Vicariance Biogeography

Vicariance Biogeography

A Critique

Symposium of the
Systematics Discussion Group of the
American Museum of Natural History
May 2–4, 1979

**Edited by Gareth Nelson
and Donn E. Rosen**

Columbia University Press   New York

Library of Congress Cataloging in Publication Data
Main entry under title:

Vicariance biogeography.

   Proceedings of a symposium held at a meeting
of the Systematics Discussion Group.
   Bibliography: p.
   Includes index.
   1. Biogeography—Congresses.   2. Paleobio-
geography—Congresses.   3. Continental drift—
Congresses.   I. Nelson, Gareth J.   II. Rosen,
Donn Eric, 1929-   III. Systematics Discussion
Group, New York.
QH84.V49   574.9   80-15351
ISBN 0-231-04808-4

Columbia University Press
New York   Guildford, Surrey

To the memory of
Robert Francis Scharff (1858–1934)
and
Alfred Lothar Wegener (1880–1930),
whose vision penetrated the limits
of their times and places

Contents

Preface

DISCUSSIONS of current issues in systematic biology have always animated the Scientific Staff of the American Museum of Natural History. Over 30 years ago, however, a small group was formed by Ernst Mayr, then a curator on the museum's staff, in which graduate and undergraduate students working in or associated with the museum's collections discussed their own research or reviewed items in the current scientific literature. The group met at irregular intervals, sometimes as often as each week, and initially included about a dozen students—most of whom now are professionally engaged in systematic research. When Mayr left the American Museum of Natural History to assume a position at the Museum of Comparative Zoology, Harvard University, the group remained active because of the students' interest. In the early 1960s the group named itself the Systematics Discussion Group (SDG), adopted a program of monthly meetings for the academic year, was assigned a meeting room at the museum, and was officially acknowledged by the museum's administration. Much of the discussion that led to this symposium took place at the meetings of the SDG. This symposium, therefore, represents SDG's grandest meeting to date, fully reflecting the museum's tradition of encouraging discussion of current issues in systematic biology.

SDG meetings, sometimes unruly, have been governed only by the absence of formality, which has come to be known as the "New York Rules" of discourse. Meetings have featured a hard-core group of activists—persons with a seemingly unquenchable thirst for dialogue or, in some cases, diatribe. Although conceived in the spirit of SDG meetings, this symposium—with its international array of participants—called for a minimum of control over those persons who might desire to speak and over how long and how often they might do so. The symposium required, therefore, someone not normally found in SDG meetings—a moderator to impose reasonable limits upon the vocal members of the audience and to encourage the less vocal members to participate. The role of moderator seemed especially important in a meeting that was destined to attract 350 persons (as compared with the 50 or so who normally attend SDG meetings). Ideally, the moderator also was to be well informed about the issues likely to be discussed at the symposium, so that attention could be turned in a profitable direction. When the organizing committee reviewed the possibilities, they agreed that one person was uniquely suited by her clarity of thought, intelligence, humor, and fearlessness. Besides, she was well informed about biogeography. Virginia Ferris (Entomology Laboratory, Purdue University), in her role as moderator of the entire symposium, fulfilled and even went beyond the committee's expectations. As one reviewer of the symposium said, "Dr. Ferris alternately wielded a velvet glove and a mailed fist." To an important degree the success of the symposium was her accomplishment.

The members of the organizing committee included Roger L. Batten, Ernst Kirsteuer, Charles W. Myers, Norman I. Platnick, Richard H. Tedford, and, as an ad hoc member, Karl F. Koopman—all of the American Museum of Natural History. On behalf of the SDG we thank them and the museum's administration, especially Director Thomas D. Nicholson and President Robert G. Goelet, Jr., for their support of the symposium and the Systematics Discussion Group.

Gareth Nelson and Donn E. Rosen
American Museum of Natural History
New York City

Contributors

Batten, R. L.   Department of Invertebrates, American Museum of Natural History, Central Park West at 79th Street, New York, New York 10024

Ben-Avraham, Z.   Department of Mathematics, Weizmann Institute of Science, Rehovort, Israel

Brundin, L. Z.   Sektionen för Entomologi, Naturhistoriska Riksmuseet, 104 05 Stockholm 50, Sweden

Connor, E. F.   Department of Biological Science, Florida State University, Tallahassee, Florida 32306

Croizat, L.   Apdo. 7344, Coro (Edo. Falcón), Venezuela

Edmunds, G. F., Jr.   Department of Biology, University of Utah, Salt Lake City, Utah 84112

Eldredge, N.   Department of Invertebrates, American Museum of Natural History, Central Park West at 79th Street, New York, New York 10024

Erwin, T. L.   Department of Entomology, National Museum of Natural History, Washington, D.C. 20560

Farris, J. S.   Department of Ecology and Evolution, Division of Biological Sciences, State University of New York, Stony Brook, New York 11794

Haffer, J.   Tommesweg 60, 4300 Essen-1, West Germany

Hallam, A.   Geological Sciences, University of Birmingham, P.O.
                         Box 363, Edgbaston, Birmingham B15 2TT, England

Haugh, B. N.   Department of Invertebrates, American Museum of
                         Natural History, Central Park West at 79th Street,
                         New York, New York 10024

Heck, K. L.   Benedict Estuarine Research Laboratory, Benedict,
                         Maryland 20612

Howden, H. F.   Biology Department, Carlton University, Ottawa,
                         Ontario K1S 5B6, Canada

Koopman, K. F.   Department of Mammalogy, American Museum of
                         Natural History, Central Park West at 79th Street,
                         New York, New York 10024

McCoy, E. D.   Department of Biology, University of South Florida,
                         Tampa, Florida 33620

McKenna, M. C.   Department of Vertebrate Paleontology, American
                         Museum of Natural History, Central Park West at
                         79th Street, New York, New York 10024

Mankiewicz, P.   New York Botanical Gardens, 200th Street and
                         Southern Boulevard, Bronx, New York 10458

Melville, R.   Royal Botanic Gardens, Kew, Richmond, Surrey TW9
                         3AB, England

Nelson, G.   Department of Ichthyology, American Museum of
                         Natural History, Central Park West at 79th Street,
                         New York, New York 10024

Niklas, K. J.   Department of Botany, Genetics, and Development,
                         Cornell University, Ithaca, New York 14853

Nur, A.   Department of Geophysics, Stanford University,
                         Stanford, California 94305

Parenti, L. R.   Department of Ichthyology, American Museum of
                         Natural History, Central Park West at 79th Street,
                         New York, New York 10024

Patterson, C.   Department of Palaeontology, British Museum (Nat-
                         ural History), Cromwell Road, London SW7 5BD,
                         England

Platnick, N. I.   Department of Entomology, American Museum of

Natural History, Central Park West at 79th Street, New York, New York 10024

Prance, G. T.   New York Botanical Gardens, 200th Street and Southern Boulevard, Bronx, New York 10458

Rosen, D. E.   Department of Ichthyology, American Museum of Natural History, Central Park West at 79th Street, New York, New York 10024

Schuh, R. T.   Department of Entomology, American Museum of Natural History, Central Park West at 79th Street, New York, New York 10024

Schweickert, R. A.   Lamont-Doherty Geological Observatory, Route 9W, Palisades, New York 10964

Simberloff, D.   Department of Biology, Florida State University, Tallahassee, Florida 32306

Short, L. L.   Department of Ornithology, American Museum of Natural History, Central Park West at 79th Street, New York, New York 10024

Slater, J. A.   Department of Biology, University of Connecticut, Storrs, Connecticut 06268

Springer, V. G.   Division of Fishes, National Museum of Natural History, Washington, D.C. 20560

Smith, C. L.   Department of Ichthyology, American Museum of Natural History, Central Park West at 79th Street, New York, New York 10024

Smith-Vaniz, W. F.   Department of Ichthyology, Academy of Natural Sciences of Philadelphia, 19th and the Parkway, Philadelphia, Pennsylvania 19103

Solem, A.   Department of Zoology, Field Museum of Natural History, Roosevelt Road at Lake Shore Drive, Chicago, Illinois 60605

Tattersall, I.   Department of Anthropology, American Museum of Natural History, Central Park West at 79th Street, New York, New York 10024

Tedford, R. H.   Department of Vertebrate Paleontology, American Museum of Natural History, Central Park West at 79th Street, New York, New York 10024

Terborgh, J.   Department of Biology, Princeton University, Prince-
                       ton, New Jersey 08540
Udvardy, M. D. F.   Department of Biological Sciences, California State
                       University at Sacramento, 6000 J Street, Sacra-
                       mento, California 95819
Wolfe, J. A.   Branch of Paleontology and Stratigraphy, United
                       States Geological Survey, 345 Middlefield Road,
                       Menlo Park, California 94025

Vicariance Biogeography

Introduction

D. E. Rosen

> All is not golde that hath a glistering hiew, But what
> the touchstone tries and findeth true.

PANBIOGEOGRAPHY, the term first used by Leon Croizat (1958) to designate a world view of biotic interrelationships, is not just a germinal concept out of which modern vicariance biogeography has emerged. For Croizat, and for at least some of today's vicariance biogeographers, it is also a touchstone for a methodologically and conceptually new evolutionary biology. It is also true, however, that the traditional Darwinian and Neo-Darwinian views of the distributional histories of plants and animals are an integral part of more inclusive views on biological evolution; they are, in fact, necessary consequences of the axioms of Darwinian evolutionism. These axioms, concerned with competition, fitness, and adaptation, are considered by present-day evolutionists—as they were by Darwin over a century ago—a collective explanation of organic change through time and the observed diversity of the modern world.

A recent thorough review of these axioms (Brady 1980) has convincingly shown that Darwinism is in reality, however, a metaphysical and not a true science because its basic statements about the natural world are framed in a way such that a given prediction will always be realized. The expositional technique of Darwinism is the narrative—a story about how competition between individuals or species will lead to new adaptations that, by definition, confer higher fitness. Darwinian dispersalism, the biogeography of the last one hundred years, is one part of this metaphysical nexus. Organisms compete, and those that consequently are improved either force the less fit to disperse to regions of lower competition, or with their newly found strengths, themselves disperse to extend their spheres of conquests. Although such a simplistic statement invites ridicule (for after all, how could there be so little substance to a doctrine influential for over a century?), I believe that it nonetheless embodies the nuclear attitudes of Darwinians and Neo-Darwinians toward the twin problems of diversity and distribution. Croizat's panbiogeography, as much as it is a way of thinking about patterns of plant and animal distribution, is an attack on the Darwinian fabric.

For many systematists opposition to the narratives and scenarios of Darwinian evolutionism was mandated by the ideas of phylogenetic systematics espoused by Willi Hennig. Hennig's general work in English on the theory of systematics (1966) was not at first warmly welcomed, for it seemed to some persons to deny the evolutionary taxonomist access to his favorite pastime—describing life's course of events. In reality, phylogenetic systematics had no such perfunctory requirement. Instead, it asked only that a scientifically formulated statement of genealogical relationships be made prior to historical inference. Phylogenetic systematics, or as it has more recently come to be called, cladistics, thus initially asks questions about patterns and their generality and makes predictions about what patterns will be discovered by additional investigations of nature. The evolutionary taxonomy of Darwinians and Neo-Darwinians asks questions initially about how processes assumed to be necessary can "explain" certain observations of nature and, as such, is really investigating the explanatory power of a theory about nature rather than the structure of nature itself. The theory that is the subject of investigation is Darwinian selection (competition, fitness, and adaptation)—a theory that was conceived by the biological application and affirmation of 19th-century axioms about human social values. During the century of their application to the organic world, these axioms have taken on a life of their own, and the study of organisms in space and time has been richly adorned with Darwinian fabric—the emperor's clothes.

Discussions of cladistic methodology at the American Museum of Natural History, where I have worked for the past 18 years, immediately polarized the curatorial staff. Strongest opposition to cladistics came, not unexpectedly, from departments most closely tied to the interests of the Darwinian tradition. By 1973, the polarization had not disappeared, but the balance of those questioning and defending orthodoxy had changed. Of about

30 systematic curators, slightly more than half were actively pursuing cladistic studies or were positively disposed toward them; the remainder either rejected cladistics as without any use at all or stood aloof from the controversy. The initial open hostility between the two camps had somewhat abated by 1973, and agreement on an armed truce was reached. On the recommendation of three scientific departments, Willi Hennig received the museum's Gold Medal in 1975.

That year, however, battle lines were instantly reformed when Croizat's panbiogeography (and its consequences for Darwinian dispersalism) was brought into the debate. Following so closely on the heels of the stern challenge by cladistics, the advocacy of panbiogeography and its explicit criticism of traditional dispersalism proved to be intolerable for the museum's ardent Darwinians. Accusations were plentiful, but mostly they were about the morality and intellectual competence of the advocates of vicariance theory. It was to be many months before there were useful discussions about the conflicting ideas. In fact, one letter from an irate curator to the chairman of the museum's scientific council of curators expressed incredulity at the nomination of Croizat as a Corresponding Member of the museum and asked that this letter be disposed of lest it be used in a libel suit. Following a later recommendation by eleven staff members to award Croizat the museum's Gold Medal, another curator threatened resignation. A third curator stopped me one day in the museum's halls to ask why I (and others) continued to raise issues that were so clearly disrupting staff harmony. In turn, I asked if he would keep to himself, or share, new ideas that might be viewed as fundamental to our science. There was no reply then, or since, and that was years ago.

Thinking to bring the scientific questions into open debate and to stem the local bitterness about personalities and gold medals, the museum's director, T. D. Nicholson, promised financial support for a symposium on vicariance biogeography in a memorandum dated December 2, 1977, and formed a planning committee which included curators of divergent systematic and biogeographical interests. For a year the committee foundered at the hands of still another curator who opposed the very idea of the symposium and consistently blocked productive discourse. It was not until late in 1978, after the director had replaced our reluctant committee member—three years after the onset of orthodox reactionism—that plans for an open debate of the issues were formulated. It was the decision of the altered committee that the symposium should include speakers who, except for Croizat, had never before written on vicariance theory and who represented recognizably different points of view in biogeography. It was also decided that each main speaker would be assigned two or more discussants, whose task would be to appraise the speaker's success in dealing with the general question: Is vicariance theory and method, as recently discussed by various authors, useful, useless, or irrelevant for dealing with the problems of historical biogeography?

For the readers of this volume who may wonder why the views of certain leading Neo-Darwinians are not represented, it should be recorded that P. J. Darlington, Jr., E. Mayr, and G. G. Simpson were invited to participate as principal speakers but declined. One person, D. I. Axelrod, accepted the invitation and then withdrew rather late in the proceedings. He was replaced by J. A. Wolfe. Otherwise, the speakers represented in this volume are those who initially and enthusiastically agreed to address the question.

It is helpful to recall that the debate concerning the relationship between the history of the earth and its life—the central question of vicariance theory—is a very old one. The roots of the debate go back to Linnaeus and Buffon in the eighteenth century (Nelson 1978). It is also helpful to recall, especially with regard to the modern discussions of earth history, that it was biological necessity that engendered geological debate. Already in the mid-nineteenth century, Edward Forbes (1846) had concluded that the distribution of certain marine fossils was inconsistent with the idea of a stable geography. Only a few years later, Antonio Snider-Pelligrini (1859) used the idea of continental drift to explain the occurrences of fossil plants. One of Alfred Wegener's principal criteria for supporting the idea of continental drift involved the occurrences of fossil and living plants and animals, especially terrestrial and freshwater forms.

What, one might ask, has transpired in the days since Wegener's (1912a, 1912b, 1915) detailed statement about the patterns of continental displacement? The answer here is that there are three noteworthy things. The first is that geophysicists have thoroughly corroborated the main elements of Wegener's patterns of spatial relationships among continental fragments (with the possible exception of some Pacific elements) using paleomagnetic lineations and computer matching of continental boundaries. The second is that Croizat, as did Scharff before him (1895, 1899, 1907, 1911), has thoroughly documented the biological necessity for an unstable geography. A third accomplishment of note is an outgrowth of the other two and is embodied in Croizat's concepts of taxogenesis and form-making (cladogenesis plus anagenesis) as a direct consequence of a sequence of events of earth history that lead to biotic fragmentation. The phoenix that has risen from this apposition of our ideas about organic and inorganic histories derives its strength from the concept of relatedness as expressed by a branching diagram, or cladogram. It seems doubtful, at least to me, that the notion of congruence between geographical and biological patterns could ever be formulated in a testable way without cladistic information, just as there seems here the promise that the study of cladistic congruence between the earth and its life will be the next "revolution in the earth sciences"—an integrated natural history of geological and biological systems.

It was in such a hopeful and expectant frame of mind after the three strenuous days of conference (May 2–4, 1979) that I solicited a reaction from one of my more conservative and ideologically orthodox fellow curators. Possibly the reader has already guessed my paraphrase of his response: "The symposium served no useful purpose because its focus was uninteresting and its conception too narrow." Perhaps. I leave the reader to judge.

1

The Riddle of Dispersal: Dispersal Theories and How They Affect Vicariance Biogeography

M. D. F. Udvardy

What is Biogeography?

IN MY SCHEME of the biological sciences (1969) I attempted to pigeonhole the various disciplines into categories arrived at by intermeshing two sets of criteria (figure 1.1):

(1) *Levels of complexity*. For an organismic biologist, all studies of parts of organisms fit into one level; studies of individual organisms fit into another. Populations, considered as biological species or small interacting units, form the next level. Finally, interrelations among populations correspond to supraspecific entities and form the highest level of complexity.

(2) *Structure, function, time, and space*. Studies within each level of complexity may be pursued with emphasis on structural, functional, temporal, or spatial factors.

This system of pigeonholes may be considered as if it were a building, where the "classical" branches of biology are the basement and ground floor. The newly evolving branches of biology, or rejuvenated ones, would be the upper levels, similar to additions built upon an old foundation.

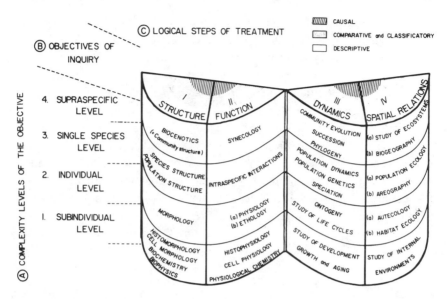

Figure 1.1. A system of biological sciences. From Udvardy (1969:3, fig. 1.1).

Among the space-related disciplines, the individual level is the subject of classical ecology. The population level also has a spatial factor—the area occupied by a species. Space and time have to be studied side by side because space occupancy is dynamic and ever changing. In addition to studies of populations and the areas occupied by them, there is the subject of population dynamics, involving formation and extinction of populations and species. The supraspecific level more directly pertains to evolution, which studied in time is *phylogeny*, and studied in space is *biogeography* (which reminds us of Croizat's 1964 title: *Space, Time, Form: The Biological Synthesis*).

We should bear in mind, however, that ecosystems are supraspecific entities recognized by their functional rather than their morphological attributes. Ecosystems are true entities, comparable to the individual, the population, and the species. They also have their phylogenies and geographies, although I would accept the criticism that my recognizing them in 1969 did not noticeably advance their study during the last decade or so. I was criticized (Howden 1971) because I did not stress higher taxa and their studies. Taxa are artifacts of our classificatory mind; thus they fit into the second step of the diagram. When our methods require that we use groups of species rather than other kinds of groups, we should use genera, families, superspecies, etc., if their use helps our understanding of the subject, just as we use concepts such as fauna, plant formation, life zone, and similar abstractions. He who equates higher taxa with common descent will have to turn to higher taxa as a means of grouping and ranking, but these are rarely necessary at the elementary level, where the biogeographer compares a bird with a beetle more often than he compares a parulid warbler with one of sylviid relationship.

Returning now to the place of biogeography in our system, we notice that in the spatial sector we progress upward from habitat ecology to areal study, and from there to higher integratory levels of biogeography. Vuilleumier (1978) divided the domains of biogeography into four classes that correspond to the subdivisions applied to other branches of geography: (1) present space occupancy, viewed as a snapshot-like assessment; (2) successional changes within a short time span; (3) spatio-temporal changes leading to speciation; and (4) paleobiogeography through global space and evolutionary time. I take the liberty of modifying this scheme for the present symposium (figure 1.2; the space and time units are arbitrary).

The fact of occurrence today of every individual organism (or species) on the surface of the globe, the static geographical picture, is not yet biology but rather biological geography—the starting point of all biogeographical studies from Candolle to Croizat. The first field, with the secular scale of time (±100 years) and the smallest divisions of space (some 100 km), is the field wherein the dynamism of distribution, spreading, and dispersal is actually studied as biological phenomena, strongly backed up by ecological, and especially synecological, studies. The biogeographer of the present allocates much of his time and energy to gather morphological, physiological, ethological, and life-history knowledge of his subjects in order to understand the biological aspects of areal occupancy and the expansionary potential of plant and animal species. A good example is the life work of the late Carl Lindroth (e.g., 1945–49, 1961–69), which shows what the combination of ecological and taxonomic zoogeography can achieve at this level. The biogeographer of the present must and does consider the historical factor, but cannot preoccupy himself with more than the immediate past—that which lies within the next and expanded view of the Quaternary biogeographer.

The researcher of the second and larger quadrangle deals with the dynamic events of the immediate geological past, the Pleistocene, when largescale climatic fluctuations culminated in glaciations of the higher latitudes, which drew life away from, and then allowed life to return to, considerable areas of the globe. These fluctuations also caused large-scale displacements and splittings of the zones of life of lower latitudes. The limits to

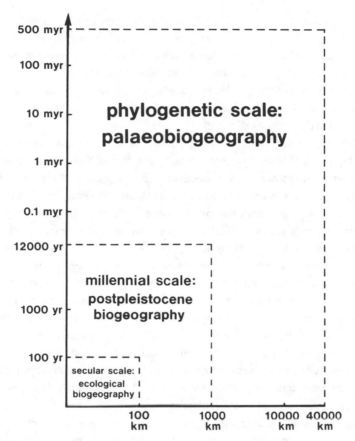

Figure 1.2. A division of biogeography into three spatio-temporal entities.

the interest of the Quaternary biogeographer are not necessarily where I draw the lines, which signify merely that his interest is higher on the axes by an order of magnitude or so than that of the recent biogeographer, and that his approach is different.

Paleoecology is best developed in the area of the millennial scale, in its concern with Wisconsin and post-Wisconsin events, involving also changes in the outlines of continents and seas. A consideration of the present biota in terms of ecofaunas, ecofloras, or biomes, applies also to the millennial scale, for therein lie the immediate roots of the present. We still lack a global synthesis at this level, for many integrators of Quaternary paleoecology and paleontology are missing. What happened to Antarctica during the great interglacial stages? What happened to eastern Asia? How did the pluvials affect the Asiatic dry belt? Did the great extinction of large-bodied animals have some parallel among plants? If, as commonly assumed, most passerine bird species resulted from vicariance during the Pleistocene events, what was avian diversity like before that? What controlled the insect predators of vascular plants before the diversification of passerine birds? Are species cycles (Wilson 1961; Ricklefs and Cox 1972) modern phenomena, or did they affect archipelagoes of the past?

The largest quadrangle on my graph encompasses the evolutionary time of all biota and is limited in space only by the size of Tellur, the planet earth. In this realm of the historical biogeographers, the ecological theater is largely unknown, yet the evolutionary play had many scenes revolving with the drifting continents. It is within this phylogenetic scale that the recent revolution of plate tectonics shook the foundations of the leading paleontologists of the past decades, while vindicating other persons with foresight and imagination. This is the area of many participants of this symposium, with the notable exclusion of at least myself. My task, then, is to qualify and discuss certain basic tenets of the present-day biogeographer. I believe that much misunderstanding can be cleared up by discussing these tenets and relating them to one, two, or all three of the delimited fields of biogeography: the present (secular scale), immediate past (millennial scale), and the remote past (phylogenetic scale). If I seem pragmatic, so be it. Pragmatism about the concepts that we debate may create some understanding during this symposium. First, however, I wish to emphasize once more that I see that the biogeographers assembled here travel on at least three different errands in time and space, carrying with them different tasks, methods, and evidences of varied nature and magnitude (figure 1.3).

What is Dispersal?

In the dynamic sector of our biological system, the individual level includes the temporal sequence of events within the life of the individual organism. I call these, for short, *ontogeny* (developmental mechanisms, broadly construed) and *life cycles* (all functional mechanisms, whether cyclically repeated throughout one or more generations—e.g., the seasonal generations of aphids, or the haploid-diploid cycles of certain plant groups). Cole (1954) called them "life history characteristics." Change of domicile is one relevant factor. Thus, we arrive at the notion of dispersal.

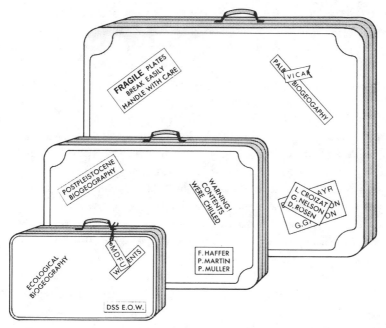

Figure 1.3. Biogeographers carry different tasks, methods, and evidence.

Dispersal, according to my dictionary, is "the process or result of spreading by active migration or of passive transfer of organisms from one place to another." My definition is essentially the same: "the process whereby an organism is able to spread from its place of origin to another locality" (Udvardy 1969:10). This use has been scrutinized by Platnick (1976), who thought that the above concept (my definition) is better termed "dispersion," and that the term "dispersal" is better restricted as a property of taxa, rather than as a property of individual organisms. Armstrong (1977) defended my usage, pointed out some of its weaknesses, and noted that some persons use "dispersion" when they mean only "dispersal" in Platnick's sense. I would add that Croizat (1958, 1964, 1968a) uses "dispersal" when he means merely "distribution" (perhaps following the permissiveness of the Oxford school of dictionary makers). I wonder whether Croizat's usage might have influenced Platnick, when he emphasized the "dispersal" (distribution) of higher taxa.

Armstrong, Platnick, and I seem to agree on one point: all of us accept the meaning that Webster's dictionary attributes to the geographical use of the word. This meaning of "dispersal" follows logically from a meaning of the verb "disperse," which is "to spread or distribute from a constant source" (Webster: *disperse* 2). However, "disperse" also means "to cause to break up and go in different ways" (Webster: *disperse* 1). Baker (1978:31) apparently based his definition on this meaning, for he writes: "to disperse: to increase the main distance between the individual members of a group of organisms." Baker's "dispersal" is the opposite of "convergence" or "concentration." Our "dispersal" is included in his usage of "migration" (Baker: 21): "the act of moving from one spatial unit to another." His subdivision for our concept is "removal migration" (Baker: 26): "a migration away from a spatial unit, which is not followed by a return." The ambiguous usage of the English word "dispersal" is emphasized also in Schwerdtfeger's (1968) treatise on population ecology. I believe that the ambiguity is partly caused by the fact that the word may mean the process as well as the result of the process. This ambiguity is one of the birth pains of a unified science of biogeography. Such birth pains are unavoidable, for scientists are individualists. They find it difficult to squeeze their thoughts into strictly uniform patterns. Similar ambiguities, leading to highly productive disputes, are found also in related disciplines.

I repeat that dispersal that results in spreading into localities outside the distributional area (range) of a species is of focal interest to biogeographers because it causes a temporal change in the distributional area. This change is the dynamic phenomenon studied by biogeographers at all three spatial and temporal levels of their inquiries.

Armstong (1977) noted that all forms of dispersal are "points on a continuum." From the standpoint of contemporary (ecological) biogeography, he is correct. I concur that forms of dispersal "simultaneously serve habitat occupation, dispersion and expansion" (Udvardy 1969:92). Because a comprehensive monograph of dispersal is still not extant (cf. Johnson 1969, for aerial dispersal of insects; and Baker 1978, for "migration" of individual animals), I refer to figure 1.4. Dispersal as a biological phenomenon is based on the ability of every organism (animal or plant) to change domicile when such change is adaptive (through successful reproduction) for the survival of a population. Polymorphic dispersional mechanisms might be based on cytogenetic, sexual, locomotive, behavioral, and other mechanisms (I use "dispersional" in its dual meaning—dispersion *sensu stricto* as well as expansion). The mobile component may simply facilitate settling of offspring so that they do not compete with surviving parental organisms; it may help deme replacement (with or without deme extinction); or it may provide means for finding a new domicile in cases of temporary or ephemeral habitats. On the larger time scale all habitats change shape and position

Examples discussed in chapters 2 and 3	Nature of morph or phase	Characteristic of morph maintaining local population	Characteristic of morph promoting expansion
Aphids[1] Carabid beetles, ants[2], termites[2]	Structural	Winglessness (aptery) Brachyptery (flightlessness)	Wingedness (alateness) Macroptery (fully winged, flying individuals)
Vertebrates: fish, newt, reptiles, birds, mammals	Behavioral	Philopatry	Vagility (nomadizing)
Western tent caterpillar	Physiological–behavioral	Sluggishness, slow metabolism	Activeness, fast metabolism
Migratory locusts[3], "expansive" butterflies[3]	Structural, physiological, and behavioral	Solitary phase Normally colored phase	Gregarious phase Dark gregarious caterpillars becoming expansive imagoes
Crustaceans: Notostraca[1], Daphnia[1], Aphids[1], Bugs[1]	Cytogenetic	Parthenogenetic (asexual) reproduction	Sexual reproduction
bagworm moth[4], beetles[4], millipedes[4], isopods[4], earthworms[4]	Cytogenetic	Sexual reproduction, diploidy	Parthenogenetic reproduction with polyploidy

NOTE:.   [1]Morphs are cyclically alternating generations.   [2]Only the sexual forms are winged.   [3]Phases are phenotypic.   [4]Morphs are sequential generations.

Figure 1.4. Polymorphic dispersional systems in animals. From Udvardy (1969:74, table 4).

because of climatic and other environmental alterations. Species that have survived to our day evidently were able to cope with these alterations by shifting—partially or even totally—their distributional areas. For these species or for their ancestors, expansion (through dispersal) was a necessity for survival. For species that became extinct, expansionary adaptations evidently were too slow, or they were missing, and adaptations to survive the alterations were inadequate. On the phylogenetic scale the same reasoning applies. As noted by Croizat et al. (1974:265): "all species are components of biotic systems (biotas) that tend to persist through time despite their more or less gradual *change in distribution* and species composition" (emphasis added).

I now consider dispersal of composite units, which are entities other than species populations. Biotic communities are considered by many persons as co-adapted entities of life that cover the earth's surface by their stands. Other kinds of entities are biotas. To separate a biota into fauna and flora is a somewhat antiquated system. Where do we classify assemblages of viri, bacteria, and certain protists? Biotas are designated on geographical grounds. Because their species composition changes through time, biotas have no intrinsic, but some heuristic, value in biogeographical considerations. (Also, the term "biota" is not commonly encountered beyond scientific English.) Higher taxa are abstractions, which contain a number of species—living and fossil—and which for the phylogenetically thinking biologist are ideally of monophyletic origin. *Dispersal of higher taxa* is a permissible figure of speech, necessary for tracing phylogenies historically and, at the same time, geographically.

Biogeographers of the present have observed that ranges of species often expand, and that some species even cross barriers while expanding their range. Through study of barrier crossing, ecologically inclined biogeographers have postulated, discovered, and studied dispersal-related settling mechanisms and extinction mechanisms (MacArthur and Wilson 1967; Simberloff 1974). Other biogeographers have accumulated evidence about wholesale change of distributional areas of ecologically related species, that is, of whole ecosystems during the immediately past millennia (Wright and Frey 1965). Paleogeographers speak of changing geography of phylogenetic units—of taxa as well as geographical biota. Although paleoecological evidence is as yet largely unexplored, I believe that, in addition to the shifting positions of land and ocean, dispersal has contributed to the kaleidoscopic distribution of life on the largest time scale.

I now briefly consider modes of dispersal in biogeography. Dispersal affects all forms of life: viri, protists, plants, and animals. The geography of viri and protists is still a separate and rather neglected study in the western world (but not in Soviet biogeography: e.g., Baroyan 1965); hence I will not deal with it. Among plants and animals, dispersal mechanisms seem to have evolved along parallel lines. In both kingdoms there are examples of random dispersal of propagules and—especially among animals—of whole organisms and populations. By "random dispersal" I mean dispersal by means of land-slides that result in rafts, by means of hurricanes that siphon away plants and animals, by means of volcanic explosions that create vacant land, etc. Such events seem restricted to certain geographical areas, and involuntary waifing as a regular dispersal agent might be questioned. Yet there is considerable literature to the effect that flightless Rails, and composite plants that have lost wind dispersability, have evolved as a result of island colonization.

Because higher plants are rooted or otherwise tied down, active dispersal by self-generated movement is rather rare and restricted among them relative to non-sessile animals, which form the majority of the animal world. When active dispersal occurs in plants it seems primarily to serve disper-sion—movement away from the mother plant. In addition to mechanical devices that shoot, catapult, or broadcast seeds a short distance (Van der Pijl 1969), vegetative spreading is a mode of active dispersal. Because vegeta-tive spreading implies no genetic change within the clone, it is adaptive only within the growing distance of the parent plant, or if coupled with passive dispersal, it favors quick reproduction and formation of local populations (clones) that prepare the way for sexually reproducing generations.

Active dispersal involving locomotion is the more widespread alternative among animals, and there is no need for me to add to the voluminous litera-ture on this subject. I should perhaps emphasize that, whereas locomotor capacities usually (but not always) are able to cope with the process of changing locality within the habitat of a species, that is not always the case in strange habitats, especially if behavior is a factor. Open-country birds shy away from forested areas, and forest animals often perish in non-forested habitats. Thus, ecological barriers on land might render unlikely colonization and speciation by barrier crossing.

Passive dispersal, involving water or wind as a carrier, is widespread in both plant and animal kingdoms—perhaps more so among plants. Recent monographs reveal an increasing and impressive number of adaptations that indicate passive dispersal often is not random (Van der Pijl 1969 and Janzen 1971, higher plants; Johnson 1969, insects; Baker 1978, animals in general). Passive dispersal is a mechanism; it might even be called a syndrome that, at least in animals, includes special functional adaptations and responses for timing of takeoff, length and direction of route, and termination of dispersal movement.

Passive dispersal by way of living carriers is more common among plants than among animals. Plants using other plants as carriers seem rather rare; epiphytes come to mind. Animals using plant carriers might suggest rafting, or spreading of phytophages on the propagules that they inhabit and utilize. Still, I do not know of any treatment in which man is not the primary carrier. Of course, plants as well as animals utilize motile animals as carriers. Many botanists now seem to agree that the evolution of fruit in many cases shows close adaptations to attract the animal carrier and to repel the usurper-consumer. Thus the fruit seems to be a device, or tool, of dispersal strategy that assures transportation of the seed(s) by animals (Janzen 1971). Stebbins (1971) details the evolution of dispersive function from earlier protective functions of structures surrounding the seed; he also believes that animals are effective carriers in long-distance dispersal. In the system of carrier dispersal (zoologists' "phoresy") used by Van der Pijl (following Ridley 1930), there is room even for saurochory—dispersal by way of reptiles. (Could this have been more common before the advent of endotherms?) I deplore with Stebbins (1974) the fact that such studies are as yet uncommon. When speaking of zoochory, or combined zoochory and anemochory (animal and wind dispersal) and its role in spreading plants and animals in the southern hemisphere, we face a controversy debated for decades (e.g., McDowall 1978).

Dispersal Centers

The ecological biogeographer of the present daily experiences and observes dispersal and its results. Even though anthropogene dispersal now overrides all other kinds and threatens to obscure the distributional (and dispersal-related) status of the total biota of our planet (e.g., the oligochaete controversy related by Ball in 1976), long-distance pioneering events do occur and are witnessed within the lifetime of every field biologist.

One of the meanings of "disperse" is gradually to move away from the point of origin. This meaning is important in tracing past distributional areas and also in tracing the chorological aspects of evolution. Hence, it is important in vicariance biogeography and in cladistic phylogeny.

Croizat et al. (1974) singled out, as an epigram for their discussion of "centers of origin," my statement (Udvardy 1969) that: "Every animal species originated from a few ancestors in a limited area; if a particular species is now found to be widespread, it must of necessity have reached parts of its present range at an earlier period."[1] Then they discussed certain attempts in the biogeographical literature to find the "center of origin" of species and other taxa. I concur with most of what was said there (cf. Udvardy 1969:238, 240). To avoid repetition, I shall not discuss here whether primitive or advanced forms occupy the geographical center of a taxon's range.

Were I a historical biogeographer, I would most likely pursue two great tasks: (1) to find the place of origin, traced through the wanderings, of the taxon or taxa of interest to me; and (2) to find the place of origin of the taxa comprising the fauna (or biota) of interest to me. Were I a phylogenetically inclined evolutionist, I would vigorously pursue the first task, but I would find both tasks challenging.

I judge that I am not alone in these temptations. Even Croizat (1964:184) writes:

It is of course obvious that vicariant form-making calls for the recognition of particular *centers* of taxonomic individualization which, readily identifiable on a statistical basis of comparison by competent (pan)biogeographical analysis (e.g., Guayas River in Ecuador), lie entirely beyond the scope of "zoogeography" and "phytogeography" operating by "casual means."

The adherents of vicariance biogeography more or less violently protest against the pursuit of "centers" in biogeography, especially centers of origin of species. Let us look at certain centers in the framework of the biogeographical divisions as they were presented above.

One task of the present-day biogeographer is to search for orderly patterns of distribution in the living world. In separate but parallel ways, plant and animal geographers alike try to discern ecofaunas, ecofloras, and vegetational units by comparing distributional areas. They find that ecologically related and (at least partially) sympatrically distributed organisms share one or several (Müller 1973) "centers" of their present distributional areas. Two questions arise: (1) Why do these areas possess overlapping (sympatric) centers? and (2) what causes the differences in the peripheral distributions?

To answer these questions, with reference to geographically overlapping

---

[1] The first half of my statement is not now under scrutiny; if we accept it for the sake of argument, the second half must be valid.

groups on a large scale, Eric Hultén (1937b) studied plants of the far northern parts of the Holarctic Region. I consider Hultén's work to have had a seminal effect on the development of a school of biogeographers who were, and are, trying to explain present distributional patterns of species under the impact of the Pleistocene, and who consider the forces of dispersal (and the lack of dispersal, which causes speciation or extinction) causal factors of these distributional patterns. No doubt Willis' ideas were known to Hultén, as they were to Ekman and other Scandinavians, and Willis' ideas might have been inspirational for Hultén. Hultén's *equiformal areas* unite species areas that reflect more or less complete radiation from centers wherein all areas of a certain geographical pattern overlap. He considered these centers glacial refugia from which the progressive and plastic species radiated, while the rigid species remained in and around the refugia. Although he did not study areas to the south, he also postulated that south of the glacially affected land, pluvial refuges must have existed, as relicts due to the extension of dry belts during interglacial periods.

Applying a similar approach to animals, Reinig (1937, 1950) considered more southerly and non-glaciated expanses of the Palearctic Region. Simultaneously, Stegmann (1938, 1939) used the same equiformal area method (without calling it that—independent of Hultén and Reinig), and applied it to the total avifauna of the Palearctic Region, deriving the fauna from seven major preglacial centers. In these same years, Meusel in Germany and Soó in Hungary, among others, applied the method to the flora of various European and Eurasian distributional groups. Among zoologists the most persistent follower of the method was Lattin (1967), who in contrast to Hultén emphasized the "centrant" elements (Hultén's term, not used by Lattin), which remain in refugia (Lattin's "Kerngebiete" is no doubt identical to Haffer's "core areas" and Müller's "areas of congruence").

In North America, meanwhile, Udvardy (1963a, 1963b), Mengel (1964), and Hubbard (1973) analyzed bird groups with distributions that Hultén would have called "radiant" (distributions that exemplify expanding, retreating, splitting, and speciation in various biomes). Lattin's synthetic view (1957, 1967) sees the Holarctic fauna as composed of three major ecological elements, each with a number of geographical centers across the northern continents. These elements are the arboreal (wooded), eremial (arid), and oreotundral (arctic and alpine highland). He believed that the arboreal centers survived the last glacial period *in situ*, and that the arboreal centers are therefore glacial refugia (an interpretation that still awaits corroboration and collating with the floral refugia proposed by Hultén and others). Lattin extended his theory to the total biota of the earth, in the sense that treeless cold and arid ecosystems could play roles antagonistic to those of forest and mesic ecosystems; when one ecosystem expands, then the other retreats into refugia, and vice versa. In the 1950s Moreau (1952, 1963) applied the alternating expansion-regression theory to the avifauna of Africa without areal analysis, and Keast (1961) applied it to Australia's Quaternary history.

Haffer (1974) and Müller (1973) each proceeded along the same general lines when studying South American distributions of various animals. Müller explicitly condemned those persons who assume that the center of the range of a group (or its center of greatest diversity) is its center of origin—that is, those persons who historically interpret the concept of centers. I find it interesting to follow the semantics. Müller most likely refers to paleobiogeographical time dimensions when he uses words such as "origin" and "historical" in his opposition to a priori recognition of centers. But after finding the centers on the basis of partial sympatry of species or subspecies ranges, he claims that the centers acted as refugia during regressive phases of the environment. Dr. Haffer shall no doubt speak for himself and his centers later in this symposium. He also searches for core areas by areographical analysis. Core areas and secondary contact zones of related taxa might help to define likely dispersal centers, or refugia.

Figure 1.5 is a sketchy history of some of the main flows of ideas among European biogeographers of the areography school. It is a superficial

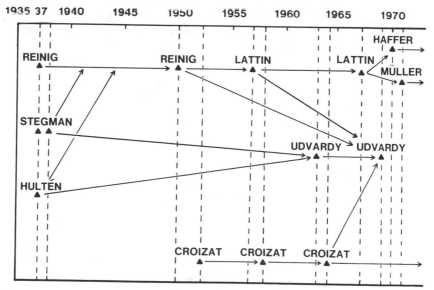

Figure 1.5. Flow of main ideas about centers of distribution.

sketch without the ramifications of recent phytogeography, and without the workers of this school, such as Voous (1963) in Holland and Varga (1975) in Hungary. A review article in English would be timely.

Figure 1.6–1.9 and figure 1.12, show examples of the area-superposition method of locating core areas or possible refugia. Figures 1.10 and 1.11 (by Croizat and Rosen) indicate that the proponents of the vicariance school use the method if not its underlying theory. And I conclude that Croizat's "vicariance" method is based on this same superposition technique, applied to paleobiogeography (his "panbiogeography"). Although the purpose of his method is to elucidate ancestral distributions, it is based on coincident distributional patterns of species. His "general track" thus seems to me a super-

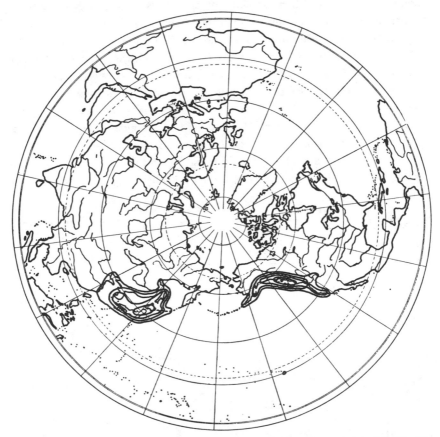

Figure 1.6. Disjunct, equiformal areas of five plant species. From Hultén (1937b:43, fig. 6). This particular pattern strongly resembles the "generalized track" concept of Croizat et al. (1974), and the "bicentric" species concept of Müller (1973).

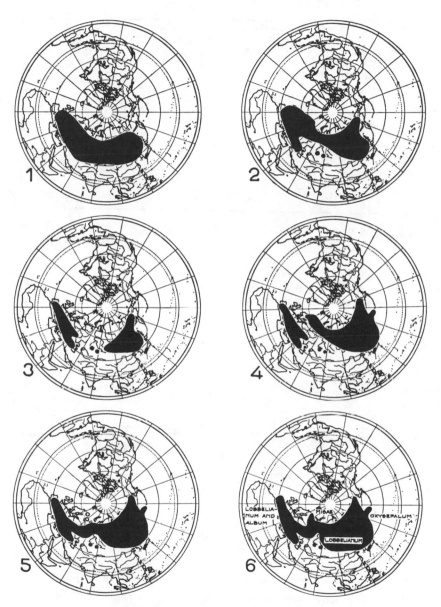

Figure 1.7. Past and present areas of *Veratrum album*. From Hultén (1937b:112, fig. 9). From present distribution and taxonomy, Hultén hypothesized expansions and disjunctions during the vicissitudes of the Pleistocene: (1) hypothetical D-interglacial area before maximum of drought; (2) hypothetical D-interglacial area after maximum of drought; (3) hypothetical area during maximum glaciation; (4) hypothetical E-interglacial area; (5) hypothetical area during Würm glaciation; (6) present area.

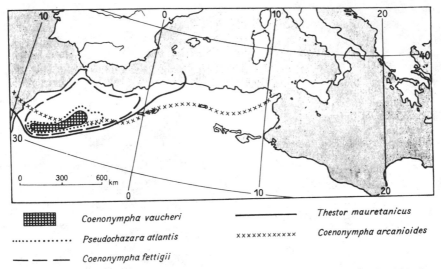

▦	*Coenonympha vaucheri*	———————	*Thestor mauretanicus*
·············	*Pseudochazara atlantis*	xxxxxxxxxxxx	*Coenonympha arcanioides*
— — —	*Coenonympha fettigii*		

Figure 1.8. Areas of some Mauretanian faunal elements. From Lattin (1967:365, fig. 109). Used with permission of Gustav Fischer Verlag.

imposed multiple-area map, somewhat simplified, but with the possibility of one or more centers ("nodes" in his terminology).

Dispersal of Fauna and Flora

What of dispersal theories among post-Pleistocene biogeographers? Evidence for dispersal is often indirect, arising through comparison of recent distributions and Quaternary geology. Often an ample fossil record (e.g., pollen) suggests climatically triggered transpositions of various life belts and biotas. An excellent sample is the work of Guilday et al. (1964); their study involves both the use of the superposition method and ample fossil evidence (figure 1.13). A karst sinkhole contained a vertical sampling of a mammalian microfauna. The upper layers yielded fossils of species now living and distributed around the sinkhole; the lower layers yielded fossils of an oreotundral-boreal fauna that today lives far away in the high northern latitudes of the continent. Dispersal and regression seem well documented in this example.

Dispersal Across Barriers

Long-distance dispersal mechanisms, often with barrier-crossing capabilities, exist in the plant and animal worlds. How effective are these mechanisms, and how common is their successful employment?

The theory of island biogeography is founded on the assumption that these mechanisms are effective and commonly employed. Island and archipelago speciation studies (e.g., Salomonsen 1976) likewise suggest over-water dispersal. It seems to me, however, that adherents of island biogeography and founder-group speciation theories concern themselves only with organisms that are capable of long-distance dispersal. And I would avoid generalizations about the barrier-crossing abilities of faunas or main-

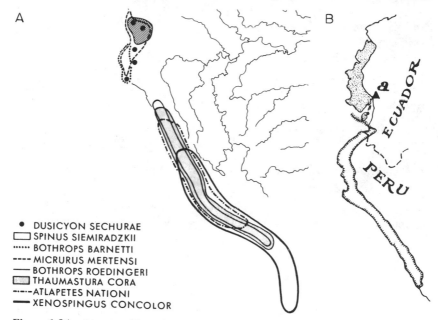

A

B

- • DUSICYON SECHURAE
- ☐ SPINUS SIEMIRADZKII
- ⋯⋯ BOTHROPS BARNETTI
- ---- MICRURUS MERTENSI
- —— BOTHROPS ROEDINGERI
- ☐ THAUMASTURA CORA
- —·—·ATLAPETES NATIONI
- ▬▬ XENOSPINGUS CONCOLOR

Figure 1.9A. Ranges of faunal elements of the two northernmost subcenters of the Andean Pacific Center of South America (Ecuadorian and Peruvian Subcenters). From Müller (1973:102, fig. 45). Used with permission of Dr. W. Junk B. V.

Figure 1.9B. "Vicariant form-making (replacement) in . . . *Thryothorus superciliaris* . . . The two races (subspecies) making up species *T. superciliaris* (stippled = *superciliaris* s.s.; hatched limits = *baroni*; triangle *a* marks mouth of Rio Guayas) are perfect geographic and taxonomic vicariants by a standard biogeographical limit (approaches of Río Guayas)." From Croizat (1964:185, fig. 43). The area of the bird species chosen by Croizat agrees neatly with the Ecuadorian Subcenter of Müller (1973).

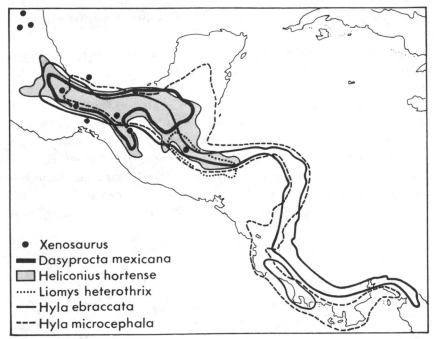

Figure 1.10. Ranges of faunal elements of Müller's Central American Rain Forest Center. From Müller (1973:11, fig. 6). Used with permission of Dr. W. Junk B. V.

land biotas. Also, I wonder whether there is a contradiction in Rosen's "vicariance model of Caribbean biogeography" when he states (1976a:445) that: "Dispersal theories, if they attempt to deal at all with distributions in a rigorous way, . . . incorporate a major, unexplained ingredient—namely the coordinated movements via active migration and chance dispersal of countless organisms of vastly different biological properties." In the same paper he states (p. 453) that "The . . . vicariant model . . . requires dispersal . . . (e.g., across subsiding island stepping stones)," and that "the South American elements that have crossed over continue to disperse northward." Rosen's postulates (which I have no reason to doubt) are hard to reconcile with his earlier anti-dispersalist statement. Also, it is hard not to imagine that island-hopping or sweepstakes-winning species would not include some that speciate after crossing the barrier.

The situation on continental land areas seems different. When I established eight distributional area-types (Udvardy 1969:187) based on theoretical considerations of ecological valency, vagility, and habitat distribution (figure 1.14) and when I searched for examples of each, I combed the whole terrestrial vertebrate fauna of North America (using mammalian areas

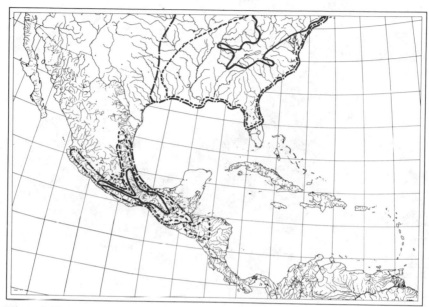

Figure 1.11. "Co-occurrences" of three species of trees. From Rosen (1978:163, fig. 7). Note the similarity of method exemplified by figures 1.6, 1.8, 1.9, and 1.10.

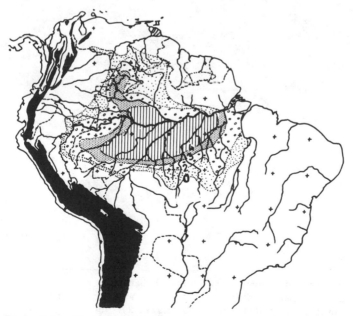

Figure 1.12. Distribution of central Amazonian birds. From Haffer (1978:58, fig. 9, superimposed ranges of four species). Used with permission of Bonner Zoologischer Beiträge.

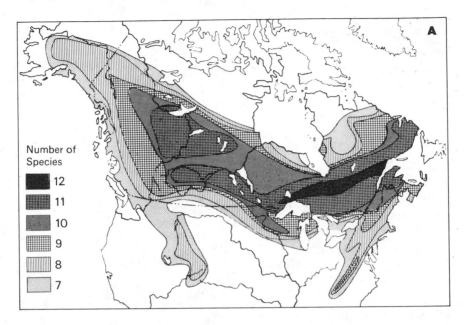

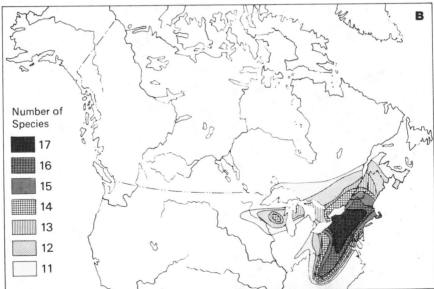

Figure 1.13. Superimposed distributional areas of mammalian species from cave deposits in New Paris, Pennsylvania (cave 4). A, fauna of cave fill from 6–9 meters; B, fauna of cave fill from 0–6 meters. Redrawn from Guilday et al. (1964).

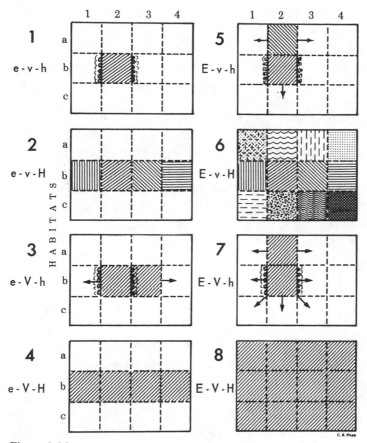

Figure 1.14. Models of continental distributional (areal) types resulting from interactions of adaptability, mobility, and habitat distribution. Each model represents a theoretical continent within a major climatic zone, consisting of three habitat types (*a*, *b*, and *c*) and four geographical regions (1–4) separated by lesser barriers (dashes running vertically). The area of habitat *b* in region 2 is delimited by strong physical barriers which are represented by semicircles in models 1, 3, 5, and 7. Crosshatching and the like covers the distributional area; different crosshatching within a model indicates subspeciation. Since our models illustrate extreme cases, no subspeciation is indicated in models 4 and 8, although slight subspeciation is possible in both instances. Only types 1, 2, 4, 6, and 8 seem to occur with more or less permanency (dynamic changes could not be considered on these models). However, types 3, 5, and 7 may exist as transient stages in new or rejuvenating areas; the arrows (small where mobility is restricted; large in strongly vagile species) indicate the transitional

of Hall and Kelson 1959, reptilian and amphibian areas of Stebbins 1966, and avian areas from my own work) in search of area-types that would suggest previous barrier crossing. But I found that all of the actual distributions were explainable by ecogeographical factors and postglacial area splitting. For bird species, my findings seem corroborated by the much more thorough taxonomic analysis of Mayr and Short (1970).

Organisms other than land vertebrates and plants might, of course, include examples of speciation by founder effect (barrier crossing). Yet, with the exception of certain *Drosophila* species, Bush (1975b) was not able to cite a single example. Lack of evidence, needless to say, is not proof. More research and synthesizing work are needed, especially regarding the ecogeographical aspects of speciation geography, behavioral aspects of dispersal (Udvardy 1970), weeds, tramps, and supertramps versus climax species and K-selected species, etc.

Uniformitarianism and Dispersal

The geological theory of uniformitarianism states that presently acting forces offer satisfactory explanations of geological changes that have occurred in the past. For phylogenetic studies, a proponent of this theory is G. L. Stebbins (for "reversed" uniformitarianism in biogeography, see Udvardy 1969:366). Stebbins (1974:15) discusses genetic uniformitarianism and states that "the basic processes of evolution are constant; phenotypes, genotypes, environmental conditions are variable." Among his corollaries especially worth mentioning are: his emphasis on adaptive radiation, which he believes has been the "primary basis of diversification among those populations that, in the remote past, gave rise to distinct genera and families of

nature of these areas which would in time become types 4, 6, and 8, respectively.
    e = restricted ecological valency = narrow range of adaptability = stenotopy
    E = large ecological valency = wide range of adaptability = eurytopy
    v = restricted mobility or vagility
    V = high vagility or mobility
    h = restricted habitat
    H = widespread habitat
    1, 2, 3, 4 = geographic regions of a continent
    a, b, c = habitats (zonally arranged; horizontally related habitats).
From Udvardy (1969:187, fig. 4-32).

modern times"; and his belief that "the initial divergence that led to the origin of major categories took place under conditions similar to those that promote maximal diversification of populations and speciation in the modern world" (pp. 13–14).

Does geological and genetic uniformitarianism allow us to think about ecological uniformitarianism? If it does, then I submit it—with caution about uncritical use—to vicariance biogeographers for consideration and possible incorporation into their theories.

Discussion

L. L. Short

I WRITE as an ornithogeographer who has some misgivings about the generalizations often made in biogeographical works. Reflecting on Prof. Udvardy's interesting presentation, I hope that each symposium participant will endeavor to make clear his use of problematical terms so that we understand each other and do not lose valuable time in semantic arguments.

Udvardy has indeed clarified much background and terminology relating to dispersal. Certainly semantic problems are difficult to avoid early in the history of a science. In literature on a highly mobile group such as birds, dispersal terminology is well entrenched. I note the special use of "dispersal rates" by avian ecologists and "migration" for movement in both directions—that is, a return movement—as well as "emigration" for what Baker (1978) termed "removal migration." There may be some difference in the effective meanings of these and other terms as they are applied to individuals, populations, species, larger taxonomic units, and even biotic units.

I emphasize two key factors in biogeographical analysis. First, we need to base our findings upon the best possible systematic knowledge. It is my distinct impression that many of those who generalize in biogeography encounter great difficulty securing appropriate systematic data from fields other than their own, and thus their results often are clouded by taxonomic uncertainty. Second, we must strive for better evaluation of ecological and other natural history aspects of species—both in plotting distributions and in conducting biogeographical analyses. I cannot believe that beetles (or even families of beetles), any more than birds, are all so alike in habits as to allow some of the gross generalizations to which many of us are prone. As an example, the Sahara is a vast desert area with, I suppose, a "desert avifauna." The species of desert birds are, however, exceedingly diverse; some birds—usually excellent flyers—require water once or twice a day and exist only within access to water. Are such species part of the "desert avifauna" or should that concept include only species that can exist where water is unavailable at the surface? If the latter, does one include birds of rocky cliffs—usually predators (e.g., vultures and falcons)—that indeed live under true desert conditions in the presence of such cliffs, but also live beside rivers and elsewhere near water? Such considerations are germane, but often are not evident in biogeographical reports.

I am dubious about our ability to trace biotas through their histories, especially beyond the Pleistocene, because I suspect that the rate of shifting of their component species is too rapid. It also is difficult to treat many large vertebrates that have extensive ranges and thus may be represented in several diverse biotas. Some individual migratory birds actually seasonally represent different biotas. Ever-occurring allopatric speciation often results in ecological shifts such that the newly evolved sister-species come to represent different biotas.

Some of the more or less semantic problems and problems of over-zealous use of terms by both dispersalist and vicariance biogeographers are alluded to by Udvardy. In a sense, dispersal inevitably must precede every vicariant event. Occurrences such as orogenies that might result in vicariance also require dispersal. For example, a montane forest species affected by massive mountain-building may be separated into vicariant units on each side of the mountain mass, but displacement of the montane forest might well result in dispersal of all individuals of the original population to areas outside its former range. A large rise in sea level could split a population as well, and with concomitant climatic shifts, the two resulting vicariant populations might come to occupy ranges formerly unoccupied by the ancestral population.

We can argue about past dispersals, but there are many instances of dispersal occurring in the present; these must be accepted and considered in evaluating the past dispersal capabilities of appropriate extant taxa. The Cattle Egret (*Bubulcus ibis*), a heron, dispersed from Africa to South America in the 1920s, became established, and has since spread northward through

Central America and North America as far as the New York region. This clearly indicates the dispersal capability of herons and suggests that over time many other herons and allied species may have dispersed from Africa directly to South America, rather than reaching the New World from the Palearctic through North America. The taxonomy of various ducks, gulls, lapwings, kingfishers, and others (Short 1975) indicates a high probability of such trans-oceanic dispersal within at least these groups. Although accidental in occurrence, and so far with few instances of establishment in Europe, the frequent dispersal (tens of species over the past decade alone) of North American birds to Europe, even including small sparrows and other land birds, gives testimony to the dispersal capability of birds. Over geological time the Hawaiian Islands have been reached by diverse birds: with dispersal from Asia and the South Pacific of honeyeaters (Meliphagidae), white-eyes (Zosteropidae), a flycatcher (Monarchidae), and thrushes (Turdidae), while a hawk (Accipitridae), a shorebird (Recurvirostridae), a goose (Anatidae), and a crow (Corvidae) seem to have arrived from the Americas.

The Northern Mockingbird (*Mimus polyglottos*) has shifted its range northward over the past two decades from southern New Jersey as far as Maine. Perhaps it is preferable for biogeographers to treat dispersal at the level of species and above to include only movement outside the "normal" range of the species considered, recognizing of course that individuals of a species at the limits of its range are constantly dispersing (usually with fatal consequences) short distances beyond those limits.

To some persons it might seem reasonable to exclude birds from biogeographical consideration because of their great mobility. Other persons might simply accept certain groups of birds as useful and ignore others. It rather seems to me that avian evidence ought to be evaluated case by case on the basis of proven dispersal capability and likely probability of long-distance dispersal.

One ought not to confuse centers of origin with distributional centers obtained by plotting limits of systematic species. Areas in which the vegetation and climate shift are the usual borders of the ranges of species and subspecies; these borders are often fluid. Plotted dispersal centers and refugia are not the actual centers of origin in most cases; one may distinguish such distributional centers correlated with recent geological, phytogeographical, and climatic history, but their location *in situ* for a time period of sufficient duration to consider them true centers of origin is doubtful.

I note the usefulness of plotting distributional centers from accurate data. Accurate plotting not only directly assists the biogeographer; it also calls attention to intervening areas of paucity of species between the centers. The works of Haffer (1969, 1974) and Müller (1973) led to the checking of such areas in Amazonian South America by phytogeographers (Prance 1973; Simpson and Haffer 1978) and by specialists in other groups (e.g., Brown 1976), providing corroborative evidence that these intervening areas are depauperate and that they show indications of recent vegetational shifts. With the dearth of palynological and other data bearing on historical processes this evidence is very important.

Udvardy in my view is correct to state that vicariance and dispersalist techniques are essentially similar, being based upon plotting of actual, super-imposed distributional patterns. Regarding birds, I suspect that whatever the techniques, it generally will be found that vicariance and dispersal both have played major roles in the evolution of continental avifaunas, and that dispersal has been predominant in archipelagoes and oceanic islands.

Discussion

N. Eldredge

IT SEEMS reasonable to assume that historical inquiry in science contains at least two elements: pattern and process. In the area of evolutionary biology, the pattern is the phylogenetic history of life—the single genealogy that we assume underlies the nested pattern of resemblances among organisms. The processes in evolution are all those mechanisms theorized to have produced that genealogy and that nested set of resemblances.

Likewise, in historical biogeography we find questions of pattern and process. For pattern, we ask: Are the elements of the biota distributed in an orderly fashion? If so, what is that order? Has the nature of the distribution changed through time? If so, what is the sequence of events of that change? For process, we ask: How are distributions modified through time? What are the units (i.e., biological entities) in nature that exhibit change—individuals, populations, species, genera and taxa of even higher rank, or some sort of ecological unit? Are changes in biotic distribution a function of (1a) random or (1b) deterministic movements of organisms themselves, i.e., dispersal;[1] or (2a) random or (2b) deterministic results of passive response by organisms to changes in physical geography? Dr. Udvardy clearly focuses on process ques-

---

[1] This is my definition of dispersal. Udvardy's concept of "passive dispersal" is comparable to my second category: changes in distribution passively reflect changes in physical geography.

tions here, and appears to favor a theory along the lines of (1a) random movements.

The next step is to ask: What is the relationship between pattern and process? In our typically western approach to science, we assume that all phenomena we see in nature have an underlying cause. Process produces pattern. But epistemologically, what is the appropriate relationship between pattern and process? How should scientists combine these two components for their historical analyses?

The usual response, as reflected in most historical analyses in evolution and biogeography, is neatly summarized by Bock and Von Wahlert (1963:140):

> Any study of a historical subject, be it organic evolution, geology, western civilization or whatever else, has three major aspects which are: (a) the description of the sequences of events and changes (i.e. historical configurational sequences) which have occurred during time; these events are only described or listed without comment—the listing usually being in chronological order; (b) the study of the mechanisms and the processes, including causes, consequences, interrelationships with other influences, etc. (i.e. immanent properties and processes), by which the subject matter changes; and (c) the overall explanation of the events and changes which have occurred using the known mechanisms of change.

To paraphrase succinctly: We have a pattern, we have notions of process, and the logical connection between the two in historical analysis is the explanation of the pattern in terms of ideas about process. For example, in evolutionary biology we would have a phylogeny—the pattern or theory of history of relationships among a series of organisms. We would adopt one of the several general sets of theories about how organisms evolve. We would then explain the phylogeny in terms of the notions of process, producing what is best described as a *scenario*. Tattersall and Eldredge (1977:208) remarked that "in devising a scenario one is limited only by the bounds of one's imagination and by the credulity of one's audience. . . ." The evolutionary literature is replete with such *just so* stories. They are usually criticized as untestable inductive narratives representing poor scientific practice.

But scenarios have another feature more germane to the present discussion; if we take notions of process and use them to explain patterns, we automatically abdicate any position allowing us to improve our theories of process. In other words, contrary to item (c) suggested by Bock and Von Wahlert, we should take our patterns and compare them with patterns predicted to result from various theories of process. If the predicted patterns do not agree with patterns we believe actually exist in nature,[2] we can discard some of our competing notions of process. There is no other way, as I see it, to improve our theories of process, be they evolutionary or biogeographical.

Scenarios permeate the literature of biogeography every bit as much as the literature of evolution. If we believe that migration (of species, not annual migration of individuals within a species) is the dominant mechanism of changes in biotic distribution, we write scenarios about how North American mammals invaded hapless South America. If we think that organisms passively reflect changes in physical geography, we write scenarios about butterflies with Gondwanan distributions that reflect the breakup and subsequent scatter of pieces of this hypothesized great southern land mass. In neither case are we setting up a situation that would allow us to examine critically the notion of process that we are applying, in a purely axiomatic fashion, to explain an apparent pattern. I share with Udvardy the belief that processes or mechanisms that account for changes in patterns of distribution of organisms are of great scientific interest. Although I do not dispute that the physiology of dispersal—as well as modes of change in relatively recent examples of range modification—can in fact be studied, I am concerned with the more general problem of dispersal as a mechanism of change in historical patterns of distribution. Biogeography, like evolutionary theory, desperately needs to have the study of pattern rigidly divorced from *a priori* notions of process, and to study processes underlying pattern by using pattern to test specific theories of process. Testing is effected by generating expected patterns from theory and comparing them with patterns obtained independently from biogeographical analysis.

The very occurrence of this symposium is tacit testimony to our mutual agreement that there is indeed order in the distribution of the elements of the earth's biota. So, in detail, we need to ask: What is the exact pattern and how has this pattern changed through time? Clearly we need a methodology for capturing the pattern. We do not need, it seems, an *a priori* theory of how that pattern arose (which would bias our attempt to perceive the pattern). We need, instead, some sort of mapping procedure. Udvardy suggests that Croizat et al. (1974) and other panbiogeographers or vicariance biogeographers all use more or less the same mapping technique as non-vicariance biogeographers. I am not equipped to evaluate this suggestion, but it is

[2] Of course we do not "observe" patterns in nature. Such patterns can never be more than highly corroborated hypotheses about the nature of the world.

interesting. If pattern is methodologically disassociated from process, there seems to be no reason why dispersalists, vicariantists, etc., cannot all use the same technique to discover the pattern that they all try to explain with their disparate notions of process. It is hoped that this symposium will offer, among other things, a survey of existing methods of capturing biogeographical patterns. Surely improvement in this area is a desideratum and, divorced from notions of process, could truly advance biogeography in general.

Most of the recent debate in historical biogeography seems to be over process; is it dispersal or vicariance? Here we see the beginnings of what I consider a more appropriate juxtaposition of pattern and process; when biogeographers argue the relative merits of vicariance vs. dispersal, they ask which process best accounts for the pattern. With a more explicit discussion of what sorts of patterns each process might be expected to generate under a given set of circumstances (kinds of organisms, habitats, etc.), we can anticipate further improvement. But we cannot expect to proceed very far if we persist in spinning the scenarios that still constitute the bulk of biogeography.

As an approach to studying process in historical biogeography, we might ask: Would dispersal theory in general predict the generation of new regular patterns from old patterns? Specific predictions would be related to the kinds of organisms (i.e., in terms of their dispersal physiologies) and general environments within the area under consideration. Certainly it has been hypothesized that dispersal can create new, orderly patterns from old ones. If the scenario of the North American mammalian invasion of South America is correct, the answer is "yes"; dispersal can change a biogeographical pattern and leave in its wake a new pattern, fully as orderly as the first. Dispersal remains a viable hypothesis.

We might also ask: Can drift create new regular patterns from old ones? Can plate tectonics or the expanding earth, or eustatic changes, climatological changes, or changes in oceanic and wind circulation patterns, change biotic distributions in an orderly fashion? The notion that organismic distributions passively reflect environmental distributions so that changes in physical geography change the geographical distributions of organisms, leads to the general prediction that patterns of biogeographical change should be isomorphic with patterns of physical geographical change. Detailed predictions in any one case would be that the change in physical geography recognized by others, on other criteria (e.g., by geologists and geographers), would be similar to the general pattern exhibited by *all* organisms in the area affected, regardless of their differences in dispersal physiology.

It is difficult to write about the hypothetico-deductive approach to the study of process in historical biogeography. But that is no excuse for not pursuing the matter. Pattern is interesting and important per se. Systematists, for example, are naturally interested in the geographical distributions of their species. But pattern alone is not enough; it should be applicable to other problems in science. One further use of biogeographical pattern that seems to be emerging these days is testing of hypotheses of changes in topology of different segments of the earth's crust. In other words, one goal of biogeography is paleogeography. There is a real parallel between biogeography and biostratigraphy (the study of the temporal distributions of organisms). The goal of biostratigraphy is to capture patterns of equivalence of bodies of rock. By restricting our attention wholly to biogeographical patterns, eschewing the processes underlying change in these patterns as untestable, biogeography also seems to be capturing patterns of equivalence of rock bodies—in this case, slices of the earth's crust. While this is laudable, it is geography, not biology. So I applaud Udvardy's desire to study dispersal as a mechanism of change in patterns of biotic distributions. But let us utilize our patterns to test our theories of process in a hypothetico-deductive manner, and avoid the axiomatic application of ideas of process to explain away these patterns.

Response

M. D. F. Udvardy

DR. SHORT, a fellow ornithologist, mentions several pitfalls that the avian geographer should try to avoid. His remark that birds are good dispersers, and his examples (herons, etc.) reveal a paradoxical aspect of the various biogeographical schools. The vicariance school is criticized for omitting from consideration the good dispersers, or widespread forms that live on cosmopolitan, but historically (temporally) and locationally ephemeral, biotopes (e.g., wetlands). The equilibrium school, in contrast, might be criticized for chiefly considering the good dispersers, namely those forms that indeed pioneer by crossing barriers. This paradoxical situation adds weight to my original notion (figure 1.3) that our facts and evidences are contained in several separate suitcases.

I agree with Short and his warning to use caution in tracing biotas beyond the Pleistocene. But here is an occasion to test the principle of ecological uniformitarianism. "Biota" is a much overgeneralized term without an equivalent in any other scientific language. Our discipline would be well served if this term would henceforth be restricted to biological geography and paleogeography.

I also agree with the constructive additions Eldredge makes. I feel, however, that my "dispersal" concept contains less of the random element and more of the deterministic movements of organisms, whether through active dispersal (locomotion), or by way of a carrier secured by structural or behavioral means.

2

There Have Been No Statistical Tests of Cladistic Biogeographical Hypotheses

D. Simberloff, K. L. Heck, E. D. McCoy, and E. F. Connor

IS THE FACT that the red mangrove species *Rhizophora mangle* thrives on the Atlantic coasts of both the Americas and Africa a reflection of the tree's great powers of dispersal or of the former proximity of these continents? Such questions have recently become a central focus in historical biogeography, giving rise to two major competing hypotheses to explain faunal and floral similarities among widespread locations: center-of-origin/long-distance dispersal and vicariance. The center-of-origin/long-distance dispersal hypothesis envisions that the place of origin of a taxon is that area in which it is most diverse, and suggests that areas of lesser diversity result primarily from decreased dispersal from the ancestral center of origin. The vicariance hypothesis envisions that current distributional patterns reflect the existence of previously widespread biotas that have since become modified by tectonic events, speciation, and extinction.

In a recent contribution on vicariant patterns, Rosen (1978) emphasizes the differences between historical and island (equilibrium) biogeographies (MacArthur and Wilson 1963, 1967; Simberloff 1974)—the former merging with systematics and geology, the latter integrating with ecology. Rosen suggested that the two are, and will remain, independent and even mutually exclusive. We are less pessimistic. We view the only real differences between them as their time frames and geographical scales. Island biogeography usually concerns itself with processes operating in ecological—in most instances post-Pleistocene—time periods (Diamond 1972; Simberloff 1974; Simpson 1974; Terborgh 1974), whereas historical biogeography seeks to explain existing patterns of similarity and difference in the earth's fauna and flora by considering factors operating from the most recent to the most distant past (e.g., Cracraft 1974a). Island biogeography attempts to explain taxonomic distribution patterns among islands in archipelagoes; historical biogeography attempts to explain patterns among presently widespread locations. Thus the time frames of the two overlap in the very recent past, and their geographical scales overlap in large archipelagoes, such as the West Indies. Below we draw some parallels between the two biogeographies. We attempt to determine if certain island-biogeographical techniques can aid in resolving the controversy between the proponents of dispersal and those of vicariance.

Null Hypotheses in Island Biogeography

What appears to be a single problem—explaining species-distribution patterns (in the historical-biogeographical context, determining whether the patterns are caused by individual dispersal or vicariance)—is in reality a series of problems. First, one needs to determine the degree of relatedness among locations: is the similarity between the biotas of sites A and B greater than, say, that between sites A and C? Second, one wishes to know whether or not the suite of pairwise similarities differs from a null distribution based upon a random assortment of species: If all taxa in each of the areas were placed into a bucket and sampled randomly, subject to various constraints, what is the chance that the observed distribution of taxa among areas—with its attendant distribution of pairwise similarities—would result? Finally, having decided that there is a distribution that is unlikely to be due to chance alone, one needs to determine what mechanism is most likely responsible for it.

To approach this series of problems in island biogeography (Connor and Simberloff 1978; Simberloff 1978), one constructs an r × c binary matrix **M**, where the r rows represent species and the c columns represent locations, and each entry m is 1 if species i is present at location j and 0 if it is absent. One then examines the matrix by grouping sites (analogous to Q-mode analysis in numerical taxonomy) or by grouping species (analogous to R-mode analysis (cf. Simberloff and Connor 1979). Grouping by sites is more common, and one usually judges similarities between sites with a standard index (Jaccard's, Sorensen's, etc.). The problems inherent in these ad hoc indices are well known (references in Simberloff and Connor 1979): two critical problems are that the indices are sample-size dependent and that their sampling distributions are unknown, so that one cannot assess the statistical significance of some observed pairwise similarity value.

    Connor and Simberloff (1978) and Simberloff (1978) have derived a technique for dealing with these debilitating shortcomings of classical Q-mode similarity analysis in island biogeography. They calculate the expected number of species held in common by two islands and the associated variance, under the null hypothesis that the observed number of species shared between the two islands is no different than would be expected if the species were random samples from a common species pool. Random colonization models can rest on either of two sets of assumptions. One assumption is that all species are equally likely to colonize any island, which yields an expected similarity (E_{AB}) and its associated variance ($V_{E_{AB}}$):

$$E_{AB} = \frac{\sum_{i=0}^{m} \binom{p-n}{i} \binom{n}{m-i} (m-i)}{\binom{p}{m}} = \frac{mn}{p}$$

$$V_{E_{AB}} = \frac{\sum_{i=0}^{m} \binom{p-n}{i} \binom{n}{m-i} (m-i-E_{AB})^2}{\binom{p}{m}}$$

where m species are on one island, n on the other, $m \leq n$, and the pool contains p species. The other assumption is that the p species possess different dispersal and persistence capabilities, and for this model E_{AB} and $V_{E_{AB}}$ can be determined by repeated simulation (Connor and Simberloff 1978). Knowing the expected number of species in common between two islands and the associated variance allows a probabilistic analysis of the set of compositional similarities associated with some observed distribution of species on an archipelago of islands or set of sites.

R-mode analysis is less frequent in island biogeography and is similarly plagued by lack of sound statistical procedures for determining whether some observed distribution of similarities among the sets of sites shared between pairs (or larger groups) of species is conceivably due only to chance individual colonization (Connor and Simberloff 1979; Simberloff and Connor 1979). The observed data of interest in R-mode analysis are, in a sense, exactly opposite to those of Q-mode analysis, because one is typically interested in an extreme dissimilarity—namely, a pair (or larger group) of species that share *no* sites and are therefore geographically mutually exclusive. The proper parsimonious null hypothesis here is that the number of such exclusively distributed pairs, or "missing combinations" (Simberloff and Connor 1980), is that expected were chance alone operating; but an alternative hypothesis (competitive exclusion) is always adopted with either an incorrect statistical test (Abbott 1977; Abbott et al. 1977; Grant 1970) or no test at all (Diamond 1975; M'Closkey 1978). For example, Diamond (1975) suggested that one "rule" governing community assembly on islands is that some groups of species are found nowhere in an archipelago of interest. He attributed this rule primarily to the idea that inter-specific competition precludes the persistence of these groups; yet one would expect such missing combinations to occur even if an archipelago were colonized randomly subject only to the constraints that certain islands contain more species than do others (because, i.a., they are larger), and certain species are found on more islands than are others (e.g., because they are better dispersers). For example, there are 56 bird species in the New Hebrides, distributed over 28 islands. There are therefore $\binom{56}{2}$ = 1,540 pairs of birds, and of these, 63 are found nowhere in the archipelago. Yet on an archipelago filled randomly with birds—subject only to the constraints that each species exist on the number of islands on which it actually exists, and that each island contain the number of species that it actually contains—one would have expected 63.2 such pairs (s.d. = 2.9; Connor and Simberloff 1979). This expectation is deduced by repeatedly producing a random binary (0–1) matrix, with number of rows = r = number of species = 56; and number of columns = c = number of islands = 28, maintaining only the distributions of row and column sums (to simulate constrained island totals and species occurrences). Each such matrix M, with m_{ij} = 1 representing species i's presence on island j, and m_{ij} = 0 representing its absence, is then scanned to see how many pairs of rows had no matching 1's in even a single column; such a pair of rows represents an exclusively distributed species pair.

Null Hypotheses in Cladistic Historical Biogeography

We describe this method in some detail because it is pertinent to the key problem in historical biogeography, center-of-origin/long-distance dispersal vs. vicariance. Historical biogeographers seem to be concerned more than are island biogeographers with the need to use objective, probabilistic methods to test biogeographical hypotheses, despite philosophical disagreement about what actually constitutes hypothesis testing (cf. Rosen 1976a vs. McDowall 1978; also Heck and McCoy 1979). Rosen (1978) has attempted to apply probability theory to the testing of historical-biogeographical hypotheses. Using the principles of phylogenetic systematics, he constructs cladograms to measure similarity among poeciliid fishes of the genera *Heterandria* and *Xiphophorus* in North and Central America. By replacing taxa on the cladograms derived for *Heterandria* and *Xiphophorus* with numerals representing geographical areas where they occur, Rosen converts his cladograms of species into cladograms of areas (his figure 2). He then eliminates from the cladograms those sites (areas) that are not shared among the genera. Shared elements in the reduced-area cladograms include five areas (1, 4–5, 10, 8, and 2 in his figure 2) whose significance, Rosen asserts, is that they occur in the same cladistic topology.

Rosen then asks: What is the probability that the geographically transformed, reduced-area cladograms of *Heterandria* and *Xiphophorus* will be concordant by chance alone?[1] To illustrate how he calculates probabilities, he uses a three-taxon system. Theoretically, there are three possible dichotomous cladograms: areas 1 and 2 vs. area 3; areas 2 and 3 vs. 1; and areas 1 and 3 vs. 2. He then reasons that the null probability that a second group sympatric with the first will duplicate its branching pattern is one in three. Thus 33 percent of the time, he says, we would expect to find two 3-taxon reduced-area cladograms that are concordant, as would be those of *Heterandria* and *Xiphophorus* were they further area reduced to any three shared sites. A third concordant taxon, such as the tortoise genus *Terrapene*, would be expected by chance only one of nine times, or 11 percent of the time; fourth and fifth concordant taxa would lower the probabilities to 1/27 (4 percent) and 1/81 (1 percent), respectively. For the 5-member reduced-area cladograms of *Heterandria* and *Xiphophorus*, he finds the null probability of concordance to be 1/105 = 1 percent, for there are 105 possible dichotomous 5-member cladograms (Felsenstein 1978).

[1] We use "concordant" to indicate topological identity and "coincident" to indicate geographical distributional identity.

There are several errors and assumptions in Rosen's analysis—some statistical and others biological and/or paleontological—that render his particular result questionable and that, taken together, suggest to us that it is very unlikely that sufficient data exist on any group for one to apply this sort of analysis to test for the probability that some observed set of biogeographical distributions is due to chance dispersal of individual taxa. We first outline our statistical objections and describe the correct procedure should an appropriate data set become available.

Rosen assumes that all possible n-member cladograms are equiprobable, while for n > 3 there are not only several distinguishable cladograms (the exact number can be determined from Felsenstein's formula), but several distinct topological *types* of cladograms; our feeling is that these types are equiprobable, or at least that this is a parsimonious testable hypothesis. Otherwise one is in a situation analogous to comparing apples and oranges. We defer to appendix 2.1 the algorithm for calculating the number of types of dichotomous cladograms for any n, but we offer an example here for n = 5. There are three types, depicted in figure 2.1, of which there are 60 distinguishable cladograms of type 1a, 15 of type 1b, and 30 of type 1c. By assigning equal probability to each of the 105 cladograms, Rosen is saying that type 1a is four times as probable as type 1b, and twice as probable as type 1c. Why should this be so? Surely there is no *a priori* reason for thinking that type 1a is more likely to occur just because there are more distinguishable arrangements of five numbers among its tips. In principle this is a testable proposition, with two tests of our hypothesis of equiprobable types coming immediately to mind if there is a sample of n-member cladograms. First, one might compare by a χ^2 test, the observed distribution of cladograms among types to an expected distribution in which they are equiprobable. Second, particularly because the size of the sample of cladograms is likely to be small, one might look simply for the number of types *not* represented in the sample, and determine by Maxwell-Boltzmann statistics (Feller 1950)

Figure 2.1. The three topoiogically distinct types of 5-member cladograms.

whether absence of this many or more types is improbable if the types are equally likely. This entire procedure would be a fascinating exercise in its own right, particularly should one find that certain topological types are, in fact, more likely than others. Without such a test, however, we assume that types are equiprobable, so that each particular cladogram (i.e., distinguishable arrangement of numbers on the ends of the branches) of type 1a, for example, is only one-half as likely to occur by chance alone as is each clado-gram of type 1c, and only one-fourth as likely to occur by chance as is each cladogram of type 1b.

We observe in passing that another reasonable underlying distribution for the null probabilities of the different types would be that generated by a strictly Markovian dichotomous branching process with branching points equiprobable (cf. Raup et al. 1973; Gould et al. 1977; Sepkoski 1978). That is, if one assumes at any instant that the location of the next branching node is equiprobably distributed among all growing tips (i.e., independent of the topological position of each tip), one can allocate null probabilities to the different cladogram types; these are neither equiprobable nor proportional to the number of distinguishable arrangements of each type. For the three types a, b, and c of 5-member cladograms (figure 2.1), for example, the equiprobable hypothesis assigns probabilities 1/3, 1/3, and 1/3 respectively; the proportional-to-distinguishable-arrangements hypothesis assigns probabilities 4/7, 1/7, and 2/7 respectively; the Markovian hypothesis assigns probabilities 1/3, 1/6, and 1/2 respectively. Finally, *any* asymmetry among the probabilities of the distinguishable cladograms *increases* the null probability that a random pair of cladograms will be concordant.

A second flaw is Rosen's procedure for area reduction of cladograms. Although area reduction is proper for pairwise examination of any two cladograms, it is not in general permissible for comparison of three or more cladograms, as in his extension of the *Heterandria-Xiphophorus* comparison to *Terrapene*. Consider figure 2.2, of three hypothetical 5-member cladograms, 2a–c. The only three areas shared among all three cladograms are 1, 2, and 4, although each pair of cladograms share at least four sites. All cladograms, when area-reduced by Rosen's procedure, become cladogram 2d, so that he would have viewed them as concordant, with chance probability of 11 percent. Each of the three pairs of cladograms, when area-reduced to its common sites, however, becomes a pair of incompatible cladograms. Platnick and Nelson (1978) give a similar example (their figure 2), in which two large, mutually incompatible (not coincident) general pat-

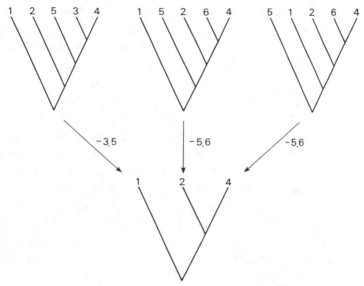

Figure 2.2. Examples of three pairwise discordant 5-member cladograms that appear concordant when area-reduced to sites shared by all three.

terns share some elements in a limited area where they are sympatric, and in that area they produce concordant cladograms. When adding a new clado- gram to a pre-existing set of s n-member cladograms, then, one must always compare pairwise each of the s new pairs formed by adding the new clado- gram to the set—to insure that each pair is concordant over all its shared sites, and not only the $m \leq n$ sites held in common by all $s + 1$ members of the new set.

A third fundamental statistical error in Rosen's approach is precisely that committed by Diamond (1975) in his "tests" of his community assembly rules, discussed above. Namely, Rosen considers only those examples consistent with his hypothesis whereas, in order to assess the probability of finding, say, two concordant 5-member cladograms, one must first delimit the universe of endemic 5-taxon systems from which the sample cladograms are drawn. Let us consider Rosen's two concordant 5-member poeciliid cladograms in this spirit. He says that the null probability of such concord- ance is $1/105 = .0095$; if types were equiprobable, as explained above, it would be $1/3 \times 1/3 \times (1/60 + 1/30 + 1/15) = .0130$. In either instance, this is only the null probability that *Heterandria* and *Xiphophorus*, the two genera *specified in advance*, have concordant cladograms. The probability that *some* pair of 5-member cladograms will be concordant is much greater. For poeciliids (Rosen and Bailey 1963), we find 21 genera, of which seven have more than five species, and 30 monophyletic species groups, of which ten have more than five species. Therefore there are at least $\binom{7}{2} = 21$ cladogram pairs in the universe, and if we were to use all available cladistic information, there are $\binom{10}{2} = 45$ cladogram pairs. For this universe size, if all the taxa were endemic to their current sites, it is not apparent that the existence of a single event with probability in the neighborhood of 1 percent is that unusual, for there are 45 such events to examine. One cannot simply multiply 45×1 percent to calculate the probability that at least one such event occurs, because the events are not independent. If we know taxon A's cladogram is not concordant with that of taxon B, and that taxon B's cladogram is not concordant with that of taxon C, we know something about the probability that taxon A's cladogram is concordant with that of taxon C. In Appendix 2.2 we outline an algorithm, based on that of Connor and Simberloff (1979) for the assembly rules, that gives the expected number of concordant n-member cladograms and its variance, for comparison to an observed data set. Because only taxa endemic to their current sites bear on Rosen's procedure, the universe of cladograms in specific instances may be very small, especially for n as large as five. If the universe were as small as two or three cladograms, a single observed concordance would be of doubtful significance with respect to a causal geographical hypothesis. We would know simply that one or a few "trials" were run and that one apparently unlikely outcome was observed.

Rosen (1978) quite explicitly looks only for confirmatory evidence. After finding that the tortoise *Terrapene* has a reduced-area 3-member cladogram concordant with those of the two poeciliid genera (which he claims is nonrandom at the 89 percent confidence level), he states:

The discovery by random search within other monophyletic groups distributionally coincident in North and Middle America of another cladogram that coincides with those three would alter the estimate of nonrandomness to the 96% confidence level, and of still one more to the 99% level. This is merely another way of saying that the discovery of additional cladistically congruent distributions can only reduce the probability or likelihood that the observed coincidence has resulted from random historical factors.

This is incorrect; one would have to know also the sampling universe at each step. By adding *Terrapene*, Rosen expands the universe to include at least the Middle and North American lower vertebrates. How many genera of these are there with at least three endemic species? If there were 100, there would be $\binom{100}{3}$ = 161,700 trios and $\binom{100}{4}$ = 3,921,225 quartets of cladograms in the universe. That a particular trio or quartet is concordant when such an event would have a null probability of 5 or 10 percent would tell us nothing; we would have expected such concordant trios and quartets to occur. Suppose that a true, 6-faced die is repeatedly tossed, and that we scan the sequence of outcomes for the event "two successive outcomes identical." Such an event for a given pair of tosses specified in advance has probability 1/6, but in a string of several tosses we are nevertheless likely to observe such an event at least once. Rosen would have us believe that such an observation (e.g., successive 4's) would imply that the die is non-random, and that his hypothesis would be strengthened by scanning the sequence of outcomes further until we found three 4's in a row.

We note also that the concept of generalized "tracks" (e.g., Croizat et al. 1974) has never been tested statistically and could well be a statistical artifact, for the same reason that two concordant 5-member cladograms might be expected given chance dispersal of individual taxa. A generalized track is a set of coincident distributions, and the existence of a number of such coincident distributions is viewed as prima-facie evidence that individual taxon dispersal could not have produced the distributions. Nowhere does one specify the universe of distributions from which the coincident sample is drawn. Once again, one is seeking confirmatory rather than falsifying data. A track of eight coincident taxa, for example, might be quite improbable if one had specified in advance which eight taxa were to be examined, but if there were, say, 100 taxa in the region, the fact that there are $\binom{100}{8}$ = 1.86 × 10^{11} octets should be sobering.

McDowall (1978) has discussed in some detail the difficulties inherent in testing hypotheses concerning the mechanisms that have produced present biogeographical patterns and in drawing inferences from tracks. Platnick and Nelson (1978), however, in an apparent reversal of earlier contentions that the construction of generalized tracks alone can lead to testable biogeographical hypotheses (Nelson 1973b; Croizat et al. 1974), have recently suggested that vicariance hypotheses can be falsified, but only when cladistic methods are used to reconstruct the phylogenetic history of the taxa of interest. In this manner, they state that the recency of interconnections among geographically separate areas can be determined and compared with geological evidence to determine the cause of the distributions in question. Procedures similar to those outlined above can be applied to their suggestion, but a new sampling problem arises: namely, to define the universe of cladograms about which we wish to draw some inference, and to demonstrate that the sample of cladograms available for analysis is a random sample. For continent-sized land masses this universe would be quite large and very difficult to define; to show that a particular sample from that universe is random would be a monumental task.

Platnick and Nelson (1978) take a tack different from Rosen's. They first hypothesize a given pattern and schedule of land movement (e.g., "that areas b and c are more recently connected to each other than either is to area a"), then ask whether any of the sample of available cladograms falsify the hypothesis. At the outset they have adopted what seems a peculiar criterion for falsification:

> If we find [3-member] groups showing the first mentioned set of relationships [taxa in areas b and c are each other's closest relatives], our hypothesis is corroborated, but if *none* of the available test groups shows the set of relationships we can reject the hypothesis that the distribution of our original groups reflects a general pattern of interrelationships of areas and their history (emphasis added).

We argue that the proper parsimonious null hypothesis is that the distributions were produced by chance dispersal of individual taxa, and that the criterion for rejection of this null hypothesis in favor of the alternative hypothesis of vicariance should be an observed fraction of the available cladograms consistent with the posited geographical relationship far in excess of that which might reasonably have occurred by chance. In an example of three 3-member cladograms, because there are only three distinguishable cladograms and all three are of one type, the null distribution of cladograms among the arrangements is in accord with Maxwell-Boltzmann statistics (Feller 1950), so that the null probability that two or more of them would show a given set of relationships is $7/27 = .259$, while the null probability that all three would show a given set is $1/27 = .037$. Clearly an observation that two of the cladograms show the hypothetical set of relationships could not be construed as strong support for the alternative, vicariance hypothesis; a result at least as extreme would occur by chance alone 25.9 percent of the time. If there were four 3-member cladograms, the null probability that two or more will be consistent with an *a priori* geographical hypothesis is $33/81 = .407$, while the null probability that at

Figure 2.3. The two topologically distinct types of 4-member cladograms.

least three will accord with the posited pattern is 9/81 = .111. Once again we would have to observe all cladograms consistent with the hypothesis to view the result as strong support for the vicariance alternative.

For a four-site geographical hypothesis, with four taxa and with no taxon occurring in more than one site, the calculation of a null probability for some observed degree of agreement with the geographical hypothesis is vastly more complicated, and rests on the assignment of null probabilities to the *types* of cladograms (of which there are two, depicted in figure 2.3) as discussed above. Consider the geographical hypothesis plus six observed cladograms (three 4-member plus three 3-member ones) shown in figure 2.4. Of these, one 4-member cladogram (4a) and two 3-member ones (4b and 4f) are consistent with the hypothesis. What is the null probability that a set of three 4-member and three 3-member cladograms, randomly drawn from the universe of possible cladograms, would produce this much or more consistency with the hypothesis? First, because in a sense we compare lizards and oranges, we must adopt the subjective convention that a 3-member cladogram's consistency with the geographical hypothesis is worth as much as that of a 4-member cladogram. Alternatively, one might weight them as inversely proportional to their null probabilities. Second, because we compare apples and oranges, we must adopt a convention concerning the null relative probabilities of the two 4-member topological types. For this example as well, we assume them equiprobable (the Markovian hypothesis has 3a half as probable as 3b). Consistency with the geographical hypothesis at least as extreme as that observed could then be achieved by any of the ten dispositions of six cladograms among consistent and inconsistent arrangements shown in table 2.1. Because we use Maxwell-Boltzmann statistics, the probability of any particular arrangement within each of these dispositions must be multiplied by the number of distinguishable ways in which such a disposition can be achieved—also shown in table 2.1. For 4-member

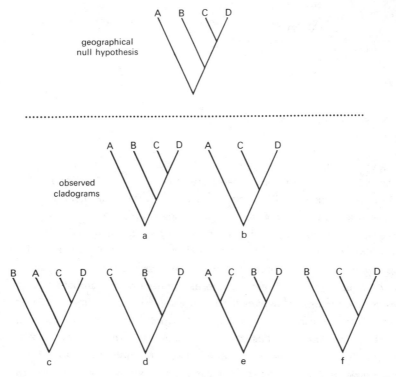

Figure 2.4. A geographical null hypothesis plus six observed cladograms to be tested for consistency with the null hypothesis.

cladograms, the two types are equiprobable; there are twelve distinguishable arrangements of type 3b, the observed type; the null probability that a 4-member cladogram is consistent with the geographical hypothesis is $1/2 \times 1/12 = 1/24$; and the null probability of inconsistency is $23/24$. For 3-member cladograms with no taxon sharing sites, Platnick and Nelson (1978) show that the null probability of consistency with the geographical hypothesis is $1/3$, and null probability of inconsistency is $2/3$. The null probability of each disposition is therefore easily tabulated as in table 2.1, and the total null probability of a result as extreme as that observed is .063.

    This laborious calculation can be avoided by using parts of the simulation of appendix 2.2. Given a geographical hypothesis concerning s sites, and r observed cladograms such that r_3 of them are 3-member, r_4 are 4-member, $\ldots$, r_s are s-member $\left(\sum_{i=3}^{s} r_s = r \right)$, one could do the following: (a) perform

Table 2.1 Probability of Various Dispositions of Six Cladograms, Based on Random Dispersal Model

Consistent 4-member cladograms	Inconsistent 4-member cladograms	Consistent 3-member cladograms	Inconsistent 3-member cladograms	No. of Ways	Null probability of each	Total probability of disposition
1	2	2	1	9	$(1/24)(1/3)^2(23/24)^2(2/3)$	.026
2	1	2	1	9	$(1/24)^2(1/3)^2(23/24)(2/3)$	.001
2	1	3	0	3	$(1/24)^2(1/3)^3(23/24)$	.000
2	1	1	2	9	$(1/24)^2(1/3)(23/24)(2/3)^2$	.002
3	0	0	3	1	$(1/24)^3(2/3)^3$	.000
3	0	1	2	3	$(1/24)^3(1/3)(2/3)^2$	.000
3	0	2	1	3	$(1/24)^3(1/3)^2(2/3)$	.000
3	0	3	0	1	$(1/24)^3(1/3)^3$	.000
0	3	3	0	1	$(23/24)^3(1/3)^3$	.033
1	2	3	0	3	$(1/24)(23/24)^2(1/3)^3$	.001

step (2) pairwise between the hypothetical cladogram and each of the observed cladograms, keeping a running tally of the number of concordances (consistencies with the geographical hypothesis); (b) perform step (1); (c) repeatedly perform steps (3), (4), (5), and (6), thereby generating random sets of cladograms subject to the same constraints as the observed set, and determining the number of concordances for each random set; (d) place the observed number of concordances determined in step (a) in the statistical distribution produced in step (c) to see if the observed degree of consistency with the geographical hypothesis would likely have been produced randomly.

Biological and Paleontological Caveats

In appendix 2.2 and above we present solutions to statistical problems associated in the past with determining null probabilities of a given degree of cladistic and biogeographical concordance, but there are a number of biological and paleontological problems that are not so easily solved—some of which may, in fact, never be deductively solved. These must stand as explicit assumptions before the statistical analysis is done, and to the extent that these assumptions are unrealistic, the statistical results, even when done properly, are cast into doubt.

First is the problem of "ghosts," taxa that are part of a lineage but are now extinct (figure 2.5). It is clear, for example, that the cladogram depicted in figure 2.5 is concordant with that in figure 2.6B (cladogram 3) only if the ghost is unseen. What can we say about unseen ghosts? First, if they were seen, they would only lower the number of observed instances of con-

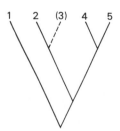

Figure 2.5. A recent 4-member cladogram with a "ghost" taxon, now extinct (represented by the dotted line).

Figure 2.6A. Topological types of 1-, 2-, and 3-member cladograms.

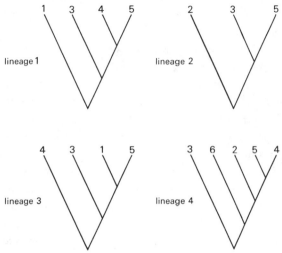

Figure 2.6B. Hypothetical set of cladograms with complete information on biogeographical distributions. Numbers at tips represent sites.

cordance because they can render a previously concordant group of cladograms discordant, but they can never effect the opposite transformation. However, the effect of ghosts on the null probability of an observed amount of concordance (appendix 2.2) is not obvious, and clearly depends on the way ghosts are produced in nature with respect to the topology of the cladogram in which they are embedded. Perhaps the most reasonable null hypothesis for this production, in the absence of paleontological evidence to the contrary, is that ghost production is Markovian and equiprobable; that is, the probability of extinction in the next interval of time is the same for each extant growing tip of a cladogram, independent of the topological location of the tip. We say "reasonable" because we find it unlikely that the probability of extinction of a taxon would depend on the phylogenetic path that the taxon took to reach its present topological position in the cladogram. No doubt one could suggest that increased competition between topologically near (phylogenetically closely related) taxa would increase their extinction probabilities relative to that of a taxon topologically distant from all others and thereby concoct a different distribution of probabilities for the topological location of ghosts. Because there is little evidence that taxonomic related-ness strongly increases probability of geographical exclusivity (Simberloff 1970, 1979; Connor and Simberloff 1979), we view this hypothesis as less likely. Whatever pattern of ghost production actually obtains, it will affect the null expectation of amount of concordance by determining the null prob-abilities of the different cladogram types—step (4) of appendix 2.2—which we have so far assumed equal.

Heck and McCoy (1978) present an example of the importance of ghosts in influencing the interpretation of biogeographical patterns. Of the seven extant genera of hermatypic corals found in the eastern Pacific, five occur also in the Indo-West Pacific. Marine biologists infer from these data that these corals drifted eastward across the Pacific in the post-Paleocene. If genera that have gone extinct in the eastern Pacific since the Paleocene are also included, however, a much weaker connection with the Indo-West Pacific is indicated; of the additional five genera of corals, none implies an Indo-West Pacific relationship. It is interesting to note also that because only post-Paleocene events are involved here, the presence of a generalized track across the Pacific is taken as evidence for a series of dispersal events, rather than for vicariance. This observation reinforces the contention of Platnick and Nelson (1978) that additional evidence, particularly fossils, may readily change the interpretation of a present distribution from vicariance-mediated to dispersal-mediated, or vice versa.

A second caveat is that one assumes whether characters are primitive or derived in constructing the cladograms, for the criteria determining this "do not have absolute validity" (Hennig 1966) and are subjective. In this sense, the results of cladistic similarity analysis differ from the Q-and R-mode island biogeographical analyses discussed above, in which the only data considered given and compared to a null distribution are directly observed species presences and absences.

A third caveat is the assumption that allopatric speciation is the means by which related taxa end up in different areas. While we do not doubt that allopatric speciation usually occurs among sexually reproducing animals, it is clearly true that stasipatric and sympatric speciation are much more common than previously suspected (Bush 1975b; Endler 1977; White 1978), espe-cially among parasites and parasitoids. This assumption is important because sympatric speciation with subsequent dispersal of the new species to new sites could not be distinguished from allopatric speciation (vicariance) and invasion of the original range. In short, if sympatric speciation occurs one cannot conclude that (Platnick and Nelson 1978):

The sympatric occurrence of two or more members of a single monophyletic group has been caused by the dispersal of one or more of these taxa into sympatry. Thus a question arises as to the cause of the distribution pattern of a group only when it contains allopatric elements (that could be the result of vicariance alone or of dispersal).

In fact, sympatric and allopatric distributions both raise questions concerning the cause of the distributions.

Inference from Island Biogeography and Cladistics

In spite of the three undemonstrated assumptions that one must make in order to test cladistic patterns as we outlined, we still believe that cladistic information can be important. An observed amount of concordance among cladograms—or consistency between a set of cladograms and a geographical hypothesis—no greater than that predicted by chance, would severely impugn the vicariance hypothesis and support an alternative hypothesis of individual dispersal, while levels of concordance or consistency far above chance expectations would tend to support the vicariance hypothesis despite the biological and paleontological caveats and would weaken the dispersal hypothesis. Our aim here has been to show that, in spite of claims to the contrary, no statistically valid support for the vicariance hypothesis or against the dispersal hypothesis is available, and that the sorts of data that must be brought to bear on the debate for a proper statistical test are formidable indeed.

We show above how the degree of relatedness among regions can be correctly determined and how one can decide whether cladistic patterns or regional similarities in species composition differ from those expected if taxa were randomly and individually distributed among regions. We have not yet completely discussed how to determine the mechanism that produced the observed pattern. In island biogeography our tactic is to employ a parsimony criterion: If the similarities among islands are no different from those expected by chance, then there is no need to propose any deterministic mechanism (e.g., competition) to explain the species abundance patterns (Simberloff 1978; Connor and Simberloff 1978, 1979; Simberloff and Connor 1979). Chance individual colonization is a sufficient explanation for the observed patterns. This does not mean, however, that competition or other deterministic factors have not been important; rather, it means that the data themselves cannot be used as supportive evidence (Connor and Simberloff 1979; cf. Raup 1977). If the patterns do differ from those expected under the null hypothesis, then we conclude that deterministic factors (e.g., vicariance, competition) are probably responsible for these differences.

In historical biogeography we have two methods for determining relatedness among areas: species similarity (number of species shared among sites) and cladistics (number of sister groups shared among sites). Some persons (e.g., Brundin 1966) have noted the importance of the number of shared sister groups, but no one has done so probabilistically. Because cladistic similarity has no analog in island biogeography, it would seem that historical biogeography might have an advantage. This apparent advantage may produce complications. For example, if we compare the expected cladistic relationship between two sites with that based on species similarities, there are nine possible results (table 2.2). For the three cases that allow unique interferences (1, 5, and 9) we follow the same procedure described for reaching conclusions in island biogeography. For the other six cases, however, it is not clear what can be concluded. Consider, for example, case 7, where there are fewer species in common but a larger number of sister groups than expected. Some possible explanations for this pattern are: (a) the two areas were closely connected and then widely separated with subsequent close connection of one of the areas with a third; (b) the two areas were never closely connected, but some of the organisms in question were particularly good dispersers; or (c) a founder species from a third area underwent an adaptive radiation in one of the two areas after they had separated.

We conclude that cladistic relationships provide an additional piece of evidence with which one can evaluate the relative merit of dispersal vs. vicariance explanations. Yet even when correct probabilities are employed it

Table 2.2 Possible Relationships of Species Similarity Analysis and Cladistic Similarity Analysis

		Species Similarity		
		<	=	>
Cladistic Similarity	<	1	2	3
	=	4	5	6
	>	7	8	9

NOTE: >: greater than expected; <: less than expected; =: expected. Based on null hypothesis of random dispersal of individual taxa.

is difficult for taxon-area cladograms to provide rigorous tests (*sensu* Popper) of biogeographical hypotheses, because of the paucity of data and the biological and paleontological assumptions necessary to produce data. McDowall (1978) and Heck and McCoy (1979) have also pointed out that with available data, neither long-distance dispersal nor vicariance is falsifiable for any particular theater and taxon discussed to date. The problem is exacerbated with increasing antiquity of the putative causal events. It therefore seems pointless to continue rhetorical discussions concerning the testability of the two major biogeographical hypotheses and, particularly, pharisaical denunciations of dispersal explanations as unscientific.

We recommend the following inductive approach based on a parsimony criterion as the preferred method of resolving questions concerning the origin of specific biogeographical patterns. First, use the random draw and expected similarity analyses to determine if the patterns differ from the random, individual dispersal null hypothesis using both the species similarities and cladistic-area data sets. These similarity analyses should serve as a criterion of subtraction. If they do not differ from the expected, random individual dispersal is the most parsimonious explanation of existing patterns. If they do differ, use all other available evidence concerning past continental configurations, dispersal abilities, and fossil data to reach a conclusion best supported by the facts.

Acknowledgments

We thank Dr. John Sepkoski for illuminating discussion on the existence and importance of ghosts.

Appendix 2.1

Let $P(I \mid J,K)$ be any partition of an integer $I > 0$ into two integers $J > 0$ and $K > 0$ such that $I = J + K$. Let $N(1)$ be the number of topologically distinguishable types of dichotomous cladograms with I tips. Clearly $N(1) = N(2) = N(3) = 1$ because there is only one type of cladogram for each of these numbers of tips, namely those depicted in figure 2.6A. For any $I > 1$, each type of dichotomous cladogram must be a unique union of two sub-cladograms (because the cladogram is dichotomous) of sizes J and

Table 2.3   Distinguishable Dichotomous Cladograms and Topological Types of Dichotomous Cladograms

n	N(n)	D(n)
1	1	1
2	1	1
3	1	3
4	2	15
5	3	105
6	6	945
7	11	10,395
8	23	135,135
9	46	2.027×10^6
10	98	3.446×10^7
11	207	6.547×10^8
12	451	1.375×10^{10}
13	983	3.162×10^{11}
14	2,145	7.906×10^{12}
15	4,816	2.135×10^{14}
16	10,837	6.190×10^{15}
17	24,495	1.919×10^{17}
18	55,705	6.333×10^{18}
19	127,232	2.216×10^{20}
20	291,983	8.201×10^{21}

NOTE: D(n) = number of distinguishable dichotomous cladograms (Felsenstein 1978) and N(n) = number of topological types of dichotomous cladograms as functions of n, the number of tips.

K respectively, where $P(I \mid J,K)$ is a partition of I. Furthermore, if we compare two unions of two sub-cladograms each of which (A1 and A2, B1 and B2) forms a larger cladogram (A and B), in order for A and B to have the same size and topological type, we must have either $((A1 = B1) \cap (A2 = B2))$ or $((A1 = B2) \cap (A2 = B1))$. If any of the sub-cladograms is unique, A and B cannot be topologically identical. This means that if there is no $P(I \mid J,K)$ such that $J = K$, $N(I) = \displaystyle\sum_{\forall J,K \ni : E P(I \mid J,K)} N(J) \cdot N(K)$.

Finally, if there is some $P(I \mid J,K)$ such that $J = K$ (i.e., if and only if I is an even number), the number of topologically distinguishable I-member cladograms that can be constructed of two J-member branches is the sum of N(J) (both branches identical) and $\binom{N(J)}{2}$ (the branches different). The recursion equation for N(I) is therefore:

$$N(I) = \left(\sum_{\substack{\forall J,K \ni: \\ 1)\ \exists P(I \mid J,K) \\ 2)\ J \neq K}} N(J) \cdot N(K) \right) + \underset{\substack{(\text{if } \exists\ J \ni: \\ I = 2J)}}{} N(J) + \binom{N(J)}{2}$$

Using this equation, we tabulated the number of types of n-member cladograms for $1 \leq n \leq 20$ in table 2.3.

		Site						
		1	2	3	4	5	6	Σ
Lineage	1	1	0	1	1	1	0	4
	2	0	1	1	0	1	0	3
	3	1	0	1	1	1	0	4
	4	0	1	1	1	1	1	5
	Σ	2	2	4	3	4	1	16

Figure 2.7. Binary matrix M for cladograms of figure 2.6B.

Appendix 2.2

Given complete information on biogeographical distributions (figure 2.6B), in order to determine whether some observed set of cladograms (e.g., of *all* the poeciliids) is unlikely to have arisen by chance individual dispersal, one would have to do the following:

(1) Construct an r × c binary matrix M, where r = the number of lineages and c the number of sites. This matrix will have m_{ij} = 1 if lineage i has a representative at site j; otherwise m_{ij} = 0. For our example, figure 2.7 depicts this matrix.

(2) Scan the collection of cladograms to see how many concordant, reduced-area cladograms of 3, 4, 5, etc. taxa there are. Each time that three or more cladograms are found to be concordant and at least two of them have been area-reduced, all pairs of cladograms within the trio (quartet, quintet, etc.) of concordant cladograms are examined over all sites shared pairwise. If any of these pairs is *not* concordant over all sites shared pairwise, the trio is judged *not* to be concordant. Table 2.4 presents this scan for the exemplary data of figure 2.6B. Note that if a subset of cladograms share two or fewer sites, we need not examine them further, because all 2-member cladograms are concordant. From table 2.4 we see that there is only one case of cladistic plus geographical concordance in the exemplary data set, namely that lineage 1 and lineage 4, when their cladograms are area-reduced to the

Table 2.4   Scan of Cladograms in Figure 2.8 for Concordant groups

Lineages	Shared sites	Concordant
1 × 2	3,5	
1 × 3	1,3,4,5	no
1 × 4	3,4,5	yes
2 × 3	3,5	
2 × 4	2,3,5	no
3 × 4	3,4,5	no
1 × 2 × 3	3,5	
1 × 2 × 4	3,5	
1 × 3 × 4	3,4,5	no
2 × 3 × 4	3,5	
1 × 2 × 3 × 4	3,5	

		Site						
		1	2	3	4	5	6	Σ
	1	0	1	1	1	1	0	4
	2	1	0	1	0	1	0	3
Lineage	3	1	0	1	1	1	0	4
	4	0	1	1	1	1	1	5
	Σ	2	2	4	3	4	1	16

Figure 2.8. Random binary matrix M′ with same distributions of row and column sums as in the observed matrix M of figure 2.7.

three shared sites, are concordant, with the taxa at sites 4 and 5 a sister group, and the common ancestor of this pair constituting a sister group with the taxon at site 3.

(3) Now generate a *random* r × c binary matrix M′ subject only to the constraints that the distributions of row sums and column sums for M′ be the same as those for M (Connor and Simberloff 1979). In other words, each site will still contain the same number of taxa as in the real data (in accordance with the species-area relationship and other rules governing diversity patterns), and each cladogram will contain the same number of taxa that it contains in nature. An example is given in figure 2.8.

(4) Randomly assign each row in M′ (each lineage) a cladogram type. That is, rows 1 and 3 in the example have four members, so each has two possible types, row 2 has three members, so there is only one cladogram type, and row 4 has five members, so there are three cladogram types (depicted in figure 2.1). As discussed above, we assign each type equal probability, though this part of the algorithm could easily be changed if, for example, we decided to assign the probabilities associated with the Markovian paradigm for cladogenesis.

(5) Randomize the order of the sites at the tips of the cladograms. Figure 2.9 depicts the cladograms resulting from one possible random choice of cladogram types (step 4) and site order for the random matrix of figure 2.8.

(6) Now repeat step 2 for this random set of cladograms. For the example of figure 2.9, the scan is depicted in table 2.5. The result is that there are two pairs of lineages whose reduced-area, 3-member cladograms are concordant, lineages 1 and 3, and lineages 3 and 4. Note that lineages 1 and 4 are *not* concordant. Recall that

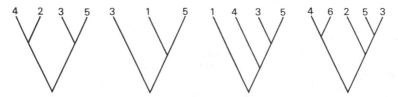

Figure 2.9. Cladograms of the lineages in random matrix M′ of figure 2.8, generated by random choice of cladogram type followed by random ordering of sites over cladogram tips.

Table 2.5   Scan of Cladograms in Figure 2.10 for Concordant Groups

Lineages	Shared sites	Concordant
1 × 2	3,5	
1 × 3	3,4,5	yes
1 × 4	2,3,4,5	no
2 × 3	1,3,5	no
2 × 4	3,5	
3 × 4	3,4,5	yes
1 × 2 × 3	3,5	
1 × 2 × 4	3,5	
1 × 3 × 4	3,4,5	no*
2 × 3 × 4	3,5	
1 × 2 × 3 × 4	3,5	

* Lineages 1 and 4 are not pairwise concordant over all their shared sites.

for the observed data there was only one pair of lineages with concordant, reduced-area, 3-member cladograms.

(7) Repeat steps 3, 4, 5, and 6 many times, to generate mean number of expected concordant groups of size s, of n-member cladograms, plus variance, for s = 2, 3, etc. and n = 3, 4, etc.

(8) Place the observed set of cladograms in the distribution generated in (7) to see if the observed degree of cladistic and biogeographical concordance is greater than chance distribution of the individual taxa among sites would likely have produced.

We have a computer program available which will do steps (1)–(8), given complete observed cladistic and biogeographical data, but we have yet to find a data set with all this information.

Discussion

J. Terborgh

I WANT TO begin by commending Professor Simberloff and his colleagues for performing a valuable service to this symposium in their roles as devil's advocates. In their stance as unabashed skeptics they raise what I believe are substantial criticisms of cladistic analysis as it has been used to discriminate between dispersal and vicariance interpretations of distributional patterns. But because cladistic analysis is not a technique with which I have any personal experience, I will leave discussion of the relevant portions of their paper to my co-discussants. Instead, my remarks will pertain to the Florida State group's advocacy of random models as applied to island biogeography—particularly whether or not certain pairs of species occur together more or less often than would be expected by chance.

On the surface, a random model might seem the ideal way to interject objectivity into an unwieldy mass of data in which an unknown number of variables play a part. As I shall demonstrate, however, an overzealous quest for objectivity—when untempered by a regard for complex underlying patterns—can lead to a misrepresentation of biological reality. This is because any model, even if random, makes assumptions about the system it purports to represent. In the case of the so-called R-mode analysis employed by Simberloff et al., the simulations explicitly assume that any species may occur on any island with a probability that depends only on the number of islands occupied by the species and the number of species found on each island (row totals held constant).

I will now show that this assumption, which is at the heart of their analysis, misrepresents two important biogeographical features of many archipelagoes, including one specifically mentioned in their text—the New Hebrides. To make matters worse, the two ways in which nature departs from the assumption of randomness lie in opposite directions, so that the two discrepancies could potentially cancel to produce a result indistinguishable from that yielded by the model. Under these circumstances we could be beguiled into thinking that nature was behaving randomly when, indeed, the truth could be quite the contrary.

Intuitively, the notion that any species may occur on any island in an archipelago seems reasonable, but it will not be true unless the species pool of the archipelago has come to equilibrium with respect to dispersal. This would be a reasonable expectation for a tightly clustered group of islands such as the Galapagos, or for a string of islands all independently colonized from a common source (e.g., the California Channel Islands). It is probably not true where colonization proceeds down an island chain, stepping-stone fashion, such as along the Malay Archipelago or the Aleutians, or where a group of islands is exposed to invasion from more than one source. In the case of the New Hebrides, avian colonists have emigrated from three sources that lie in as many directions from the center of the group: Australia to the southwest, New Guinea and the Bismarks to the northwest, and Fiji to the east (Diamond and Marshall 1976). A similar situation exists in the West Indies, which have received their fauna from Central America, North America, and South America (Bond 1948).

To take a concrete case, let us focus on the Lesser Antilles, a long chain of islands that provides a potential stepping stone pathway between the Greater Antilles and the South American mainland. One can recognize several categories of species in the avifauna of these islands: (1) widespread species found throughout the Greater and Lesser Antilles, and frequently on one or more of the nearby mainlands as well; (2) species with distributional centers in North or Middle America or the Greater Antilles that have invaded the Lesser Antilles from the west; (3) species of South American origin that have invaded the Lesser Antilles from the south; and (4) Lesser Antillean endemics (here "endemic" is used in a broader sense than when I later refer to species restricted to the Lesser Antilles as a whole; four barely reach the Greater Antilles).

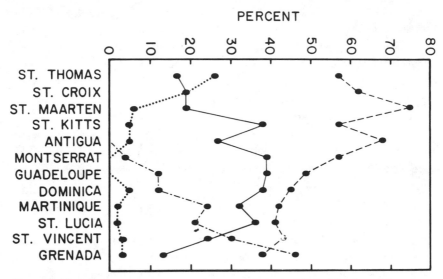

Figure 2.10. Countercurrent distributional patterns in the Virgin Islands and Lesser Antilles, expressed as the percentage of breeding land birds on each island belonging to four categories of species: (— — — —) widespread; (———) endemic to the Lesser Antillean chain; (· · · · · ·) invading from the west (Greater Antilles); (— · — · — · —·) invading from South America.

Now we can see whether dispersal has come to equilibrium by asking whether each of the four categories of species is equitably distributed along the island chain. Figure 2.10 shows that this is decidedly not the case. The South American faunal component attenuates rapidly with distance from the source, as does the Greater Antillean component. The widespread and endemic species groups also show trends in relation to position in the archipelago, although they are somewhat more equitably distributed than the first two faunal components. Such pronounced countercurrents of distribution will clearly engender departures from a model which allows any species to occur on any island. Species derived from different sources will be concentrated at opposite ends of the island chain. These will create an excess over expectation in the number of species pairs that nowhere occur together. Moreover, the resultant down-chain gradient in species composition assures that nearby islands—other factors (area, habitats, etc.) equal—will share more species than will more distant islands. This is something I demonstrated a number of years ago (Terborgh 1973).

For the major islands of the Lesser Antilles, a regression of faunal similarity against interisland distance indicates that the species composition of these islands is about 90 percent determined by their locations, with most of the remainder accounted for by interisland variation in species number. This analysis does not shed any light on the extent to which the species composi- tions of island faunas are molded by interspecific competition, because species that were unable to coexist would occur on different islands and thus be factored out in the regression against distance. Complementarity between two currents of dispersal could imply competitive obstruction of one current by the other, or it could just as well represent limited powers of dispersal on the part of species emanating from both sources.

Another deviation from randomness is found in the distributions of rare species (here defined as those inhabiting only one or a small number of the islands in an archipelago). In the analytical presence or absence scheme employed by Simberloff et al., single island endemics represent the ultimate in rare species. In their simulations these are allowed to occur on any island and consequently will frequently be assigned to small islands where different endemics would be unlikely to occur together (the extent to which this hap- pens will depend on the relative numbers of large and small islands included in the simulation). Yet if we again defer to data, we see that endemics have

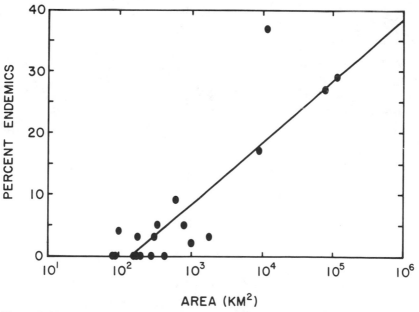

Figure 2.11. Regression of percent of single-island endemics against log island area for the bird faunas of the Greater and Lesser Antilles. The largest islands contain not only the highest proportions of endemics, but the greatest total numbers of species as well. This means that endemics are highly concentrated in the few largest islands.

highly clumped distributions because most of them occur on the largest islands (figure 2.11). Thus, the number of pairs of endemics which will be predicted to occur nowhere together by the simulation will be far greater than is the actual case.

We now see that by ignoring countercurrent dispersal the random colonization model considerably underestimates the number of pairs of species that occur nowhere together; and by randomly assigning endemics (and other rare species) to any island in proportion to the number of species in its fauna, the model greatly overestimates the number of pairs that occur nowhere together. Within certain ranges of conditions the two departures from reality will cancel out to create conformity with an illusory model of random distributions. The moral of the story is not that we should shun random models in the worthwhile procedure of testing null hypotheses, but that we should apply them with circumspection. Otherwise we run the risk of submerging important biological patterns in a statistical mirage.

Discussion

C. L. Smith

PROFESSOR SIMBERLOFF and his colleagues present a most interesting paper and their warnings are certainly timely and pertinent in view of the current interest in historical and equilibrium biogeography. I find myself in disagreement with the authors' optimism that historical biogeography and equilibrium biogeography will become closer in the future. It seems to me that equilibrium (island) biogeography is specifically aimed at the consequences of dispersal into new areas and the balance between colonization and extirpation as the authors emphasize near the end of the paper, when they point out that island biogeography has no analogies with cladistics, that is, it contains no tools for assessing relationships among organisms. This is only partly true because detailed studies of the ecology and adaptations of the species involved in island populations do provide functional relationships, but certainly the time frame of equilibrium biogeography is in no way comparable to that of historical biogeography.

One interesting difference between island biogeography and equilibrium biogeography is that when setting up null hypotheses for equilibrium biogeography, according to Simberloff et al., the similarity between two areas can be expressed in terms of the numbers of species that are common to both areas. Nelson has repeatedly pointed out that in historical biogeography such comparisons are only of limited usefulness because the species that occur in both areas are either *good* dispersers or *poor* evolvers but never carry labels saying which they are. Nelson's point is that widespread species are like plesiomorphic characters in systematics; they carry no information about relationships.

Simberloff et al. critically review Rosen's attempt to formulate a null hypothesis for historical biogeography of a given region. Their criticisms focus on three points: (1) the probability of coinciding cladograms should be calculated on the basis of topologies rather than individual patterns of relationships; (2) the method of area reduction used by Rosen may lead to concordance between cladograms that are really not concordant; and (3) the calculation of corroboration probability must be based on the entire biota rather than on groups that show concordance. All of these points are well taken and together they serve as a warning that calculating null hypotheses is at best a tricky business. One should bear in mind, however, that the generation of a null hypothesis against which patterns could be tested is only a minor part of Rosen's detailed analysis of the Middle American biota, and certainly is not the central thrust of his paper.

Simberloff et al. later take issue with Platnick and Nelson (1978), who described a method of cladistics for testing geographical hypotheses, suggesting that one look, instead, for deviations from randomness. This seems to confuse two different stages in their suggested approach. They recommend that first a test for deviation from randomness should be made, and if any deviation is found, then hypotheses about observed patterns should be formulated. The hypotheses should finally be tested by attempts at falsification. This is fine if there is any question about the existence of patterns, but the biogeographer who is considering systematics at the same time already knows that there are patterns; it is therefore proper for him to proceed immediately to the hypothesis testing stage.

Simberloff et al. moreover point out that failure to prove deviation from randomness does not necessarily mean that there are no deterministic processes at work; it means merely that the data do not show them for some reason. They cite as an example the fact that equilibrium biogeography does not propose deterministic mechanisms to explain species distribution patterns: "This does not mean, however, that competition or other deterministic factors have not been important; rather, it means that the data themselves cannot be used as supportive evidence." This profound point is easy to overlook in our zealous search for absolute objectivity. Competition is certainly an established principle in biological communities; one has to look no further than succession in plant communities to see its effects and often its mechanisms; yet the statistical verdict must be considered "not proved." This seems a paradox worthy of epistemological attention. A thorough analysis could have profound effects on science.

Simberloff et al. have identified some sources of noise in the analysis of cladistic patterns that apply equally to the falsification procedure and to the formulation of null hypotheses. The most important seem to be the problems of area reduction procedures, ghost species, and incorrect polarity in cladistic analysis. Area reduction should be a two-step procedure. First, by elimination of areas that provide no information, simplified patterns emerge that may lead to hypotheses. Left at this stage, the criticisms raised by Simberloff et al. are valid, but there is no real excuse for leaving the subject here. If we again add the species until inconsistencies appear, we can then evaluate the inconsistencies in terms of the hypothesis we attempt to falsify, and vice versa.

The second question, ghost species, is also important and points up once again the need to consider all available evidence—paleontological as well as neontological. Certainly it is not acceptable to ignore the fossil record when it is available. The point that ghosts can never increase concordance, although they might falsify it, is well taken. In my opinion, the third problem, reverse polarity in systematic analysis, would rarely be serious. In theory, of course, it can be troublesome, but in practice such matters rarely occur. A good systematist will always maintain a *what if* attitude that will enable him to identify possible problems and devise acceptable tests of competing hypotheses.

The authors raise the point that sympatric speciation may be more common than usually accepted. Obviously, sympatric speciation is rare and difficult to detect, which is why systematists are so skeptical about it. Whenever nearest-relative species are found together, we usually invoke secondary dispersal as an explanation. Sympatric speciation might make some cases much tidier, but it would in general have little effect on our search for explanations of patterns of distribution. If sympatric speciation is common and if we can come up with a reliable detection method it will sharpen our view of vicariant patterns.

One final point: It is common practice to focus a discussion by attempting to define clearly the opposing points of view. One must be careful, however, not to put words in the opponent's mouth. When we talk about center of origin/dispersal as the opposite of vicariance theory I think we have to take care not to think of the center of origin as a point. Certainly such a concept would be acceptable only to a special creationist or a macroevolutionist. What, then, is a center of origin? Presumably, the center of origin for a species is the area occupied by its gene pool, or perhaps by a smaller unit that is the home of what the fishery biologist defines as a *unit stock*, that is, the area through which mating is more or less random. Certainly there are localized areas of high endemism; are these always also centers of origin? What is the center of origin of a higher taxon? In the final analysis, is there a center of origin school or are we all on the same team? After all, the theory of vicariance biogeography recognizes a cosmopolitan phase, a vicariant phase, and sometimes a redispersal phase.

Discussion

J. S. Farris

SIMBERLOFF et al. attempt to establish their thesis—that "there have been no statistical tests of cladistic biogeographical hypotheses"—solely through criticism of Rosen's (1978) study of North and Central American biogeography. The relationship between their discussion and Rosen's conclusions is questionable because none of their considerations suffices to render his observations less significant than the conventional 5 percent level. One might conclude, therefore, that the validity of their argument is largely moot and deserves no further attention. I take a different view, for I am interested primarily in the form of statistical reasoning as such. Several aspects of their criticism of his work seem to me to present opportunities to consider points that may be of general value in biogeographical discussion.

They object to his procedure on three statistical grounds. The first is that he is not justified in taking all possible dichotomous cladograms for his taxa as equally probable a priori. They observe that, when more than three terminal taxa are considered, there are two or more topologically distinct types of cladograms. They then argue that "our feeling is that these types are equiprobable, or at least that this is a parsimonious testable hypothesis. Otherwise one is in a situation analogous to comparing apples and oranges."

One question raised by this argument is why Rosen presented no defense of his probabilities. On asking him, I discovered that it had simply never occurred to him that the probabilities might be other than he had supposed. If his defense is not much of a justification, it is at least understandable, for he is a biologist rather than a mathematician. They, however, raise the issue of probabilities of cladograms in ostensibly mathematical discussion, and from them one might expect a more rigorous defense of their position. To me, however, their arguments to this point are deficient in a number of respects. Their observation that equal probability of cladogram topologies is a testable hypothesis is presumably correct, but, plainly, any probability distribution of cladograms is testable in just the same way. Testability, then, seems no reason to prefer their "feeling" over his intuition. Their characterization of their hypothesis as "parsimonious" also seems arbitrary. To take all probabilities as equal might reasonably be termed "parsimonious" in some sense, but one could describe his assignment of equal probabilities to all cladograms as "parsimonious" in the same sense. Nothing in the concept of a "parsimonious testable hypothesis" seems to distinguish their assumption from his.

The intent of their comment on apples and oranges is not immediately apparent. From the context they seem to claim that some logical error is committed unless topologies are taken as equally probable. The claim is both false and inconsistent with other parts of their discussion, for they later mention the possible application of a Markov model in assigning different probabilities to distinct cladogram topologies. The claim is also misleadingly worded. Criticisms of "comparing apples and oranges" are usually, and correctly, applied to manipulations in which quantities measured in different units are combined in a way such that the units of the result are ill defined. In the procedures under discussion, however, cladograms are combined only through their probabilities. Whatever else might be said of the resultant probability, it can scarcely be regarded as having mixed units. The outcomes of a toss of a coin and a toss of a die are by no means in the same physical units, but it is utter nonsense to claim that "the probability of a head and a 3 is 1/12" involves an error in units.

They state further: "Surely there is no *a priori* reason for thinking that type 1a [a cladogram topology of their figure 2.1] is more likely to occur just because there are more distinguishable arrangements of five numbers among its tips." This statement is true in a way, but, again, it seems inconsistent with other aspects of their discussion. They call attention to their use of "Maxwell-Boltzmann statistics." They do not explain the term, which comes from physics and is seldom encountered in biological literature. If the term is not intended simply to obscure the argument, its purpose could be only to call attention to the distinction between the various types of "statistics" (probability models) used in physics. Maxwell-Boltzmann statistics refers to a law in which the probabilities of structurally distinct arrangements of particles are determined by the number of ways in which particles may be distributed to yield those arrangements. Bose-Einstein statistics, in contrast, refers to a law in which each structurally distinct arrangement has the same probability, regardless of how particles might be disposed to produce the arrangement.

For a simple analogy, consider a process in which each of b balls is placed randomly into one of two urns, the two placements having equal probability for any one ball. In Maxwell-Boltzmann statistics, the probability that urn A receives a balls is proportional to $\binom{b}{a}$—the number of ways of choosing a balls from b candidates. This probability, of course, leads to the familiar binomial distribution. In Bose-Einstein statistics, the b + 1 possible values, 0, 1, . . . b of a would be equally probable.

The binomial distribution in this case may seem intuitively correct; and the Bose-Einstein distribution, less so. Which distribution is actually correct depends on the nature of the objects distributed. If these are ordinary balls, then we may think of them as having individual identities—as being in principle distinguishable—even if by concentrating on the count we ignore which individual balls are counted. For this reason the $\binom{b}{a}$ different arrangements combine in probability to make some values of a more likely than others. If the balls are photons, however, they may behave as if they have no individual identities—as being in principle indistinguishable—so that it is incorrect to speak of $\binom{b}{a}$ possible assignments: all dispositions with the same a are one and the same arrangement. Each of the b + 1 possible values of a can then arise in only one way, so that equality of their probabilities becomes more understandable. A more technical discussion of these ideas is given by Feller (1957:39–40). As he sums it up: "Note that 'Maxwell-Boltzmann statistics' is the physicist's term for what we call random placement of balls into cells."

Simberloff et al. are certainly correct in asserting that they use Maxwell-Boltzmann statistics, for they employ arguments based on ordinary binomial probabilities. Yet they maintain that there is no reason to regard as more probable those cladogram topologies that can arise from a greater number of arrangements of individual taxa. The analogy with Maxwell-Boltzmann vs. Bose-Einstein statistics seems quite precise. In Bose-Einstein statistics, and in assigning equal probabilities to cladogram topologies, structurally distinct configurations are assigned the same probability regardless of how those arrangements can arise. In Maxwell-Boltzmann statistics, as the binomial distribution, distinct configurations acquire different probabilities as a consequence of the number of ways in which distinguishable components may be distributed. The components distributed on cladograms, however, are individual taxa, and so are presumably quite distinguishable. From the analogy with physics, then, it seems rather suspicious to treat cladograms in probability as if under a Bose-Einstein model. In objecting to the idea that number of distinguishable arrangements affects probabilities of cladograms, while themselves using "Maxwell-Boltzmann statistics," they seem to offer an argument that is at best incomplete. It may well not be that all cladograms are equally probable, but neither is there any obvious basis for claiming that topologies subsuming many arrangements of distinct taxa are no more probable than other cladogram shapes. Certainly they make no effort to demonstrate any such basis. Like their parsimony notion, their contention about distinguishable arrangements amounts to no more than the flat assertion that Rosen's probabilities might be incorrect.

There would be little point in discussing assignment of probabilities to cladograms unless it were supposed that Rosen's choice of probabilities is crucial to the justification of his conclusions. They hold that such is the case. They state: "Finally, *any* asymmetry among the probabilities of the distinguishable cladograms *increases* the null probability that a random pair of cladograms will be concordant." Their idea, discussed further below, is that his observations are less significant than he claimed. Whereas he attributes a probability of 1/105 to the chance concordance of two fully resolved 5-taxon cladograms, they assign a probability of 0.013 (about 1/77) to the same event under their postulate that topologies are equally probable. While their point is correct as far as it goes, it is also misleading, because it is presented so as to conceal another issue. By his probability assignment, all chance concordances between cladograms have the same probability under the null hypothesis, so that any concordance provides as much evidence against that hypothesis as does any other match. Under their model, however, matches between fully asymmetrical cladograms, if observed, provide more evidence hypothesis than are agreements between other cladograms. Matches between fully asymmetrical cladograms, if observed, provide more evidence against the null hypothesis than would other matches. The two 5-taxon poeciliid cladograms used by him are fully asymmetrical. The probability of such a match is only (1/3) (1/60), or 1/180 under their model (the factor 1/3 derives from the equal probability of three cladogram types; there are 60 ways to arrange five taxa on a fully asymmetrical cladogram). By discussing only the probability of agreement between some pair of cladograms, they gloss over the fact that his observation is less probable under the null hypothesis according to their probability model than according to his own.

As their second objection, they criticize his use of area-reduced cladograms. A suite of three or more cladograms that agree on the sites common to all three, they observe, may include cladogram pairs that disagree on other sites. They conclude from this that his procedure, "is not in general permissible for comparison of three or more cladograms." They do not explain their reasoning on this point, and their conclusion seems questionable. Their claim seems to imply that agreement between cladograms provides no evidence against random distribution unless the agreement is perfect—in effect that two cladograms give no evidence for vicariance unless they give no suggestion at all of dispersal. There seems no reason for adopting such a view, however, for neither he nor any other vicariance biogeographer maintains that patterns of vicariance cannot be affected by episodes of dispersal.

Their third objection arises from a misunderstanding of the way in which he obtained cladograms for his study. They contend that "Rosen considers only those examples consistent with his hypothesis whereas, in order to assess the probability of finding, say, two concordant 5-member cladograms, one must first delimit the universe of endemic 5-taxon systems from which the sample cladograms are drawn." They amplify this claim by noting that, if one searched the cladograms of ten 5-taxon groups of poeciliids, the probability of finding two congruent would be greater than the probability that any two randomly selected cladograms are congruent. They make a similar point by noting that one is likely to find runs in a long series of tosses of a fair die. It is, of course, true that one's chances of observing some particular event increase with the number of cases sampled. As a criticism of his procedure, however, this fact is irrelevant unless it is supposed that he searched out just those two cladograms that conform to his hypothesis, deceitfully concealing the existence of incongruent distributions. In fact, he "selected" cladograms simply by using all cladograms that were both available and relevant to his problem. That only two poeciliid cladograms met these criteria may imply something about poeciliids, but it is hardly evidence against Rosen's honesty. Their idea thus has nothing to do with his study. Some of the other comments that they make in connection with this objection nonetheless call for further discussion.

They emphasize that probabilities of concordance between cladograms that appear in his argument apply to pairs of cladograms specified in advance. In a similar vein they stress the importance that the cladograms comprise a random sample. The second of these points touches on the question of the statistical universe studied, to which matter I shall return below. The two points mentioned here, however, have a common element in seeming to imply the necessity of quite stringent criteria for the acquisition of data. If cladograms are not a random sample, or if groups used as evidence have not been chosen prior to the study, they seem to say, then, that concordance of cladograms is to be expected, and that the seeming significance of concordance is misleading. I would observe simply that such strong restrictions on admissibility of evidence are unnecessary. Concordance probabilities of the sort used by him are applicable provided only that cladograms are obtained in a way independent of concordance. For his argument it is necessary only that his procedure allow discordant cladograms, if they exist, the same chance of being sampled as that enjoyed by concordant cladograms. It does not matter to his argument whether the cladograms used are "randomly" chosen in any other sense, nor does it matter when cladograms are "specified," as long as the means of specification are unaffected by concordance.

Some part of their discussion is phrased so as to imply that samples in studies such as his are picked from a large universe of possible cladograms. In other places, however, they admit that only a few cladograms may be relevant to the relationships of areas considered. They capitalize on this possibility in an interesting way: "If the universe were as small as two or three cladograms, a single observed concordance would be of doubtful significance with respect to a causal geographical hypothesis. We would know simply that one or a few 'trials' were run and that one apparently unlikely outcome was observed."

The word "significance" is pivotal here. The word may be interpreted in either its statistical or its common sense; probably it is meant to convey both concepts together. Both interpretations suggest a weakness in their reasoning. If "significance" is taken in the statistical sense, then the implication of the quoted statement would be that unlikely outcomes in small samples are not as significant as equally unlikely outcomes of large samples.

They feel, it would seem, that only large-sample results can truly be significant; they confound, in effect, statistical significance and sample size. There is nothing in the theory of statistics to support such a view. In some experiments, it is true, high significance cannot be achieved without a large sample size. In testing the hypothesis that a coin is fair, the error rate of a decision rule admitting of rejection cannot be less than $(1/2)^n$ for n observations in a one-tailed test. This hardly means, however, that large samples are coincident with high significance in general. Even when sample size is large, a false null hypothesis might still be rejected at only a moderate level of significance—or be only marginally rejectable, or not rejectable at all. Further, a large sample size is required to make high significance possible only when no observations are possible that are highly unlikely under the null hypothesis, as in hypotheses about fair coins. When some possible observations are very unlikely under the null hypothesis, even one or two such observations may make it possible to reject that null hypothesis at a very high level of significance. Significance level (error rate) in statistical theory refers just to the probability that a rejection criterion will be satisfied when the null hypothesis is true; in the mathematical theory, "significance" has no other meaning or implication. If his observed concordance occurs with probability no greater than 1 percent under the null hypothesis, then that concordance can serve as a basis for rejection of that hypothesis at the 1 percent level, and that rejection enjoys precisely the same theoretical status as would a rejection at the 1 percent level by a t-test based on 100 observations. To take any other view is simply to discard the statistical theory of hypothesis testing.

When conclusions are based on small samples, there is perhaps a tendency to feel intuitively that the results are unconvincing because further sampling might change the conclusion. That new data will dispute what seems already known is always possible, but this possibility provides no logical basis for criticizing any particular conclusion. There is no mandate in statistical theory for further sampling when a significant difference has already been found. If there were such a requirement, then sequential tests would be impossible. At a more general and philosophical level, one might add that the possibility that further data will give different results has little to do with the validity of small samples. The same possibility of future refutation exists for conclusions based on large samples—indeed, for conclusions reached in any empirical way whatsoever. The conclusion to be drawn is not that additional data should not be sought, but rather that the possibility of future refutation is not a criticism of any particular conclusion already formed. The relevant issue about any present theory is not whether in the future it might be refuted, for any theory might be refuted. Rather, one should inquire whether an existing theory is supported over alternatives by available data. If statistical significance testing is used to assess relative support of theories, then it is quite possible that a theory may be much better supported than its alternatives even when few data are available—when sample size is small.

The second possible interpretation of "doubtful significance with respect to a causal geographical hypothesis" arises from the common usage of "significance." This usage might itself be interpreted in two ways. One way is that concordance of two cladograms, while not due to chance, may nonetheless imply little about the cause of the concordance; the cause might possibly not be geographical. While they put forward this possibility in the context of small samples, this possibility, in fact, has little to do with the number of cladograms involved. For any suite of concordant cladograms, one might claim that the concordance is due to something other than a geographical cause. In order to discuss this possibility further, other causes must be specified, of which they provide no hint. The second way to interpret "significance," perhaps more applicable to small samples, is that concordance between two cladograms, while not due to chance, possibly reflects a pattern common only to a small suite of groups of organisms, not a pattern common to many groups. This possibility cannot be denied, but it would seem to have little to do with the validity of conclusions of non-random association of groups. Vicariance biogeographers, after all, do not maintain that all groups in an area must show the same pattern. Not all groups are supposed to respond to geographical events in the same ways.

In addition to their statistical objections, they offer three "caveats" of a more biological nature. The first of these concerns "ghosts" (extinct lineages). They state: "What can we say about unseen ghosts? First, if they were seen, they would only lower the number of observed instances of concordance because they can render a previously concordant group of cladograms discordant, but they can never effect the opposite transformation." I suppose that they intend "lower or leave unmodified" rather than "only lower." Even on this favorable interpretation, however, their claim is false as can be seen from figure 2.12. In figure 2.12a, two related groups, A, B, C and X, Y, Z (as his two genera of poeciliids), show the same pattern of relationships among areas 1, 2, 3. In figure 2.12b, another related group, P, Q, R, is added which seems to show a different geographical pattern. In figure 2.12c newly discovered "ghosts" P', P'', Q' are incorporated so that the seemingly incongruous P-Q-R pattern is converted into two copies of the A-B-C pattern. In making their claim about the effects of "ghosts," they rely on their own inability to imagine certain kinds of distributions of extinction, rather than on a logical property of extinction itself.

They state that: "A second caveat is that one assumes whether characters are primitive or derived in constructing the cladograms, for the criteria determining this 'do not have absolute validity' (Hennig, 1966) and are

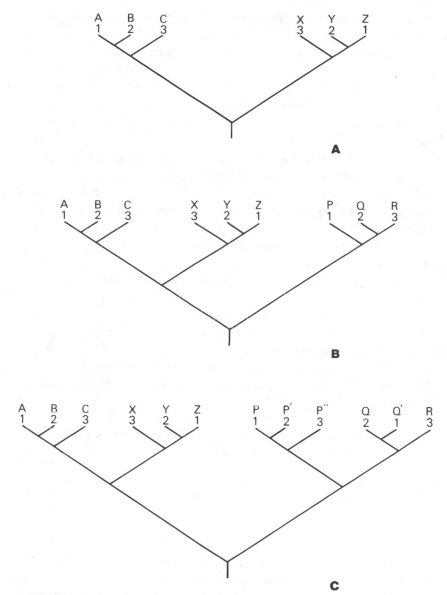

Figure 2.12. A, cladogram for two groups (ABC, XYZ) having concordant distributions; B, the same cladogram with addition of a third group (PQR) with a discordant distribution; C, the same cladogram with the addition of three "ghosts" (P'P"Q') that cause concordance in distribution of four groups (ABC, XYZ, PP'P", QQ'R).

subjective." Hennig, of course, knew better than to equate the possibility of error with subjectivity (the quote is from Hennig, 1966:146). Any empirical and objective test of a scientific hypothesis is potentially capable of leading to an erroneous conclusion, a fact of which they are presumably aware, as they refer elsewhere to tests "*sensu* Popper." If possibility of error implied subjectivity, then the statistical methods advocated by them would have to be called subjective, for certainly any of their methods admit both Type I and Type II errors.

As their third caveat they raise the possibility of sympatric speciation. They contend that the routine presumption of allopatric speciation in vicariance studies is critical "because sympatric speciation with subsequent dispersal of the new species to new sites could not be distinguished from allopatric speciation (vicariance) and invasion of the original range." They contend that several studies have shown that "stasipatric and sympatric speciation are much more common than previously suspected."

I would agree that vicariance biogeographers should treat allopatric speciation as a hypothesis rather than as an axiom, but beyond this I find their argument simply confused. If studies have indeed shown that sympatric speciation has occurred, then there must be some means of distinguishing that phenomenon from allopatric speciation.

Two further quotations, one from the section on statistical objections and one from the section on island biogeography and cladistics, serve well to summarize their view:

> We argue that the proper parsimonious null hypothesis is that the distributions were produced by chance dispersal of individual taxa. . . .
> An observed amount of concordance among cladograms—or consistency between a set of cladograms and a geographical hypothesis—no greater than that predicted by chance, would severely impugn the vicariance hypothesis and support an alternative hypothesis of individual dispersal. . . .

There is a close relationship between these two ideas. That relationship, however, lies not so much in the logical content of the statements as in the statements' joint role in bolstering the position that Simberloff et al. wish to establish. The first claim aims to restrict null hypotheses to those that they find acceptable; the second attempts to confer on null hypotheses a special safety from refutation.

Their argument for dispersal as a null hypothesis seems to depend entirely on parsimony. As before, they misapply this concept, although here in a new way. Truly "proper" application of the parsimony criterion in choosing among hypotheses involves only a preference for eliminating untested assumptions. Only untested assumptions can be discarded on these grounds; phenomena with established existence are quite immune to shaving away by Occam's Razor. This is true even in cases in which recognizing the relevance of some factor may seem subjectively to render a question needlessly complex. They probably feel that the ability of organisms to disperse is already known and is therefore not an assumption so that recognition of vicariance is unnecessary and therefore unparsimonious. But if dispersal is well documented, the mechanism of vicariance is no less so, for vicariance amounts to no more than that organisms tend to persist in the areas occupied by their ancestors. Neither the existence nor the relevance to distribution of either of the two effects, dispersal and persistence, can reasonably be doubted. Neither phenomenon, therefore, can be rationally discounted on grounds of parsimony.

The null hypothesis preferred by them postulates that dispersal, and dispersal alone, is the explanation of distribution. But if vicariance patterns are a consequence simply of persistence, then dispersal can no more constitute the sole cause of distribution patterns than can vicariance alone. This conclusion might be taken to imply simply that they have picked the wrong null hypothesis, for there is little point to testing a hypothesis that is absurd at the outset. In fact, I would suggest that the implication is rather different; it is that the problem of explaining distributions should not be treated formally only through hypothesis testing. Because distributions will generally be caused by a combination of dispersal and persistence, the problem to be legitimately investigated is: Which aspects of distribution are best explained by dispersal, and which by persistence? A problem of this sort, it would seem, can be more usefully approached through estimation than through testing preconceived theories.

A hypothesis-testing approach has advantages of its own, of course, but even if this approach is followed, its results cannot validly be interpreted in the way that they seem to wish. It does not follow from failure to reject a hypothesis through statistical testing that the hypothesis is supported or an alternative impugned. Lack of significance in a statistical test means only that the data are inadequate to distinguish between hypotheses, that is, to decide between hypotheses with adequate confidence. This meaning is a standard principle of applied statistics and does not require much discussion, but one of the reasons why it is important in interpreting statistical results is perhaps especially relevant here. The principal value of a statistical approach to hypothesis testing is to allow the probability of reaching false conclusions to be evaluated and, therefore, controlled. However, only the probability of erroneous rejection of a null hypothesis is controlled. The probability of failure to reject a false null hypothesis can seldom be evaluated. If failure to reject a null hypothesis implied concluding that hypothesis to be true, then the probability of error of a decision would not be known. Only by regarding failure to reject as implying no conclusion at all can the probability of error be controlled through choice of a significance level.

When failure to reject a null hypothesis is treated as the conclusion that the hypothesis is supported, the probabilistic consequence is only that the probability of a false conclusion becomes unknown. The more general consequences are more disturbing; the result is to form a conclusion that depends on the arbitrary choice of one of the competing hypotheses as "null." Hypotheses taken as null in statistical tests are treated in a rather special way. Because rejection criteria are designed to keep the probability of rejection of a true null hypothesis low, null hypotheses can be discarded only on fairly strong evidence. When data are not adequate to distinguish strongly between alternative hypotheses, it may well occur that choice of either of two hypotheses as "null" would lead to failure to reject. If such is the case, then it is clear that "acceptance" of a null hypothesis—concluding it to be true because it has not been rejected—can lead to the conclusion of truth of any of several hypotheses depending on which one is selected as "null." If that selection is based on arbitrary criteria, then so will be the conclusion. This, I would suggest, is the most important philosophical weakness of their argument. They attempt to justify a conclusion of truth of a null hypothesis on the basis of failure to reject that hypothesis, while defending their choice of a null hypothesis only through a specious application of the concept of parsimony.

Response

D. Simberloff, K. L. Heck, E. D. McCoy, and E. F. Connor

WE ARE PLEASED to reply to our discussants, both because this dialectical process makes our own thinking more critical, and because their objections to our contribution center largely on what we, in concert with vicariance advocates (e.g., Rosen 1974b; Ball 1976), feel is the essential goal of biogeographers today: to transform the discipline from a melange of more or less plausible scenarios (narrative explanations) to an attempt to provide rigorously objective criteria for choosing among alternative hypotheses.

In this spirit we note that Professor Terborgh's eminently reasonable scenario of countercurrent dispersal is not buttressed by any statistical analysis whatever. He states that the four categories of Lesser Antilles birds (widespread, endemic, invading from the west, invading from South America) are not equitably distributed along the island chain, but he presents no support for this assertion save for visual inspection of his figure 2.10. How do we know that these four components, except for sampling error, are not pairwise identically distributed? How do we know that they achieved their distributions in the fashion he proposes? In any event, there is nothing in our model that forbids two source areas, with specified functions for the probability that species i in source j reaches an island of distance d_j from source j. Our point is that there must be *some* null hypothesis with stated criteria for rejection, or biogeography will be hopelessly restricted to perpetual advocacy of subjective, more or less reasonable, schemes.

With respect to single-island endemics, Terborgh's assertion about our projected results does not jibe with our actual results. In fact, endemics in our simulations do *not* frequently end up on small islands, and almost never end up together on small islands. Because the probability that any species is placed on island a vs. island b is proportional to (number of species on a)/(number of species on b), most endemics, when randomly and individually placed, will be found on large islands, as Terborgh says that they are in nature. Terborgh states that "the number of pairs of endemics which will be predicted to occur nowhere together by the simulation will be far greater than is the actual case," but he presents neither data nor statistical analysis. For the West Indies, Connor and Simberloff (1979) randomly place species on islands *only* in the size ranges in which they actually occur in nature, and find no significant change in the number of mutually exclusive pairs and trios of birds. We agree with Terborgh that separate examination of endemics may be informative, but the results of this sort of simulation cannot simply be intuited, nor, of course, can their statistical significance.

Terborgh feels that "the moral of the story is not that we should shun random models in the worthwhile procedure of testing null hypotheses, but that we should apply them with circumspection. Otherwise we run the risk of submerging important biological patterns in a statistical mirage." We agree that circumspection is called for, but we assert, along with Popper (1962), Feyerabend (1975), and Strong (1980), that even more important than circumspection to advance our mechanistic understanding is the need for *some* model, along with stated criteria for its falsification. Terborgh has not provided data that falsify our model; he has not even suggested what sort of data could conceivably falsify his countercurrent model; and he has not attempted the falsification. We ask that "statistical mirage" be precisely defined. "Mirage," according to Webster's dictionary, denotes "illusory," whereas probabilistic statistics ought to be used, and we attempt to use them, only to reject illusion, not to erect specious patterns.

Dr. Smith takes us to task for, i.a., our index of faunal similarity, which he suggests is not very powerful. Its virtue is to allow falsifiable hypotheses. In most of our studies, we reject purely random and individual colonization by the use of this index. We never claim it to be the only, or the most refined, or the most informative way to represent faunal relationships; we observe that almost all commonly used indices are sample-size dependent and have unknown sampling distributions. Smith similarly misunderstands our discussion of cladogram topology. Our chief point is *not* that one must calculate probability of coincident cladograms "on the basis of topologies *rather than* individual patterns of relationships" (emphasis added). We specifically state (cf. our table 2.2) that both sorts of information must be used to infer mechanism. Our claims with respect to topology are simply that *some* set of null probabilities of concordance must be stated before testing to see if observed concordance is unlikely due to chance, that there are several ways in which one may interpret cladogram topology for this purpose, and that these ways produce different sets of null probabilities.

Smith assails us for addressing only part of Rosen's detailed analysis of Middle American biota. We were continuously and forcefully urged by the conference convenors to focus narrowly on the issue of vicariance biogeography, and to criticize its methods and accomplishments. We deal with those portions of Rosen's and other papers that we view as relevant to this narrow focus.

Central to Smith's arguments is his claim that "the biogeographer who is considering systematics at the same time already knows that there are patterns; it is therefore proper for him to proceed immediately to the hypothesis-testing stage." Such unsupported assertions must be purged from biogeography. *How* does the biogeographer "already know that there are patterns"? Smith does not provide the objective criteria. To us, "pattern" connotes repetition, which in turn suggests non-randomness. But even if one accepts a clearly defined random arrangement as a pattern, one must state how one knows that the pattern is adhered to. This, as we pointed out, is not normal procedure for biogeographers. Croizat et al. (1974) suggest that tracks are patterns, and infer vicariance from tracks. Yet the *Oxford English Dictionary* defines "pattern" as "a part shown as an example of the rest," and the track is only the part; no examination of the rest is attempted. We again note that to test hypotheses one must clearly state not only the hypothesis but also what data are necessary for a rigorous attempt at falsification.

Smith finds no excuse for our leaving the procedure for comparing area-reduced cladograms where we do and enjoins us to add the omitted species to search for inconsistencies. This is *exactly* what we do (and what Rosen 1978, does *not* do), when we state explicitly that one must compare any two higher taxa over all *their* shared sites, not just over the sites shared by all taxa in the set of interest. We omit no taxon-by-area information.

Smith seems to feel that we claim that a center of origin must be one point, and that this claim is necessary for our models. We never claim this;

we run similar models with multiple species pools (Connor and Simberloff 1978, 1979); and, as we note in partial answer to Terborgh, our concern is that, with one, two, or many species pools, one must generate some testable prediction with statistical grounds, clearly understood, for its rejection. We agree completely with Smith, that several forces have almost certainly acted in concert to produce extant biogeographical distributions, and that species disjunction must be one of them; but vicariance theory suggests that much of the disjunction of species occurs in concert, whereas dispersalists envision species disjunctions occurring primarily alone. As we point out, it is currently likely "that with available data, neither long-distance dispersal nor vicariance is falsifiable for any particular theater and taxon discussed to date." We suggest simply that a dispersalist interpretation is as reasonable a stance to take as is vicariance in lieu of adequate data, and we produce some statistical tests should adequate data appear.

Dr. Farris says our statistical thesis is based solely on criticism of Rosen (1978). We address also Nelson (1973b), Croizat et al. (1974), Rosen (1976a), and Platnick and Nelson (1978). We feel that these are a fair representation of the vicariance school. Farris pillories us on a number of statistical points, on some of which we take issue, and on others of which we feel we have been misunderstood. We proceed seriatim.

We do not claim that the only testable probability distribution of topologies is the equiprobable one. We specifically mention two other possible distributions and view them all as testable, but as yet untested. Our claim is, as we note in our reply to Smith, that the specific distribution chosen determines the null probability of some observed degree of concordance, so that one must state the distribution and, if possible, defend the choice. This has not been done so far. Our metaphor of apples and oranges is intended to show that viewing cladograms of two different topologies as having equal a priori probability requires an assumption about equivalence or non-equivalence of different topologies. We never claim that a *logical* error is committed by *not* assigning equal probabilities, and we agree with Farris that such a claim is false. We agree with Farris also that this claim is inconsistent with other parts of our argument; this is why we never make the claim. Of course one can toss a coin and a die, and calculate the probability of a given outcome; one generally assumes the faces of the die equiprobable, and the coin true. Clearly, there is no such a priori distribution presently available for cladograms, although we may assume one if we state our assumptions.

We regret causing difficulty by introducing Maxwell-Boltzmann statistics, which are hardly new to the biological literature (cf., Abbott 1977;

Abbott et al. 1977; Gardiner and Haedrich 1978; and Underwood 1978, among ecologists, plus several applications to DNA sequencing). To insure that we were not obscure we included the reference to Feller (1950), which Farris cites. We do not, as Farris claims, introduce Maxwell-Boltzmann statistics in our discussion of the probabilities of various cladogram topologies in Rosen's model, but rather with respect to the Platnick and Nelson (1978) model, in which they are implicit. For the purpose of that discussion we observe that there is no a priori reason to accept Maxwell-Boltzmann statistics, but that *even if one does*, the authors adopt a peculiar criterion to determine whether a set of observed biogeographical and cladistic data corroborates their model. As for whether Maxwell-Boltzmann statistics are, in fact, appropriate for the probability distribution of cladogram topologies, Farris' own discussion of photons is applicable: that is at best a testable proposition, and in the absence of a test is no more defensible than any other assumption. As we observe, the distribution of topologies that seems to us to flow most naturally from a phylogenetic model of cladogenesis is neither Maxwell-Boltzmann nor Bose-Einstein, but rather that associated with the Markovian model. So we agree completely with Farris that our "contention about distinguishable arrangements amounts to no more than the flat assertion that Rosen's probabilities might be incorrect." This is precisely our contention. Farris errs, however, in his calculation of the null probability of Rosen's matching 5-taxon poeciliid cladograms, by failing to keep his eye on our clearly stated null hypothesis, that a given two genera, specified in advance, will match. We did not postulate the compound hypothesis that they will match *and* that they will both have topological type a, nor do we see any reason why one should adopt such a null hypothesis.

Farris' defense of Rosen's area-reduction procedure similarly fails to state a clear null hypothesis and the possible observations that would be construed as falsifying it. All we point out here is that Rosen's procedure for generating the data with which one will test a cladistic biogeographical scheme throws out some data that can be inconsistent with a vicariance hypothesis. What degree of non-matching would Farris accept before he would view such an hypothesis as falsified?

We apologize for misunderstanding Rosen's procedure for obtaining his cladograms, and we very much resent Farris's assertion that we comment on Rosen's honesty. Of course, our analogy of the die does not apply if the cladograms depicted are the only ones available. We should be pardoned for our misunderstanding, however, because Rosen nowhere explains how he chose the cladograms, nor gives a further reference, and even speaks at times as if there were others available. For example, he states (p. 181), "But if a third congruent three-taxon area-cladogram is added to the system, *for example* the forms of *Terrapene carolina*, then the probability that two three-taxon cladograms will be congruent with the first one is one out of 3^2, or 11%. . . ," (emphasis added). To us, "for example" implies that others could have served the same purpose.

Nowhere do we state that evidential taxa must be chosen prior to a study and that if they are not, cladogram concordance is to be expected. Rather, we say that the null probability of an observed concordance is much higher if we do not state beforehand which taxa will be examined. Such a null probability, for an unspecified pair, trio, etc., of cladograms, can still be computed, as we outline.

Farris excoriates us for our use of the term "significance" in our discussion of a very small universe of cladograms. As he notes, the word may be taken either statistically or commonsensically. We, of course, mean commonsensically; hence our qualifier is "doubtful" rather than "marginal." Further, the entire sense of this discussion appears to us clearly not aimed at defining a significance level, and we are surprised to be misunderstood. In any event, we address only Farris' argument with our common sense.

He perfectly paraphrases our feeling, "that concordance between two cladograms, while not due to chance, possibly reflects a pattern common only to a small suite of groups . . ." He claims this has "little to do with the validity of conclusions of non-random association of groups" because "vicariance biogeographers . . . do not maintain that all groups . . . must show the same pattern." Once again, it seems as if the criteria for falsification of vicariance either do not exist or are unstated. If vicariance biogeographers take groups showing the same pattern as evidence for their hypothesis, then they must surely recognize groups *not* showing the same pattern as evidence against it, or else all observations must be viewed as supporting their hypothesis. The potential universe of cladograms that vicariance advocates define is biased, because it includes only taxa endemic to their current locations. These are disproportionately likely to be poor dispersers, so that one ends up looking at exactly those groups whose disjunctions are most likely to have arisen according to the vicariance scenario. Even if we are willing to accept this biased universe, however, we ask simply that the criteria for rejection be stated; if no amount of cladogram discordance can cause rejection, then there is no justification for adducing cladograms in the first place. If the universe of available cladograms is very small and there are one or a few concordances, even if these are unlikely to be due to chance individual dispersal, one should view them as weakly corroboratory and defer provisional acceptance of so comprehensive a theory as vicariance biogeography until a larger sample size is available, for the very reason that Farris states: A larger sample size will lower the possibility of "a pattern common only to a small suite of groups."

We apologize for our wording on ghosts; we intend that a *given ghost*, not suites of ghosts, can only lower or leave unmodified the observed instances of concordance. As both Farris and Platnick and Nelson (1978:figure 11) show, *a group* of ghosts *certainly* can change apparent discordance to concordance. We contend that our main point—that assumptions about the topological locations of ghosts affect the null probabilities of observed concordances—remains well taken. And we add that randomly produced ghosts are less likely to increase the number of concordances than to decrease them. There are almost certainly fewer possible placements of ghosts that would generate concordance than would produce discordance.

Our caveat about the subjectivity of cladograms is not properly taken. We do not deny that any of our methods could produce erroneous conclusions; any conclusion drawn from empiricial data as opposed to syllogistic reasoning is conceivably erroneous. We note simply that cladistic data have a potential source of error in addition to those possible for distributional data, namely that the cladograms themselves are not observed but rather are subjectively constructed, albeit as intelligently as possible. And there is no more reason to discount the importance of sympatric speciation than to exaggerate it. Farris appears to think that in the absence of a demonstration that a particular speciation event was sympatric, one should assume allopatric speciation. Again, this is usually a subjective matter, and even if we bring all our intelligence to bear on it and conclude that allopatric speciation is the more common mode, there is no *logical* basis for uniformly assuming allopatric speciation. This is another potential source of error from inferring unobserved events.

We never claim that dispersal is the only appropriate null hypothesis. We point out simply that individual dispersal is at least as appropriate a null hypothesis as is vicariance, that it is falsifiable by stated statistical criteria, and that such criteria for vicariance have been either non-existent or erroneous. We attempt to remedy this by describing what sorts of information would be needed in order to render vicariance a truly falsifiable hypothesis, and we show that although vicariance is falsifiable in principle, it does not seem that sufficient data are currently available for rigorous testing. We must maintain our claim that individual dispersal *is* the more parsimonious hypothesis (while recognizing that Occam's Razor has no logical force). For Farris' claim that "vicariance amounts to no more than that organisms tend to persist in the areas occupied by their ancestors" transmogrifies vicariance. Platnick and Nelson (1978:2), for example, aver that the critical difference between dispersal and vicariance hypotheses is that the latter postulates that range disjunctions arise simultaneously with geographical barriers, while the former postulates that barriers precede disjunctions. This in turn implies that in vicariance, range disjunctions for species in different higher taxa arise together (as the barrier arises), while in dispersal, range disjunctions for species in different taxa arise individually and sequentially. This is the aegis for the vicariance advocates' present search for concordant cladograms. And we maintain for this reason that dispersal *is* more parsimonious than vicariance: both hypotheses suggest that disjunctions arise; vicariance *in addition* suggests that they arise simultaneously and by the same event.

Finally, although we suggest individual dispersal as a null hypothesis (for reasons of both parsimony and falsifiability), we never claim that "dispersal, and dispersal alone, is the explanation of distribution." We explicitly state that distributions of entire taxa are likely to be generated by both sorts of events—those whose importance has been advocated by dispersalists and those emphasized in vicariant explanations. And we agree wholeheartedly with Farris that failure to disprove an hypothesis does not mean that it is proved and an alternative impugned. We make no such claim, and Farris' final sentence is completely in error when he attributes to us a conclusion of truth for a dispersalist null hypothesis. Our goals are to suggest that one cannot attempt to disprove an hypothesis without properly stating what observations would be accepted as disproof, to show that this has not been done for vicariance, to suggest ways in which it might be done, and to observe that there is no *a priori* reason to choose vicariance rather than individual dispersal as the null hypothesis.

Farris suggests that the resolution of the debate over dispersal and vicariance "can be more usefully approached through estimation than through testing preconceived theories." Aside from "preconceived" (what theories are *not* preconceived?) we do not at this time dissent from this view. It is a welcome retreat to modesty from the assertions, i.a., that generalized tracks are the "only scientific basis for biogeographic analysis" because the hypotheses are testable (Rosen 1974a:321), that Croizat's work allows "at last... a science of biogeography that depends on rigorous methods of analysis and the formulation of testable hypotheses" (Rosen 1974b:289), and that vicariance theory allows us "to formulate explicit methods of statistical analysis... that yield unambiguous and repeatable results" (Croizat et al. 1974:277).

3

Croizat's Panbiogeography versus Phylogenetic Biogeography

L. Z. Brundin

WE ARE TODAY entitled to believe that causal historical biogeography is leaving its former position as a mainly speculative discipline among the biological sciences. I do not hesitate to postulate that Hennig's elaboration of the methods for reconstructing nature's hierarchy, under simultaneous cross reference to the implication of vicariance patterns between sister groups, has been a milestone in connection with that development. Practical application of Hennig's principles to the study of biogeographical problems (especially intercontinental vicariance patterns) by several authors since the early 1960s has clearly demonstrated the potentials of the new approach for a realistic reconstruction of the history of life in time and space since the middle Mesozoic.

When we state, however, that biogeographical research of today has entered a period of comprehensive reevaluation of former concepts and estimates, it should be understood that this situation is only partly due to application of the principles of phylogenetic systematics as the basic tool. Another important factor has been the availability—and rapid development toward general acceptance—of the theory of plate tectonics and continental displacement. In a remarkable way the development of this theory has run parallel to that of phylogenetic biogeography. The biogeographer now seems to be in possession of the previously lacking paleogeographical background that is a prerequisite for a realistic estimate of the time and space dimensions of those events that formed the major disjunctions.

The fact that biogeographical research of today is in a period of critical reappraisal of former concepts and opinions is due, not least, to a third major contribution represented by the firebrand raised by Croizat again and again, with restless intensity, in a long series of comprehensive volumes. His *Panbiogeography* (1958) was a complete break with traditional bio-geography, in favor of a vicariance model that leaves comparatively little room for dispersal. It is important to note, however, that although Croizat's panbiogeography developed independently of Hennig's phylogenetic systematics and its biogeographical implication (phylogenetic biogeography), many of the views and conclusions reached by Croizat concur well with those arrived at by adherents of phylogenetic biogeography. Yet at present, there is undeniably a controversy centered on the role of dispersal and the methods necessary for a meaningful treatment of that phenomenon and its corollaries—directions of dispersal and areas of origin.

This paper is written for a symposium devoted to a discussion of the pros and cons of the vicariance model in biogeography. In order to give a constructive background to my criticism of some of the methods and prin-ciples of the vicariance model, I have chosen to present the tentative outlines of a phylogenetic biogeography that is symbolized by an alternative model and based in principle on personal experience acquired by studies of circum-Antarctic and amphitropical vicariance patterns.

What is Phylogenetic Biogeography?

Hierarchy in Time and Space

Through the ages the dormant potentials of the first gene pools have given rise to a unique hierarchical sequence of millions of species comprising many dead ends, it is true, but the hierarchy is still represented today by a biota displaying tremendous diversity of form and adaptive pattern. The realization and persistence of this dynamic multiplicity have been possible thanks to the processes of species cleavage, where life, via the deviation rule, has been able to work with the alternatives of conservatism and change—properties that have been equally necessary for the preservation and progressive development of life and its innate potential to colonize all the nooks and crannies of the earth. An expression of this process is the fact that we still have before us the long sequence from simple unicellular, akaryotic organisms to the representatives of the most advanced evolutionary experiments among the higher phyla. In other words, the hierarchy formed by Recent species mirrors the main outlines of the anagenetic and hierarchical evolution that has occurred since the start of life on the globe. This conclusion seems justified in spite of the fact that many groups have become extinct during the course of evolution. Perhaps with the exception of some of the very first groups, those now extinct were constituent members of the hierarchy formed by the Recent groups because the Recent groups belong to sectors that represent the never-broken continuity of the hierarchy. This is the reason why fossils cannot be placed properly without previous reconstruction of the hierarchy formed by the Recent groups.

The development of the hierarchy has taken place not only in time but also in space. There are several potential kinds of multiplication of species, but the evidence is strong that allopatric speciation, brought about by the subdivision of the ranges of ancestral species, has been predominant and decisive and that the abundant phenomenon of geographical vicariance is a direct expression of this process. If so, there is good reason to expect that the study of correlations among hierarchical structure, vicariance patterns, and known geological-geographical changes will yield important information about the history of the actual groups in time and space. Moreover, with reference to the model of allopatric speciation, it should be reasonable to conclude that sympatric distribution of closely related groups is an indication that dispersal has occurred.

Definitions

The young branch of evolutionary biology that I call *phylogenetic biogeography* has grown out of the insight touched on above. Phylogenetic biogeography is the study of the history of monophyletic groups of nature's hierarchy in time and space. The branch can be methodologically defined as the study of the causal connections between *phylogenesis* (development of the hierarchy in time and space), *anagenesis* (transformation of characters in time and space), *allopatry* (vicariance), *sympatry* (dispersal), and *paleogeographical events*.

It is important to distinguish between phylogenetic biogeography and *ecological biogeography*. Both are branches of historical biogeography, but ecological biogeography comes close to functional biology because of its connection with general ecology; it may be defined as the causal study of the distribution and history of populations, species, and biotic communities as members of ecosystems. Hence the ecological biogeographer predominantly works with problems connected with the Pleistocene and post-Pleistocene epochs, and the phylogenetic perspective is left aside.

Hierarchical Reconstruction

Because phylogenetic biogeography is the study of the history in time and space of monophyletic groups of nature's hierarchy, it is evident that this study must begin with an investigation of the relationship between the hierarchical structure and the vicariance pattern(s) of the relevant group(s). It matters little, however, if the work is started because of one's interest in a particular group and its history or because of the temptation to try to solve the history behind a particular vicariance pattern. The first task of the biogeographer will always be that of a cladist, i.e., reconstruction of the actual sector(s) of the hierarchy by applying the principles of phylogenetic systematics (Hennig 1965, 1966). While a general discussion of those principles is hardly called for in this context, it would perhaps be worthwhile to touch on a few points.

Inside and outside parallelism. As indicated by the literature, the occurrence of parallelism is generally considered a burden that causes much embarrassment in connection with hierarchical reconstruction. There is certainly some reason for this attitude, especially in groups for which our understanding of the direction of evolutionary trends is very limited, and for which we have very few credible apomorphies. We are far from always facing such critical situations, however, and the specialist does not often find it too difficult to construct a hierarchy of sister groups wherein the components are kept together by one or two seemingly credible synapomorphies. Yet, because hierarchical reconstruction is based on a sequence of hypotheses, every additional evidence of true synapomorphy and monophyly becomes important. Evidence of that type is the occurrence of unique parallelism inside a group that is supposed to be monophyletic, meaning that a unique apomorphy has evolved independently within each of two subgroups making up a major group. Several examples of *inside parallelism* are presented in my 1966 work and are discussed again in a paper written in 1976. The high supporting indicator value of *unique inside parallelism* (Brundin 1976:140) is a consequence of the fact that not only true synapomorphy, but also parallelism (incomplete synapomorphy) are expressions of the canalized evolutionary potential of the stem species of a monophyletic group. Saether (1977), who is able to rely on a very wide experience of hierarchical reconstruction, makes a similar judgment. Saether (p. 30) remarks, moreover, that an accordant opinion was already expressed by Crampton in 1929 (Brundin and Saether 1978).

It is important to observe also that we are not obliged to resort solely to synapomorphies that appear to be unique. Consider an example of family *A* wherein all species possess an apomorphic character *x*. We know, however, that character *x* has evolved by parallelism also within other families. But as long as we have reasons to suppose that none of the genera inside family *A* is related phylogenetically more closely to groups outside *A* than to other members of *A*, we are entitled to regard character *x* as a constituent character of family *A*, i.e., as a true synapomorphy for all species of that family (Hennig 1970:4, 1972:5). The implication is that in the search for synapomorphies an apomorphic character need not be rejected solely for the reason that its occurrence within a particular group is combined with a pattern of *outside parallelism* (Brundin 1976:140-41).

Dichotomy and polytomy.   The view expressed, even quite recently, by some critics (e.g., Blackwelder 1977) that the "search for the sister group" does presuppose that all speciation is dichotomous, is easily refuted (Brundin 1972a, 1972b). But what is the reason why dichotomy seems so predominant and cases of polytomy so rare? Suspected cases of multiple splitting refer to monophyletic groups wherein we are able to establish autapomorphies for different species but wherein, at least according to our present knowledge, we cannot find synapomorphies joining two or several species within the group. However, on theoretical grounds dichotomy seems to stand out as a far more probable result of allopatric speciation than does polytomy.

In his treatment of the speciation process among higher animals, Mayr (1963) points out that the geographical isolation of a peripheral population means the start of a risky existence caused by several bottlenecks, such as reduction of the diversity of the gene pool and the often very strong selection pressure exerted by the local conditions that deviate more or less markedly from those of the mother population. Mayr stresses that only a minority among the isolated populations are able to survive this process. On the other hand, in no other situation are there greater opportunities for breakthrough of evolutionary novelties. Most species bud off peripheral isolates, but nearly all isolates either reestablish contact with the mother population or die. Speciation is another illustration of the opportunism of evolution. What does it matter, asks Mayr, if 98 or 99 of 100 isolates become extinct? All is well and evolutionary progress is assured as long as one of them once in a while transforms into a new species.

According to Mayr there are good reasons to suppose that accomplished speciation in the vast majority of cases results from simple dichotomy and that polytomy is a rare phenomenon. Mayr's theory, based on population genetics, agrees well with the reconstructions of different sectors of the hierarchy made till now. My results, as well as the results of others, unanimously indicate that dichotomy has been dominant. I myself have never encountered a suspected case of multiple cleavage. But this is probably not the whole answer.

Croizat (1964:209) compares the development of vicariance patterns to the cracking of a framed piece of glass by successive blows, apparently assuming that at least the main part of the isolated fractions of the ancestral population would give rise to new species. But would suspected cases of polytomous speciation not be far more common than they seem? Admittedly, we do not know very much about these matters. There is reason to assume, however, that young groups rich in species very similar to each other might offer examples of polytomous speciation; but in the particular cases decisions are hampered by a persisting and far from unreasonable suspicion that the lack of inside synapomorphies is due to insufficient knowledge of the character spectra. Here phylogenetic systematics encounters its limits.

Andersson (1977:16) suggests that the predominance of dichotomous speciation indicated by the reconstructions of different sectors of the hierarchy to date might be only apparent because the reconstructions have concentrated on old groups: "Dichotomy in old groups can in fact be due to a secondary dichotomy resulting from extinction . . . and it is questionable if the reconstruction of the phylogeny of surviving old rest groups really depicts the true pathways of evolution." His is a good point and is well illustrated by his figure 5, which shows how an original hierarchy in the reconstruction is transformed into an incorrect hierarchy because of the presence of parallel character transformation and subsequent extinction of certain taxa—meaning that primary parallelisms are mistakenly treated as synapomorphies (also Hennig 1966:209-16).

It is evident that the biogeographer must be well aware of sources of error of the kind touched on here. Their existence emphasizes that reconstruction of the hierarchy and history of a particular group is often of limited value until it can be shown to conform to a generalized pattern of firm correlation among hierarchical structure, vicariance, and paleogeographical events. Important also are the special risks connected with treatment of old relict groups. Monotypic genera showing marked morphological gaps in relation to their Recent sister groups are often problematical links in biogeographical reconstructions, for there might be reason to suspect that the high degree of deviation signifies earlier extinction.

Vicariance Patterns

By reconstructing the hierarchy formed by a monophyletic group, one arrives at a picture of the geographical distribution of the group. The emerging distribution pattern will be composed of more or less clearly separated areas, meaning that the subordinate groups and the individual species are restricted to certain geographical areas (ranges) that may be separated by continents or oceans but in other cases may be in close contact or may overlap. The apparent patterns of vicariance form an important complement to the argumentation, based on supposed synapomorphy, that we have applied during cladistic analysis. Already in his classic work of 1950, Hennig stressed the importance of the "chorological method" in this connection. Not too rarely a revision of a supposedly monophyletic group will turn our attention to a group occurring far outside the apparent main range. Such cases require a critical testing of the relationships in accordance with the principles of phylogenetic systematics.

The value of a vicariance pattern as an indicator of the credibility of the cladistic analysis is far from always the same but is generally well illustrated when it can be shown that the pattern is repetitious, i.e., orderly. But reference to repetitious occurrence of simple vicariance between two groups living, for example, on each side of the South Atlantic, is of course a weak argument. In such cases we have to rely solely on the credibility of the applied synapomorphies. If we are able to refer to a wider hierarchical perspective, however, even a simple two-area pattern can be deeply meaningful. Within chironomid groups (Diptera) of southern origin it seems a common phenomenon that Patagonian groups of low rank have their sister groups in the tropical high Andes; a broad reconstruction of the involved hierarchies indicates that the latter groups are comparatively young (and comparatively apomorphic) offshoots of major, older aggregates in Patagonia. There is little doubt that the actual two-area pattern is the result of comparatively late dispersal from the south in connection with the rise of the Andes.

Complex vicariance patterns generally deliver the best tests of the credibility of the cladistic analysis. It is good if one can refer to a series of identical multiple vicariance, but still better if one can show that within several supposedly monophyletic groups there is a relationship between hierarchical structure and the areas of a multiple vicariance pattern. An example is offered by chironomid midges of southern origin, for which it could be demonstrated that within each of three subfamilies (Podonominae, Aphroteniinae, Diamesinae) the endemic groups of New Zealand and southeastern Australia all have their closest relatives (sister groups) in Patagonia, and that within each subfamily, the partial groups of South America, southeastern Australia, and New Zealand together form a monophyletic group whose closest relatives occur in South Africa and/or Laurasia (Brundin 1966).

By investigating vicariance patterns, phylogenetic systematics transforms into phylogenetic biogeography. But there is always a close integration, and the procedures of phylogenetic biogeography imply, after all, a continued test of the credibility of the cladistic analysis, as is also the case with the successive inclusion of arguments delivered by transformation series of characters not applied by the original cladistic analysis but made available by our increasing insight.

Paleogeographical Background

The solidity of cladistic argumentation is strengthened and the historical picture in time and space of a group is deepened if we are able to link the origin of vicariance patterns with paleogeographical events during certain epochs. In this respect the possibilities have improved rapidly during the last fifteen years thanks to intensive research devoted to further development of the theory of plate tectonics and continental displacement and our increased knowledge of the adhering time scale. Because the old supercontinent Pangea was fragmented according to a fairly well known and datable sequence, the biogeographer is now able to form a reliable picture of the causal history of the subdivision of ancestral ranges that once were continuous. But this presupposes that he can show a correlation of branching sequences with the presumably known sequence of continental separations. For example, such a correlation could be demonstrated for Gondwanian chironomid groups with circum-Antarctic distribution (Brundin 1966) and for the order Palaeognathiformes among birds (Cracraft 1974b).

Thanks to a great number of strategically placed deep-sea drillings, it seems well documented that southern Africa and East Antarctica were separated at the latest during the Lower Cretaceous (Larson and Ladd 1973; Stapleton and Beer 1976); that the connection between New Zealand and West Antarctica was broken in the Upper Cretaceous (Heirtzler et al. 1968; Pitman et al. 1968); and that the break between Australia and East Antarctica occurred during the transition between the Paleocene and Eocene (Weissel and Hayes 1972). As for the period when South America separated from West Antarctica, there is still some uncertainty, but available evidence points to the lower Tertiary, or roughly to the same period as the break between Australia and East Antarctica (Dalziel and Elliot 1971; Foster 1974; Kennett et al. 1974). The conclusion that the circum-Antarctic vicariance patterns of the chironomid midges developed as a consequence of these paleogeographical events between the Upper Jurassic and the Paleocene-Eocene does presuppose that the main outlines of the chironomid hierarchy were already in existence in the Upper Jurassic and that some Recent genera are at least of Lower Cretaceous age. Are these dates realistic? Multiple correlations like those mentioned are strong evidence; likewise the occurrence of the chironomid genus *Archaeochlus* in the Drakensberg Mountains of southern Africa and in southwestern Australia apparently demonstrates that the genus occurred in East Antarctica before the fracture between that continent and southern Africa (Brundin 1976). But we deal with hypotheses, and in this and similar cases, confirmation by fossil evidence would be a strong additional argument.

The insight that the particular type of intercontinental vicariance, and hence the degree of engagement of a group in the Pangean breakup, is an expression of the minimum age—and often also of the maximum age—of a group, lessens the often expressed but rarely satisfied need for relevant fossils. This insight is great progress, and there is reason to expect that many plant and animal groups, not least among the mammals, will turn out to be essentially older than still believed on the basis of inconclusive fossil findings.

In this connection it is important to remember that vicariance between two sister groups goes back beyond the time of origin of the two groups to the time of the partition of the range of the common ancestral species. In addition, as Hennig (1954, 1966, 1969) repeatedly stressed, there might be an essential difference in time between the age of origin of a group and the age of its differentiation into the Recent species.

Evidence of Fossils

From what has been set out above, it is evident that reconstruction of phylogenetic relationships and of important aspects of the history in time and space of a group is possible even if relevant fossils are not available. But fossil findings may give significant and even decisive biogeographical information of a different kind, if the fossils are so well preserved and so complete that their position in the hierarchy can be established with precision. For the methods and principles that have to be applied in this connection, it may suffice to refer to Hennig (1954, 1966, 1969). Here I will give two examples of the importance of fossils to insect biogeography.

The recent findings in Canada, Lebanon, and North Siberia of fossiliferous amber from the Cretaceous attract a special interest due to ever increasing evidence that the distribution patterns of the Recent biota have been strongly influenced by geological-geographical events during this dynamic epoch. In Lebanon, in amber embedded in strata of the Neocomian (the lowermost Lower Cretaceous) directly overlying marine Jurassic strata (Schlee and Dietrich, 1970), Schlee has found a member of the chironomid subfamily Podonominae. On the basis of several apomorphies, this fossil species, *Libanochlites neocomicus* Brundin, from the northern margin of Gondwanaland (that during the Neocomian was in a state of fragmentation), belongs to the tribe Boreochlini. The available characters indicate that *Libanochlites* is either the sister group of *Paraboreochlus + Boreochlus* or the sister group of *Paraboreochlus*. These close relatives of the fossil form are Laurasian genera that form a sister-group pair in the Recent fauna (Brundin 1976). *Libanochlites + Paraboreochlus + Boreochlus* make up the sister group of the highly plesiomorphic genus *Archaeochlus* and at least the common ancestral species of *Paraboreochlus + Boreochlus* must have existed at the transition between the Upper Jurassic and the Neocomian. To the biogeographer the documentation thus accumulated becomes a proof that even subordinate groups high in the chironomid hierarchy are sufficiently old to have taken part even in the early stages of the Pangean fragmentation. Even from this viewpoint there is a well founded theory to suppose that the amphitropical and circum-Antarctic vicariance patterns of the Chironomidae are a consequence of the subdivision of formerly continuous distribution areas during the Mesozoic and lower Tertiary.

My second example refers also to Chironomidae. In 1966 I described representatives of a new subfamily, Aphroteniinae, based on material from Patagonia, southeastern Australia, and the Cape Province of southern Africa. These very small rheobiontic midges seemed to deviate from the evidently common pattern that groups with circum-Antarctic or amphi-Antarctic distribution are more or less directly involved in amphitropical (bipolar) vicariance. The Aphroteniinae are not exceptional, however; at the 6th chironomid symposium in 1976, Dr. N. S. Kalugina demonstrated fossil midges that doubtlessly belong to Aphroteniinae embedded in amber from Cretaceous strata on the Taimyr Peninsula in northern Siberia.

Global Aspect

To a biogeographer engaged in analytic work it is important never to forget that his attempt to reconstruct the history of a group refers only to a limited sector of nature's hierarchy and that every group has an ancestral species in common with another group, which the two groups—provided that we are dealing with dichotomy—do not share with any other group in the Recent biota. One of the leading theses of phylogenetic biogeography is therefore that a firm grip on the history of a group cannot be achieved if we do not know its sister group and where the sister group is living. But knowledge of the sister group is a minimum requirement, and it is normally recommended, if not required, to continue the reconstruction of the hierarchy several steps further in order to secure a satisfactory perspective in time and space. The procedure cannot be overextended. These viewpoints are seemingly often neglected in today's all too theoretical discussions of the methods and principles of historical biogeography.

When, for example, an entomologist from the northern countries visits Patagonia, Tasmania, or New Zealand, the most striking and interesting impression will not be exoticism of the fauna (because it is expected), but the familiar features that are there in spite of the vast distances between the northern and southern areas of comparison. One is reminded of the relative insignificance of geographical distance relative to the global coherence of biogeographical events. The supply of time has been so rich that it becomes comparatively insignificant in principle if we study birds, beetles, or limnic crustaceans of the groundwater. Indeed, even a limited area on the northern continents, such as Sweden or Minnesota, has a biota with species probably representing hundreds of northern groups that have their sister groups in the southern continents; the reverse is the case if we start from an area in the southern temperate zone. "For whatever of nature is northern is bound to have a southern counterpart, whatever its kind, degree and obviousness" (Croizat 1958:195).

Such considerations, based on experience, lead to the view that biogeographical analyses of groups involved in vicariance patterns of limited geographical extent easily become fragmentary and inconclusive because of an insufficient survey of the time and space perspectives. It is therefore recommended that the hierarchical reconstruction be carried far enough so that we face cases of vicariance of global extent, thus also securing an adequate survey of the occurrence of sympatry at different sister-group levels, in turn facilitating a realistic discussion of dispersal and areas of origin on a worldwide basis. It may be added that integration of the global aspect already is called for because hierarchical reconstruction requires the use of synapomorphy, which presupposes that we have a satisfactory survey of the exclusiveness of the actual apomorphic characters.

Dispersal and Areas of Origin

We here approach the most difficult and controversial, as well as the most fascinating, matter within historical biogeography. A great challenge has always been posed by vicariance patterns that display wide disjunctions between closely related groups. With little help from geologists, biogeographers have long felt free to calculate dispersal via former land bridges or long-distance dispersal by a few or single "founders." But even if the present general acceptance of a comparatively well contoured dynamic paleogeography has eliminated several reasons for controversy, there is still disagreement about approach and methods, and the meaning and role of dispersal.

Essential for an adequate estimate of dispersal, directions of dispersal, and areas of origin of ancestral species is, first and foremost, a comprehensive preparatory work of the kind discussed in the foregoing sections. Hardly less important, but at present often neglected, is acknowledgment of certain anagenetic phenomena connected with allopatric speciation and dispersal.

Allopatric speciation. Loose discussions of the relations in time and space between "primitive" and "derivative" groups, so common among traditional biogeographers, easily lead to ambiguous or erroneous conclusions. During the evolutionary process the transformation of characters has taken place within the framework of the developing hierarchy. This means that if differential degrees of transformation of the character supply of different species and species groups are to be used as meaningful biogeographical arguments, they must refer to comparisons between sister species and sister groups of a reconstructed sector of the hierarchy. In this respect every kind of compromise is indefensible.

Reconstruction of a sector of the hierarchy, signified by the stepwise search for the sister group based on synapomorphy, soon reveals that one of the components of a pair of sister species or sister groups generally differs more or less markedly from the other by a more apomorphic design. This means that it deviates more from the common ancestral species than does the sister species or sister group that stands out as conservative or plesiomorphic (or, from a more general aspect, plesiotypic). This massively confirmed phenomenon, Hennig's (1950) deviation rule, is of fundamental evolutionary importance because the apomorphic component signifies the experiment in a potentially progressive process through time and space that, if successful, means a further development of novel trends; while the conservative component signifies persisting possibilities for breakthrough of the potentials of the ancestral species if the experiment symbolized by the sister species proves unsuccessful (Brundin 1968, 1972a). If the apomorphic species starts to increase its range, the direction of dispersal will be centrifugal, at least in the initial stages, because persistence of the primary barrier will prevent invasion of the domains of the plesiomorphic sister species, obviously to the advantage of a free, further development of the hierarchy.

The experience of the existence of a rule of deviation gained by hierarchical reconstruction apparently confirms Mayr's (1963) view, based on the results of population biology, that speciation generally is the result of geographical isolation of marginal populations and is brought about by barriers subdividing the continuous range of an ancestral species. Such unequal cleavage of the ancestral gross population means the start of a more or less opportunistic experiment at the species border that often results in failure, but that in case of success will give rise to a new species in a peripheral position. This species, the product of changed conditions of life, will stand out as apomorphic (apotypic) in relation to its conservative sister species that is the result of genetic and environmental conditions that were more or less identical to those of the mother species, a situation that might mean preservation of biological identity (complete plesiotypy).

During the evolutionary process the rule of deviation has been maintained irrespective of whether allopatric speciation occurred before or after dispersal. But the actual rule is a rule and not a law (or close to a law) only if allopatric speciation was not preceded by dispersal. Equal or approximately equal cleavage of an ancestral gross population by preservation of roughly similar conditions on both sides of a barrier might happen, and if reproductive isolation is brought about after a long period of time, the degree of anagenetic change and the influence of the deviation rule would probably be minimal. However, this is one extreme possibility that signifies something like a blind alley (Mayr 1963:542). The other extreme is the isolation of a single fertilized female, signifying an utterly optimistic experiment.

It should also be noted that the action of the deviation rule might become more or less blurred or diluted in connection with a comparatively rapid development of complex local vicariance patterns, not least if they are due to simultaneous multiple splitting of the area of an ancestral species and concomitant polytomous speciation resulting in "superspecies," i.e., aggregates of very similar species expressing patterns of very modest anagenetic progression. Such a process might appear an evolutionary parenthesis. Yet it might mean the very start of potentially important preadaptations; the best chance for a real breakthrough would probably be the subsequent geographical isolation of marginal populations followed by dichotomous speciation clearly expressing the rule of deviation. Alternating periods of low and high evolutionary rates probably have been common in the history of particular groups and biotas in general.

Dispersal. There is a polarity between the center-of-origin/dispersal model of the traditional biogeographers and the vicariance model of Croizat and his adherents (Croizat et al. 1974; Nelson 1975, 1976). With all respect to the essential progress symbolized by the latter model, there seems to be reason to ask if the strong deemphasis of the role of dispersal and the limited interest for investigation of areas of origin really are expressions of a balanced approach and effective methodology that hold out the prospect of a realistic reconstruction of historical events in their actual complexity and difficulty of access. It seems symptomatic that the formalizations of the vicariance model hitherto given (Croizat et al. 1974; Nelson 1975) do not define the meaning of allopatric speciation and dispersal and dismiss Hennig's "progression rule" as "a rejectable apriorism" (Nelson 1975).

Disregarding cases of long-distance dispersal over pre-existing barriers by one or a few individuals, we can define *dispersal* as the stepwise progression in space by marginal portions (border populations) of the gross population of a species. There is a steady fluctuation back and forth at the border of ever living species, but the general incitement to dispersal of some magnitude will be the disappearance of a former barrier, quite as the appearance of barriers will be the incitement to allopatric speciation and vicariance. Because progression in space means exposure to new conditions of life, the result of subsequent isolation and speciation cannot be but one: peripheral, more or less strongly accentuated apomorphy. In other words, there must develop a parallelism between morphological and chorological progression in the time perspective. This parallelism must be conceived as an expression of a close correlation between the rule of deviation and the results of dispersal seen in the time perspective.

The above discussion is based on data given by life itself. For example, studying the vicariance patterns of chironomid midges, we face many groups that stand out as comparatively young and geographically distant offshoots of older groups. In more than 30 cases of vicariance between sister groups in Patagonia–southeastern Australia, Patagonia–the tropical High Andes, and the Gondwanian continents–Laurasia, it can be demonstrated by reference to sympatry and other circumstances that dispersal has occurred. In all these cases the comparatively young offshoots stand out as apomorphic in relation to their proximally situated sister groups and often display the last step(s) in proximally started multiple-step trends. The causal connections are obvious. They signify the existence of the following "law" that is nothing but a transcription of the "law" of parallelism between morphological and chorological progression (Hennig 1950, 1966:232), but they express the biogeographical meaning of dispersal more clearly:

Dispersal by an incipient ancestral species followed by isolation and speciation will give rise to peripheral apomorphy, not to peripheral plesiomorphy.

It is irrelevant whether the species that started to extend its range was plesiomorphic or apomorphic in relation to its vicariant sister species, because the latter was not involved in the actual process. It must be acknowledged that possibilities for dispersal are open to all living species, independent of their relative apomorphy/plesiomorphy. Fatal for our attempts to reconstruct particular dispersal events would be application of Darlington's rule of thumb (1957, 1970a), that derivative groups tend to mark the places of origin, and that there is reason to expect "most non-dominant or primitive forms to be in distant-peripheral areas." These assumptions, an echo of Matthewian doctrines, are not based on relevant evidence (Cracraft 1975a:234). They are also basically *beside the point*. What matters most are the consequences of dispersal of incipient ancestral species, not the relation between apomorphy/plesiomorphy and aptness to disperse or to keep a certain range. My earlier writings on these matters (Brundin 1972b:72, 1975:20, etc.) are admittedly far from adequate. The consequences of dispersal within directly involved monophyletic groups should be formulated as follows:

If dispersal has occurred, then the comparatively plesiomorphic species or group will be closer to the initial range of the common ancestral species than the apomorphic sister species or sister group.

This is a rule and not a law. Exceptions are possible, e.g., if the hierarchical structure of a group has been torn by extinction (see also Hennig 1966:232). Within a simple vicariance pattern between two sister groups, however, the mere ocurrence of the comparatively plesiomorphic group within one part of the total range, and of the apomorphic sister group within another part, should not in itself be used as evidence of dispersal and direction of dispersal. But if other conditions such as sympatry and the structure of the hierarchical connections outside the two groups indicate dispersal, then the geographical distribution of general plesiomorphy/apomorphy becomes important additional evidence of direction of dispersal and the area of its origin, in accordance with Hennig's progression rule.

Speaking for themselves in these respects, independent of presence or absence of sympatry, are those cases of preserved multi-area vicariance where, in conjunction with a reconstruction of the actual hierarchy, several steps in morphoclines can be followed over the map and used as conclusive evidence of dispersal and the area of its origin. An example is Schminke's reconstruction (1973) of the global dispersal history of the Parabathynellidae, syncaridan crustaceans of the groundwater.

Ancestral species, areas of origin, and dispersal. A study of the literature reveals that biogeographical discussions often suffer from negligence or unawareness of the causal connections among ancestral species, areas of origin, and dispersal. The following points are worthy of note: (1) the area of origin of a monophyletic group is always the area of its ancestral species (in singular); (2) the area of an ancestral species can be estimated by addition of the ranges of the descendant species if, and only if, the range of the group has not been increased by secondary dispersal of some of its members, or reduced by extinction; and (3) if the occurrence of a group within a certain area is solely the consequence of prior dispersal, then the group—*including its ancestral species*—(see no. 9 in figures 3.1–3.2) cannot have been directly involved in that process. It is evident that dispersal must have been performed by members of a species (no. 7; all groups are identified by the number of their stem species) that was the incipient ancestral species of the actual group and its sister group (no. 8). Hence the area of the latter group marks the approximate area of origin (start) of the supposed dispersal and at the same time the area of origin (initial area) of an ancestral species that eventually, after subdivision of its range by a barrier, gave rise to a vicariance pattern between its two daughter species that were the ancestral species of the two sister groups. Consequently, if we say, as we generally do, that for example a Laurasian group is of Gondwanian origin, we must be aware, if our dispersal hypothesis is right, of the kind of historical events that have taken place.

Analysis in theory. The starting point for our attempts to estimate dispersal is the insight that sympatry between closely related groups is an indication that dispersal has occurred because primary allopatry has been transformed into secondary sympatry. But the problem about direction of dispersal and areas of origin still has to be resolved; that problem includes questions about whether one member of a sympatric pair did disperse; if so, which member dispersed, or whether both dispersed (Croizat et al. 1974). Facing these intricate questions, the biogeographer has at his disposal means that are certainly not infallible, but that will often give him a fair chance to arrive at defensable answers.

Let us first have a look at some theoretical examples referring to amphi-Atlantic vicariance between sister groups in Africa and South America. Figure 3.1 shows the assumed hierarchy of such a pattern. It is assumed also that the South American group (number 9) clearly stands out as apomorphic in relation to its sister group in Africa (number 8). This does not tell us very much when seen in a limited time perspective, but becomes quite meaningful when we are able to establish that the group 8 + 9 forms a young and comparatively apomorphic sector of a hierarchy that is firmly anchored in Africa via the branching points that gave rise to the older African groups (numbers 6, 4, and 2). Hence the South American group stands out as a young and apomorphic offshoot of an older aggregate in Africa. Because this establishment refers to one of the components making up a sympatric pair, we have strong reason to conclude that the range of stem species number 1 was restricted to present Africa and that the occurrence of the young and apomorphic group number 9 in South America is due to dispersal of stem species number 7 from Africa into present South America before the existence of the South Atlantic (figure 3.2). In other words, we have reason to suppose that stem species number 7 was preceded by a sequence of stem

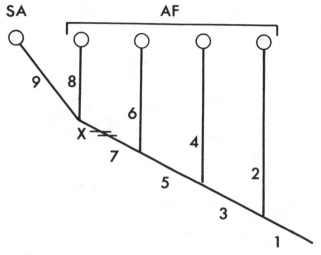

Figure 3.1. Hierarchy of a major group assumed to be one of the components of a sympatric pair involved in amphi-Atlantic vicariance. Groups numbers 9 and 8 + 9 are relatively apomorphic. X represents the break caused by the opening of the South Atlantic.

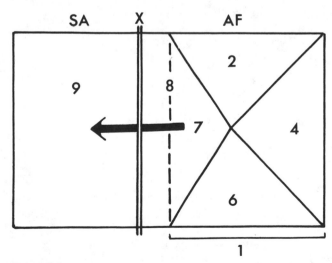

Figure 3.2. History of the supposed vicariance and dispersal of the group referred to in figure 3.1.

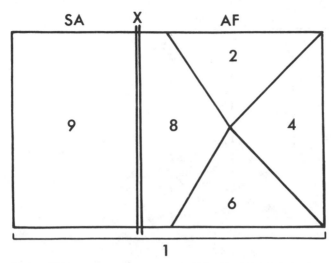

Figure 3.3A. Alternative hypothesis based on the hierarchy in figure 3.1. Stem species number 1 occurred also in South America and the whole pattern is the result of vicariance events.

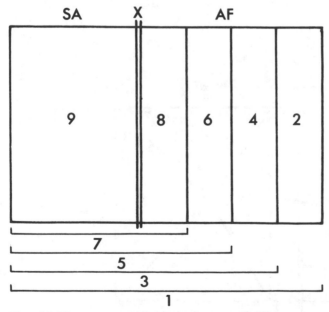

Figure 3.3B. As in Figure 3.3A, but the diagram illustrates the role played by stem species 1, 3, 5, and 7 in space. The area of stem species 1 was parted in areas 2 and 3; the area of stem species 3 in areas 4 and 5, etc.

species (numbers 1, 3, and 5) that speciated without engagement of populations in South America simply because such populations did not exist in South America during earlier periods of the subdivision of the range of stem species number 1.

An alternative hypothesis, based on the assumption that stem species number 1 occurred also in South America and that its range comprised the total area of the descendant species, meets with difficulties. If the extant vicariance pattern would be the result solely of stepwise subdivision on the spot of the range of stem species number 1, we are evidently forced to assume a development of the type shown in figure 3.3, where figure 3.3B is constructed so as to enable an illustration of the role played by stem species numbers 1, 3, 5, and 7 in the space dimension. It seems strange that while a steady speciation was taking place in the African area of stem species number 1, there was no allopatric speciation within the South American area until after its isolation due to the birth of the South Atlantic. This lengthy evolutionary vacuum in South America would be hard to explain, as would be the phenomenon that the gross population inhabiting the vast South American range—the rest of the range of stem species number 1—would at last have given rise to the apomorphic stem species and group number 9. Under the supposed conditions a plesiomorphic status of number 9 as a consequence of a probably modest "phyletic gradualism," would be the more reasonable alternative, but it cannot be considered in the actual case.

Following up the matter, we have reason to ask which type of pattern would be the most probable if a stem species corresponding to number 1 of figure 3.1 occurred on both sides of the present South Atlantic and occupied an area equal to the total area of the descendant species. The tentative answer is that such a situation would give rise to a pre-Atlantic vicariance pattern involving both Africa and South America and conforming in principle with the pattern shown in figure 3.4. If we also consider the secondary, radical break (X) caused by the opening of the South Atlantic (figure 3.4), the result will be the hierarchy shown in figure 3.5. Characteristic seems to be the presence on each side of the South Atlantic of a mosaic of subgroups of different ages forming a hierarchical/geographical pattern that does presuppose the occurrence of stem species 1, 3, 5, and 7 in Africa as well as in South America.

If the distribution pattern of a monophyletic group is a consequence of vicariance events without involvement of dispersal, the distribution of general apomorphy/plesiomorphy among the species and species groups inside the total range may be supposed to form an irregular mosaic pattern that cannot

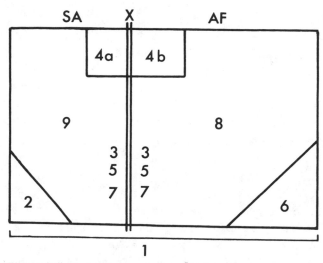

Figure 3.4. Probable type of an amphi-Atlantic vicariance pattern if a stem species corresponding to stem species 1 of figure 3.1 occurred on both sides of the South Atlantic and occupied the total area of the descendant species.

be predicted. We have the right to expect only that the distribution patterns of the subordinate taxa as exponents of apomorphy/plesiomorphy will mirror the history of the local abiotic and biotic conditions and that the actual patterns probably will be repeated by other, but not necessarily all, biotic components inhabiting the same area. Hence the geographical distribution of

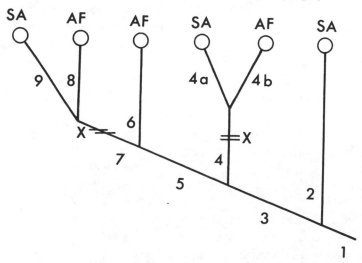

Figure 3.5. The hierarchy of the vicariance pattern in figure 3.4.

extant groups as exponents of comparative apomorphy/plesiomorphy becomes an irrelevant argument when we are dealing with vicariance patterns that developed *in situ*.

Analysis in practice. Experience teaches that hierarchy/vicariance relations of the type shown in figure 3.1 are common in connection with cases of sympatry. But often there are, as could be expected, complications of a different kind. Figure 3.6 shows a reconstruction of the hierarchy formed by the tribe Podonomini (Chironomidae: Podonominae). The strongly diversified genera *Podonomus* (44 species) and *Podochlus* (27 species) show a three-area pattern including southeastern Australia, Patagonia, and New Zealand, while the genera *Rheochlus* (three species) and *Podonomopsis* (seven species) have developed a two-area pattern comprising southeastern Australia and Patagonia. Together the above genera are involved in multiple sympatric vicariance between Patagonia and southeastern Australia. Because the Australian group of each genus stands out as a young and comparatively apomorphic offshoot of an older group in Patagonia, we evidently deal with cases that are compatible with the theoretical case discussed above and illustrated in figures 3.1–3.2. We are thus entitled to apply the same arguments.

It seems well founded to conclude that the occurrence in southeastern Australia of representatives of the genera *Podonomus, Podochlus, Rheochlus,* and *Podonomopsis* is due to dispersal from South America and (or) East Antarctica of the stem species that those representatives have in common with their respective sister groups in Patagonia. The dispersal evidently occurred before the break between East Antarctica and Australia at the transition between the Paleocene and Eocene. Within the comparatively young and apomorphic genus *Podonomopsis,* however, there are two cases of two-area vicariance, and the terminal subgroup that developed from stem species number 9 includes only three species, one of them forming the monotypic Australian group that is simply the sister group of its two relatives in South America. But in this case the presence of sympatry, the very strongly marked apomorphy of the Australian species, *P. discoceros* (Brundin 1966), and reference to a congruent general pattern are sufficient arguments for dispersal and the area of its origin.

The hierarchy pictured in figure 3.6 shows that the New Zealand groups differ principally from the Australian groups by their older relative age. Those New Zealand groups that belong to the genera *Podonomus* and *Podochlus* are also each the sister group of the South American groups, of which the

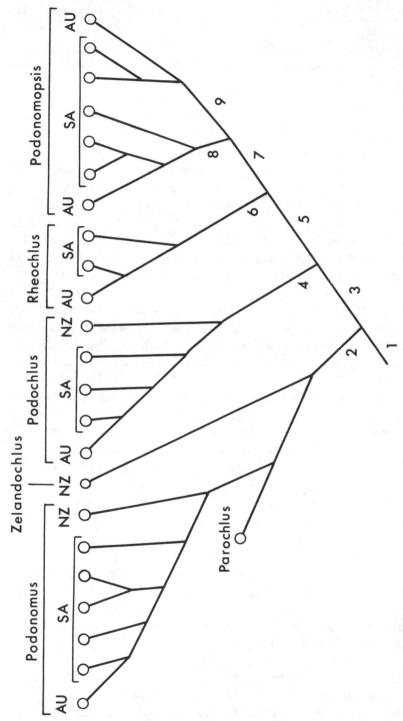

Figure 3.6. Partial reconstruction of the hierarchy of the tribe Podonomimi (Chironomidae: Podonominae).

Australian groups are younger offshoots. The genera *Rheochlus* and *Podonomopsis* are not represented in New Zealand, and if they ever occurred in West Antarctica, they were probably too young to reach New Zealand before its separation from West Antarctica in the Upper Cretaceous. There is reason to assume that the latter two genera had their area of origin in Patagonia or in Patagonia + East Antarctica. As for the tribe Podonomini itself, it seems safe to conclude that the tribe had its area of origin within the axis New Zealand–West Antarctica–southern South America. There are some indications, however, that the proper area of origin did not include South America: (1) the most plesiomorphic genus of the tribe, the monotypic *Zelandochlus*, is endemic to New Zeland; (2) *Zelandochlus* is the sister group of *Podonomus* + *Parochlus*; (3) the sister group of these three genera is formed by *Podochlus* + *Rheochlus* + *Podonomopsis*, and *Podochlus* is the plesiomorphic sister group of the two other genera; (4) within *Podochlus* as well as within *Podonomus* the New Zealand group is plesiomorphic in relation to its South American-Australian sister group; (5) points 1–4, together with the fact that *Podochlus* and *Podonomus* are involved in sympatric amphi-Antarctic vicariance between New Zealand and South America, indicate some early dispersal toward South America from West Antarctica-New Zealand. It seems to be an open question which of the basic stem species did disperse, or if both dispersed. A precise judgment is severely hampered by the probable status of *Zelandochlus* as a relict species that must be regarded against a background of extinction of unknown extent. Be that as it may, New Zealand evidently has played a role in the early history of Podonomini that was at least as important as that of Patagonia. It would certainly be a grave mistake always to look upon New Zealand as a receiver.

A closer consideration of the genus *Parochlus* in the above discussion was not possible but would not have influenced the general conclusions. *Parochlus* was excluded because the hierarchy formed by the numerous (16) species of the amphi-Antarctic and amphitropical *araucanus* group could not be confidently reconstructed. According to our present knowledge of this group, only pupal characters can be used for phylogenetic argument and for the purpose of identification. I am now of the opinion that the hierarchy of the *araucanus* group shown in figures 46 and 634 of my 1966 work is partly based on parallelisms, a possibility already discussed in detail in that work (pp. 120–23).

This handicap, however, cannot jeopardize the status of the species *Parochlus kiefferi* of Laurasia as a comparatively young and apomorphic offshoot of the Gondwanian *P. araucanus* group. Its closest relatives are most probably *araucanus* of Patagonia, *bassianus* of Tasmania, and *maorii* of New Zealand. Since *kiefferi* must have been preceded by a very long sequence of stem species (leading back to the very origin of Podonomini) that speciated without engagement of populations in Laurasia, it is clear, without reference to sympatry, that the occurrence of *kiefferi* in Laurasia is due to transtropic dispersal from the south. But whether the dispersal was performed by populations of an ancestral species during the Pliocene-Pleistocene, or during an earlier epoch, is problematic. The demonstrated occurrence of the true *kiefferi* as far south as Sierra Nevada in California, and the finding at the crater lake of Nevado de Toluca in Mexico (leg. F. Reiss) of imagos that might belong to *kiefferi*, could be points in favor of the former alternative as well as an indication of the dispersal route.

We now turn our attention to the chironomid subfamily Diamesinae, which is only distantly related to Podonominae. The Diamesinae display a double amphitropical distribution. The dominant and most plesiomorphic diamesine group of the southern temperate zone is the tribe Heptagyini, which is represented by 11 species in Andean South America, two species in southeastern Australia, and five species in New Zealand. The sister group is the relatively strongly apomorphic and monotypic tribe Lobodiamesini of New Zealand. The reconstruction of the hierarchy pictured in figure 3.7 shows that the basic branchings of the stem species number 1 lead to groups in South America without engagement of populations in New Zealand and Australia. Stem species number 2 has given rise to the genera *Heptagyia* and *Paraheptagyia*—the former monotypic, the latter with five South American species. The southeastern Australian subgroup (two species) of *Paraheptagyia* stands out as a young and apomorphic offshoot of an older group in South America also comprising the genus *Heptagyia*. We evidently deal with a case similar to those of the Podonomini. Because the same pattern occurs also within each of the genera *Aphroteniella* and *Paraphrotenia* of the subfamily Aphroteniinae (Brundin 1966), there is little doubt that we deal with a generalized pattern of dispersal and vicariance. In this perspective it is irrelevant that we cannot refer to sympatric vicariance between groups in Patagonia and Australia within the little diversified tribe Heptagyini. Because of the lack of any indication that the heptagyine stem species numbers 1, 2, and 4 (figure 3.7) ever occurred in Australia, the conclusion is that the occurrence of a subgroup of *Paraheptagyia* in southeastern Australia is due to dispersal from Patagonia-East Antarctica of the stem species number 6 before the end of the Paleocene.

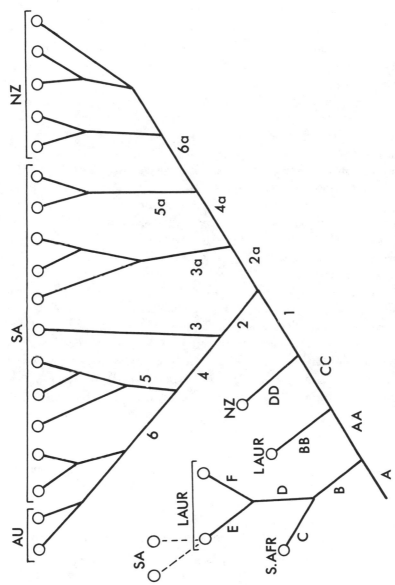

Figure 3.7. Partial reconstruction of the hierarchy of the subfamily Diamesinae (Chironomidae): 1, Heptagyini; 2, *Heptagyia*; 3, *Paraheptagyia*; 3a, *Reissia*; 5a, *Limaya*; 6a, *Limaya*; A, Diamesinae; C, Harrisonini; E, Diamesini; F, Protanypodini; BB, Boreoheptagyini; DD, Lobodiamesini.

The branching of the heptagyine stem species number 2a has given rise to the sequence *Reissia*, nom. nov. (= *Araucania* Brundin 1966),[1] with three species in South America; *Limaya*, with two species in South America; and *Maoridiamesa*, with five species in New Zealand. The fact that *Maoridiamesa* is closer to the branching point of stem species number 1 than is the Australian *Paraheptagyia* group agrees well with the early separation of New Zealand from West Antarctica during the Upper Cretaceous. Also, *Maoridiamesa* stands out as a comparatively young and apomorphic offshoot of an older group in South America; the pupae and imagos show the extreme stages of several morphoclines whose first steps occur in *Reissia* and *Limaya* of Patagonia. And the plesiomorphic genus *Reissia* is the sister group of *Limaya* + *Maoridiamesa*.

Against this background, the question arises whether the amphi-Antarctic vicariance between *Maoridiamesa* and *Limaya* should be considered a southern parallel to that involving *Paraheptagyia*. The structure of the phylogenetic relationships and the geographical direction of multiple-step morphoclines are apparently positive evidence for the hypothesis that the occurrence of *Maoridiamesa* in New Zealand is a consequence of dispersal via West Antarctica of stem species number 4a, and there seems to be no argument in favor of the other alternative: speciation in New Zealand without preceding dispersal. In this case, however, we are able to refer neither to sympatry with a closely related group, nor to a well established generalized pattern of dispersal from Patagonia–West Antarctica into New Zealand. Without further evidence, the history of the *Maoridiamesa-Limaya* vicariance has to be regarded as somewhat doubtful. The monotypic genus *Lobodiamesa* of New Zealand, forming the sister group (Lobodiamesini) of Heptagyini, should not be drawn into the discussion because the morphological gap suggests a background of extinction.

The search for the sister group of Heptagyini + Lobodiamesini leads to the tribe Boreoheptagyini of Laurasia, a strongly apotypic group, even ecologically (Brundin 1966:365). Going one step further down in the hierarchy, we face another amphitropical group (*B* in figure 3.7) that is the sister group of the former aggregate (*AA*). Group *B* is composed of the plesiomorphic, monotypic tribe Harrisonini of southern Africa and its Laurasian sister group

[1] Mr. B. Villegas López (University of California, Davis) has kindly informed me that the generic name *Araucania* Brundin (1966:398), is a junior homonym of *Araucania* Pate (1946:219) of the family Sapygidae (Hymenoptera: Aculeata). Because no replacement is available, I propose the name *Reissia* nom. nov. for *Araucania* Brundin. The genus is named after Dr. Friedrich Reiss (Zoological Museum, Munich), in appreciation of his excellent contributions to the systematics of the chironomid midges.

comprising the tribes Diamesini and Protanyini. The hierarchical structure does not give much advice, but the broad overlapping in Laurasia of the comparatively apomorphic descendants (*BB, E, F*) of two Pangean sister species (*AA* and *B*) that evidently once vicariated in southern Gondwanaland, indicates that the Laurasian sympatric pattern is due to transtropic dispersal northward (probably during the Jurassic) of the incipient stem species *AA* and *B*. A secondary dispersal southward, into the domains of Heptagyini, is evidently exemplified by the occurrence in the Andes of Bolivia and Patagonia of three markedly apomorphic members of the northern tribe Diamesini comprising about 70 species in Laurasia (Brundin 1966:366; cf., figure 3.7). In accordance with his thesis of predominance of vicariance events without preceding dispersal, Croizat (1971:383, referred to by Croizat et al. 1974:283), has expressed the view that the Andes have risen under the roots and feet of the immediate ancestors of the species still living there today. This is, however, untenable as a generalization because the tropical Andes, evidently foremost in Croizat's mind, are inhabited not only by a former tropical lowland biota, but also by elements of distant origin. The presence of a northern element, exemplified by members of the Laurasian group Diamesini, has already been mentioned.

When the Andes arose during the Tertiary, Patagonia, Antarctica, southern Australia, and parts of southern Africa were inhabited by a very old and well-diversified temperate biota without direct connections with the biota of the tropical lowlands of South America. Many species of the southern temperate biota availed themselves of the opportunity for dispersal toward tropical latitudes offered by the development of the Andean mountain chains. Among the chironomids the result is the occurrence in the Andes of Bolivia, Peru, and Ecuador, at altitudes between 1700 and 4850 m, of endemic species and species groups that have their closest relatives far to the south, with the essential barrier the desert zone of northern Chile. Solely within the subfamilies Podonominae and Diamesinae there are about 20 examples in the genera *Parochlus, Podonomus, Podonomopsis, Paraheptagyia,* and *Limaya* (Brundin 1966). The conclusion that the North Andean–Patagonian vicariance patterns have developed as a consequence of northward dispersal along the Andean mountain chains by Patagonian stem species is based on the following data and considerations: (1) reconstruction of the actual hierarchies down to the base of respective subfamilies; (2) knowledge of the minimum age of different groups as indicated by their degree of engagement in the breakup of Gondwanaland; (3) the insight that the Andes are comparatively young and that the tropical high Andes arose during the

Pliocene-Pleistocene; (4) the demonstration that the stem species of the northern Andean species groups are situated high in an old hierarchy of the Jurassic whose basal branchings were anchored in Patagonia–Fuegia and Antarctica; (5) the Podonominae and Diamesinae are cool-adapted, rheophilous and polyoxybiontic groups that have never been found in tropical lowlands; (6) all the north Andean groups of the actual genera stand out as apomorphic in relation to their sister groups in the south.

Hence it is a well founded hypothesis that the northern Andean–Patagonian vicariance patterns arose during the Tertiary by a northward extension of the primarily southern ranges of incipient ancestral species. It should be noted that the argumentation could be performed without reference to sympatry, but the fact that northern Andean–Patagonian sympatric vicariance really occurs, especially within the genus *Podonomus*, is a further confirmation of the reliability of the conclusion. I think that the above examples of practical application of our means for investigating dispersal and its corollaries show that an objective analysis is possible on the basis of biological data. We must accept that the reliability of the conclusions changes from group to group, however, because we meet problems that present varying degrees of difficulty. Occasional presence of morphologically strongly deviating, monotypic relict groups creates a problem that is hard to estimate. Experience teaches that the best guarantee for reliable results is a broad approach that makes it possible to show that particular cases conform with generalized patterns.

Croizat's Panbiogeography

Leon Croizat is primarily a botanist and a specialist in Euphorbiaceae. The results of his causal studies of distribution patterns among plants and animals are published in an impressive series of bulky volumes; the first appeared in 1952. No one has objected more sharply and intensively than Croizat to the philosophy and methodology of traditional biogeography as introduced by Darwin and Wallace and further developed by Matthew, Simpson, Mayr, and Darlington. In his criticism Croizat has turned especially against the aprioristic treatment of centers of origin, migrations, chance dispersal, means of dispersal, and the overrating of the importance of fossils, as well as against the traditional distinction between phytogeography and zoogeography.

Croizat's documentation is of tremendous scope. Starting from botanical and zoological monographs, revisions, and checklists, he has inserted on maps the geographical vicariance patterns formed by thousands of plant and animal groups, thus making available very impressive material that had never before been put together. Joining by lines on the map the areas of each group, Croizat obtained a picture of what he considered was the total range of the stem species. How the lines are drawn is perhaps subjective, but it is important to note that the lines are laid out independent of the extension of the oceans on the present world map. Yet Croizat did not commit himself to the theory of continental displacement.

Croizat has been able to show in a convincing way that the distribution pictures of plant and animal groups are not random but fall into a limited number of more or less uniform vicariance patterns; these form what Croizat calls *generalized tracks*. There is reason to believe that this concept will be long lived. According to Croizat, the numerous components that make up a generalized track have a similar history; he arrived at the conclusion that most of the generalized tracks must have developed during periods when the geography of the world differed essentially from that of the present day. His extensive analyses of the biota of the tropical zone and its connections to the north and to the south, as indicated by generalized tracks, have special merit. For example, his explanation of the history of the Galapagian biota (1958:746–859), as confirmed by recent geological-geophysical research (Holden and Dietz 1972; Malfait and Dinkelman 1972; cf. Croizat et al. 1974; Rosen 1976a), bears witness of his biogeographical intuition and common sense.

What Croizat has written is a pioneering work with a perpetual reminder to all present and future biogeographers. Because his arguments, however, often tend to be diffuse, and his attitude about dispersal and correlated phenomena far from consistent, it is not easy to get a firm grip on his biogeographical message. I refer to a summary he gave (1964:189), where the following points are of special interest: (1) immobilism (vicariant form-making) and mobilism (dispersal) do constantly alternate and interplay; (2) vicariant form-making excludes mobilism; (3) vicariism arises by local form-making in immobilism within ranges that may have been acquired, in an ancestral stage, by mobilism; (4) the massive preponderance of vicariant form-making is proof that "vicariant form-making by immobilism does by far exceed spells of mobilism in biogeographic significance." I agree with theses 1 to 3. But thesis 4 stands out as a subjective conclusion open to criticism.

Everywhere in Croizat's writings he stresses that the patterns of geographical vicariance are the results of allopatric speciation—of a stepwise subdivision on the spot of the ranges of ancestral species by the formation of geographical barriers. Only sympatry or overlapping ranges of closely related species and species groups is accepted as evidence of dispersal. This cautious attitude is well justified in principle. But in those instances where there are cases of sympatric distribution, Croizat does not consider the problem of direction of the actual dispersal, or even the primary range of the ancestral species. On the contrary, discussions of areas (or centers) of origin are often explicitly labeled unwarranted. The ancestral species "was already there," and in practice Croizat avoids discussion of what may have happened beforehand. This attitude is contradictory, not least in relation to his theses 1 and 3. Hence I am forced to conclude that Croizat, in his endeavor to emphasize the fundamental role of allopatric speciation and development of vicariance in immobilism, has at the same time underrated the role of mobilism, i.e., dispersal. I here touch upon a marked weakness of Croizat's panbiogeography.

One reason why Croizat has underrated the role of dispersal, especially during the post-Pangean epochs, seems to be a tendency to analyze the distribution patterns formed by groups of low rank (not least among the birds), where cases of inside sympatry may be comparatively rare, often because such cases are not yet developed. Because this is combined with a general lack of knowledge of the phylogenetic relationships outside the actual groups, it is understandable that Croizat easily misapprehended the real frequency of sympatry (dispersal) among closely related groups.

Croizat's sharp reaction against traditional biogeography and its aprioristic operation with centers of origin, dispersal, and dispersal potentials must be received with great satisfaction. The situation is aptly summarized by Ball (1976), who writes that Croizat's works and theses have released us from the tyranny of those prior concepts. At the same time it is evident that every objective discussion of the role of dispersal in the history of a group does presuppose comprehensive preparatory work and a critical approach of a kind that has been largely neglected even by Croizat.

My acquaintance with Croizat's thoughts more than fifteen years ago in his *Panbiogeography* was a highly refreshing experience. But at the same time I felt a lack of certain indispensable arguments; in my 1966 paper on Gondwanian vicariance patterns I wrote (p. 61) that Croizat's approach is "not wholly sound." When studying Croizat's methodology and biogeographical argumentation, one is struck by the fact that he constantly accomplishes his discussions of the meaning of different vicariance patterns without reference to strict analyses of the relevant phylogenetic relationships. Hence his views of the history in time and space of particular groups very often stand out as subjective and questionable. Contributory is his negligence of the connection between sympatry and the geographical distribution of closely related groups as exponents of relative apomorphy/plesiomorphy and of the biogeographical implication of these phenomena.

Representative is, I think, Croizat's treatment of the history in time and space of the Picumninae, a group of pantropical woodpeckers to which he often refers. There are four "standard genera": (1) *Picumnus* (with about 25 species in tropical America south of Honduras and Nicaragua with a main massing in Brazil, and one species, *innominatus*, fully disconnected in southeastern Asia and Indonesia); (2) *Nesoctites* (one species in the Greater Antilles); (3) *Verrauxia* (one species in West and Central Africa); (4) *Sasia* (two species in southeastern Asia and Indonesia). Croizat (1964:190) remarks that certain ornithologists prefer to credit the disconnected species of *Picumnus* in the Orient and Indonesia, *P. innominatus*, to a monotypic genus *Vivia* and declares that this clearly does not interest the student of dispersal because *innominatus* is an "integral part of the *Picumnus* complex." This is, however, an optimistic approach that is far from convincing. The *Picumnus* complex has not been subjected to an analysis according to the principles of phylogenetic systematics, and it is still an open question whether the similarity between *innominatus* and the American species of *Picumnus* is due to convergence, symplesiomorphy, or synapomorphy. Only the latter alternative would have biogeographical significance. But according to Croizat (1964:208) the drastic geographical disjunction within the genus *Picumnus* is nothing but a normal case of "wing dispersal" (whence and whither?) and "recombination of characters." In another work (1968a:435), Croizat points out that the very same genus may be "recombined" at an enormous distance, and *Picumnus* is referred to as a "thoroughly transparent" example of this. But if the 25 *Picumnus* species of tropical America and *innominatus* of southeastern Asia/Indonesia really form a monophyletic unit, then the presumed recombination in immobilism would mean the dual origin of an incipient stem species in South America and Asia. That seems utterly improbable. A better guess would probably be that "*Picumnus*" *innominatus* and *Sasia* are simply sister groups.

Croizat (1968a:431–35) visualizes a general post-Permian/pre-Cretaceous "spread and radiation" of incipient ancestral species as a background to the history of the extant vicariance patterns of plants and animals. I think that such a process, though lasting into the Middle Cretaceous, has been fundamentally important, and I do not disagree with Croizat when he assumes an early pantropical spread of the forerunners of Picumninae. But every attempt to go any further into the history in time and space of Picumninae would be meaningless as long as we lack a reconstruction of anagenetic development and phylogenetic relationships inside and outside the group. In causal historical biogeography the concept of geographical vicariance must refer, in principle, to sister species and sister groups of nature's hierarchy.

The pioneering work Croizat performed is unique and will remain unique. It is largely based on shortcuts, i.e., compilations from the literature, but in the situation he faced, he was forced to adopt these shortcuts and to trust in the monophyletic status of the groups he treated. He took the risk with an open mind and one must admit that his results, including the main body of his general conclusions, are well worth the tremendous effort.

Vicariance Model

Vicariance versus Dispersal

In their important paper "Centers of Origin and Related Concepts" (1974), Croizat et al. present a much needed and concentrated survey with comments on Croizat's biogeographical theses. Here one is struck by the prevailingly immobile aspect that is laid upon the biogeographical process. I cannot escape the impression that there is still a tendency to underrate or suppress the mobilistic aspect, i.e., the role played by dispersal in connection with the development of the biotic distribution patterns we try to explain. Indeed, it seems to me that the authors go some steps further in this respect than did Croizat in his earlier papers.

The authors stress that all species are components of biotic systems (biotas) and that a generalized track estimates the composition and geographical distribution of an ancestral biota before it subdivided (vicariated) into descendant biotas. It is pointed out that the components of one generalized track are geographically and biotically more closely related among themselves than they are to the components of some other generalized track. Therefore, descendant biotas (vicariants) resulting from the subdivision of an ancestral biota are biotically and geographically more closely related among themselves than they are to the subdivisions of some other ancestral biota.

This is well worth careful consideration. But what Croizat et al. have stressed here remains fragmentary when they at the same time do not underline the phylogenetic (genealogical) aspect. From the biogeographical viewpoint it is also very important that the biota of a generalized track forms a heterogenous phyletic assemblage where the taxa to a very large extent are more closely related phylogenetically to taxa of other generalized tracks than they are among themselves. Via its subordinate groups even a monophyletic group of comparatively low rank may be a component of several tracks symbolizing very different biotic and abiotic historical events. It must be assumed that many—perhaps thousands—of monophyletic groups of higher rank are components of practically every generalized continental track on earth. All components of a biota are at the same time integral parts of one and the same phylogenetic hierarchy whose successive development in time and space evidently has gone on via local form-making that was predominantly allopatric. According to our present insight it seems quite clear that there are not gross populations of continental or intercontinental extent that transform as such into the comparatively apomorphic component of a phylogenetic branching. On the contrary, in accordance with the results of population genetics we have to assume that there are isolated local populations that are responsible for the new, keen experiments and which, via vicariance and dispersal in reciprocal action, have been able to realize the potentials of the hierarchy over continents and oceans. Considering further the very fact that we face—except in areas that offer extreme conditions of life or that have long been isolated—an impressively harmonic representation of the terrestrial/limnic and marine sectors of the hierarchy, it seems evident that biotic dispersal on a very grand scale has occurred and has been fundamentally important.

Closely connected with the harmonic diversity of the local and regional biotas, and pointing in the same direction about the role of dispersal, is the widespread and abundant phenomenon of sympatric distribution between closely related groups. From my own experience I wish to refer to the global pattern of multiple sympatric distribution interweaving the old Antarctic element of the dipteran family Chironomidae.

In Patagonia about 80 species of the tribe Podonomini of the subfamily Podonominae form a complex aggregate of sympatric sister groups, from the specific to the generic level. In New Zealand all Podonomini groups occur sympatrically, and all of them have their closest relatives in Patagonia, which means a multiple pattern of sympatry based on sister-group relationships between New Zealand and Patagonia. A corresponding situation applies to all

Podonomini groups of Australia-Tasmania that likewise have their sister groups in Patagonia. The tribe Podonomini moreover shows amphitropical distribution, like its sister tribe Boreochlini, and the two tribes have a broadly overlapping distribution in Laurasia with threefold overlapping in the northern continents within Boreochlini. The sister group of Podonominae, the subfamily Aphroteniinae, likewise has an amphitropical distribution; and two sister-group pairs within Aphroteniinae display sympatric vicariance between Patagonia and Australia, where they occur together with Podonominae, often in the same mountain streams. Further, the sister group of Podonominae + Aphroteniinae, the subfamily Tanypodinae, also has an amphitropical distribution within certain of its subdivisions and is represented by numerous species within the distribution areas of its sister group in Laurasia and the southern continents.

The abundant occurrence of local to global sympatry at widely differing hierarchical levels demonstrates that intra- and intercontinental dispersal played a very prominent role in the history of the chironomid midges before the fragmentation of Pangea. This is certainly not exceptional. There is every reason to assume that in relation to their absolute age other insect groups, and in general many components of the terrestrial/limnic biota of the globe, show a pattern of sympatry corresponding in principle to that of the Chironomidae.

Croizat et al. (Abstract:265) suggest that "on a global basis the general features of modern biotic distribution have been determined by subdivision of ancestral biotas in response to changing geography." This view of the matter, by omission of the role of dispersal, is a step backward in relation to Croizat's earlier views. Still, in 1968 Croizat did logically calculate with a general post-Permian "spread and radiation" before the breakup of Pangea. Referring to what has been set out above, I am forced to conclude, like Croizat, that the main outlines of the modern distribution patterns to a very high degree were formed thanks to world-wide biotic dispersal during that epoch. The main features thus created were, of course, the generalized Pangean tracks that Croizat so eloquently discussed. We are able to reconstruct them on the basis of the still existing major vicariance patterns, which in turn were a consequence of Pangean fragmentation and other geographical changes. The fundamental process was not, however, the post-Pangean biotic subdivision, but the preceding formation of a network of generalized tracks extending continuously over all the continents before the breakup of Pangea, Laurasia, and Gondwana (Croizat 1958:figure 259). And if sympatry is understood in the very broad sense used by Croizat et al. when mentioning sympatry between a fish species and a crustacean species (p. 278, n. 3), the authors have indirectly admitted that the generalized tracks, to cite my own conclusion, "to a very high degree were formed thanks to world-wide biotic dispersal." Against this background, it is remarkable that Croizat et al. not only clearly underrate the role of dispersal, but also show a marked disinterest in this process. They point out that sympatry is evidence of dispersal, but do not recommend or stress the need for investigation of the corollaries of this abundant phenomenon: direction of dispersal and areas of origin. Available means for this are neglected or dismissed. This is contradictory.

If we drive the restrictive attitude about dispersal to extremes, we are forced in the last resort to operate with primarily Pangean stem species (primary cosmopolitanism) in order to explain by immobilism the history behind the common phenomenon of amphitropical vicariance. This would presuppose that the stem species primarily occupied a range extending "from pole to pole." But when Croizat et al., for excellent reasons, calculate with local form-making within the areas of the vicariance patterns, why should not also the Pangean stem species have been the result of local form-making? There is, of course, every reason to suppose that it was. The logical conclusion will be that the range of a Pangean stem species is the result of dispersal from some minor area of origin. Hence it becomes important to try to determine that area. When faced in practice with a corresponding case—for example, the Galaxiidae of Gondwana and their sister group, the Salmonidae of Laurasia—Croizat et al. (p. 279) refer to the possibility that the two fish groups are vicariants formed as a consequence of the fracture of Pangea, adding: "If so, then the ancestral species common to both groups may already have been widespread over Pangea, and the question of dispersal of the ancestral galaxiid species becomes unnecessary and, perhaps, irrelevant." But a conclusion that an ancestral species "was already there" is a poor explanation free of any obligation because it refers to a *fait accompli* and evades the problem of primary dispersal and the area of origin. Yet Croizat et al. are aware of the existence of that problem: "We do not deny that, at some point or other, dispersal might have played a role in the formation of the ancient Pangaean distributions, of which we now have only the vicariant remnants." But for unaccounted reasons, this admission, as we see, becomes very restrictive.

Two main points of the vicariance model are formulated by Croizat et al. (p. 279) as follows: (1) "Allopatry is the rule and sympatry the exception in present-day distributions of the species of a given group"; and (2) "Vicariance is, therefore, of primary importance in historical biogeography, and dispersal is a secondary phenomenon of biotic distribution." These theses are, according to my opinion, untenable generalizations and open to criticism. Surveying the matter, I propose that the following three theses signify a more dynamic and, I think, more coherent explanation of the development of distribution patterns: (1) The gradual subdivision by local form making of the ranges of ancestral species, a biotic process that is immobile in space, has been fundamental; (2) the gradual widening of the ranges of incipient ancestral species, a biotic process that is mobile in space, has also been fundamental; and (3) these processes, vicariance and dispersal, have been each other's corollaries. Discussions of the general relative importance of vicariance and dispersal are, after all, meaningless.

Croizat et al. (p. 269) identify geological change as the general causal principle of vicariance, but declare that they are unable to identify a general causal principle of dispersal. But the solution is close at hand: if appearance of barriers instigates vicariance, then disappearance of barriers instigates dispersal.

Investigation of Dispersal

It is generally agreed that sympatry indicates that dispersal has occurred. Hence, if we face sympatry, the phylogenetic biogeographer's task is inescapable: to try to estimate the direction(s) of the indicated dispersal and the area(s) whence it started or, more exactly, the area of origin of the stem species that gave rise to the actual cases of sympatric distribution. When making this statement, however, I focus on the controversy that for the present separates Croizat's panbiogeography from my phylogenetic biogeography. So far as I can see, the controversy refers to the following points that are not or are only partly acknowledged by panbiogeographers.

Deviation rule.   Apparently as a consequence of their negligence to formalize the meaning of allopatric speciation, Croizat et al. have not made any reference to the *rule of deviation*. But this rule—that allopatric speciation symbolizes experiments in conservatism and change, performed by sister species expressing differential evolutionary rates—is a phenomenon that has deeply influenced the history of life in time and space. When reconstructing a sector of the hierarchy, the biogeographer first surveys the occurrence of apomorphy/plesiomorphy among sister species and sister groups in relation to their hierarchical position and geographical distribution. Continued work might result in the appearance of a meaningful general pattern. In connection with analyses of ancestral distributions and dispersal, the documentation delivered by the action of the deviation rule is always important and often decisive.

Progression rule. Acknowledgment of the deviation rule logically leads to acknowledgment of the progression rule and its implications. Analyzing vicariance patterns and facing cases of sympatry, the biogeographer must not be satisfied with indications that dispersal has occurred and leave the matter at that. He misses something fundamental if he does not start an investigation of the nature of the indicated dispersal by exploiting the connection between sympatry/dispersal, hierarchical structure, and the geographical distributions of the involved monophyletic groups as exponents of apomorphy/plesiomorphy. Croizat et al. (but indeed not Rosen 1974a) ignore the whole matter and claim (p. 273) that the use of apomorphy and plesiomorphy in discussions of dispersal is objectionable because it would refer to different kinds of aprioristic thinking. But they overlook, like Darlington (1970a), Goin and Goin (1973), Briggs (1974), and even Ball (1976), that we deal here with the *results* of dispersal by incipient ancestral species, not the secondary question of the relation between apomorphy/plesiomorphy and aptness to disperse or to keep a certain range. By not acknowledging the potential relevance of the geographical distribution of apomorphy/plesiomorphy, Croizat et al. deprive themselves of essential means to estimate the history of distribution patterns. Their attitude is understandable only in relation to a condemnation of the search for areas or origin. I here touch upon a major weakness of the vicariance model.

It is only fair to point out that the attitude of Croizat et al. about these matters means a step backward even in relation to the view of many traditional biogeographers that by presupposed dispersal the range of the "primitive" subgroup marks the area of origin of a group. Analyses of dispersal and areas of origin must be the last step in a synthetic procedure; it is clear that such analyses should be applied only if available data suggest dispersal and allow a meaningful discussion.

Wide perspectives. Analysis of vicariance patterns and dispersal and its corollaries does generally presuppose reconstruction of the actual hierarchy including several steps of hierarchical splits beyond the group that marked the start of the analysis. As for this request for a wide phylogenetic and geographical perspective that must be conceived as essential, the position of Croizat et al. is far from clear and at least occasionally open to criticism. For example, referring to Wiebes (1968) and Croizat (1971), Croizat et al. (p. 273) discuss a small group of four species forming a subgenus of the beetle genus *Goliathus* and living in Central Africa. The range of *G. russus* takes a central position, while the ranges of the three other species are situated to the east and west of *russus* (Croizat 1971: figure 2*B*). Because the latter species is said to differ more sharply from the other species than these differ among themselves, Croizat considered this vicariance pattern an example of "wing dispersal" (whence and whither?), and Croizat et al. seem to agree. This is poor biogeography based on several apriorisms; and the authors have apparently forgotten their own claim that sympatry is the only reliable evidence of dispersal.

Further Comments

Nelson's formalization.   In his attempt to present an alternative formalization of the procedures of historical biogeography, Nelson (1975) concludes that his previous formalization (1969) of Hennig's (1966) and Brundin's (1966) procedures is defective in resolving dispersal "in cases where no dispersal occurred, and needs improvement to eliminate that defect." Nelson points out that biogeographical practice is based on a priori acceptance of dispersal and exemplifies this by citing Hennig (1966:133): "Every species originally occupies a certain area, and the breaking up of a species into several reproductive communities usually, if not always, is closely related to the dispersal of the species in space."

Referring to Rosa's (1918) theory of hologenesis and the works of Croizat, Nelson suggests that for a given group "the distribution of ancestral species can be estimated best by adding the descendant distributions." He pretends that the resolution of dispersal, as evidenced by sympatry, is accomplished more efficiently than before if the procedure is combined with estimation of ancestral distributions and the history of the biota of which a given analyzed group is a part. But he does not discuss the arguments that must be applied in the particular cases, which is the decisive point.

It may be that Hennig does express a traditional a priori acceptance of dispersal; but would we be free of aprioristic thinking if we say with Nelson that "estimation of ancestral distributions may be considered simply additive (hologenetic)"? The answer is negative. The area of an ancestral species can be estimated by simple addition of the ranges of the descendant species only if the range of the group has not been increased by secondary dispersal of some of its members, or reduced by extinction. Every particular vicariance pattern must be carefully analyzed . The rough approach Nelson recommends will easily lead to his "Type-II error" (not resolving dispersal when dispersal did occur), which is hardly better than a "Type-I error" (resolving dispersal when none occurred: Nelson, 1975: footnote 2).

Formalizations of the procedures of historical biogeography cannot avoid influence by the formalizer's conception of the meaning and consequences of dispersal in the time perspective; his conception becomes objective only if based on analytic experience of particular cases illustrating relevant causal connections. Rosa's and Croizat's writings are not very helpful in this respect, but I am convinced that if Nelson, starting from a relevant background of personal insight, had made an attempt to formalize the meaning and consequences of dispersal, he would not have dismissed Hennig's progression rule as "a rejectable apriorism."

Another generalization open to criticism is Nelson's statement that it would be aprioristic to try to resolve centers of origin and dispersal without reference to general patterns of vicariance and sympatry. Reference to general patterns of vicariance is certainly desirable, but Nelson overlooks the fact that occurrence of sympatry is far from always a necessary prerequisite for establishment and satisfactory analysis of dispersal (for example, the parabathynellid crustaceans and the northern Andean–Patagonian vicariance patterns among the Chironomidae mentioned earlier).

Finally, I comment on Nelson's figures 1–2 and the adjoining theoretical discussion of a three-area pattern formed by two species ($A1$ and $A2a$) in South America and one species ($A2b$) in Africa, where $A2a + A2b$ are the sister group of the species $A1$. It is supposed beforehand by Nelson that this vicariance pattern developed without involvement of dispersal. According to Nelson, at least some of the procedures of Hennig (1966), Brundin (1966), and Ross (1974) would lead to the conclusion that the ancestral species of the three-species group was exclusively South American and that the presence in Africa of species $A2b$ is due to dispersal into Africa of the ancestral species of $A2a + A2b$ before the separation between South America and Africa. Nelson points out that both conclusions would be false under the given conditions. Answering for myself, however, I want to stress that Nelson's theoretical case is irrelevant because I would not be ready to draw any conclusion on the basis of the available meager data.

Platnick and Nelson.   Platnick and Nelson's paper (1978) is a comprehensive methodological discussion of our means for constructing and testing hypotheses about the history of vicariance patterns. There are several good points, it is true, but I consider it a weakness that the treatment of the matter is highly theoretical and refers to examples that are even geographically imaginary. At least to me, the relevance and applicability of some of the results appear doubtful. I restrict myself mainly to the section on "Applications" that ends:

When investigating given areas, we must choose from monophyletic groups all their members endemic to the areas of interest, but we can ignore all their members occurring outside those areas (although they must obviously be taken into consideration whenever the scope of the hypothesis is expanded to include the areas in which they occur). Thus, we need only to obtain hypotheses of relationship between and among those members of test groups that occur in the areas of interest to any particular problem.

The above thesis, however, cannot have general validity. Let us assume that we investigate vicariance patterns, comprising South America (Patagonia), Australia, and New Zealand, of a monophyletic tribe containing three monophyletic genera, each of which has four species groups; genus A has only one group in the three Gondwanian areas (in New Zealand), genus B has only one group in the south (in South America), and genus C has only one group in the south (in Australia). Following Platnick and Nelson's reasoning (1978:16), we are entitled to argue that a group containing only the three mentioned species groups (and excluding the other nine groups) would be polyphyletic, but can still serve as a test of a three-area hypothesis for the area comprising New Zealand, Australia, and South America, referring for example to the cladogram for the genus *Podonomous* shown in figure 3.6. But what happens if we assume that the nine non-Gondwanian groups all occur in Laurasia and that the three Gondwanian groups are young and apomorphic members of their respective genera (figure 3.8)? Can we use a cladogram including only the three Gondwanian groups of the genera A, B, and C (figure 3.9) as a test of our three-area hypothesis symbolized by the cladogram in figure 3.6)? Obviously not, because the cladogram of figure 3.9 means a distortion of the hierarchy and vicariance pattern formed by genera A, B, and C. The occurrence in South America, Australia, and New Zealand of subgroups of the Laurasian genera A, B, and C is best interpreted as caused by independent ancestral dispersal from Laurasia into Gondwanaland.

In accordance with the Platnick and Nelson thesis a polyphyletic group of Laurasian origin has been used as a nonsensical test of a three-area hypothesis referring to a monophyletic group of Gondwanian origin. In our

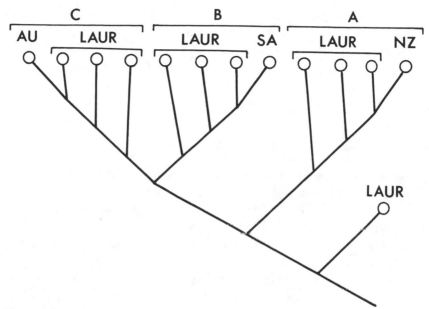

Figure 3.8. Hierarchy presupposed as a starting point for the test of a three-area hypothesis comprising New Zealand, South America, and Australia.

"test" the southern groups of genera *A, B,* and *C* stand out as young and apomorphic offshoots of northern groups. The test probably would become meaningful only if northern subordinate groups were young and apomorphic offshoots of southern groups, i.e., if the southern groups were paraphyletic. Polyphyletic groups probably can never serve as meaningful tests of vicariance hypotheses.

I think that their attempt to formalize a method of analysis for historical biogeography exemplifies the dangers connected with a purely theoretical approach. Indeed, we easily err if we do not ponder data given by life itself

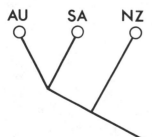

Figure 3.9. Fictitious testing by illegitimate elimination of the Laurasian groups in the hierarchy of figure 3.8.

and compare particular cases that are real. If I understand them correctly, Platnick and Nelson are of the opinion that an objective estimate of directions of dispersal and areas of origin of ancestral species is not possible on the basis of biological data. For these problems, their arguments are seemingly restricted to indirect evidence delivered by earth history, such as "the fusion of India with mainland Asia or the appearance of the Panamanian isthmus"—events providing opportunities for dispersal by the disappearance of barriers, it is true, but as such telling nothing about the direction of actual cases of dispersal. But by exploiting relevant biological data, the biogeographer is far from helpless regarding these matters. The situation is highlighted by the question: Why are we conviced that the presence of murid rodents in Australia is the result of dispersal from Asia? There is good reason to expect that a broad investigation of the connections among vicariance, hierarchical structure, and the geographical distribution of murid rodent groups as exponents of comparative apomorphy/plesiomorphy would serve as a relevant and convincingly positive test of our hypothesis. But we look in vain in Platnick and Nelson's paper for any reference to that type of approach.

Summary and General Conclusions

Phylogenetic biogeography in my sense, and panbiogeography in its modern form as symbolized by the vicariance paradigm of Croizat et al. (1974), are both primarily based on reconstructions of nature's hierarchy according to the methods and principles formalized by Hennig. This consensus on a fundamental point is a good guarantee for a steadily evolving understanding of the factors that determined the development in time and space of the distribution patterns of nature's consanguineous units above the species level. It is agreed that critical investigations of the connection between vicariance patterns and sequences of hierarchical branching points in their relation to sequences of datable geological-geographical events are a master key for realistic insight, and that analyses of particular groups often are of limited value until the groups can be shown to conform with generalized patterns. Further, there is agreement concerning the fundamental importance of vicariance events *in situ* and the need for application of the principle that involvement of dispersal should not be considered if there is no indication that dispersal has occurred. The consensus is far reaching, but it is not complete.

There is disagreement about an essential point, which refers to the meaning and role of dispersal and the method that must be applied in order to secure an optimal treatment of that intricate problem and its corollaries: direction of dispersal and areas of origin of ancestral species.

The vicariance model is stamped by the endeavor to eliminate the influence of the traditional center of origin/dispersal model on bio-geographical thinking. The intention is good, and the presentation of the meaning and consequences of vicariant events is excellent. But in their eagerness to stress their point, the adherents of the vicariance model have gone too far and have become markedly one-sided and dogmatic. The formalization of the vicariance model gives the impression that the influence of vicariance events has been so overwhelming that a closer study of dispersal—its meaning and consequences—becomes a matter of subordinate importance. Sympatry is said to indicate that dispersal has occurred, but nothing palpable is said about methods to investigate its corollaries. It seems symptomatic that Croizat et al. do not mention the progression rule and that Nelson (1975) dismisses it as aprioristic. There is a marked tendency to use the generalized tracks simply as starting points and to concentrate the biogeographical analyses on the history of the subdivision of the tracks. In spite of its merits, the vicariance paradigm does not signify the harmonic integration of all biogeographical aspects that would be the embodiment of a biogeographical synthesis.

Phylogenetic biogeography thus seems to signify a more balanced approach and a more effective methodology than the vicariance paradigm. Phylogenetic biogeography is best symbolized by a more dynamic model that may be called the *vicariance/dispersal paradigm*. The following considerations are basic: (1) fundamental is gradual subdivision by local form-making of the ranges of ancestral species via the appearance of barriers, a biotic process that is immobile in space; (2) also fundamental is the gradual widening of the ranges of incipient ancestral species via the disappearance of barriers, a biotic process that is mobile in space; (3) these processes, vicariance and dispersal, have been each other's corollaries.

In critical discussions of methods and principles of causal historical biogeography it is sometimes difficult to avoid a partial smashing open of doors. Among the adherents of the vicariance model there are signs of certain differences in opinion as well as signs of individual shifts in attitude that hamper a completely adequate criticism. It should be noted, for example, that in their recent paper Platnick and Nelson (1978:7) declare that "the vast number of patterns of large, world-wide groups whose subgroup interrelationships reflect the fragmentation of Pangaea all require episodes of biotic dispersal promoting cosmopolitanism to account for the (sympatric) Pangaean distributions of the single ancestral species of each of those groups." This is an advance compared with the views expressed by Croizat et al. (1974).

Worthy of special attention in this context is Rosen's paper on the phylogeny and zoogeography of salmoniform fishes (1974a). The treatment of the matter is in accordance with the methods and principles of phylogenetic biogeography, and discussions of dispersal events are based on application of the progression rule. Indications like these raise expectations of a settlement of the controversy in the near future. The disagreements are to a large extent methodological. It seems obvious that unity on a sound basis is a first-rate desideratum to historical biogeography, which still offers so many great problems that have been mistreated or hardly touched.

Acknowledgments
I am very grateful to Dr. Per Brinck, University of Lund, and to Dr. Joel Cracraft, University of Illinois (Chicago), for their useful comments on my manuscript.

Discussion

J. A. Slater

I SHOULD LIKE to confine myself chiefly to three aspects of Professor Brundin's paper. These are: (1) the acceptance of the allopatric species model as the major (only?) method by which new species are produced; (2) the belief that the most plesiomorphic component of two or more sister groups occurs closest to the *place* or *area* where the group originated; and (3) the need to differentiate between disjunct distributions due to extinction of a group in intervening areas and disjunctions due to crossing unsuitable intervening areas.

Acceptance of the allopatric species model in biogeographical analysis is not, of course, by any means confined to Brundin, who says:

> There are several potential kinds of multiplication of species, but the evidence is strong that allopatric speciation, brought about by the subdivision of the ranges of ancestral species, has been predominant and decisive.... it should be reasonable to conclude that sympatric distribution of closely related groups is an indication that dispersal has occurred.

In so stating, Brundin essentially echoes Rosen's position (1978:175) that cladogenesis and allopatric speciation seem synonymous. He says that "several groups of taxa had different histories of cladogenesis (allopatric speciation events)." Brundin also echoes the position of Platnick and Nelson (1978) and Croizat et al. (1974).

This rather blind acceptance of the allopatric species model by Brundin and leading authors of the vicariance school is surprising, first, because there is a great deal of evidence from plant, invertebrate, and vertebrate groups that sympatric speciation is a widespread and common phenomenon. It is surprising, second (and perhaps this applies more to the aforementioned authors than to Brundin), because it does not, at first glance, seem consistent with the thesis that dispersal has been overemphasized as a causal factor for explaining disjunct distributions. It would seem reasonable to suppose that students desiring to marshall evidence that dispersal has been overemphasized would tend to embrace the evidence for sympatric speciation rather than to accept a model that requires dispersal. One may speculate that they have not done so because they cling to early Hennigian and Brundinian ideas about the pervasive occurrence of dichotomous branching in evolution.

The evidence for sympatric speciation has been accumulating rapidly in animal groups in recent years. Remember also that both Brundin and Croizat deplore the maintenance of a differentiation between phytogeography and zoogeography. Botanists, with their understanding of the significance of speciation by karyotypic modification (automatically sympatric), have, of course, long accepted the phenomenon as important (although some seem to limit sympatric speciation to cases of polyploidy). It is a little ironic that we meet in New York today, with the allopatric speciation model apparently alive and well, while from May 24–27 of this year a three-day symposium on sympatric speciation in animals convenes at Washington University in St. Louis.

Acceptance of the allopatric speciation model seems also slightly ambivalent on the part of those who support "falsifiability" as a doctrine for proper scientific procedure.

This is obviously not the place to attempt to document the evidence for sympatric speciation. The subject is extensively reviewed by White (1978). Examples of significant papers for animal sympatric speciation, among many others, are those of Alexander and Moore (1962), Bush (1975a, 1975b), Lloyd and Dybas (1966), Schultz (1969), and Wasserman (1970).

My reason for emphasizing the importance of not placing total reliance on the allopatric speciation model in a symposium on vicariance biogeography is that its adoption will lead the investigator to false conclusions where sympatric speciation has occurred, and also that it tends to cause the investigator to search for the sister group of a given taxon in a different geographical area rather than in an area of sympatry. Brundin appears to support allopatric speciation because he views speciation events chiefly as simple cases of dichotomous branching. He says that he has never encountered a case of multiple cleavage (polytomy), but sympatric speciation events strongly suggest that polytomy may be widespread. Brundin does note that Croizat may possibly have been more perceptive, prior to his 1974 paper, when he compared the development of vicariance patterns to the cracking of a framed piece of glass. If we view the fragments of the glass as piled together at our feet, we probably have a crude picture of what a significant part of the process of speciation in some groups has been. By this I do not suggest that allopatry has not been an important speciation process. What I do suggest is that both phenomena are important; to ignore sympatric speciation in many groups of organisms is to bind oneself to a restrictive and outmoded model, acceptance of which cannot but lead to an absolutely false interpretation of past geographical events as they relate to the present composition and distribution of many groups.

The second point I would like to make relates to Brundin's ideas concerning the geographical position of the relatively plesiomorphic and apomorphic taxa of a given group. Brundin believes that the expansion of range by a species followed by allopatric speciation will result in peripheral apomorphy, not in peripheral plesiomorphy. He severely criticizes Darlington's (1957) thesis that "derivative groups tend to mark the places of origin" and that plesiomorphic groups tend to be in peripheral areas. This, parenthetically, is not exactly what Darlington said. My understanding of Darlington's position is that relatively plesiomorphic groups will be found in either or both of two places. One will be in the area of origin because this is the area most favorable for the survival of the group; therefore, older (less dominant) groups can often survive there in specialized habitats even when in competition with more "dominant" (i.e., apomorphic) groups. The second place the plesiomorphic elements may survive is in distantly isolated peripheral areas which the more dominant (apomorphic) elements have not yet reached. According to Darlington the one place one would not expect to find plesiomorphic elements would be in intermediate areas between the most favorable "center" and the most distant peripheries. Brundin apparently believes that such ideas are beside the point. I am not at all sure that they are beside the point for vicariance biogeography. If Darlington's thesis has validity we would expect to find that a plesiomorphic taxon and its sister group were geographically separated, with a more apomorphic group interposed between the two. Such a disjunction would then not be due to any geographical and/or climatic changes, but only to past and present competition between evolving biological entities. Accepting a general rule of "peripheral apomorphy" would seem tantamount to accepting a rule that taxa with the most progressive evolutionary innovations will not be able to live in the most favorable areas.

Brundin has also postulated a "rule" that if dispersal has occurred (remember that according to Brundin we establish dispersal by evidence of sympatry), the more plesiomorphic element will be closer to the initial range of the common ancestor than will be the apomorphic element. This position seems based upon a vision of an amazingly static set of climatic and ecological conditions in given areas at the same time that continents drift through degrees of latitude, ice caps advance and retreat, and mountain cordilleras rise and wear away. For example, let us hypothesize a species (or group) originating in North America in the Cretaceous at say 35°N. This species would of course have an original range; that range would presumably be one that adapted the species to subtropical conditions. This ancestral species (or group) then gives rise to an apomorphic sister species from an isolated peripheral northern population, and this apomorphic sister species is adapted to cool temperate conditions at, say, 70°N. Suppose that these species have not further speciated and have remained very "static" ecologically so that we have the same two species in existence at present. I would suggest that there is little doubt that today the apomorphic species would be closer to the original range of the common ancestral species than would the plesiomorphic species.

Brundin, although he is critical of "immobilist" positions, envisages a much more stable climatic world than seems credible. It may well be that his viewpoint has been influenced by his concentration upon elements of the fauna of the cool-temperate southern hemisphere. Given the large water-to-land ratio in the southern end of the world, subsequent to the loss of faunal exchange between the various land masses and the destruction of the Antarctic faunal elements, it is possible that stability may have been greater there than in many other parts of the world.

Actually, the whole question of the area of origin of a monophyletic group seems to me largely fruitless, unless possibly we are talking about huge areas and major groups. Brundin has suggested three criteria as necessary to determine an area of origin. That the area of origin of a group is always the total area of its ancestral species is a point with which I'm sure we would all agree. Yet I cannot visualize how one can possibly ascertain the total area, because Brundin tells us that in order to do so we need to know whether the total range of the group has or has not been increased by "secondary dispersal" or reduced by extinction. To know whether there has been dispersal (increase) or extinction (decrease), we surely must know the original range. I have a vision of the old dictionary cliché: "Camel, see Dromedary"; "Dromedary, see Camel."

Finally, I would like to comment very briefly on two additional things. I find it surprising that Brundin criticizes Platnick and Nelson as being too "purely theoretical" for attempting to formalize a method of analysis for historical biogeography (quite aside from how much I may or may not agree with their method). This criticism is particularly surprising because it comes from Brundin, a person whose work is often portrayed as the outstanding application of Hennig's rigidly formal methodology and theoretical approach to systematic relationships.

Brundin's paper illustrates very well the need for further refinement in the use of the word "dispersal." Brundin frequently uses dispersal to mean the expansion of a range, with subsequent extinction in part of the area, so that a disjunct range results. He sometimes fails to differentiate this from a disjunct distribution caused by a taxon's "saltating over" an intervening area without ever inhabiting the intervening area. This perhaps can best be thought of as the "colonizing" or "propagule" concept. It does seem that terminology is needed to separate these two causes of disjunct ranges.

Having said all of this, I would like to say that I agree with what I consider Brundin's major point, which is that in reaction to an essentially dispersalist view of present organic distribution, Croizat et al. (1974) and Rosen (1978) have tended to adopt a much too "immobile" view of the distribution of organisms. Brundin seems correct in believing that immobilism, dispersal by saltation, and dispersal by range expansion and contraction are all parts of an interdigitated process (that he calls the vicariance/dispersal paradigm), and that the degree to which each part is involved in the patterns we see today varies enormously from group to group.

Discussion

N. I. Platnick

The Progression Rule or Progress
Beyond Rules in Biogeography

I'M PLEASED TO HAVE the opportunity to respond to Lars Brundin, for without his pioneering (1966) study of trans-Antarctic relationships, none of us would today be attending a symposium devoted to the synthesis of cladistics, biogeography, and historical geology. However, I must beg Brundin's indulgence. Despite his curious contention that there is something intrinsically dangerous about theoretical inquiries, my discussion of his paper will be theoretical, for it is at that level that I believe his proposals are inadequate.

Brundin has outlined an approach that he terms "phylogenetic" but that I will call "progression-rule biogeography" because it is neither more nor less phylogenetic than any other approach involving cladistic analyses of the interrelationships of organisms. Brundin has accurately identified the main feature of his approach not found in vicariance theory: the use of Hennig's (1966) deviation and progression rules. I will argue that neither of these rules is acceptable in a rigorous system of biogeographical analysis. Brundin has also presented some criticisms of vicariance theory; I will argue that his criticisms overlook the major feature of the vicariance approach not found in progression-rule biogeography.

A key to evaluating progression-rule theory may be found in the dipteran cases that Brundin cites in order to justify his claim that "practical application of our means for investigating dispersal and its corollaries [shows] that an objective analysis is possible on the basis of biological data." We would all agree than an objective analysis is desirable, but persons might disagree about what constitutes objectivity in that sense. Brundin's paper contains only one overt statement about objectivity, to the effect that a "conception becomes objective only if based on analytic experience of particular cases." Given this inductive view, it is not surprising that Brundin finds the progression rule satisfactory, for the rule can always be applied to particular cases and will always yield an apparently definitive result.

In this respect, however, the progression rule is no different from what Brundin calls Darlington's (1957) rule of thumb. The view that the center of origin of a group is marked by the range of the most apomorphic member of the group can be applied to particular cases just as easily as Brundin's opposite view, and it will also yield an apparently definitive result. Because Darlington's rule, too, was presumably based on his "analytic experience of particular cases," it must be judged equally objective under Brundin's concept.

There is, of course, an alternative view of objectivity, developed by Popper (1959), under which the source of a theory is irrelevant and a conception becomes objective only if it is testable, that is, if we can detail in advance what conceivably obtainable evidence would compel us to give up the idea if that evidence were actually obtained. From that view of objectivity, namely falsifiability, I will examine Brundin's contentions.

My first criticism of Brundin's argument involves his confusion of two very different concepts when he speaks of apomorphic species or groups. One of these concepts involves only the relative positon of a taxon in a cladogram; of two taxa which branch off a cladogram at different nodes, the one that originates farthest from the base of the cladogram is the most apomorphic (in position). Of two taxa which branch off a cladogram at the same node, neither can be said to be more apomorphic in position than the other because branches can always be rotated at a node. This concept of a positionally apomorphic taxon is both unambiguous and unobjectionable.

The second concept of an apomorphic taxon stems from the deviation rule, by which Brundin means that "one of the components of a pair of sister species or sister groups generally differs more or less markedly from the other by a more apomorphic design." He believes that this is a "massively confirmed phenomenon," the confirmation stemming from the experience "gained by hierarchical reconstruction." But the deviation rule is not a necessary axiom of cladistic analysis or hierarchical reconstruction; indeed its use in systematics has been criticized and rejected by Banarescu (1978). The rule is in fact a phenetic rather than a cladistic concept because it refers not to particular characters of organisms, but rather to degrees of general similarity, not only among extant groups of organisms but among their hypothetical ancestors as well. Although cladistic techniques involving ontogenetic evidence or outgroup comparison allow us to test hypotheses about the relative apomorphy of particular characters, neither Hennig nor Brundin has suggested a test for hypotheses about the relative apomorphy of whole organisms, much less groups of them.

My own experience in hierarchical reconstruction does not indicate that the deviation rule fares any better as an empirical generalization than as a methodological tool. For example, the fundamental dichotomy among spiders is apparently between the Mesothelae and Opisthothelae (Platnick and Gertsch 1976). Although the Mesothelae retain a number of characters thought to be primitive for spiders in general, most of these characters are found also in some Opisthothelae; and there are other characters, thought to be derived for spiders, which are unique to the Mesothelae (as of course there must be for any group judged to be monophyletic). Which group is generally more apomorphic? I don't know. One might contend that whichever group has the larger number of recognized autapomorphies is therefore the more apomorphic in general, but the spider cladogram, like others, involves relatively few characters at a given node; these can hardly be said to constitute an adequate sample of the total character set of even one organism, much less the dozen species of Mesothelae or 35,000 species of Opisthothelae.

Brundin (1966:26) cites Agnatha versus Gnathostomata, Crocodilia versus Aves, and Marsupialia versus Placentalia as cases where "the relative plesiomorphy of one of two sister groups is so marked that we have right to feel confident." Would he feel equally confident if the relative numbers of species in those pairs of sister groups were reversed? If there were 35,000 marsupials in the world and only a dozen placentals, would not the marsupials include the positionally apomorphic groups, and would not the placentals be regarded, in Brundin's sense, as just a primitive group of mammals with a peculiar mode of development?

Most importantly, however, Brundin admits that the deviation rule "is a rule and not a law," in which case we must ask how to distinguish those groups in which it has functioned from those in which it has not functioned. Brundin provides no answer, and the question becomes critical when the deviation rule is applied to biogeography by means of the progression rule.

Brundin provides a scenario involving speciation through dispersal followed by peripheral isolation, and argues that the process will give rise to peripherally distributed apomorphic groups. By apomorphy Brundin means here not positional apomorphy in terms of cladograms, but taxic apomorphy in terms of the total character set of entire groups of organisms and their hypothetical ancestors. This is evidenced by his refusal to apply the progression rule to Nelson's (1975) example of the simplest system in which the rule could function: a three-taxon problem formed by two South American species and a positionally apomorphic peripheral species in Africa. Brundin indicates that he "would not be ready to draw any conclusion on the basis of the available meager data," leaving no doubt that the crucial additional data he would need to apply the progression rule in this case are precisely those data on general taxic apomorphy for which he has provided no objective test.

But let us admit, for the moment, that Brundin's scenario of speciation by dispersal plus peripheral isolation may well have been true in many cases. It is still an elementary error in logic to conclude that because all cases of dispersal plus peripheral isolation result in peripherally distributed apomorphic taxa, all cases of peripherally distributed apomorphic taxa must therefore be due to dispersal plus peripheral isolation. They may be, but they need not be. Suppose that in some case peripheral taxic apomorphy had a different cause. Suppose, for example, that the immediate ancestors of Brundin's Australian midge groups did not disperse to Australia but evolved there *in situ*? How might we discover the error we would make by applying the progression rule to this case? Brundin has suggested no way, and until he does, the axiomatic application of the progression rule cannot be considered objective in Popper's sense. Only one possible source of falsification comes to mind: discovering a fossil member of the group that occurred in both the peripheral and central areas (Platnick and Nelson 1978). It should be obvious that any method that depends on finding all the right fossils in all the right places will simply be inapplicable to the vast majority of organisms. I therefore conclude, on the basis of the arguments presented to date, that the progression rule does not represent an acceptable method of biogeographical analysis.

Turning to Brundin's comments on vicariance biogeography, let's consider first the theoretical example treated in Brundin's figures 3.1–3.3, with four African groups arising sequentially and a positionally apomorphic South American group that is putatively also taxically apomorphic. Brundin argues that:

the South American group stands out as a young and apomorphic offshoot of an older aggregate in Africa. Because this establishment refers to one of the components *making up a sympatric pair*, we have strong reason to conclude that the range of stem species number 1 was restricted to present Africa and that the occurence of the young and apomorphic group number 9 in South America is due to dispersal of stem species number 7 from Africa into present South America *before the existence of the South Atlantic* (emphasis added).

Here Brundin claims to use sympatry as evidence that dispersal has occurred, but his figure 3.2 indicates that there is no sympatry whatsoever in the example; the four African groups are all parapatric. Moreover, even if there were sympatry among the African groups, at most that would be evidence of dispersal within Africa, not between Africa and South America.

Brundin's analysis of this example is a vicariance explanation, in that the allopatric elements are explained by the appearance of a barrier (in this case the proto-Atlantic Ocean), not by dispersal across a pre-existing barrier (Platnick and Nelson 1978). There is nothing in Brundin's analysis, however, indicating that the dispersal between Africa and South America, which he believes occurred, did not take place across the Atlantic Ocean rather than prior to the ocean's appearance. The requirements of the progression rule would be satisfied by dispersal at either point in time. In other words, the interesting aspect of Brundin's (1966) midge analyses, the conclusion that the fragmentation of the midge groups was coincident in time with the fragmentation of Gondwanaland, was not (and could not have been) supplied by application of the progression rule.

The vicariance explanation of the interrelationships of the allopatric taxa in Brundin's example, on the other hand, is unaffected by whether stem species number 7 occurred in South America as a result of dispersal prior to the appearance of the Atlantic or as a result of *in situ* development. Brundin objects, however, to the latter of these two possibilities (his figure 3.3), arguing that, "It seems strange that while a steady speciation was taking place in the African area of stem species number 1, there was no allopatric speciation within the South American area until after its isolation due to the birth of the South Atlantic." But there is no a priori reason to expect the earliest barrier affecting the group to occur between Africa and South America (Brundin's figure 3.4) rather than somewhere within modern Africa. Indeed, if Brundin were consistently to maintain his scenario of peripheral speciation, it is more likely that the earliest barrier to divide a species widespread over two continents would appear at one end of the total area, not at the middle.

This brings us, however, to Brundin's major criticism of vicariance biogeography. He correctly points out that the vicariance model requires the existence of widespread ancestral species whose ranges have subsequently been divided by the appearance of various barriers, and that in the extreme cases, ancestral species may have been virtually world wide or Pangean in distribution. He then argues:

> why should not also the Pangean stem species have been the result of local form-making? There is, of course, every reason to suppose that it was. The logical conclusion will be that the range of a Pangean stem species is the result of dispersal from some minor area of origin. Hence it becomes important to try to determine that area.

Here of course, we may stop and ask: important to whom, and for what reasons? With regard to the history of some particular group of organisms, it may well be an important question. But with regard to the problems that vicariance biogeography attempts to solve, and to which Brundin's classic study of trans-Antarctic relationships was directed, Croizat et al. (1974:279) are correct in stating that "the question...becomes unnecessary and, perhaps, irrelevant."

To see why that should be the case, let us remember what vicariance biogeography attempts to discover (Nelson and Platnick 1979). Given areas in which endemic taxa of a wide variety of groups co-occur, vicariance biogeography asks how the areas themselves may be interrelated. It asks whether there is a single cladogram of areas, or more than one, which can summarize the interrelationships of the endemic taxa of all the groups represented in the areas, or of a larger number of such groups than might be expected by chance alone (Rosen 1978). It then asks whether there is a correlation among known geological, geographical, or ecological events and the branching points in the cladogram(s) of areas, and whether the correlation indicates a causal connection.

Let us then examine the hypothetical example in Brundin's figure 3.8 and ask what that group might tell us about the interrelationships of the areas in which it occurs (Australia, South America, New Zealand, and Laurasia). Brundin argues that the group contributes no meaningful evidence regarding the interrelationships of the three southern areas because their occupants obviously dispersed there independently from northern areas. It should be noted that: (1) the sympatric taxa in this example, if any exist, are in Laurasia, hence the only dispersal evidenced by sympatry occurred within Laurasia; (2) even if the southern groups did disperse from the north, the dispersal could have occurred prior to the isolation of the southern areas, just as Brundin assumes but does not demonstrate in the case of the midges that he believes dispersed to Australia before its isolation; and (3) the cladogram may indicate only that the area called Laurasia is a composite of three different areas most closely related not to each other but to different southern areas.

The information about the interrelationships of the three southern areas contributed by the example thus remains the same (shown in Brundin's figure 3.9) whether the ancestors of the southern groups dispersed there or not. One might ask, of course, whether the information is true. If Brundin is correct, and the example contains no meaningful evidence about the southern areas, there is no reason to expect other groups of organisms in those areas to show the same pattern of relationships among the areas, and we will find that the cladogram (Brundin's figure 3.9) is not true for all the groups with endemic representatives in the areas, or for a larger proportion of them than would be expected by chance alone. But the cladogram might be true in most or even all cases, and we will never know whether distribution is that orderly—whether as Croizat (1964) said "Nature forever repeats,"—if we use a priori rules to explain the history of groups without inquiring whether their history does or does not differ from that of the remainder of the world's biota.

Response

L. Z. Brundin

IN HIS COMMENTS on my paper Dr. Slater begins with a discussion of allopatric versus sympatric speciation. He thinks that my acceptance of allopatric speciation as the predominant pattern means an oversight of the results of recent research indicating that sympatric speciation has played a far more prominent role than yet supposed. I refer to Mayr's (1979) review of White's (1978) comprehensive work on modes of speciation. It appears that White, one of the leading proponents of the prominent role of sympatric speciation even among animals, has not been very successful in his attempt to convince the informed reader, and Mayr remarks that the "*terra incognita* of speciation is still very extensive." There is hardly a reason for Slater to say that allopatric speciation is an "outmoded model, acceptance of which cannot but lead to an absolutely false interpretation of past geographical events as they relate to the present composition and distribution of many groups." Even if sympatric speciation has played a more prominent role than supposed by most biogeographers, I doubt that this would markedly devaluate the results reached by phylogenetic biogeographers.

Slater thinks that I fail to do full justice to Darlington's "rule of thumb" when treating the consequences of dispersal of an incipient ancestral species. In spite of Slater's protests, I am still of the opinion that Darlington's discussions are beside the point. A meaningful discussion must be based on reconstructed sister-species and sister-group relationships, not on primitive, derivative, or "dominant" groups lacking the phylogenetic background. Slater's reference to a "general rule of peripheral apomorphy" lacks relevance because the progression rule, by definition, refers to cases of dispersal followed by isolation and speciation.

Dealing with my second "dispersal rule," Slater remarks that there are exceptions and gives a hypothetical example that contradicts the rule and appears credible. I myself have pointed out that exceptions are possible, and I deplore the fact that I could not discuss the details of the matter in the symposium paper. According to Nelson (1975), the area of an ancestral species can best be estimated by adding the descendant distributions. I have stressed that this is correct only if it can be shown that there has been no dispersal or extinction. I agree with Slater that these demands are difficult to meet. But I do not agree when he contends that establishment of dispersal presupposes knowledge of the original range. On the contrary, if there are indications of dispersal (sympatry, etc.), a further analysis may show its probable direction and also, more or less roughly, the original area of origin.

Slater is of the opinion that the "whole question of the area of origin of a monophyletic group" probably is "largely fruitless, unless possibly we are talking about huge areas and major groups." He is partly right. It seems clear that comparatively exact results are attainable if a group developed *in situ* without dispersal and under relatively stable conditions. But for a general understanding of the history of life in time and space, it is important to know, for example, the meaning of amphitropical vicariance patterns—which Laurasian groups are of Gondwanian origin and contrariwise. In such cases a precise knowledge of the area of origin of the common ancestral species is not a first-rate desideratum. "Major groups" are far from always actual. The two models of dispersal have recently been discussed by Platnick and Nelson (1978), who used the terms "dispersal in the absence of a barrier" and "dispersal across a barrier." I saw no reason to treat the matter further in my paper.

Dr. Platnick's criticism of my paper demonstrates that he is an adherent of an extreme type of vicariance biogeography in which there is no room for the study of dispersal, the existence of the deviation rule is denied, the application of the progression rule rejected, and the goal of the biologist is to discover how the geographical areas inhabited by endemic groups may be interrelated. Hence it is no wonder that there are several points of disagreement. I will treat Platnick's points in due order.

Theoretical inquiry.   Platnick starts by pointing at my "curious contention that there is something intrinsically dangerous about theoretical inquiries." What I have done is to stress the dangers connected with the present tendency to apply a purely theoretical approach to attempts to formalize a method of analysis for historical biogeography, adding that we easily err if we do not ponder data given by life itself and do not compare particular cases that are real. For these difficult matters, the quality of our formalizations depends on our understanding and knowledge of particular cases.

"Progression-rule biogeography."   Platnick introduces this designation for phylogenetic biogeography in my sense "because it is neither more nor less phylogenetic than any other approach involving cladistic analyses of the interrelationships of organisms." His measure is unjustified for two reasons: (1) he has not observed that my definition of phylogenetic biogeography clearly classifies it as one of two branches of historical biogeography (ecological biogeography is the second); (2) he neglects the important point that the progression rule, according to my arguments, can be applied only in those cases where there are indications that dispersal has occurred (sympatry, multiple-step morphoclines that can be followed over the map, etc.). A more adequate name for my biogeography would be "Phylogenetic biogeography according to the vicariance/dispersal model."

Objectivity and falsifiability.   In my paper I express the opinion that an objective analysis of dispersal on the basis of biological data is possible. But according to Platnick I trust in a weak sort of objectivity when writing that, a "conception [of the meaning and consequences of dispersal] becomes objective only if based on analytic experience of particular cases." He cuts off the end of the sentence, however, which runs as follows: ". . . illustrating relevant causal connections," which are demands that highly increase the quality of the argumentation. In practice, objectivity becomes a concept of relative significance, but even in practice there is in biogeography a clear limit between objectivity and subjectivity or speculation. But the objectivity of the progression rule, according to Platnick, is no different from Darlington's "rule of thumb." I can conclude only that this proves a careless reading of my paper (see, for example, my analysis of the 20 cases of northern Andean-Patagonian vicariance patterns). In this connection Platnick refers, not surprisingly, to Popper (1959), for whom the source of a hypothesis is irrelevant, and a conception becomes objective only if it is testable and falsifiable. Platnick however, overlooks the fact that in biology a falsification is far from always possible, and that the test often becomes a choice between greater or lesser degrees of credibility.

Rules of deviation and progression.   As hinted above, Platnick does not accept application of these rules in connection with biogeographical analysis. He starts his discussion with the assertion that I confuse two different concepts when speaking of apomorphic species or groups with respect to taxa that are comparatively "apomorphic in position" in the cladogram (i.e., situated comparatively far from the base of the cladogram) and those that are apomorphic in relation to a sister taxon. In reality I keep those concepts strictly separated. Instead of speaking of taxa that are "apomorphic in position," I prefer to consider them simply as taxa that are comparatively young.

As to the deviation rule, Platnick cannot have devoted much attention to the matter. He is highly skeptical, however, and tries to convince the reader of its non-existence by referring to his experience that he cannot decide which of the two basic sister groups among the spiders is more apomorphic than the other. I am personally not impressed because we have limited knowledge of transformation series and hierarchical structure inside and outside this vast order. And is Platnick's conclusion not highly inductive?

If Platnick would look upon nature's hierarchy without prejudice, he could hardly avoid perceiving its tremendous display of anagenetic progression. But this progression can be nothing other than an expression of life's incessant work with the two alternatives, conservatism and change, as realized by species cleavage via the rule of deviation.

Since Darwin's time biologists have worked with the concepts of "primitive" and "derivative" groups. Is Platnick of the opinion that this represents an unsound outgrowth of evolutionary theory, or that it is based on imagination? If not, he is evidently forced to accept the existence of the deviation rule.

Estimates of the relative plesiomorphy of sister groups and sister species are based on our survey of plesiomorphic/apomorphic character states used for the hierarchical reconstruction. Thanks to that survey we are able to estimate the basic design (ground plan) of a group, i.e., the character pattern of its ancestral species, and to compare the design with that of the ancestral species of the sister group. A higher number of plesiomorphies in a basic design shows that the branching process started from an anagenetic level lower than that of the sister group. If this is combined with a comparatively limited general change of ancestral conditions (low evolutionary rates), the result will be a relatively plesiomorphic group. In connection with outgroup comparison we are often faced with unidirectional multiple-step trends that become reliable indicators of the comparative plesiomorphy/apomorphy of sister groups. I mention especially Fittkau's (1962) comprehensive study of multiple-step trends and their great importance for an understanding of plesiomorphic/apomorphic groups and species within Chironomidae.

Considering Platnick's rejection of the deviation rule, I refer also to the concept of "evolution index" introduced by Illies (1961) in connection with his attempt to analyze more exactly the anagenetic levels of different plecopteran families. The calculation consists of assigning the value 1 for the plesiomorphic state and the values, 2, 3, 4, etc., for the number of evolutionary steps within respective trends. The arithmetic mean of the step values of all trends gives the evolution index whose lowest value equals 1. The method has been used with some modifications by Wagner (1962), Schlee (1968), Hirvenoja (1973), and Saether (1970, 1971, 1976). Saether (1970) introduced an "adjusted evolution index," which gives all trends and steps equal value according to the scale 1–2.

The last word about estimation of relative plesiomorphy/apomorphy among species and groups certainly has still not been said. But it seems evident that the experienced specialist is able to form a credible estimate of relative anagenetic progression by reference to morphology, ecology, etc.; hence, this anagenetic insight becomes an important argument in connection with our attempts to analyze old dispersal, which is one of my main points.

According to Platnick it is important that I "admit" that the deviation rule is a rule and not a law, because this allows him to ask "how to distinguish those groups in which it has functioned from those in which it has not functioned." He says that I provide no answer. The most exact answer seems to be investigation of the evolution index.

Platnick argues that his question becomes critical when the deviation rule is applied to biogeography by means of the progression rule and he refers to Nelson's (1975) example of a hypothetical three-taxon problem formed by two South American species and a "positionally apomorphic peripheral species in Africa." My "refusal to apply the progression rule" in this case, says Platnick, illustrates the need for "precisely those data on general taxic apomorphy for which he [Brundin] has provided no objective test." His argumentation is not very careful. First, the African species cannot be in a more "apomorphic position" than its sister species in South America; second, it should be quite clear from my paper that I would demand, for the purpose of a meaningful discussion of a group corresponding to Nelson's, extensive knowledge of the hierarchy of which the actual group is a part, positive or negative evidence of the presence of a sympatric amphi-Atlantic vicariance pattern formed by a closely related group, and general insight into patterns of anagenetic progression, especially with respect to possible occurrence of multiple-step trends including the African species. None of that knowledge was available.

Continuing his discussion of the progression rule, Platnick accuses me of "an elementary error in logic" because my reasoning would mean that "all cases of peripherally distributed apomorphic taxa must therefore be due to dispersal plus peripheral isolation." This is indeed a severe accusation. But in my paper there is no indication of such a reversal of the progression rule. On the contrary, I have stressed that "if dispersal has occurred," then the relatively plesiomorphic group is closer to the initial range. And I have added that the mere occurrence of the plesiomorphic group within one part of the total range, and of the apomorphic sister group within another part, *should not in itself* be used as evidence of dispersal. "But if other conditions such as sympatry and the structure of the hierarchical connections outside the two groups indicate dispersal, then the geographical distribution of general plesiomorphy/apomorphy becomes important additional evidence of direction of dispersal and the area of its origin" (see my figure 3.6). A further proof is my discussion of the history of the diamesan genera *Reissia*, *Limaya*, and *Maoridiamesa* (see figure 3.7). The elementary error in logic is Platnick's.

Platnick tries to support his point by referring to my Australian midge groups. He supposes that their ancestors, contrary to my conclusion, did not disperse to Australia but that they evolved there *in situ*, and he asks how we might discover the error we would make by "axiomatic application" of the progression rule. The answer is that an *in situ* explanation is very weak because all 12 apomorphic Australian midge groups (comprising all Australian representatives of their respective subfamilies) are components of 12 sympatric amphi-Antarctic vicariance patterns between Patagonia and Australia. Against this background of a general pattern of sympatry it is a perversion of facts to talk about "axiomatic application" of the progression rule. Even Platnick admits that sympatry indicates dispersal.

In addition, Platnick argues that I have not suggested a source of falsification. He can see only one possibility: the discovery of "a fossil member of the group that occurred in both the peripheral and central areas." This would be correct only if the South American fossil member of an Australian subgroup (belonging to the groups I analyze) would turn out to be clearly apomorphic in relation to the Australian relatives. Closer at hand would be the possibility of showing that my Australian midge groups are clearly plesiomorphic in relation to their sister groups in South America, or, more drastically, that my hierarchical reconstructions are wrong. In summary, I conclude that Platnick's criticism of my reference to the progression rule lacks the support of relevant arguments. That is the essential point.

Hypothetical vicariance patterns. Turning to my hypothetical examples of biogeographical analysis, Platnick at first deals with the case illustrated in figures 3.1–3.3 and finds that my figure 3.2 does not indicate the presence of sympatry—one of my prerequisites—adding that "even if there were sympatry among the African groups, at most that would be evidence of dispersal within Africa, not between Africa and South America." This is nonsense. Why should I show sympatry in my diagrams that refer to my analysis of a particular group? It is obvious from my text that the presupposed sympatry refers to congruent amphi-Atlantic vicariance patterns.

As for my treatment of the hypothetical vicariance pattern of figure 3.1, Platnick should be content with my vicariance explanation without involvement of dispersal across a pre-existing barrier. But he is not. He is disturbed by the supposed dispersal of stem species number 7, in spite of the fact that this event is assumed to belong to the pre-history of the amphi-Atlantic vicariance pattern of the group. But the probable reason is simply that he considers investigation of the pre-history of a vicariance pattern irrelevant in connection with a reconstruction of the history of life in time and space. Platnick's comments on my figure 3.3 seem meaningless.

My criticism of vicariance biogeography. I conclude in my paper that if the range of a Pangean stem species is the result of dispersal from some minor area of origin, it becomes important to try to determine that area. Platnick comments: "important to whom, and for what reasons? With regard to the history of some particular group of organisms, it may well be an important question. But with regard to the problems that vicariance biogeography attempts to solve . . . 'the question . . . becomes unnecessary and, perhaps, irrelevant'" (the latter sentence is partly a quotation from Croizat et al. 1974). This one-sidedness and disregard of the pre-history of vicariance patterns are the major weaknesses of the Croizat school. To the panbiogeographers, the intermittent interchange that must have taken place between the biotas of Laurasia and Gondwana, and post-Pangean dispersal in general, seemingly are not worthy of investigation.

Platnick ends with an attempt to meet my criticism of his method to investigate and test correlations between biological and paleogeographical cladograms (Platnick and Nelson 1978). But he cannot defend the weakness of the method that a priori permits a free distortion of the biological cladograms used for testing and that disregards the possible influence of dispersal. Vicariance patterns that are non-homologous are non-comparable.

Platnick's final and general charge—that I have used "a priori rules" to explain the history of groups—also lacks support. Indeed the rules of deviation and progression have not been simply applied but referred to so often because my own material is a perpetual reminder of the consequences of their action. Is not the blunt denial of their existence the expression of an aprioristic approach?

4

Taxon Pulses, Vicariance, and Dispersal: An Evolutionary Synthesis Illustrated by Carabid Beetles

T. L. Erwin

> I do not trust Occam's razor. The simplest explanations are not necessarily the right ones in biogeography. To choose the simplest explanation because it is simple is like a surgeon choosing to cut a patient's throat with one razor stroke rather than to perform a complex operation. Occam's razor should be used to make an exploratory cut into a problem, not to solve it (Darlington 1965).

DURING MOST of earth's long history, species diversity has been nearly infinite, limited only by time and perhaps also by the chemistry and physics of genetic recombination. The multitude of biological processes and biological responses to climatic and geological processes is complex and laminar; the processes surely must act differentially at times on the same and on various organisms, and on biotas. This laminar effect, concurrently acting at different levels and through time at different levels, has produced the present distribution of plants and animals. Hypotheses that invoke *single mechanism* causal agents to explain distribution patterns of entire biotas—e.g., continental drift—cannot do justice to the true complexity of patterns. This kind of causal agent may account for vicariance between sister species or other taxon levels, but not for whole biotas.

Investigative procedures of the past (and present) have been, perhaps necessarily, *simplistic*. Biogeographical models of classic dispersalists were

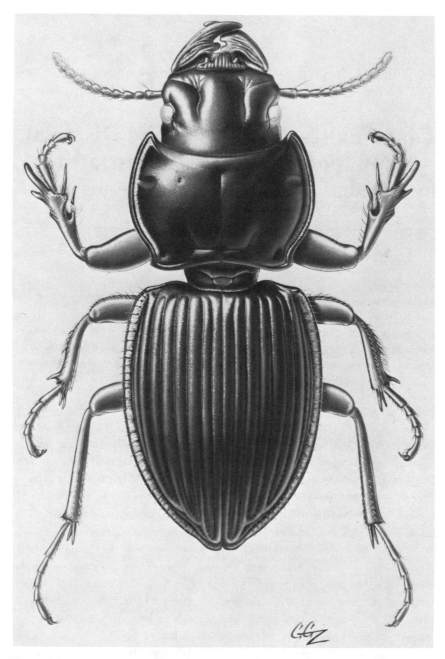

Figure 4.1. *Pasimachus cordicollis* Chd., dorsal habitus, length 16.37 mm.

based on either catalogue counts of taxa per area (e.g., Darlington 1957, 1965) or taxonomic revisions which, in retrospect, utilized fragmentary knowledge of the groups in question, both with regard to members' relationships and/or their distributions (e.g., Erwin 1970). These dispersal models proposed range expansion from a center of origin, with expansion sometimes taking the forms across barriers, where new forms arose on the other side. The suggested barriers were usually visible physical features of the landscape (water, ice, mountains, etc.). Implicit in the dispersalists' models, but almost never stated, was *isolation* of the dispersants (which crossed the barrier) and their progeny from the "base-camp" population(s); also implicit was an allopatric arrangement in which speciation might proceed given enough time. In almost all cases, pathways of dispersal were viewed on the face of the earth as it is today; in some instances mysterious missing land bridges were invented to account for difficult cases (B. B. Simpson 1978).

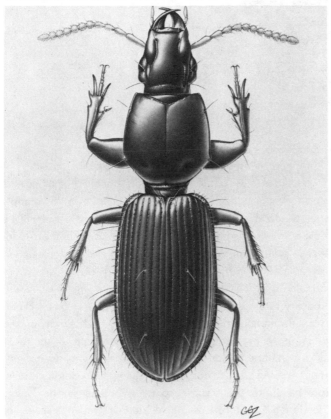

Figure 4.2. *Stratiodes* sp., dorsal habitus, length 4.85 mm.

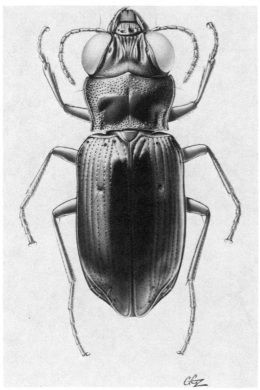

Figure 4.3. *Notiophilus specularis* Bates, dorsal habitus, length 5.72 mm.

Advocates of vicariance biogeographical models postulate that groups attain cosmopolitanism of some degree via dispersal, and that the group's range is subsequently divided by a barrier which again, as in the dispersalist's model, creates an allopatric arrangement in which speciation might proceed. The focus of vicariance advocates is continental rifting, and the envisioned barriers are physical features of the landscape—usually bodies of water. Neither group normally analyzes ecological factors, life histories, fossil records, and evolutionary rates pertinent to the group(s) under consideration (Erwin 1979a). This information must have been in the thoughts of the biogeographers writing in the past, however, because they were for the most part fine biologists and natural historians. Like classifiers who do not explain their methods or logic but come to reasonable classifications, biogeographers, too, have proposed some sound hypotheses. That these ideas are not "Popperian" in form, as advocated in recent issues of

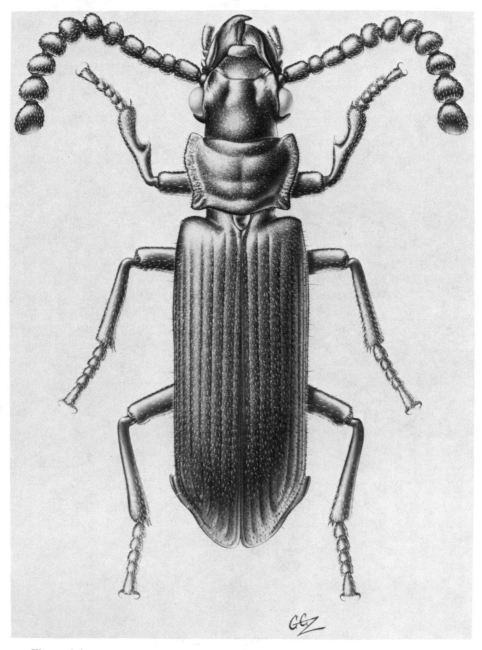

Figure 4.4. *Ozaena convexa* Bon., dorsal habitus, length 15.78 mm.

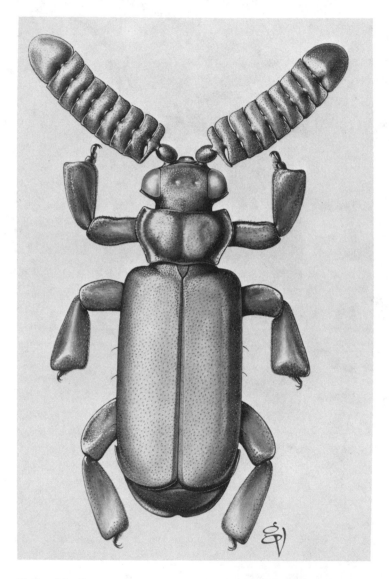

Figure 4.5. *Homopterus subcordatus* Darl., dorsal habitus length 8.46 mm.

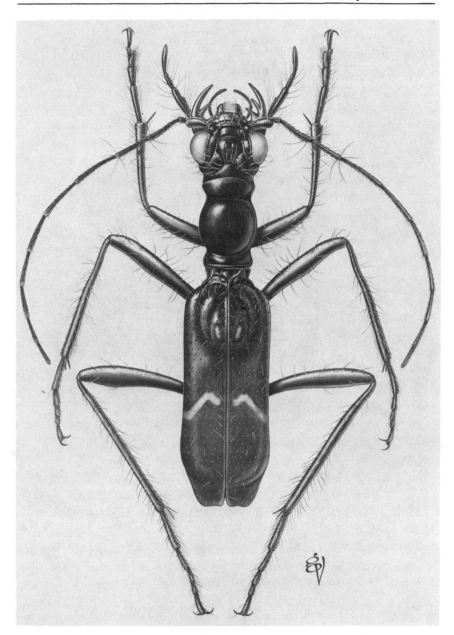

Figure 4.6. *Ctenostoma laeticolor* Bates., dorsal habitus, length 13.40 mm.

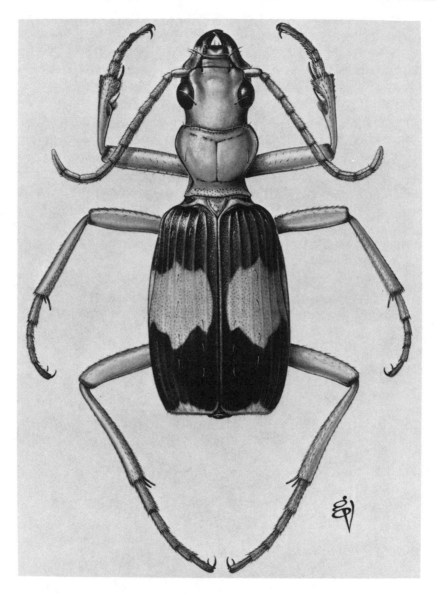

Figure 4.7. *Pherosophus aequinoctialis* L., dorsal habitus, length 16.34 mm.

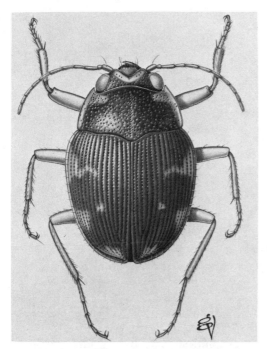

Figure 4.8. *Omophron gratum* Chd., dorsal habitus, length 6.43 mm.

Systematic Zoology (and Noonan, unpublished), does not mean that we can dismiss them outright.

The history of life on this planet can be likened to kaleidoscopic images of biological and physical events through time—the tempo counted in pulses. Simple explanations of these images do not do them justice. Nature was and is complex; an explanation of nature, if satisfactory, will also be complex.

The images with which I work are patterns observable in the distribution and nature of ground beetles of the family Carabidae. I try to stick to the carabid beetles (figures 4.1–4.10) for two reasons. First, I think they are nice animals; second and more important, I know something about them and the people who work with them, and I can better judge data reliability. Often biogeographers use various data from the literature on unfamiliar organisms and hence cannot see the data limitations. Faulty conclusions often result.

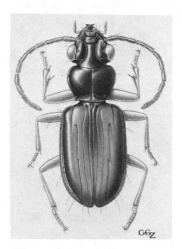

Figure 4.9. *Cnides* sp., dorsal habitus, length 2.96 mm.

Carabid Beetles

Carabid beetles have long been zoogeographical tools. Bates (1881–84) used them to discuss the nature of biotic provinces in Central America (which, incidently, still seem valid). More recently, numerous authors have analyzed carabid distributions and have drawn conclusions about earth history from these analyses (e.g., Ball 1975; Darlington 1943, 1965, 1970b, 1971; Erwin 1970, 1975; Jeannel 1926–28, 1946–49; Noonan 1973; Whitehead 1972). There are several reasons why carabids have received considerable attention. They are highly diverse (figures 4.1–4.10), yet mentally a manageable group; they are winged (vagile dispersants) or not (poor dispersants); they are found in all regions of the world (except present-day Antarctica); there are numerous species and individuals (about 40,000 species are presently described); and they are found in all communities and most terrestrial habitats, from below sea level to 5300 m+ elevation (Mani 1968). Their relationships are now under intense study, and much is known about their life histories and environmental requirements. Classical and experimental biogeographers (Darlington 1943; Lindroth 1945–49) used carabids as tools, and a tradition began. George E. Ball, greatly influenced by Darlington and Lindroth, stimulated his numerous students toward zoogeographical analysis of carabids. Many of these studies are cited here, and a more complete history is given in Erwin et al. (1979).

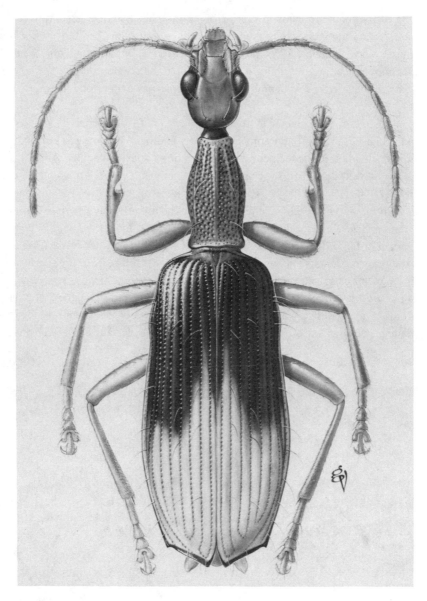

Figure 4.10. *Agra lavernae* Erwin, dorsal habitus, length 9.34 mm.

Biogeographical Factors and Definitions

One of the main problems in today's biogeographical studies is semantics. In fact, that is probably a key element in this symposium. For the immediate future, biogeographers must present clearly and in detail their definitions of biogeographical jargon (figure 4.11) in order to eliminate confusion. Perhaps some of these words will come to have a commonly understood usage!

Dispersal. Dispersal is the movement of an individual or groups of individuals from one geographical point to another. This movement and its mode, speed, and distance can be thought of as species vagility. Among the nearly 40,000 described species of carabid beetles, all states of vagility exist. In 1976 (Erwin 1979a), I reported flight records of up to 100 miles for certain highly vagile dispersants, some of which were only 3 mm in length. Other species, especially those of mountain tops, lose their wings and/or powers of flight during their evolution and can only walk; hence they are low vagility dispersants. Vagility seems to be related to habitat in a general way among carabids, especially when habitat and geographical placement are considered together. Most species of mountain tops, remote islands, and high latitudes are flightless. Species of seashores, lowland watersides (floodable plains), and lowland prairies seem to be highly vagile. Terrestrial species of

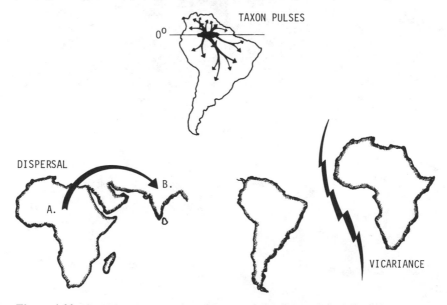

Figure 4.11. Graphic representation of taxon pulses, dispersal, and vicariance.

temperate forests are often flightless; species of tropical forests are vagile. All species of the canopies are fully winged and come to lights by flight, but their total ranges seem restricted; thus they do not appear to be highly vagile dispersants. With this kind of diversity of vagility, and apparent habitat correlations, careful analysis must be made to assure biogeographical usefulness. An understanding of a group's vagility must be a forerunner to any biogeographical study.

The importance of dispersal to a taxon is the attainment of cosmopolitanism and continued genetic contact between populations. Individual dispersants are merely genetic carriers from one population to another across an intervening gap. As long as this connection exists, a species maintains its integrity and genetic diversity; separated populations gradually diverge, and yet maintain a commonness in direct proportion to the amount of contact or genetic exchange. Only if dispersants fail to carry their genetic material between separated populations can allopatric speciation proceed. Failure results when the intervening "gap" becomes an uncrossable "barrier." This can occur in two ways: (1) changing physical features of the earth surface and/or climatic shifts; or (2) intrinsic changes in the genome, behavior, or dispersal capabilities of members of a semi-isolated population. That the first occurs is undisputed; that the second occurs is open to conjecture and needs much study (e.g., Endler 1977).

Most biogeographers think of barriers as large and dominant features of the landscape. Oceans between continents and oceanic islands are good examples. We know that insects disperse to remote islands; they cross even the Atlantic Ocean (Johnson and Bowden 1972). This capability of animals and plants spurred Mayr (1942) to suggest the "founder" principle, that is, a one-time transport across a barrier of a gravid female or small deme that becomes established (with subsequent family) in an area previously not occupied by that species. Speciation then proceeds. Under the assumption that insects, some plants, and some other animals disperse long distances, the theory of "founderism" seems reasonable. The chance that it actually happens in nature, however, is small and cannot account for many cases of species-distribution patterns, even in remote areas. That is because weather patterns, ocean currents, or other means of dispersal are not "freakish" when viewed on the geological time scale or especially on the evolutionary-rate scale. In other words, if dispersal conditions are such that a founder now finds its way across an ocean to an island, it is likely that the event will occur often over the next several thousand years until dispersal conditions change. Dispersal promotes cosmopolitanism, not isolation, if it is repeated year after year, or decade after decade. The connection to the semi-isolated population may be tenuous, but it exists; the island is therefore *within* the cosmopolitan distribution of the species. When the tenuous connection is broken for a long enough time, speciation will take place. The *event* that breaks the connection is a vicariance event; it may be climatic, continental-rifting, glaciation, host-plant switching, or anything that prevents the genetic carrier from crossing the gap long enough for a speciation event. In the case in point, the ocean is not the barrier because the species members crossed it; rather it is the weather pattern change that stopped dispersal. This concept is fundamental to biogeography. All too often biogeographers have considered some imposing geographical surface feature to be *the* barrier because it is visible. I doubt that this is often the case, at least in vagile arthropods, and suggest that we focus on more subtle features such as climate shifts or in the case of the Amazon, for example, the mosaic and shifting riverine system. Of course, in the case of continental rifting the developing ocean does eventually, after a long period, become a barrier to a majority of the fauna and flora, but this happens gradually and differentially on various biotic elements. An analysis of barriers and species vagility is an important first step in any biogeographical project.

Vicariance.   Vicariance, as I allude to it, is usually thought of as the separation of populations of a species by some geological or ecological feature in the biosphere (Platnick and Nelson 1978). It is the result when two or more portions of a species range become separated and thus allopatric. If the separation is maintained long enough, speciation takes place. Vicariance is not established as long as dispersal or genetic exchange between the populations takes place. I view vicariance events as having a wider scope of variation, however, from climatic alternations, grand continental rifting, and glaciation patterns to host switching traditionally thought of as "sympatric" speciation (Bush 1975b). Vicariance to me is merely the separation into two or more isolated pools of the genetic resources available to a species, by some external or intrinsic mechanism that allows the two or more pools to be differentially selected by external agents. The resolution at which one looks at vicariance depends on taxon level. There should be a general correlation between age of a taxon (that is, in a cladistic system, taxonomic rank of the group) and age of vicariant events. For example, sister-species pairs in the Nearctic Region probably date from a late Pleistocene vicariance event (Ball 1965; Matthews 1979; Ashworth 1979; Whitehead 1972). Two sister genera, however, probably date from an older event, perhaps mid-Tertiary (Erwin 1970; Noonan 1973; Ball 1975).

Vicariance events in the history of carabids are probably the same as those affecting many flying insects, such as subsidence patterns, rifting, flooding cycles, glaciation, desert formation, etc. There is no evidence yet that genetic switching or host alternation exists, and at present we can deal only with the traditional "allopatric" speciation model to see how it applies to observed patterns.

Taxon pulses. In a paper I gave in 1976 on carabid beetles (Erwin 1979b), I expanded the "taxon-cycle" concept, introduced by Darlington (1943) and named by Wilson (1961), into a model that accounts for habitat

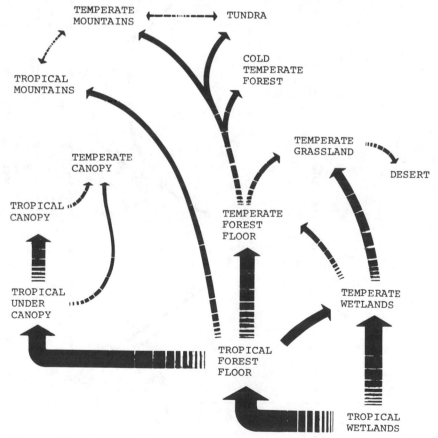

Figure 4.12. Status of life styles by fauna and area. From Erwin (1979b).

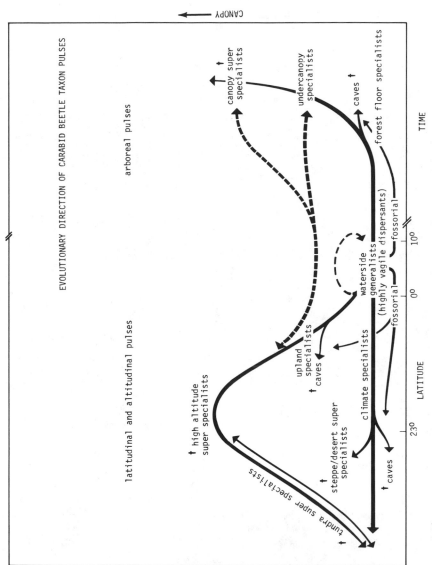

Figure 4.13. Evolutionary direction of carabid beetle taxon pulses or pathways to extinction. Dagger (†) indicates ultimate end to radiation above the species level.

shifts along certain pathways away from the complex of tropical wetland habitats (figure 4.12); this model was called "taxon pulses." Taxon pulses flow unidirectionally along pathways toward forest canopies, high latitudes, grasslands, deserts, caves, and up mountains (both tropical and temperate). Progression is along a sequence of habitats in one direction only; reverse pulses have not been observed; it was suggested (Erwin 1979b) that they do not occur. A taxon pulse (figure 4.13) is defined as a taxon's adaptive shift from one habitat into another along pathways such as mentioned above; for carabids the shift initially takes place as a tropical-wetland evolutionary generalist (*plesiotype*) radiates into a biotic zone away from the waterside surface and becomes an evolutionary specialist (*apotype*). Further along the pathway evolutionary superspecialists (*superapotypes*) evolve. Replacement of wetland plesiotypic taxa takes place, but these taxa are long persistent. Plesiotypes may generate several pulses before replacement; these pulses overtake previous pulses and replace them along the pathways. Pulse members usually show sequential relict patterns toward the termini of the pathways because of high extinction rates and replacement by succeeding waves of taxa. The driving forces behind the pulses are various and change through time (figure 4.14). These driving forces, acting on the wetland plesiotypes, keep major carabid pulses flowing and account for the incredible diversity and persistence of the family through time (probably since the Permian; see Ponamarenko 1977).

The use of this model (figure 4.13) for phylogenetic and zoogeographical studies was outlined by Ball (1978). Taxa may be categorized into sets that reflect how far they have departed from the evolutionary generalist stage. Sister-group relationships between taxa of sequential habitats can be discovered—the plesiotype at the base, same level, or lower down the sequential scale than the apotype, as in any transformation series. Correlation of habitat sequences with behavioral and structural characteristics adds power to phylogenetic and zoogeographical analysis (e.g., Ball 1978; Allen and Ball 1980). Habitat vicariance is simply geographical vicariance at a much finer resolution.

The mechanism by which this process occurs can be thought of as habitat cosmopolitanism. A wetland evolutionary generalist spends part of its time living at the edge of the adjacent drier forest or savanna and through time adapts to both habitats, i.e., broadly adapts. Competition or predation pressure increases in the wetland habitat, but not in the drier adjacent habitat, and the wetland form becomes rarer and finally extinct. Selection is toward those organisms that live only in the drier habitat; these survive. This

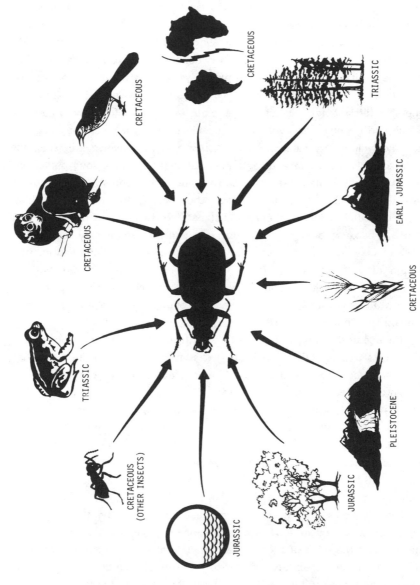

Figure 4.14. Graphic representation of evolutionary driving forces that greatly affected carabid beetles.

adaptive shift is a *pulse*. In species that occupy larger ranges, perhaps the wetland form survives locally where competition and predation are less or do not occur. Sister pairs are established between wetland-dryland (plesiotype) survivers and dryland-only isolates (apotype). Allopatric isolation of different elements of these populations sets the stage for differential selection and subsequent speciation or extinction.

Synthesis of Carabid Beetles

Extant distribution patterns of carabids result from past events; the higher the taxon level, assuming a balanced classification, the older the event. Proto-caraboid fossils, much like Recent Trachypachidae, are known from the Russian Permian (Ponomarenko 1977). At that time, the earth's land surface was a megacontinent, Pangea; plants were extremely primitive; and life in general on land had not yet begun to flourish in the great diversity that we know today. Vicariant events resulting in speciation certainly existed at that time, but what was their nature?

Much of the early diversification of carabids must have come about at that time and given rise to what we now consider primitive subfamilies or tribal complexes. The structural and behavioral nature of members of these tribes suggests selection by primitive predators (Erwin 1979b). The question is of vicariance mode. On a solid land mass, vicariance events could take the form of glaciation, riverine mosaics, climatic shifts, inland-sea development, or habitat sequencing as already outlined. In these early lineages there appears to be no host specificity, and host switching probably was not a mechanism of speciation available to early carabids. Hypothesized histories of three carabid groups are given graphically in figures 4.15–4.23. The Trachypachidae, until recently regarded as a subfamily of carabids and now regarded as the sister group, are very old; they must have undergone much extinction, and today they have a simple pattern. Promecognathini, a somewhat younger group, have a similar pattern, but there is a possibility that host millipeds may have influenced the evolution of this group. A more complicated pattern in the Ozaenini-Metriini has resulted from later pulsing in a more complicated environment and much less extinction through time. Still more complicated patterns are given in Erwin (1979b). Congruence patterns among the higher taxa of carabids repeatedly show these kinds of pulses, movements, radiations, and extinction patterns. I view this as a scenario based

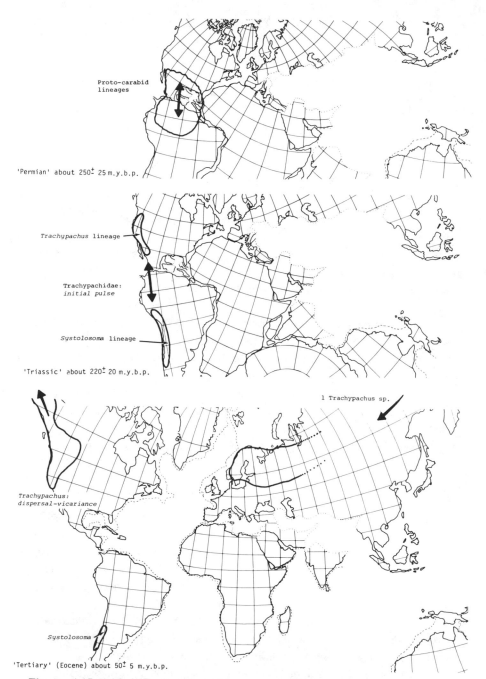

Proto-carabid
lineages

'Permian' about 250 ± 25 m.y.b.p.

Trachypachus lineage

Trachypachidae:
initial pulse

Systolosoma lineage

'Triassic' about 220 ± 20 m.y.b.p.

1 Trachypachus sp.

Trachypachus:
dispersal-vicariance

Systolosoma

'Tertiary' (Eocene) about 50 ± 5 m.y.b.p.

Figures 4.15, 4.16, 4.17. Hypothetical time sequence distribution maps of Trachypachidae from Permian. Figure 4.15: Initial taxon pulse in tropical climes. Figure 4.16: Secondary amphitropical pulse away from tropical climes into temperate environments. Figure 4.17: Dispersal of northern lineage into Old World and subsequent vicariant event at Beringia.

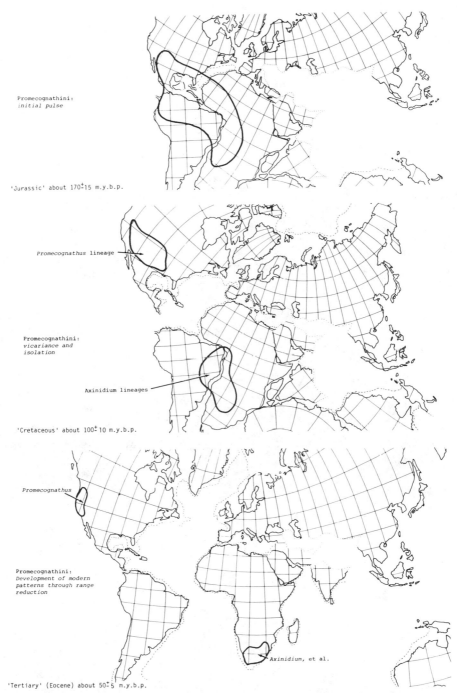

Figures 4.18, 4.19, 4.20. Hypothetical time sequence distribution maps of Promecognathini from Jurassic. Figure 4.18: Initial taxon pulse in tropical climes. Figure 4.19: Secondary amphitropical pulse away from tropical climes into temperate environments. Figure 4.20: New World-Old World vicariance, range reduction, and isolation of subtribal units.

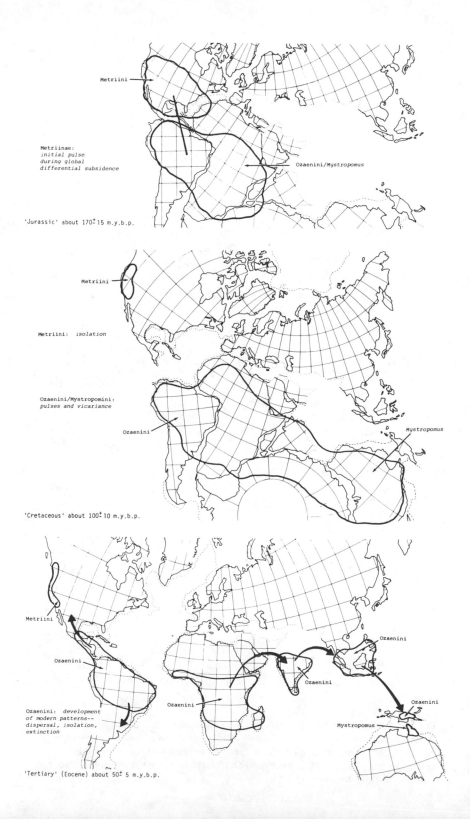

Metriini

Metriinae:
*initial pulse
during global
differential subsidence*

Ozaenini/Mystropomus

'Jurassic' about 170±15 m.y.b.p.

Metriini

Metriini: *isolation*

Ozaenini/Mystropomini:
pulses and vicariance

Ozaenini

Mystropomus

'Cretaceous' about 100±10 m.y.b.p.

Metriini

Ozaenini

Ozaenini

Ozaenini

Ozaenini

Ozaenini: *development
of modern patterns--
dispersal, isolation,
extinction*

Ozaenini

Mystropomus

'Tertiary' (Eocene) about 50±5 m.y.b.p.

on a general knowledge of the family; what remains, however, is the nitty-gritty job of cladistic analysis paired with detection of exact distributions.

In conclusion, and to make the point that I came here to make, I believe that we have to deal with a great variety of vicariant events at various levels to explain present distribution patterns of whole biotas or even groups such as the ground beetles because today's patterns are a summation of these events plus tremendous amounts of extinction. We must discover first the evolutionary processes—driving forces if you will—that impact on our special group. We must then place these in a context and in a time frame with vicariant events that have a potential effect on the group (not all events will affect all members of a biota or group because of differential powers of dispersal, lengths of time of events, speciation rates of synvicariants, and original distributions of group members in geographical relation to the events). The time frame for carabids dates from the Permian to the present; the time frame for just the Harpalini (a tribe of carabids) probably dates only from the Cretaceous. The Harpalini had a "center of origin" somewhere among the greater distribution of Carabidae evolved at that time. The proximate vicariant events, subsequent to the origin and dispersal of harpalines, acted in conjunction with taxon pulses and resulted in today's patterns. Coincident patterns with other tribes tell us the relative strength of the causal vicariant event. Coincident patterns among the carabids as a whole indicate that several vicariant events have had great impact on present-day patterns of distribution (figure 4.24). Depending upon which taxon level we, as researchers, deal with, there is a tendency to stress importance of one of these events. For carabid workers who study at the subtribal level (Reichardt 1979), continental drift, or at least South American-African rifting, is the most important. For workers dealing with Holarctic elements at the species and species-group levels in a single genus (Kavanaugh and Negre 1979), the Pleistocene glaciation and Bering land bridge are the most important. For me, at the present, Amazonian refuge forests and flooding cycles are the most

←——————————————————————————————

Figures 4.21, 4.22, 4.23. Hypothetical time sequence distribution maps of Metriinae from Jurassic. Figure 4.21: Initial taxon pulse and amphitropical pulse away from tropical climes by Metriini lineage into temperate environments. Figure 4.22: Attainment of cosmopolitanism by Ozaenini lineage; range restriction and isolation of Metriini lineage after vicariant event at Middle America disconnection; initial vicariant events between Gondwanian elements. Figure 4.23: Vicariance events isolating *Mystropomus* in Australia, Neotropical from African Ozaenini lineages, and subsequent attainment of cosmopolitanism of these two lineages through dispersal and taxon pulses.

? GLACIATION (PERMIAN)

LAND. SUBSIDENCE (JURASSIC)

LAURASIA/GONDWANA RIFT (JURASSIC)

GONDWANA RIFT (CRETACEOUS)

INLAND SEAS (CRETACEOUS/TERTIARY)

GRASSLAND/DESERT FORMATION (CRETACEOUS/RECENT)

ICE AGE (PLEISTOCENE)

FLOOD CYCLES (PLEISTOCENE/RECENT)

Figure 4.24. Geographically, geologically, or biotically induced vicariant events important in the evolution of Carabidae.

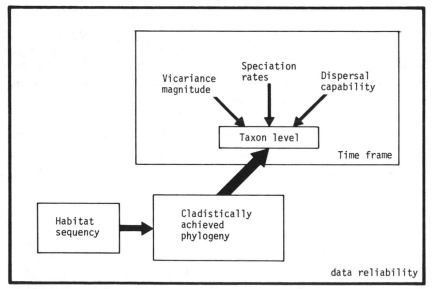

Figure 4.25. Factors that should be used in biogeography, beginning with cladistically achieved phylogeny.

important (Erwin unpublished). But all of these, in summation, affect today's total biotic patterns.

It is imperative that we as biogeographers keep in mind and utilize as many of the following as possible when we do our studies: cladistically achieved phylogenetic relationships, time frame, taxon levels, vicariance magnitude, dispersal capabilities, habitat sequencing, speciation rates, and data reliability (figure 4.25). To do less is to use Occam's razor unsharpened.

Discussion

K. F. Koopman

AS A NEO-MAMMALOGIST with considerable interest in Tertiary and Quaternary mammalian distribution patterns, my viewpoint is quite different from Dr. Erwin's. I am, however, in fundamental agreement with him concerning the importance of avoiding simplistic explanations, a subject to which I will later return. I would like to touch first on several specific points that Erwin makes and then discuss what I regard as the broader implications of his thesis.

First, while both the "dispersalists" and the "vicariance biogeographers" have at times been guilty of oversimplification, I think that the "dispersalists" have been far less inclined to do this than the "vicariance biogeographers." G. G. Simpson has certainly emphasized fossil records and evolutionary rates. Ecological factors at least (e.g., forest vs. grassland adaptation) have been taken into account. Differences in life histories (e.g., *altricial* vs. *precocial* development) have rarely been important in explaining mammalian distribution patterns.

I take issue with Erwin concerning the importance of long-distance dispersal. While the agents which can bring about dispersal are not freakish, the probability that a certain kind of organism will be able to surmount a given barrier may be very low. As Simpson (1952) pointed out, however, given a long enough time, such an event becomes very probable. I cite an example: 100 years ago, not only the Cattle Egret but the entire genus *Ardeola* (consisting of seven species) to which it belongs, was confined to the eastern hemisphere. After dispersing across the Atlantic Ocean to northeastern South America early in the twentieth century, the Cattle Egret was then able to colonize a large part of both North and South America. The dates of many similar cases of Australian birds dispersing for the first time across the Tasman Sea to New Zealand are known. In some cases, double and even triple invasions (Mayr 1963:504–6) of the same island by the same stock have occurred, spaced far enough apart in time for reproductive isolation to develop during the intervening period. Thus, while dispersal initially produces "cosmopolitanism," the end result is discontinuity, which may simulate vicariance very closely. In fact, although the presence of numerous mainland species on continental islands throughout the world (e.g., Trinidad, Fernando Poo, and the islands of the Sunda shelf) is usually explained by vicariance (as a result of rising water levels caused by melting of glacial ice), some could be the result of post-vicariant dispersal.

Concerning the timing of vicariance events in relation to the present levels of taxonomic distribution of the sister groups that are the products of these events, it is necessary to stress the importance of evolutionary rates. I certainly agree that sister taxa that have differentiated only to the species level are most unlikely to be the products of a Mesozoic or early Cenozoic vicariance event. Actually, the timing that Erwin gives to vicariance events for species and genera of carabid beetles agrees rather closely with what I would postulate for most mammals. Erwin, however, has also postulated times for several vicariance events whose products are now regarded as families, subfamilies, or tribes. The evidence for divergence of the various groups at the times postulated is not clear.

Concerning "taxon pulses," the preferred evolutionary directions for land vertebrates are not the same as for carabid beetles, although there are certain resemblances. Reversals, however, do occur at least occasionally, particularly when a *specialized group* reaches an area by dispersal (either over land or over water) and finds an area without competitors in adjacent ecological zones. Under these circumstances, adaptive radiation may occur so that some derivatives become less "specialized" than the ancestral stock. The thin-billed Darwin's finches are an example.

If I correctly understand Erwin, he believes that the concepts of vicariance biogeography (at least if vicariance is taken in a broad sense) are of some value in solving specific problems of historical biogeography, although they do not tell the whole story. As I see them, the basic principles of vicariance biogeography are as follows: (1) The distributions of all kinds of organisms are to be considered together, regardless of differences in ecology or dispersing ability; (2) groups of organisms having similar distribution patterns are assumed to have had similar histories; (3) degree of differentiation is of little or no value in assessing times of past separation (vicariant or otherwise); (4) a direct "track" connecting the separated parts of a distribution (usually reflecting tectonic plate movement) is to be preferred to a more roundabout way by which former connection might have existed; (5) dispersal as an explanation for distribution patterns is treated as a last resort, usually for distributions that do not fit common patterns.

With these principles I cannot agree. Let us take, as an example, the large number of taxa (of various taxonomic levels) that are now confined to Africa and South America. There are several ways in which such a distribution pattern could arise: (1) the ancestral stock of the taxon had a continuous distribution through both continents before they separated in the Mesozoic; (2) the taxon, requiring tropical conditions, was widely distributed in northern continents early in the Cenozoic, but became restricted to Africa and South America when tropical conditions disappeared in the north; (3) the taxon was originally confined to one of the two areas, but later dispersed across the Atlantic to colonize the other area. Because all of these explanations are possible, it is probable that if a large number of taxa of various kinds with this common distribution pattern are studied, there will be examples of each of these plus combinations of them (e.g., cases where earlier vicariance patterns are obscured by later dispersals). The point is that although all these distributions are similar and would be part of the same "generalized track," they would have had very different histories. Vicariance biogeography seems incapable of distinguishing them. A less rigid biogeographical analysis, however, would ask questions such as: (1) what is the taxonomic level of differentiation within the taxon? (2) what is known of its evolutionary rates and dispersing ability? (3) what are its ecological limitations? (4) is there any fossil record indicating former occurrence outside its present range? From the answers to these questions, some explanations of the distribution of a particular taxon could be rejected as highly improbable; others would emerge as more likely, to be tested by further evidence.

I have heard it said that because all organisms inhabit the same earth, their distributions have been determined by the same factors. This is nonsense. Corridors and barriers to distribution will differ between aquatic and terrestrial species, forest and grassland species, species requiring rocks for shelter and species requiring alluvium for burrowing—even though the species with different ecological requirements may be closely related.

The important thing in biogeography, as in other aspects of biology, is to avoid simplistic reductionism. Any aspect of an organism or the environment in which it lives may be important in understanding why it lives in some places and not in others. While there are, of course, some common patterns, basically every kind of organism has its own biogeographical parameters. Any kind of evidence that will help to elucidate these parameters should be utilized, whether it is a relevant fossil record, an ecological restriction, a relative dispersal ability, or anything else. To discard any evidence is to impoverish biogeography in its attempt to interpret the real world.

Discussion

H. F. Howden

Random and Infrequent Dispersals

DR. ERWIN MAKES many good points. Perhaps the most important is that there is no single explanation that encompasses and explains all evolutionary or biogeographical events. Rather than single out one aspect, e.g., climatic change or continental movement, all should be considered, along with their relative importance and period of greatest influence. To paraphrase Erwin, we look at a laminar mosaic. Unfortunately, both time and space limit the development of this theme, and rather than attempt to comment on all of the points Erwin raises, I will try to examine in detail only some aspects of dispersal and its role in biogeography.

Erwin includes dispersal in his consideration of taxon pulses and suggests that a pulse is unidirectional. I wonder if it is so. If semantics and new terminology are overlooked, dispersal from wet tropical areas to less favored habitats is similar to some of the ideas expressed by Darlington (1957). While in general agreement, I believe that Wilson's (1961) taxon cycle is pertinent because it considers both chance dispersal and invasion of unoccupied niches in a variety of habitats, including possible invasion of the wet tropics. The taxon cycle involves islands, and I will consider these—both oceanic islands and habitat islands—and the role they play in cycles or pulses. Rather than discuss generalities, I will mention a few specific cases and then consider how these fit into a broader picture.

I believe that for most terrestrial organisms, salt water is a major barrier. Organisms, particularly winged ones, very small ones, some weeds, etc., *are* capable, however, of long-distance dispersal over salt water. Lindroth et al. (1963), in the elegant study of arrivals on the newly formed island of Surtsey, have certainly shown that some organisms, particularly insects, disperse over salt water. Other investigators, including Freeman (1945), Holloway (1977), and Fox (1978) have documented varying dispersal abilities in a variety of animals. As Erwin points out, if the organisms can do it once, they can do it again, so what is the frequency of arrival? Does the species disperse once or many times; how often does it need to disperse to maintain gene flow; and is this gene flow unidirectional? Is a vicariant event needed to explain genetic divergence (speciation) on islands in spite of different ecological factors that most certainly are present in any two island areas separated geographically? In other words, how much does infrequent chance dispersal, particularly if unidirectional, influence biogeographical patterns?

In the Galapagos Archipelago there are several freshwater lakes that presently are covered with a species of water fern: *Azolla microphylla*. Schofield and Colinvaux (1969) took several borings to study these lakes and their past history. Evidence was found that *A. microphylla* has persisted for approximately the past 8500 years. The lakes were dry before then until approximately 45,000 years ago. In sediments dated 48,000 (C^{14}) a "fossil" species of *Azolla filiculoides* occurred, but there is no indication that *microphylla* was also present. Both species occur today on the South American mainland, but one may exclude the other in a particular habitat. The most likely explanation for the alternate occurrence of the two species of *Azolla* on the Galapagos is that some time in the past *A. filiculoides* arrived in the Galapagos and occupied all available habitats. Drought then brought about its extinction. The next time the habitat became "available," some 8–9000 years ago,—*A. microphylla* arrived first and occupied all available habitats. This case does not illustrate any break in gene flow, but does illustrate the element of chance as a factor in the first arrival at, and the filling of, an available niche, particularly since *Azolla* is supposedly carried by chance on the feet of migrating birds. This case also would seem to indicate that crossings are rather infrequent. If both species regularly can reach the Galapagos, why do all the ponds contain just one species? The likely explanation is that one species arrived, established itself in one pond, and was then transported to nearby ponds by birds resident on the islands. This explanation is speculative, although the case certainly supports long-distance overwater dispersal.

What evidence supports the founder effect and the implied interruption of gene flow? The history of the Hawaiian drosophilids is a superbly documented case, particularly because their taxonomy, ecology, chromosomal history, and biochemistry have been intensively investigated. Geologically, the present-day main islands of the archipelago supposedly formed above a "hot spot" under the Pacific Plate. As the plate drifted northwestward, volcanic eruptions occurred above the hot spot, forming a chain of islands. The present islands are not more than 10–15 million years old. How close they, or the older atolls and guyots, were to other exposed areas is not important to our discussion. Among the larger islands with present elevations above 300 m, the older islands such as Kauai lie to the west, while younger islands lie to the east, the chain terminating in the relatively recent (3–5,000,000 years) island of Hawaii. At least some of seven or eight main islands have never been connected by dry land even if the sea level was lower by 300 m at some time in the last 5,000,000 years (figure 4.26). This means that any movements between at least some of the various islands had to be by overwater dispersal. I am not concerned about the source of the original

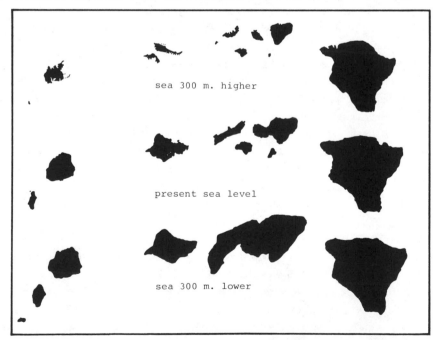

Figure 4.26. Configuration of the Hawaiian Islands at different levels of the sea. From Zimmerman (1948:40, figure 21). Published with the permission of the University Press of Hawaii.

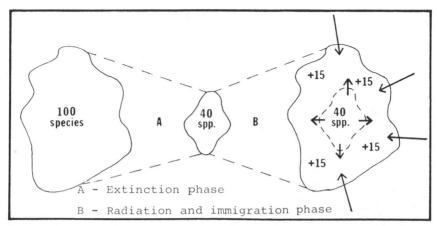

A - Extinction phase

B - Radiation and immigration phase

Figure 4.27. Possible changes due to size fluctuations of one island within an archipelago.

founders, but merely of the between-island radiation of groups that occur in the archipelago and nowhere else, and then only groups that have greatly speciated. In the case of the Hawaiian Drosophilidae, Carson and Kaneshiro (1976) estimate that there may be 800 endemic species, the largest concentration of species for any area of the world. These are all believed to have arisen from one or two original colonizing species, but it is their history of radiation within the islands that is of interest.

According to the evidence based on chromosome tracers (Carson 1970), ecology, mating behavior, etc. (Carson et al. 1970; Carson and Kaneshiro 1976), the various species not only have invaded odd niches, but also have dispersed to different islands and sometimes back, with the more ancient (plesiomorphic) groups centered on Kauai and the other older islands, and the more derived groups centered on Hawaii. Both salt water and lava flows have served as barriers. Facts too numerous to detail here are given in the papers cited, but the general types of archipelago radiation are illustrated in figures 4.27 and 4.28. Carson and Kaneshiro (1976:339) conclude from their extensive investigations:

> From its inception the whole archipelago was strongly isolated from continental regions of the globe. This necessitated strong founder effects in the establishment of the initial populations in the remote center of the Pacific Basin. As each island and volcano has successively appeared, founder events involving forms from nearby islands have apparently repeatedly occurred. Accordingly, the major pattern of evolution on the islands has been allopatric speciation with a strong stochastic element provided by the inbreeding and genetic revolutions associated with these repeated founder effects.

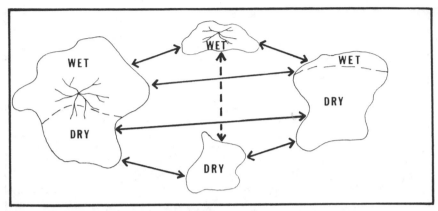

Figure 4.28. Possible types of exchange with at least seven possible combinations between four islands involving high and low, wet and dry, and large and small islands or areas; actual island examples are far more complex.

Many similar but less well documented cases of radiation appear in the classic works by Zimmerman (1948) and Carlquist (1965, 1974).

In numerous discussions of the founder effect, the argument has often (wrongly, I believe), centered around the "chance" that a single founding propagule, with no subsequent invasion, will become the ancestral stock of the island species. This single founding may possibly, but rarely, have occurred. Organisms crossing barriers may do so with varying frequency and may do so in low numbers or at infrequent intervals, perhaps once in twenty to fifty years. If they do establish in a new habitat or island, then several selective pressures can immediately influence the new population. Many factors, both physical and biological, may differ from the mainland (or large area) to an island (or small area). The climate is often different, the species composition of the biota will differ, and predators attacking the invader may be lacking or different. These and other selective pressures can rapidly change a small gene pool. Diet and behavior also may rapidly change as new niches are exploited. As the island (or area) population increases, the occasional immigrant from the mainland stock will not greatly influence the overall genetic change. Hybrids between the mainland ancestral stock and the new population become increasingly less fit until hybridization no longer occurs. In this example both allopatric and sympatric speciation are mixed. If numbers of immigrants are reduced by changes in wind patterns, etc., vicariance can then be included, but dispersal abilities, chance, and geographical or climatic change are all interwoven as parts of the evolutionary picture.

Actually, I believe that the archipelago effect (interisland dispersal and radiation) may have been more important in the past than at present if one considers past continental events and not merely present oceanic islands. During the Cretaceous, angiosperm plants, their associated winged insects, and some groups of vertebrates were rapidly evolving, and many of them radiated extensively within areas that now are continents. At that time many areas—northern Africa, much of western Europe and South America, and a large part of both North America and Australia—were under shallow epicontinental seas. Pre-Tertiary Australia, for example, was close to or contiguous with Antarctica (figure 4.29), but the continent was only partly exposed. It is interesting to note that, for at least some groups, the emergent areas of that time apparently acted both as an archipelago and as centers of radiation for at least some groups that today show a high degree of generic or tribal endemism within Australia. Key (1976) has discussed this for morabine Orthoptera, and a similar pattern of evolutionary diversification has been suggested for the scarab beetles in the subfamily Geotrupinae (Howden 1980). Similarly, the great diversity of insect genera and species groups endemic in South America may well be partly explained by an archipelago

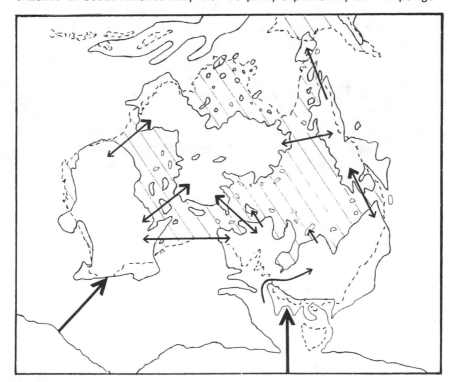

Figure 4.29. Cretaceous Australia, illustrating a possible archipelago effect. Epicontinental seas are lined.

type of differentiation. In the mid-Tertiary the uplifting Andean chain (James 1973) presented a situation paralleling today's Hawaiian Islands. This was followed by a large flooded inland area that now forms the Amazon Basin and a concurrent directional reversal of the Amazon itself. Both the flooding and the Amazon reversal produced a rapidly changing archipelago that, because of changing island sizes and distances, is analogous to that which has allowed the Hawaiian drosophilids to speciate. These Tertiary geological events in South America are briefly and succinctly summarized by Haffer (1974).

Despite my present emphasis on dispersal, I believe that it is only one of many factors. Before the Cretaceous, continental drift may have been of prime importance, but seemingly it has had little effect on the Recent biota. Both changes in land size and dispersal may have been considerably important at the time of epicontinental seas, but are perhaps less important today. Vicariance, development and invasion of new niches, competition, climatic changes, and other factors mentioned by Erwin also are important, but differ in their impact according to time and place. We can perhaps deduce one or two major factors causing allopatric speciation in a particular group at a particular time, but I do not believe there is any single simplistic answer that will explain all distributions and radiations for all of the Recent biota.

In conclusion, it would appear that the interplay of many events has influenced the development of the Recent biota. Trying to explain current diversity by utilizing only a few events such as continental drift and climatic change, despite evidence that other factors are involved, reminds me of a cartoon caption by Sidney Harris from the *American Scientist* (March-April 1979:193), which states that, "Putting a box around it, I'm afraid, does not make it a unified theory."

Acknowledgments

The comments and suggestions made by G. Carmody, J. A. Downes, E. G. Munroe, S. B. Peck, and my wife, Anne, were of considerable help to me in the preparation of this paper. I am extremely grateful for their assistance.

Response

T. L. Erwin

HOWDEN AND KOOPMAN implicitly included in their use of the term "dispersal" both movement of propagules or individuals and development of allopatry and speciation events. Vicariance biogeographers simply give different terms to these processes: "dispersal" is the movement or attainment of cosmopolitanism; "vicariant events" create allopatry; and "speciation event" is self-explanatory. When dispersalists become explicit (or vicariance biogeographers go back to being implicit dispersalists), the matter will clarify itself. With regard to Howden's comments, I reiterate that, of course, dispersal and, perhaps, "foundering" do occur, the former with great regularity. It is the "vicariant event," however, that stops dispersal and allows a breakdown in the exchange of genetic information; it is vicariance, not dispersal per se, that allows allopatric speciation to proceed.

Methodological arguments that Koopman outlines (points 1–5) can be made within schools of thought as well as among them. I do not see that these points represent "basic principles" of neo-vicariance thought any more than the concept of fixed continents represents neo-dispersalist thought (perhaps early Croizatian biogeography made use of these kinds of ideas). I do not believe that "dispersal" is unidirectional, as Howden interprets my remarks; it is the taxon pulse that appears never to reverse itself. Dispersals are made by individuals of a single taxon (species). These dispersants do not become new species or new adaptive plateaus upon arrival. A taxon pulse is the result of several processes that lead to new adaptive lineages moving away from a "center" of radiation in both time and space. "Center" is symbolic for a generalized organism at a certain place in a certain adaptive zone. Pulses are dynamic in time and space and include dispersal, speciation, adaptive radiation, and extinction. Pulses are revealed by patterns of concordance among cladograms based on structural analyses, geographical analyses, and habitat sequences. Further congruence among various taxonomic groups indicates pathways of evolution.

5

Land-Snail Biogeography: A True Snail's Pace of Change

A. Solem

REGARDLESS OF WHAT model or theory is used to interpret the distribution patterns shown by a group, or groups, of extant organisms, data from the past in the form of classifiable fossils and the evidence that they provide will be more relevant to their distributional history than will theoretical or ideological interpretations. Basic to this argument is whether fossils of a particular group can be assigned accurately to extant taxa.

This review attempts to place the radiation of land snails within an ecological context; to assess their fossil record in terms of adequacy of taxa assignability and then with regard to geographical evidence; to evaluate briefly the question whether or not one can identify generalized tracks as Croizat uses the term; and finally to examine in somewhat greater detail evidence and patterns relating to the biogeography of Pacific-island land snails.

Extant Diversity

A conservative estimate of Recent species diversity among land snails (Solem 1978b) indicates that there are approximately 25,000 species, the vast majority of which (20,500 species) belong to the higher pulmonates, superorder Stylommatophora. Most of the rest are scattered between two prosobranch orders, with less than 250 species represented by the super-orders Systellommatophora and Basommatophora.

Land snails are not a monophyletic assemblage. The seven recognized orders represent a minimum of 11 separate colonizations of the land. A recent review of land-Mollusca classification (Solem 1978b) lists 72 families of extant land mollusks and discusses the structural evidence used to derive this classification. While many questions of inter-familial relationships remain unsettled, most families are coherent units that are well characterized and that are readily identifiable on the bases both of shell (conchological) and anatomical (malacological) structures. This relatively felicitous state of knowledge has been arrived at in three stages. During the first century of the post-Linnaean era, classifications were based almost exclusively on the gross structure of the shell. During the last 120 years, far more emphasis has been placed on interpreting relationships by analysis of the soft parts. In the last two decades, biochemical data and the use of instruments such as the scanning electron microscope have permitted integrating data from the micro-structure and growth patterns of the molluscan shell much more effectively with data derived from gross dissection or histological studies of soft parts.

It must be emphasized that the basic inventory of land-snail diversity is far from complete. With the possible exception of western Europe, nowhere in the world can we draw accurate maps of the distributions of species and genera. Range extensions of hundreds or thousands of miles, depending on the area studied, are common. In many groups, discovery of new genera and species occurs with boring regularity. Nevertheless, we can prepare a basic outline of land-snail distributions.

Assignability of Fossils

Compared with vertebrates and arthropods, for example, land snails have one tremendous advantage for study. Shell growth occurs by a series of additions to the outside perimeter. Thus the adult shell contains a complete record of shell growth from the initial section formed within the egg capsule to the cessation of additive growth that occurs usually at sexual maturity. Most land-snail families can be shown to have highly characteristic, if not totally exclusive, characters and combinations of a dozen non-correlated characters such as the number and structure of shell layers, how they are bonded together, variations in the way that new growth is bonded to the previous whorls, how surface sculpture forms, whether internal partitions are resorbed or remain intact as growth proceeds, the ontogenetic time of appearance, pattern, and microstructure of apertural barriers, the way in which terminal growth proceeds as adulthood is reached (if growth does indeed terminate), basic shape patterns of growth, and the formation plus distribution of color patterns. If an extant family shows an exclusive set of these non-correlated characters relating to structure and growth (some land-snail fossils completely agree with this set of characters), then inclusion of the fossils within the extant family is by far the most parsimonious decision.

With very few exceptions, land-snail fossils can be assigned to extant families with an extremely high degree of confidence. No land-snail fossils known to me show characters intermediate between families. Only a few taxa remain problematic. Uncertainty about their position is partly based on lack of contemporary study and analysis; only rarely do land-snail fossils lack adequate structural features to permit classification. The Filholiidae, known from the Eocene to Oligocene of Europe, seem to have all the basic features of the Clausiliidae; and maintaining them as separate families can be questioned. The Anadromidae, which range from the Lower Cretaceous to Eocene of Europe, probably are a polyphyletic assemblage that requires restudy and analysis. The Grangerellidae, from the Paleocene and Eocene of western North America, may prove an early experiment by the extant family Bulimulidae, but assignment of this family to synonymy is premature.

While continuing the emphasis on use of soft-part data to work out land-snail higher taxa, work of the last 15 years has demonstrated that considerable information exists in shell microstructure and growth patterns; hence the fossil record can be effectively integrated with extant taxa for purposes of both classification and biogeography. Elsewhere (Solem 1979a, 1979b) I have presented preliminary analyses of land-snail distributions through time, starting with the new classification presented in a review of Paleozoic land snails (Solem and Yochelson 1979). Much of the following discussion is summarized or paraphrased from the above reports.

Origins and Early Diversification

The first appearance of land snails in the fossil record is in the Cumberland Group of strata in Labrador and Nova Scotia. There is a coherent fauna of three orders and five families of land snails. Because the extant orders of land snails number only seven—and one of them, the Soleolifera, contains shell-less slugs for which no fossil record could be expected or exists—the sudden appearance of half the ordinal groups is amazing. This record is equivalent to the Westphalian B or Upper Carboniferous in Europe and the Atoka Series of the Pennsylvanian in North America. This record continues through the Dunkard Group of the Lower Permian. Geographically, this fauna ranges from Illinois through western Europe slightly east of Vienna. The orders represented in the Upper Carboniferous and Permian do not have an ancestor-descendant relationship with subsequently appearing orders, and speculations on their phylogenetic affinities are outside the purview of this symposium. This early record does suggest that the basic diversity was established by the Permian.

Solem and Yochelson (1979) have speculated about what factors might have triggered the obviously successful permanent colonization of the land by snails. Information provided by several paleobotanists, particularly T. Phillips (1976), suggests a plausible hypothesis. At least in the northern hemisphere, three floristic trends in combination produced what we consider favorable conditions for the permanent colonization of the land by snails. These changes are: (1) increase in arborescent growth at the expense of herbaceous types; (2) development of lamellar foliage types in several lineages; and (3) development of a "coniferous pattern" whereby leaves are shed continuously, rather than seasonally. All three of these floristic trends gradually become more common throughout the Visean.

The culmination of these trends had major effects on the litter and its fauna. Broadening of leaves on more highly elevated trees provided increased shade and resulted in significant retardation of dessication by preventing exposure to direct sunlight. Added to this was an increase of moisture in the shaded air by leaf transpiration. Continuous leaf shedding added a regular source of raw food material to the litter, and maintained permanent shade cover. Shaded, moist, aseasonal litter provided ideal conditions for land-snail colonization and survival. These beasts have been labeled "hypochondriacs perpetually conscious of environmental conditions, especially moisture" (Rees 1964:56). The initial snail colonization of the land may well have been made possible by the floristic trends outlined above. Subsequent snail history on land can perhaps best be summarized as swings between diversification at times and places where year-round moisture conditions were favorable, and by experiments with techniques for surviving periods of temporary-to-seasonal absence of moisture.

Apparently both the Gondwana and Cathaysean floras remained deciduous rather than coniferous in their leaf shedding until a considerably later period. The much later appearance of land snails in the fossil record from Gondwanian areas (Paleocene of both Patagonia and southwestern Africa) might be a real event rather than an imperfection in the fossil record. At the time of their initial entry into the fossil record, half of the land-snail orders for which fossils could be expected are present. As summarized by Solem and Yochelson (1979) and briefly reviewed by Solem (1979b), those families represented in the Pennsylvanian and Permian are not morphologically primitive. In some cases—for example, the Discidae—they represent derived groups for which potential ancestral families are still extant. While we thus know virtually nothing about the initial radiation of land snails, it is possible to present some data concerning their distributional changes through time.

Land-Snail Fossil Record

The known record of land-snail fossils is spotty in both temporal and spatial contexts. Paleozoic records are limited to eastern North America and western Europe. The presence in both regions of two genera, the achatinellid *Anthracopupa* and the enid *Dendropupa*, is an obvious result of these areas being a unified land mass at that time. The next appearance of land snails in the fossil record is not until the Jurassic of western Europe, so far as current published data document. The Cretaceous of western Europe and of the present-day Rocky Mountain region of western North America has a relatively abundant record. Only in the Paleocene of southwestern Africa and Patagonia does southern-hemisphere representation appear. An abundant European and western North American Paleocene-to-Pleistocene record exists, but from most of Africa, all of Australia, and many portions of Asia, the fossil record is absent or insignificant. Major summaries of land-snail fossils are few, and the reports on South America by Parodiz (1969) and on North America by Henderson (1935) are major summary works. Very recently, the description of Cretaceous and early Tertiary material from southern China by Yü (1977) has added major records that remain to be integrated into the overall picture.

Within the above limitations of time and space, it obviously is not possible to present a coherent picture of past distributions on a world-wide basis.

The record is simply too fragmentary both geographically and temporally. It is possible, however, to draw several distributional conclusions.

Geographical Stability

As summarized by Solem (1979b), few land-snail taxa even begin to approach a world-wide distribution once the many effects of obvious human introductions are deleted. Only the Pupillacea and the Succineidae appear to have endemic representatives on all major continents (excluding Antarctica). The Pupillacea are terrestrial to arboreal in habitat, generally less than 4 mm in length and 2 mm in breadth. They frequently attach themselves to the underside of leaves on plants or hide in curled edges of dead leaves on the ground. They are thus "pre-adapted" for rare chance dispersal by wind. The Succineidae, in contrast, have many taxa restricted to marsh or swampy areas and to wet zones in tropical forests. They have extremely viscous mucous and account for more than 95 percent of the recorded instances of snails found on the feathers or feet of birds. Their adaptation for what apparently is routine dispersal on "feathered chariots" provides an obvious mechanism accounting for their nearly worldwide distribution. The fact that some members of the Succineidae inhabit semi-arid areas and estivate while sealed to the bark of trees (succineids from central and western Australia) is a minor exception to the general picture for the family. The only other group of land snails which has been documented more than once to occur on bird feathers or feet is the Vitrininae, which show a variety of intriguing mountain-island or oceanic-island distributional anomalies.

For most other families of land snails, the recent distribution encompasses: (1) a portion of one continent; (2) adjacent areas on two continents that are not in close proximity; (3) two noticeably disjunct areas; or (4) three noticeably disjunct areas. Of the 72 land-snail families listed by Solem (1978b, 1979b), 55.5 percent of the families have a one- or two-area continuous distribution; 20.8 percent have a two-area disjunct distribution; 15.3 percent have a three-area disjunct distribution; 2.8 percent have an indeterminate or intermediate pattern; and 2.8 percent have an essentially world-wide distribution. The remaining 2.8 percent of the families have a distribution, based on only a very few species, that defies rational classification into these categories. It is clear that contemporary land-snail family distributions are generally relatively restricted in area.

Data on the time of appearance in the fossil record for land-snail families have been summarized by Solem (1979b:tables 2–3). There are two "bulges," with 30 families (41.7%) appearing in the Cretaceous through Eocene and 27 (37.5%) for which there is either no fossil record or only a Pleistocene occurrence. There are 37 families (51.4%) that have a Paleozoic-to-Eocene time of appearance. For these relatively old families the question of continuous versus disjunct distributions is a stand-off: of the 40 families with single-area distribution, 53.8 percent appeared in or before the Eocene; of the 28 families with noticeably disjunct distributions, 51.9 percent appeared in or before the Eocene.

Of more direct interest to this symposium is the question about what changes can be detected through time. It must be emphasized that knowing the point and time of first appearance in the fossil record tells us nothing concerning the actual time and point of origin. Establishing a single distributional point for a family during the late Paleozoic tells us nothing about its possible distribution elsewhere in the world. One can, however, quite easily ask the simple question: How does the point of first appearance in the fossil record relate to the present distribution of the family unit? Does it: (1) lie within the present distribution? (2) lie several hundred miles outside the present distributional limits? or (3) lie several thousand miles outside the present distributional limits? Of the 37 land-snail families with an Eocene-or-older fossil record, 26 (70.3%) have their initial point of appearance within the current geographical range; four (10.8%) have shifted their range a few hundred miles; and seven (18.9%) show a major change in distributional limits. Of the eight families with an Oligocene-to-Pliocene appearance, only two show a change in distribution. Both the Endodontidae and Charopidae were present in the Marshall Islands during the Miocene (figure 5.5), but have become extinct as the former moist high islands became relatively dry atolls. Compared with that of almost any other group of organisms, this is an extraordinary degree of stability in space through time, encompassing up to 300 million years.

Changes in Family Distributions

As in contemporary systematic analysis, more useful biogeographical information comes from changing patterns than from stabilized situations. The Enidae were present in the Paleozoic of North America at the time it was

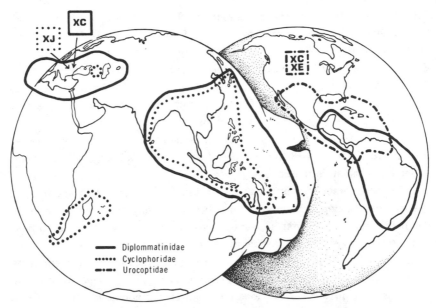

Figure 5.1. Recent distribution of the Diplommatinidae, Cyclophoridae, and Urocoptidae. Fossil records indicated by an X, followed by a symbol indicating either earliest age or range in time: J, Jurassic; C, Cretaceous; Pa, Paleocene; E, Eocene; O, Oligocene; M, Miocene; Pl, Pliocene.

connected to Europe, but subsequently there has been no New World record of this family. Today the Enidae are well represented in the Mediterranean region, with their main diversity in the area from the Near East and Africa to China and Japan. There is a very modest representation in the New Hebrides and New Caledonia (subfamily Draparnaudiinae), and a weak occurrence in Indonesia and northern Australia (*Amimopina*, Solem 1964). The Urocoptidae (figure 5.1) are recorded from the late Cretaceous of Alberta and the Eocene of Wyoming (Tozer 1956), but today their center of diversity lies in Central America and the West Indies, plus a fringe occurrence on the northern borders of South America. One genus, *Holospira*, extends as far north as central Texas and southern Arizona. The Urocoptidae thus represent a minor but distinct southern shift in distribution since the Cretaceous.

Members of the carnivorous family Streptaxidae (figure 5.2) were common in the late Cretaceous of Europe and have been recorded from the Miocene of both Kenya and Brazil. They disappeared from Europe sometime in the Pliocene, with only a single relict (*Gibbulinella*) still persisting on the Canary Islands. Van Bruggen (1967:184, figure 7) summarized the Recent distribution with its three-area pattern of disjunction and indicated the relative levels of diversity in each region. The main centers of diversity are in tropical Africa plus the wetter parts of southern Africa (Van Bruggen 1978), then southeastern Asia through Borneo and the Philippines. A smaller radiation took place in tropical South America. The Streptaxidae thus show a clear contraction of range during the late Tertiary with their extinction in western Europe.

The answer to the question about whether the Bulimulidae (figure 5.2) have an altered or stable distribution depends on how several fossils eventually are classified. Two species described from the Eocene at Fort Union, North Dakota (*Pseudocolumna teres* and *P. vermicula*) have long been controversial. Henderson (1935:153–54) placed them in the Achatinidae, but examination of the type specimens (Solem unpublished), shows that their structures are entirely consistent with their being elongated members of the Bulimulidae. Fossils from the Paleocene or Cretaceous of Alberta also have been assigned to this genus. The question of where to classify members of the Grangerellidae from the same general region and time span also is undecided at present. I suspect that both will prove to be Bulimulidae or most closely related to this family. Because the Bulimulidae frequently have been viewed as a family showing classic Gondwanaland distributions, the assign-

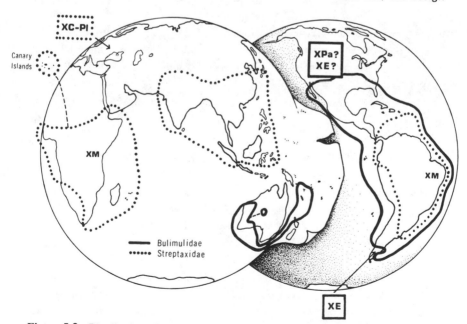

Figure 5.2. Distribution of the Bulimulidae and Streptaxidae. For explanation of symbols, see figure 5.1.

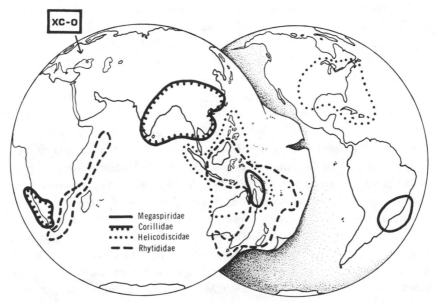

Figure 5.3. Distribution of the Megaspiridae, Corillidae, Helicodiscidae, and Rhytididae. For explanation of symbols, see figure 5.1.

ment of early Tertiary North American fossils to this family greatly changes its perspective history. With the omission of the above controversial and uncertain records, the earliest confirmed record for the Bulimulidae is of an extant genus (*Thaumastus*) in the Eocene of Patagonia (Parodiz 1969:179–81).

The several families that show a major alteration in distribution have dissimilar patterns. The Achatinellidae were modestly diverse in the late Paleozoic of North America and Europe, and they are known subsequently by a single fossil from the Cretaceous of Wyoming. Today the Achatinellidae are abundant in Hawaii, Rapa, and Juan Fernandez, with modest diversity on various Polynesian and Micronesian islands, plus a number of probable human introductions into areas around the fringes of the Pacific. The time gap between the North American records and the current limited Pacific Basin distribution is so great that speculation on their intermediate travels is impossible.

The Megaspiridae (figure 5.3) are known as fossils in Europe, ranging in age from the Cretaceous to Oligocene. In the Recent fauna they are relicts in Brazil, New Guinea, and Queensland, Australia. The Camaenidae (figure 5.4), which today have a disjunct two-area basically tropical distribution, are known definitely from the Cretaceous to Eocene of North America (Solem

1978a). Quite probably some of the fossils that Yü (1977) described from southern China will prove to be camaenids when analyzed in detail. In the New World the northern distributional limits are Costa Rica and Cuba, although Miocene fossils are reported from Florida. Thus there has been a distinct southern contraction in New World distribution since the Cretaceous.

The Strobilopsidae (figure 5.5) were abundant in Europe from the Eocene to Pliocene. Their Recent distribution is in parts of North and Central America, plus the fringes of eastern Asia, including a peculiar genus, *Enteroplax*, which has a Philippines and coastal-island-off-New-Guinea range. Possibly the Spelaeodiscinae from Yugoslavia are a modern remnant, but their position is still controversial.

The probably interrelated families Diplommatinidae, Pupinidae, and Cyclophoridae agree in having Cretaceous-to-Miocene European fossils that have been compared directly to extant taxa now living in southeastern Asia and Indonesia. The current distributions of two families in this complex are compared in figure 5.1. The Cyclophoridae have a relict group near the Caspian Sea, but then have a Malagasy and fringe-of-southern-Africa distribution, plus a typical Southeast Asia-to-the-Solomon Islands and Queensland range. A subfamily of the Diplommatinidae has a moderately wide Europe-to-Near-East range. The nominate subfamily parallels the south-

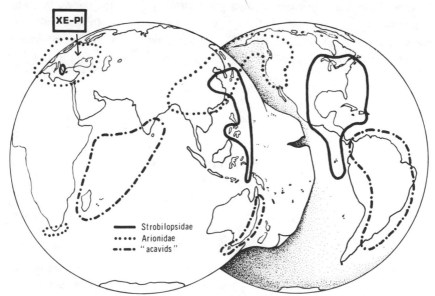

Figure 5.4. Distribution of Strobilopsidae, Arionidae, and "acavids." For explanation of symbols, see figure 5.1.

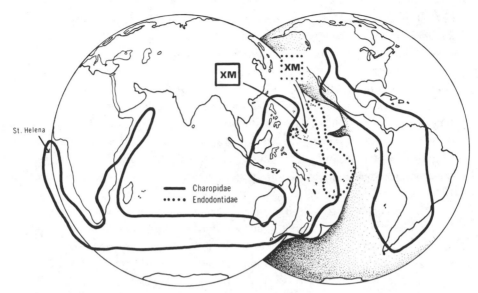

Figure 5.5. Distribution of the Charopidae and Endodontidae. For explanation of symbols, see figure 5.1.

eastern Asian range of the Cyclophoridae but extends further into the Pacific, and then recurs as a marginal group in parts of Central and South America. Despite the contemporaneity of these two families in Europe during the late Mesozoic, their present ranges have noticeable differences. No other families show significant changes in their distributions, so far as the fossil record indicates.

Changes in Faunas

There are only two areas for which the fossil land-snail record is significant enough so that we can draw meaningful conclusions about the changes in entire faunas. For both western Europe and the Rocky Mountain area of North America, there are significant Jurassic or Cretaceous-through-early-Tertiary fossil records.

The patterns for the two areas are quite different. The Rocky Mountain area shows an almost incredible degree of stability, with families such as the Oreohelicidae, Polygyridae, and Ammonitellidae in residence since the Cretaceous or Paleocene and still, at least in part, basically restricted to that region. The documented southern shift of range for the Urocoptidae and the deletion of probable Bulimulidae, such as *Pseudocolumna*, and the Grangerellidae are the only detectable changes on the family level. This contrasts greatly with western Europe, which has lost families such as the Diplommatinidae, Cyclophoridae, Pupinidae, Helicinidae (Paleocene *Dimorphoptychia*), Streptaxidae, and Strobilopsidae. Figures 5.1 through 5.7 show that for most of these families there is a distance of several thousand miles from western Europe to the nearest Recent distributional limit. The above is only a very gross outline, but pending publication of detailed European distributional maps and a modern review of late Mesozoic and early Tertiary European fossils, only the broadest outlines of such change can be documented.

Elsewhere in the world, the recorded Paleocene and Eocene land-snail fossils either occupy precisely the same area today (southwestern Africa) or Pleistocene glaciations have moved the fauna very slightly north (Patagonia). In the Pacific Basin, members of both the Charopidae and Endodontidae were present in the Marshall Islands during the Miocene, and endodontids are known as fossils from Midway Atoll. Today, members of neither family live in these areas. Otherwise the fossil record of land snails indicates distributional stability.

From this discussion, one conclusion is inescapable: land-snail families,

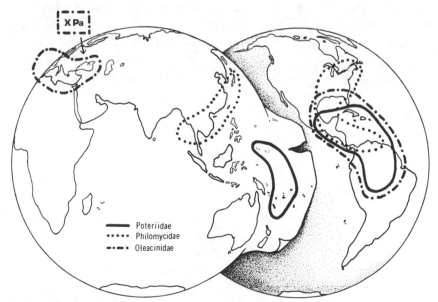

Figure 5.6. Distribution of the Poteriidae, Philomycidae, and Oleacinidae. For explanation of symbols, see figure 5.1.

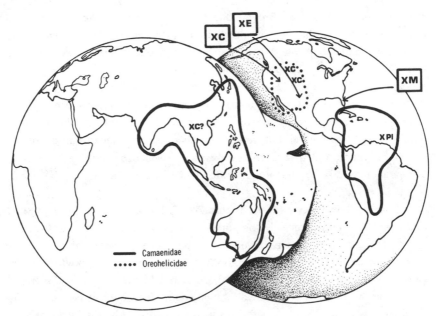

Figure 5.7. Distribution of the Camaenidae and Oreohelicidae. For explanation of symbols, see figure 5.1.

in general, show an extraordinary degree of geographical stability over a very long period of time. Only a small portion of the known families can be documented to have changed radically in distribution. This does not mean that many families cannot live successfully in most parts of the world. The number of human introductions is almost staggering, and the failure to recognize this fact makes the analysis of land-snail distributions by Te (1976) of little use. In most areas of the world, land snails of introduced status are flourishing. On the Pacific islands, for example, land snails belonging to the Arionidae, Limacidae, Philomycidae, Subulinidae, Achatinidae, Streptaxidae, Valloniidae, Veronicellidae, Oleacinidae, Bradybaenidae, and Helicidae are flourishing as a result of introduction by man, although in pre-human times they never reached Polynesia or Micronesia.

The fact that they did not reach many areas of the world in BHT (Before Human Transport) times, indicates that a low degree of dispersibility exists for many taxa, particularly because land snails are an ancient group. The geological events that determined their basic distributional patterns far antedate the appearance of extant terrestrial vertebrate families. Corroborative evidence from the distribution of other groups will have to be sought among taxa such as the primitive vascular plants and land arthropods, rather than among vertebrates.

It seems evident also that land snails were basically unaffected by the massive floristic revolution in the late Mesozoic. Snails remained in the litter, quietly chomping away on dead plant fragments, ignoring the basic change in litter source from the fern and conifer forests of the past to the angiosperm-dominated floras of today. Bakker's recent (1978) interesting suggestion that the rise to dominance of flowering plants can be correlated with changes in dinosaur feeding behavior, would have had little effect on land-snail survival; and the subsequent rise of mammals probably was equally unnoticed by the snails.

Congruence of Distributions

The extent to which distributions are repetitive is basic to any vicariance biogeography analysis. Figures 5.1 through 5.7, based partly upon a majority of the land-snail taxa that show disjunct distributions and that have an Eocene or older fossil record, indicate that these older taxa show essentially no common distributional tracks. For example, although the Diplommatinidae and Cyclophoridae occurred in Europe during the late Mesozoic, the former has a Pacific and South American modern distribution, while the latter has a Pacific and Malagasy plus fringe-of-southern-Africa range (figure 5.1). Figure 5.7 shows three unrelated families that have similar New World distributions, but completely different Old World patterns. The nearest to a common element that can be recognized (this is basically a negative statement) is the tendency for disjunct taxa that were well represented in the northern hemisphere during the late Cretaceous and early Tertiary to show a distinctly more southern distribution at the present time.

There are only two areas, the Euro-Mediterranean and India-to-New-Guinea regions, in which multiple overlapping distributional tracks can be recognized. For no other area of the world can I at this time indicate any significant degree of distributional congruence for land-snail families. I consider it highly likely that, once adequate modern distributional range maps have been prepared for Euro-Mediterranean genera and species, it will be possible to recognize some common patterns in this region. The data necessary for such recognition do not yet exist in a readily available form, although various

European mapping projects can be expected eventually to produce equivalents to Kerney (1976).

With regard to the Pacific Basin and an update of data summarized by Solem (1959), there is the common repetitive track of taxa extending from southeastern Asia for varying distances into the Pacific Basin. Eight such family level units are summarized in figure 5.8. Several more such as the Trochomorphinae, Helicarioninae, Enidae, and Camaenidae could have been included, but the map lines are confusing enough. Their inclusion merely would have confirmed the basic pattern. A more sophisticated analysis of this phenomenon is given by Van Balgooy (1971:138–39) showing the attenuation of Paleo-Oriental elements in Pacific island vascular plants. This shift is classic for many groups as summarized by Thorne (1963:314), and was recognized as early as 1825 (Hedley 1899:397–98).

The existence of this attenuated land-snail distribution pattern presents two interesting conclusions, one of which I belabored earlier (Solem 1959): Wallace's and Weber's lines have as little relevance to land-snail as to vascular-plant distributions. Second, given the now generally accepted sequence of plate-tectonic events that "Not until mid-Miocene, was the migration of Asian plants and animals into Australasia relatively direct" (Raven and Axelrod 1974:543) because of northward drift by Australia, we

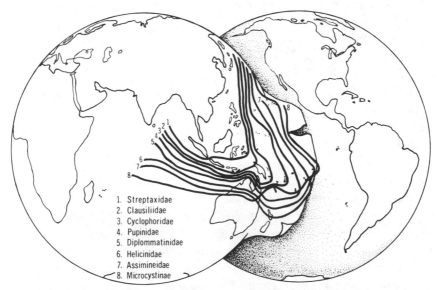

1. Streptaxidae
2. Clausiliidae
3. Cyclophoridae
4. Pupinidae
5. Diplommatinidae
6. Helicinidae
7. Assimineidae
8. Microcystinae

Figure 5.8. Distributions of Paleo-Oriental taxa into the Pacific Basin from southeastern Asia. Family units: 1, Streptaxidae; 2, Clausiliidae; 3, Cyclophoridae; 4, Pupinidae; 5, Diplommatinidae; 6, Helicinidae; 7, Assimineidae; 8, Microcystinae.

are faced with a seeming contradiction. A group of organisms with a history of great distributional stability, has, since the Miocene, undergone a major pattern of dispersion from southeastern Asia into the wetter parts of tropical Australia and onto even many remote Pacific Islands.

Is There a Gondwanaland Snail Fauna?

In my early review of Pacific Basin land-snail distribution (Solem 1959:296) I grouped several taxa and stated: "This distinctive assemblage may be called the Southern Relict fauna. The chosen name deliberately implies South African and South American associations, although a 'world wide snail geography' cannot be presented at this time." Subsequent work on the Endodontidae (Solem 1976) and Charopidae (Solem 1979c) has greatly altered part of this concept. With the exception of fossils representing the Dorcasiidae in the Paleocene in southwestern Africa and the related Strophocheilidae from the Paleocene of South America (Parodiz 1969), none of the few families that show a typical "Gondwana distribution" has an old fossil record.

Three families whose modern distribution might be interpreted as classically Gondwanian are the Bulimulidae (figure 5.2), Rhytididae (figure 5.3), and "acavids" (figure 5.5). To them might be added the Charopidae (figure 5.6), although their apparent absence from the Malagasy region and India[1] mitigate against this probability.

The suggestion was made earlier that North American Paleocene-to-Eocene fossils may be bulimulids. There is also the fact that their present distributions in Australia and Melanesia are not suggestive of a southern-continent distribution (figure 5.2). Data on the anatomical specializations in the Pacific bulimulids were summarized by Solem (1969:242, figure 7). New Hebridean and southwestern Australian taxa are the most generalized with those from New Zealand, Lord Howe, and other New Hebridean species showing a second level of specialization. New Caledonian species of *Placostylus* are more advanced in structure, with those from Fiji and the Solomon Islands presenting the greatest degree of morphological change.

[1] There are a few taxa from India—*Ruthvenia* Gude, *Glyptaulax* Gude, and *Thysanota* Albers—that may be charopids, discids, or even an aberrant helicarionid stock. Published anatomical data is inadequate to classify them and no detailed study of their shell structure has been made.

Unfortunately, it still is not possible, because of inadequate work on South American taxa, to relate these degrees of specialization to those that occur in Neotropica. Until this is accomplished, any attempt to discuss the phylogeny of the Bulimulidae will be impossible. Nevertheless, the possibility that this family is of northern-hemisphere origin and now relict in the southern hemisphere cannot be dismissed.

Patterns of relationships within the Rhytididae (figure 5.3) also remain uncertain. Although many anatomical data for the southern African taxa have been presented by Watson (1934), no equivalent review of the Australian and New Zealand taxa has appeared. The Rhytididae have a very limited representation in Indonesia and on the Seychelles. Until the phylogeny of this family has been interpreted, serious speculation on this rather remarkably disjunct distribution pattern must be deferred. It can be interpreted as a relict spread from the north, or a Gondwanian extension from the south. The absence of a significant fossil record for the Rhytididae correlates undoubtedly with the greatly reduced calcareous elements in their shell.

The one family of land snails for which a strong Gondwanian distributional interpretation can be made is the "acavids" (figure 5.5). This family includes several taxa that traditionally have been split among the Acavidae and Clavatoridae (Madagascar, Ceylon, South India), Caryodidae (eastern Australia), plus two South American genera (*Solaropsis* and *Macrocyclis*), whose positions long have been uncertain. I have been unable to obtain either Malagasy or Indian material for dissection, but the close affinity of the Australian and South American taxa is based on unpublished, detailed anatomical studies. They may well be an endemic Gondwanian radiation.

Data on the Charopidae are equivocal. Unusual facets—that a Pacific island genus (restricted to Tonga and Samoa) has its nearest relative on St. Helena, and that the charopid fauna of southwestern Australia comes nearest to bridging the morphological gap between the Pacific island endemic Endodontidae and the southern hemisphere Charopidae—hint at distributional and phyletic complexity. Detailed discussion of this must be deferred. With the one exception of the "acavids," there is no evidence for a strictly Gondwanian snail fauna. All of the taxa which show a Gondwanian distribution can be interpreted equally well as remnants from a Pangean fauna.

It has not been possible during preparation of this report adequately to review the literature from non-molluscan groups. I consider it significant, however, that the plant group Proteaceae, which Raven and Axelrod (1974:583–84) and Johnson and Briggs (1975) had interpreted as a Gondwanaland endemic radiation, has subsequently been reported by Jarzen and Norris (1975) from the Cretaceous of Alberta. The last two authors also report members of the Gunneraceae from the same formations. The general facies of the Alberta flora in the Cretaceous was tropical. The flora contains also a number of now-tropical southern-hemisphere plant taxa and thus presents similarities to the limited land-snail data. Given the length of time, with increasing destruction potential of the limited terrestrial fossil record, one can expect only occasional fragments of data to be found. The occurrence of plant and land-snail fossils suggesting that Gondwanian taxa might have northern origins is intriguing.

I am not claiming that there is no Gondwanian land-snail fauna. I am simply saying that presently available evidence is insufficient to decide in the few possible cases whether they are the result of regional diversification in Gondwana or are relicts from a northern pre- to mid-Mesozoic dispersal. Of 72 extant families, there are at most only four disjunct families (Bulimulidae, Rhytididae, Charopidae, "acavids") and four single-area families (Dorcasiidae, Strophocheilidae, Athoracophoridae, Aperidae) that have a primarily Gondwanian distribution.

Areas of High Endemic Diversity

An analysis of basic area diversity in extant land-snail families has been presented in Solem (1979b:240–244) and will not be repeated here. The above mentioned Euro-Mediterranean track with 12 restricted family units and the Indo-Malayan-Pacific track with 13 restricted family units show the highest levels, but the most intriguing aspect is the low restricted diversity on some continents: South America (two: Strophocheilidae and Systrophiidae), Australo-Zelandic area (one: Athoracophoridae), and North America (two or three: Ammonitellidae, Oreohelicidae, possibly Polygyridae). This contrasts with high diversity in island areas, such as the Pacific islands with four endemic families and one disjunct with the New World, and the West Indies as the center of diversity for six families (Poteriidae, Cerionidae, Sagdidae, Spiraxidae, Urocoptidae, Camaenidae), some of which extend abundantly to weakly into Central America and parts of South America. These data continue to emphasize the unusual facets of land-snail distributions that raise numerous questions of interpretation, and that range far beyond the limits of time and space of this symposium.

Pacific Island Endemic Families

An apparently unique aspect of land-snail distribution is the presence of family elements that are restricted to the high islands of the Pacific. While many plant and insect genera may show local endemism on the Pacific islands, I know of no other group of organisms with endemism at the family level. The land-snail families Endodontidae (Solem 1976), Partulidae (Kondo 1968, 1973), Achatinellidae (Cooke and Kondo 1960; Kondo 1962), and Amastridae (Pilsbry and Cooke 1915–16:1–65) are not known to occur elsewhere except for the diversification of the Achatinellidae on Juan Fernandez and the probably human introductions of small leaf dwelling achatinellids to the fringes of the Pacific. In addition, the land prosobranch family Poteriidae has a widely disjunct distribution (figure 5.7) based in large part on the islands of Micronesia, Samoa, Fiji, New Hebrides, and New Caledonia.

Except for the Achatinellidae, which first appeared in the Paleozoic of North America and Europe, and the Miocene record of the Endodontidae from the Marshall Islands, they have no fossil record. The Amastridae are restricted to the Hawaiian Islands, and the question as to whether they can be related to such extralimital taxa as the Cionellidae (Holarctic) or Ferussaciidae (Palearctic) remains as puzzling now as in the 1910s, when this question was last considered in print. I have speculated that the Partulidae may be related or ancestral to the Old World Enidae, but the question remains unsettled. The Achatinellidae have no known near relatives, and only the Endodontidae (Solem in press) can be related to another family with certainty. They are structurally more generalized than the Charopidae, and western Australian charopids are structurally partly intermediate between the two families. The Charopidae (Solem 1979c) are not restricted to the Pacific islands (figure 5.6), but form a significant faunal element in Polynesia and Micronesia. Similarly, the Helicarionidae and Zonitidae, monographed by Baker (1938–41), have many genera endemic in the Pacific, but they are not restricted to the Pacific Basin.

For all of those families, reasonably modern revisions exist for the Polynesian, Micronesian, and Fijian taxa, and they use the same modern data base (collections amassed by field surveys sent out from the Bernice P. Bishop Museum in the 1930s). The published data are not complete for Hawaii (Solem 1976, in press), simply because massive extant collections from there have not been analyzed. It is thus possible to consider questions of distribution, species abundance, colonizations, and diversity levels in several families from a reasonably good and fully comparable data base. Because the main purpose of this symposium is to evaluate dispersal vs. vicariance phenomena, these topics have immediate relevance.

Vagvolgyi (1976) has shown that the maximum size of land-snail species on Pacific islands is smaller than on neighboring continents, and then concluded that therefore the islands must have been colonized by aerial dispersal or rafting in quite recent times. This conclusion has been criticized by Platnick (1976) and Croizat (1978) on theoretical and logical grounds, with a brief response by Vagvolgyi (1978). Evidence in recent years from potassium-argon dating has shown that island-arc areas in the Pacific Basin may have histories of more than 60 million years (summarized in Solem in press: table 70), and other contributors to this symposium consider the tectonic history of this region in detail. Thus the time for snail colonization and subsequent survival that Vagvolgyi (1976) claimed was absent has been established by solid evidence. The existence of the Achatinellidae in the Paleozoic of North America and western Europe was demonstrated by Solem and Yochelson (1979). Both the Endodontidae and Charopidae are known from the Miocene in the Marshall Islands, with the fossil species referable to extant species groups (Solem 1976: 116–18, in press). Thus the age of at least three Pacific island family units as at least pre-Miocene is clearly established. The Achatinellidae are known from extralimital areas in the Paleozoic, but we have no way of knowing whether the other Pacific island families are relicts of formerly wider distributions or are limited area endemics.

Elsewhere (Solem 1973, in press), I have shown that land-snail species diversity levels do not follow the MacArthur-Wilson model: diversity is greater on small (5–15 mi^2) and high (over 1,200 ft) than on large (225 mi^2 plus) islands; for islands of equal size, those farthest from the Indo-Malayan core region have a higher diversity level; isolated high islands have higher diversity than less isolated islands; and extensive local speciation among land snails occurred on small islands such as Lord Howe (5 mi^2) and Rapa (14.9 mi^2). The relevance of these conclusions to this symposium rests with questions of size distributions and numbers of colonizations.

The Endodontidae and Charopidae are represented on the islands of Polynesia, Micronesia, and Fiji by, respectively, 190 and 87 species-level taxa, plus about 290 unnamed Hawaiian endodontids (Solem 1976, in press). For all of the named taxa, mean adult shell measurements are available, and a more detailed analysis of geographical variation in shell size is presented in Solem (in press). The median mean adult size, as indicated by shell diameter (the largest dimension), is 3.77 mm for the Endodontidae and 2.76 mm for the Charopidae. Figures 5.9 and 5.10 show the geographical distribution of

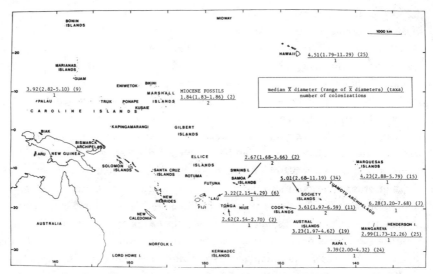

Figure 5.9. Geographical patterns of shell size and colonization frequency in the Endodontidae.

median mean sizes, range of median mean sizes, number of measured taxa, and minimum number of colonizations required to account for the known diversity in that island group. Because of their different distributions (figure 5.6) and the differences in mean sizes, the two families have been separately graphed.

The Endodontidae (figure 5.9) are restricted to the Pacific islands (figure 5.5), with 14 archipelagoes having enough taxa for this analysis. Only for Samoa, Cook Islands, and the fossils in the Marshall Islands is it necessary to assume more than one colonization to account for the level of diversity existing in the early 1900s. For the other 11 areas, single colonizations are sufficient. For all island groups except the Tuamotu Archipelago, species of less than 3 mm mean diameter were extant, and for seven groups the minimum mean diameter is 2.0 mm or less. There is a clear pattern of larger median size and larger maximum size occurring on the eastern and northern distributional fringes, while on the western and southern fringes the range and median size is significantly less than the family mean of 3.77 mm. Non-correlated anatomical structures and differences in shell growth patterns show that parallel changes in structures associated with large size have occurred. These are independent locally evolved parallel lineages rather than the result of multiple colonizations. The presence of small taxa on almost every archipelago is an indication of possible colonizer size, followed by evolution into larger size. The few multiple colonizations involve unrelated anatomical stocks now living in the same archipelago. I have suggested that the absence of Endodontidae from most of Micronesia, all of Melanesia, and the main islands of Fiji may be due to the presence of native ants, for biological peculiarities (egg laying site, restriction to ground litter) make the endodontid snails vulnerable to ant predation.

The Charopidae (figure 5.10) have a more western distribution that partly overlaps that of the Endodontidae. By coincidence, data on the Charopidae for 14 island areas have been assembled. The number of colonizations by charopids is much greater, reflecting in part their semiarboreal habitat and in part the fact that several subfamily units are present in the area of study. The median mean diameter of 2.77 mm is greatly exceeded on the outer Pacific fringes (Marianas, Samoa, Cook), where speciation was extensive on many islands, but essentially is equalled only on the Society Islands, where only part of the chain has been colonized. In contrast, on the islands nearer the New Guinea "core," the size of charopids is noticeably smaller than the average. Because these areas contain many snail taxa that could be considered competitors of the charopids, while the outer islands have fewer families represented, I hypothesize that lack of competition on the outer islands has permitted evolution to large size, but that the inner areas have not had equivalent vacant niches open for exploitation.

Analysis of the other endemic families (Partulidae, Achatinellidae, Amastridae), disjunct endemic families (Poteriidae), and intrusive families

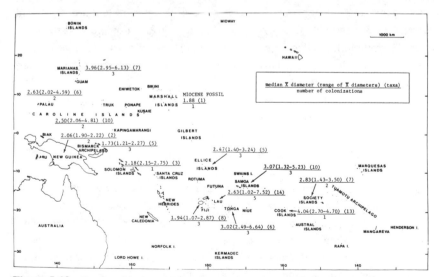

Figure 5.10. Geographical patterns of shell size and colonization frequency in Pacific island Charopidae.

(Helicarionidae, Zonitidae) gives similar patterns (Solem unpublished). Arboreal or semi-arboreal taxa show more colonizations than strictly terrestrial taxa, and there is a strong tendency in the Achatinellidae, Helicarionidae, and Zonitidae for evolution toward larger size in local areas. The latter two families, and the Charopidae, are intrusive into the Pacific, with colonization probably occurring, at the earliest, slightly before the Miocene. The Helicarionidae are derived from the wet tropics of Asia, the Zonitidae from the Holarctic (probably bird dispersal to Hawaii and Tahiti), the Charopidae probably from the New Zealand-Australian area. Their successful habitation of Pacific islands is most parsimoniously explained by hypothesizing rare overseas transport, most likely by cyclonic winds. With regard to these taxa, Vagvolgyi's concept of "relatively recent overseas dispersal" is probably correct.

The endemic Achatinellidae, Endodontidae, Poteriidae, Amastridae, and Partulidae, which show little evidence of multiple colonizations and are without extralimital ranges (except the Poteriidae), present a different problem. The first two families are known to be Miocene to Paleozoic in origin, so that a dual hypothesis of distributional mechanics seems necessary. They probably reached or evolved in the Pacific area during the Mesozoic, at a time when islands were greater in number and had narrower water gaps hindering dispersal. These families have been effectively isolated from competition with continental groups during the Tertiary by the increasingly wide water gaps as subsidence proceeded in several areas of the Pacific. They survived by exceedingly rare and accidental inter-island transport. In the case of the Endodontidae, which are restricted litter dwellers, the number of successful colonizations would have been essentially infinitesimal when viewed against the age of the Pacific arcs.

Conclusions

The land snails are an ancient, distributionally conservative, polyphyletic group. Wherever and whenever favorable moisture conditions and geographical pathways have permitted the opportunity for migration (as in Miocene-to-Recent times from southeastern Asia into the Pacific), migrations have occurred. Where effective major moisture barriers (water or desert) have prevailed, colonizations generally have not happened.

Land-snail families today show little indication of generalized tracks. Scattered bits of data from other Paleozoic-to-Mesozoic taxa will have to be pieced together before any clear picture of major pre-Tertiary distributional changes can be worked out. At present the use of cladistic analysis is not possible with regard to most land-snail taxa because revisionary and phyletic work to date has concentrated on regional rather than on world-wide projects. Land snails show evidence that pleases neither the dispersalist nor the vicariant biogeographer. Unaware of such controversies, the snails remain happily munching on litter, oblivious to changing fauna and flora. They worry about water and shelter, not about systematist or biogeographer.

As should be more than obvious by now, I view dispersal and vicariance biogeography as polar views of a continuum. The tenets of each pole will apply better to some groups than to others. Both are powerful tools of analysis, but neither is Truth.

Acknowledgments
For assistance and inspiration over many years in stimulating my interest in biogeography, I am deeply indebted to the late Karl P. Schmidt and Fritz Haas. Most of the data concerning the land-snail fossil record grew out of cooperative research with Ellis Yochelson on Paleozoic land snails, summarized in Solem and Yochelson (1979). The text figures were rendered by Marjorie M. Connors, using base maps prepared by Elizabeth A. Liebman, former illustrator, Division of Invertebrates, with support of NSF grant DEB 75-20113. Invaluable assistance in final manuscript preparation and typing was given by Valerie Connor-Jackson, Secretary, Division of Invertebrates. For all of the help I am deeply grateful.

Discussion

W. F. Smith-Vaniz

ALTHOUGH DR. SOLEM acknowledges the reality of plate tectonics and continental drift, his analysis of land-snail biogeography is permeated with the traditional concerns for centers of origin, dispersal mechanisms, and ecological considerations. Rosen (1974a) and Cracraft (1975a) have shown that the widely disjunct distributions of a large group of unrelated plants and animals with widely variable dispersal capabilities form generalized tracks that can be attributed to vicariant events associated with the orderly breakup of Pangea. Croizat et al. (1974) have emphasized that the significance of generalized tracks is that they estimate the distributions of ancestral biotas and, because of the different biological requirements and dispersal capabilities of individual species, the congruence of many individual tracts cannot be the result of chance dipersal. On a series of maps Solem outlines the distributions of most of the land-snail families occurring on two or more continents in an attempt to evaluate the question about whether or not generalized tracks in Croizat's sense could be identified. Unfortunately, these family tracks are of limited value in resolving this question because no attempt is made to distinguish the individual tracks of the component monophyletic snail taxa. The utility of the snail distribution maps could also be improved if the outlines of the major tectonic plates were indicated on the maps and if the precise localities of the individual taxa were indicated by dots, thus allowing a more accurate representation of the actual geographical range.

Solem's following observations concerning land-snail fossils and their dispersal attributes are especially noteworthy: (1) basic land-snail diversity was well established by the Permian (before the initial fragmentation of Pangea) and those families represented in the Pennsylvanian and Permian are not morphologically primitive; (2) compared with almost any other group of organisms, land snails exhibit an extraordinary degree of stability in time and space; (3) contemporary land-snail family distributions are generally relatively restricted in area; and (4) in most areas of the world land snails of introduced status are flourishing, including on Pacific islands 11 established families that in prehuman times never reached Polynesia or Micronesia.

How can these statements be reconciled with the seeming contradiction that nearly half of the 72 land-snail families have disjunct distributions, including 15.3 percent that exhibit three-area disjunctions and 2.8 percent that have an essentially world-wide distribution? One possible explanation for such distributions is vicariance of an ancestral land-snail fauna at the time of continental disruptions. The general antiquity of land snails is compatible with such a hypothesis, and no dispersal mechanisms are required. Cracraft (1975a) documented the concordance of vertebrate and floristic links (sister groups) between several major continents and concluded that in most cases such distribution patterns were best explained by vicariance. It will not be possible to make a meaningful comparison of apparently similar distributional patterns in land snails until their sister-group relationships have also been established. Some land-snail families with Laurasian representation make their first appearance in Gondwanian areas (Patagonia and southwestern Africa) as Paleocene fossils, long after the vicariant event concomitant with division of these major northern- and southern-hemisphere continental assemblages. This observation could be interpreted as supporting the dispersal paradigm. Major summaries of land-snail fossils are few in number, however, and the known fragmentary record, both geographically and temporally, likely reflects a sampling artifact.

A number of ecological factors and potential dispersal mechanisms can also be marshalled in an attempt to explain the biogeography of land snails: (1) moisture related ecological influences; (2) behavioral and physiological adaptations of snails that facilitate moisture retention; (3) vulnerability to indigenous or introduced ant predators; (4) competition with other snails; (5) human related habitat alterations; (6) island subsidences and sea level fluctuations that affected the structure and temporal distribution of islands; and

(7) factors related to wind- and bird-assisted aerial dispersal (Vagvolgyi 1976). I do not doubt that most, perhaps all, of the above factors have influenced land-snail distribution to some extent. When viewed from a historical standpoint, however, these influences generally are operational for relatively short spans of time and may affect only a segment of the total population. Only by determining the phylogeny of a group of organisms is it possible to formulate testable hypotheses about ancestral lineages and their distributions. In a brief and lucid account, Nelson and Platnick (1979) have further shown that the only adequate means of establishing biotic relationships is by determining the phylogenetic relationships of three or more allopatric (endemic) taxa comprising a monophyletic group. They stressed that conclusions about biotic relationships inferred simply on the basis of number of shared species, or even on the basis of the phylogenetic relationships of wide-spread taxa, may frequently be erroneous.

My criticism of Solem's presentation of land-snail biogeography is general and concerns methodology and concepts, specifically his failure to attempt a synthesis of present knowledge of snail phylogeny and geographical distributions. He has produced comprehensive monographs of two land-snail families (Endodontidae and Charopidae), both of which are known to have at least a Miocene history on Central Pacific islands and which appear to have greatly dissimilar distributional patterns. The preceding remarks are aimed largely at stimulating him to use his systematic knowledge of these two families to address the problem of inter-relationships and areas of endemism from a vicariance perspective.

Discussion

V. G. Springer

Comments on Solem's Land-Snail Biogeography, with an Hypothesized Explanation of the Distribution of the Endodontidae

DR. SOLEM PRESENTS a great deal of data about land snails. The data are interesting, but I consider them incidental, irrelevant, or vastly incomplete insofar as they have a bearing on the issues of vicariance and dispersal biogeography. In this discussion I will comment on the framework that Solem establishes as a basis for his presentation. I will then hypothesize an explanation for the distribution of the Endodontidae.

Solem states in his introduction that he would attempt "to place the radiation of land snails within an ecological context." I am not certain what he means by that statement, but he gives no evidence that changing ecological parameters resulted in the great numbers of land-snail species, genera, and families that exist today. He does tell us that plant conditions in the Paleozoic probably more than once permitted land colonization by snails, and that land snails are polyphyletic. This information is not very helpful, for it tells us nothing about the mechanisms that caused the appearance of those groups of families (e.g., the pulmonates) that Solem considers monophyletic.

Solem also states that he would assess the "adequacy of taxa assignability" of the fossil record. If I understand him correctly, such a discussion is out of place here. It should go without saying that, if one does not know the identity of one's organisms and cannot hypothesize cladistic rela-

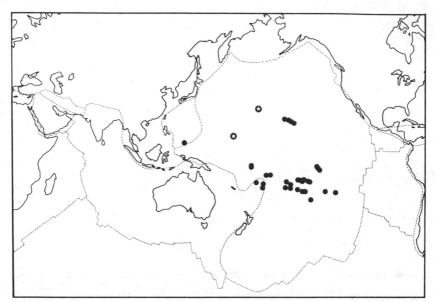

Figure 5.11. Distribution of the land-snail family Endodontidae: * = fossils; • = extant species. Compiled from Solem (1976).

tionships among them, it is futile to attempt either a vicariant or dispersal biogeographical analysis of the taxa.

Solem's search for generalized tracks demonstrates scientific canalization, for it is limited to families of land snails; hence, his concept of tracks is not generalized at all. Biogeographical exegesis does not mandate that we restrict ourselves only to one phyletic group or even to one taxonomic level. Vicariant events, at least, are independent of the organisms and taxonomic levels they affect. In any case, if, as Solem seems to believe, knowledge of land-snail families is inadequate for biogeographical analysis, he should direct his attention to a lower monophyletic taxonomic level for which he could reasonably propose cladistic relationships, and then he should seek geological, ecological, or other physical information to see if he could find a historical sequence of events that might have produced the pattern of evolution he hypothesizes. For confirming evidence he could look at other monophyletic groups of snails, but he need not; he could just as well look at fishes. In his closing remarks Solem applauds both vicariance and dispersal biogeography as powerful tools, but nowhere in his paper does he clearly make a case for or against either paradigm.

At this point continued criticism would serve little purpose unless I offer something constructive as well. I would therefore like to fill the void in

Solem's treatment of land snails by offering a possible explanation for the distribution of the Endodontidae. The information I will present is part of my ongoing study of the biogeography of the Pacific Tectonic Plate.

According to information in Solem (1976) and presented by him at this symposium, the Endodontidae and Charopidae are sister taxa (more closely related to each other than to any other family of land snails). I have plotted the distribution of the Endodontidae (figure 5.11) on a map showing the outlines of the major tectonic plates in the Indo-Pacific region. The Endodontidae are endemic to the Pacific Plate and its margins. This distributional pattern is a generalized track as evidenced by the distribution of a species (with two subspecies) of surface dwelling shorefish (*Hyporhamphus acutus*, figure 5.12), a species of marine gastropod (*Strombus maculatus*, figure 5.13; the smallest species of *Strombus*), a subspecies of alpheid shrimp (*Alpheus lobidens polynesica*, figure 5.14), and a number of other forms, particularly fish species. In each case, so far as I can determine, the sister taxon of the Pacific Plate endemic has an Indo-West Pacific distribution. The sister taxon of the Endodontidae is among the charopids of southwestern Australia, if Solem's remarks that these particular charopids come closest to bridging the

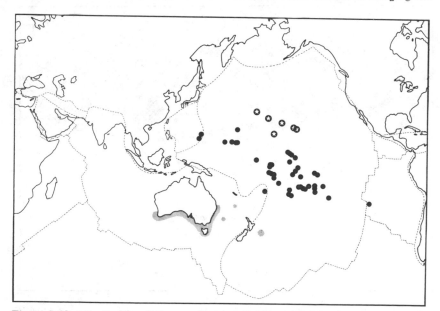

Figure 5.12. Distribution of the two subspecies of the fish, *Hyporhamphus acutus.* * = *H. a. acutus;* • = *H. a. pacificus.* Shaded area is the distribution of sister taxa of *H. acutus.* Pacific Plate localities occur on the continental shelf of New Zealand. Compiled from Collette (1974 and personal communications).

morphological gap, or are partially intermediate, between the Endodontidae and Charopidae can be so interpreted. The sister group of the fish, *Hyporhamphus acutus*, is a group of three species presently occurring, interestingly, only in the southern Australian and New Zealand area (B. B. Collette personal communication). The sister subspecies of the shrimp is widespread, but allopatric, in the Indo-West Pacific. The sister taxon of *Strombus maculatus* is not clear based on available information (Abbott 1960), but Abbott indicated that two species form a group with *S. maculatus*. Of these two species, the distribution of *S. microurceus* overlaps that of *S. maculatus* only in the Caroline Islands. The other species, *S. mutabilis*, ranges from eastern Africa to the Tuamotus and almost completely encompasses the range of *S. maculatus*.

The margins where tectonic plates meet are geologically highly active, giving rise to volcanic island-arc formation (including, but not limited to back-arc spreading and arc deformation, subduction of oceanic plates beneath continental plates, formation of deep-sea trenches, and obduction of continental plates over oceanic plates). Given the distributional patterns and

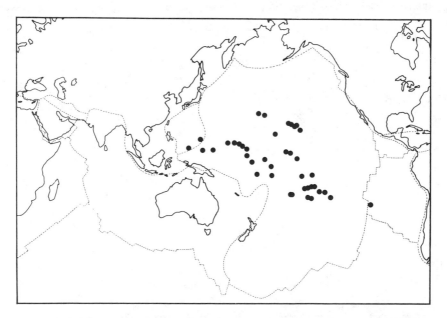

Figure 5.13. Distribution of the marine gastropod, *Strombus maculatus*. Compiled from Abbott (1960) and collections of the Australian Museum and the U.S. National Museum.

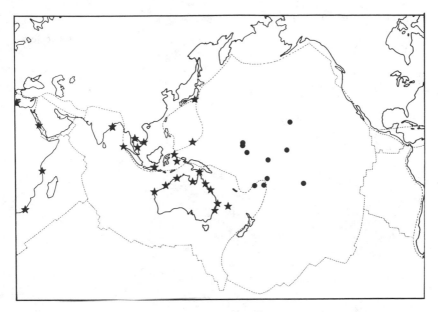

Figure 5.14. Distribution of the two subspecies of the alpheid shrimp, *Alpheus lobidens.* * _ *A. l. lobidens;* • = *A. l. polynesica.* Compiled from Banner and Banner (1974).

cladistic relationships I have described, I hypothesize that at some time in the past (pre-Miocene based on land-snail evidence), each of the Pacific Plate endemics was represented by a single widespread taxon that ranged from the continental areas of the Indo-West Pacific onto the islands of the Pacific Plate, and that geological events along the western margin of the Pacific Plate resulted in a barrier to dispersal (reproduction) between the continental and Pacific Plate populations of each taxon, allowing the populations to vicariate and attain, in the judgment of systematists, a familial, specific, or subspecific level of differentiation. The disappearance of this barrier has allowed dispersal onto the Pacific Plate of some of the forms previously restricted to the continental side of the barrier. This dispersal accounts for the extant partial sympatry of the Endodontidae and Charopidae, and possibly that of *Strombus maculatus* and its closest relative.

While my hypothesis suffers because the exact nature of the isolating mechanism along the plate margin cannot be proposed (and physical evidence may be lost forever because of plate subduction), it nevertheless seems more reasonable than a dispersal hypothesis to provide an explanation for the generalized Pacific Plate track that includes forms as diverse as land snails and marine fishes (a single vicariant event, as opposed to multiple dispersal events, resulting in numerous basically similar distributional patterns).

It may be, as Solem hypothesizes, that land snails are "oblivious" to changing biota and biogeographical controversies, but the only evidence I have confirms that they are vicariant conformists.

Discussion

R. T. Schuh

VICARIANCE BIOGEOGRAPHY ADDRESSES animal distributions from a historical perspective. Dr. Solem encourages us in this endeavor by his observations on area diversity theories and the fact that land-snail distributions, especially in the Pacific, do not generally agree with those theories as advanced by MacArthur and Wilson. Thus, Solem seems to conclude that theories of ecological geography are ineffective or insufficient to explain observed land-snail distributions, in spite of the fact that contrary claims have been made for the same groups of organisms by other authors.

Rather, Solem addresses himself to the types of data necessary for understanding land-snail distributions in a historical context. He concludes that the most important evidence will ultimately come from classifiable fossils and that this evidence will supercede theoretical or ideological interpretations. After examining available fossil evidence, he concludes that it is insufficient at this time to reveal generalized tracks. He indicates that in his estimation dispersal theory will apply to some groups and vicariance to others.

From the point of view of this symposium Solem's conclusions are dissatisfying. They suggest that, because no general distributional patterns are conspicuous in present land-snail data, an evaluation of vicariance theory can be produced for those organisms only when more data are available. Yet some of Solem's information may indicate otherwise. In his remarks on fossils, Solem notes that sufficient structural complexity exists to associate Recent and fossil groups. He states further that a reasonably diverse but geographically limited fossil fauna exists in the Paleozoic and Mesozoic of western Europe and North America, but that for most of the world, distributional information is spotty until the Tertiary.

From analysis of both geographical and temporal patterns Solem concludes that land snails show "an extraordinary degree of stability." This statement encompasses some 300 million years of geological history and a diverse geography. He further states that according to distributional evidence land snails have low dispersability, that the geological events that influenced their distributional history antedate the appearance of extant terrestrial vertebrates, and that the snails seem to have remained unaffected by a massive floristic revolution in the late Mesozoic. Such statements could be interpreted as indicating that a pattern associated with geological history should exist at some level.

If we have Solem's data in hand, and if we interpret Croizat's work as the final statement in the annals of vicariance biogeography, we might reasonably wonder just how to proceed analytically; however, several recent papers have put forward specific procedures. We must first produce a scheme of phyletic relationships for the groups in question and then examine that scheme for congruent patterns of distributional endemism among the groups. Platnick and Nelson (1978) and Rosen (1978) have given explicit statements about how this might be done. Because phylogenetic hypotheses are not easily constructed, the application of such methods to land snails may be difficult at this time. Nonetheless, certain distributional patterns are suggested by Solem's data and these may give us some clues as to where to begin.

I would suggest that a fossil record in the northern hemisphere in conjunction with a Recent record primarily in the southern hemisphere, as noted by Solem for such groups as the Streptaxidae, Megaspiridae, Strobilopsidae, Diplommatinidae, Pupinidae, and Cyclophoridae, may contain important distributional information. This observation is in conflict with Solem's remarks that those land-snail taxa that have an Eocene or older fossil record show essentially no common distributional tracks. Certainly the Cyclophoridae, Diplommatinidae, and Pupinidae form a track in Croizat's sense. Because the Recent and fossil distributions are not identical, Solem apparently assumes that no track could exist. The families Megaspiridae, Streptaxidae, and Strobilopsidae have distributions which for the most part include those of cyclophorids, diplomatinnids, and pupinids. Whether they are part of the same track cannot be determined with the information at hand. As Solem indicates for other snail groups with apparent Gondwanian distributions, these families all may be remnants of a Pangean fauna. Whether congruent patterns of distribution exist among any of these taxa will require phylogenetic hypotheses of three or more taxa for each group to determine if there are indeed common patterns of endemism. Such a fossil record does not necessarily provide evidence that land snails have migrated or dispersed from the northern to the southern Hemisphere, as Solem suggests in several places.

With respect to the western Pacific it may be a serious mistake to conclude, as does Solem, that since the Miocene land snails have undergone a major pattern of migration from southeastern Asia into the wetter parts of tropical Australia and onto many remote Pacific Islands. Such a conclusion is apparently based on certain assumptions: (1) even for potentially Pangean groups, Australia was not available for colonization until the Miocene; and (2) because there are no pre-Miocene fossils in the Pacific, the snails were not there prior to the Miocene. These assumptions seem to ignore the fact that fossil records indicate only minimum ages, that water gaps between Pacific islands and southeastern Asia may have been smaller in the past, and that many Pacific islands may be as old as 60 million years. The contradiction is that Solem recognizes these facts, but chooses to ignore them in this particular circumstance.

Land-snail distributions in the Pacific show much endemism at the family level, a phenomenon that probably occurs in few other groups. Because such endemism is unusual, one might wish to test for its reality and to establish the distributions of the nearest relatives of these Pacific endemics. Cladistic analysis seems to be the appropriate procedure for doing this. The result might be that even though much of the Pacific fauna shows considerable isolation, some common pattern of distribution actually does exist.

The foregoing comments might suggest that my disagreement with Solem is whether one believes that general patterns of distributions exist as a result of the forces of earth history—and that those patterns must be discovered before dispersal events can be deduced—or whether vicariance and dispersal as explanations of observed distributions can be interpreted simultaneously. As to whether vicariance and dispersal are poles of a continuum, with the tenets of each pole applying better to some groups than to others as Solem concludes. I would suggest that there is no continuum, but rather that the dispute involves different philosophies of science—dispersalism representing the inductivist/ad hoc approach and vicariance representing the hypothetico-deductive/analytic approach. The former seems to be an almost essentialist viewpoint while the latter seeks to discover and to test empirically some general patterns that may be true for all of life.

Response

A. Solem

I HAVE NOT BEEN, am not now, and probably never will be a card carrying cladist. This fact obviously disturbs the discussants. Hennig's techniques are only *one* of *several* useful approaches to systematic research. To claim that in the absence of cladistic analysis "it is futile to attempt either a vicariant or dispersal biogeographical analysis" (Springer) shows the enthusiasm of a naive convert, equivalent to the "all-characters-are-equal" dictum of the first pheneticists, or the recent idea that biochemical change occurs at a uniform rate through time.

It would be nice to present an adequate phylogeny of land snails, and to know detailed relationships within family level taxa that show bi- or tri-continental disjunctions. Classification of land snails into families is relatively stable, and the independent land colonization by several prosobranch lineages is certain; but whether the pulmonates are a grade or a clade is unknown and the superfamilial-to-ordinal groupings of stylommatrophoran pulmonates are nearly chaotic (Solem 1978b). Construction of phylogenetic trees, dendrograms, or cladograms at our present level of inter-family phyletic knowledge is either a student seminar exercise or simplistic reductionism, possibly with value for suggesting taxa or faunistic areas for rigorous investigation, but not leading to any overall picture of evolution either for snails or for their distributions. While a search for parsimony, or the holy grail, may stimulate efforts, well documented evolutionary scenarios are proving to be quite complex and logically messy, and they show evidence of many different phenomena. The Tertiary history of maples as outlined by Wolfe and the evolution of Hawaiian *Drosophila* alluded to by Howden in this symposium are good examples.

Vicariance events can be as small as a path pushed through a tangle of shrubs, isolating formerly interconnected crowns for a few years or decades until path disuse permits reunion, or as grand as the breakup of Pangea. Dispersal can be as modest as a snail crossing the above path, or as large as intercontinental travels of the Cattle Egret and repetitive trips by Australian birds to New Zealand. Both vicariant and dispersal biogeographical events occur repeatedly. Recently published emphasis on the grand vicariance patterns resulting from plate tectonics should not obscure the focus on finer grain vicariance events, nor subsequent dispersals, whether by the reunion through expansion of temporarily isolated wet forest patches in Amazonia (as summarized by Haffer) or the across-barrier dispersions of propagules studied by Simberloff.

Although frequently resembling one, this symposium should not be remembered as a battleground of paradigms, but rather as an attempt to communicate different approaches and levels of knowledge, and to focus on problems, be they taxa- or area-related. With regard to land snails, I could summarize recent work to indicate that: the fossil record of family units shows much greater age than for most terrestrial organisms; despite this great age, most distributions are far from world wide; comparatively few major distributional changes through time can be identified; "Gondwanaland" elements are few and may be relicts from Pangean distributions; and the Pacific islands have a complex mixture of family-level endemics and post-Miocene dispersalists from southeastern Asia. Because of inadequate phylogenetic data, I do not attempt to date the origins of the major discontinuities that resulted from both plate-tectonic vicariances and subsequent dispersals.

In the broad strokes of worldwide distributions, plotting of species points as requested by Smith-Vaniz and Springer, or indicating areas of major current diversity (not to be confused with point of origin), is not possible. Establishing that dots on a map for a variety of organisms have roughly similar spreads or congruences ("pattern") gives no data on how and when ("process") this happened. Coincidence, repetition of historical events, simultaneous vicariances, isolated dispersal events, or simple misunderstanding of data all can produce similar maps. Springer (figure 5.11, 5.13) compares the *land*-snail family Endodontidae with the *marine* snail *Strombus maculatus*. His few-point endodontid distribution, compressing 185 species-level taxa, ignores critical absences of extant taxa (real, not collecting gaps), from the Marianas, Carolines, Marshalls, and main islands of Fiji, and the phylogenetically significant data that advanced endodontids are restricted to Palau, Lau, Ellice, Tonga, and Upolu, with generalized taxa from the Manua group of Samoa to Hawaii and the Marquesas (Solem 1976). His marine distribution of one species includes all of Micronesia plus Easter Island, and omits Lau, Tonga, Samoa, Ellice Islands, and the Marquesas—a very different pattern. Similarly, Schuh lumps family units—with different times of appearance in and disappearance from Europe, which also show non-congruent Recent distributions (Solem figures 5.1, 5.4, 5.6)—as a single track, which stretches both fact and imagination.

Finally, I do not claim that "since the Miocene land snails have undergone a major pattern of migration from southeastern Asia into the wetter parts of tropical Australia and onto many remote Pacific islands" (Schuh). I do claim that some land-snail taxa are ancient relicts on the Pacific islands, that some represent post-Miocene dispersals, and that some reached the Pacific islands from the Australia-New Caledonia-New Zealand axis in Tertiary times. Vicariance *and* dispersal phenomena have been involved in the distribution of most organisms through time. To ignore data from the time dimension for individual taxa while trying to concoct "general patterns that may be true for all of life" (Schuh) is to substitute faith and dogma for science. The weakest part of vicariance biogeography as presented at this symposium is its rejection of historically generated complexity in its search for uniformity.

6

Vicarious Plant Distributions and Paleogeography of the Pacific Region

R. Melville

TRANS-PACIFIC DISTRIBUTIONS have long aroused the interest of biologists. On the return from his Antarctic voyage, J. D. Hooker (1860) gave much thought to the interrelationships of the floras of Australia, Tasmania, New Zealand, and South America. He postulated migration via Antarctica between these disjunct floras, and he assumed land connections and a milder climate at some earlier period. Antarctic land bridges could not account for the numerous vicarious species pairs on either side of the North Pacific. The most frequent hypothesis to account for these has been migration via a Bering land bridge. Had this been operative there should be at least some examples of intermediates or close allies linking Chinese and North American vicariants. Recently (Colinvaux 1964) doubt has been cast on the effectiveness of the Bering land bridge, which seems unlikely ever to have played a significant part in plant migration around the Pacific. There are, in addition, amphitropical distributions to be accounted for. Why should there be two genera of Lardizabalaceae in Chile while the rest of the family is in China and Japan with an overspill onto the Himalayas? Land bridges in other parts of the Pacific have been proposed and discussed by Van Steenis (1962), but there is no firm evidence for transverse land bridges across the Central Pacific, nor any known geophysical process that could account for them. The causes for these trans-Pacific distributions have remained enigmatic.

Guppy (1906), from his study of seed dispersal in the floras of Hawaii and Fiji, came to the conclusion that the majority of endemic species were adapted for bird dispersal, but that birds no longer seem to be effective vectors for inter-island dispersal. Bird migration routes pass from China through southeastern Asia and Malaysia into Australia in the west and along the Rockies, through Central America, and along the Andes in the east. These routes would not account for the distribution of the Lardizabalaceae, but they do fit rather closely with Croizat's (1952) concept of "Gates of Angiospermy" so far as the Pacific is concerned. Following an extensive study of plant distribution, Croizat has traced the migration routes of the angiosperms back to three regions in the southern hemisphere. These "gates," as he called them, are centered around southern Africa, western Polynesia, and the Magellanic region. The three gates all appear to be pointing back to Antarctica, which, if projected back in time, would suggest Gondwanaland as the place of origin and starting point for the migration routes. Croizat, however, did not fully embrace this concept.

Concept of Pacifica

For many years I had been concerned at Kew with the floras of Australia, New Zealand, and the islands of the Pacific, and had become intensely interested in angiosperm evolution and distribution. By 1966 I reached the conclusion that present distributions in the Pacific region could be satisfactorily accounted for only by the former existence of a Pacific continent. A tentative reconstruction of the continent was attempted (Melville 1966), using the somewhat meager geological and geophysical data then available and accepting Menard's (1964) interpretation of the Darwin Rise as a simple mid-ocean ridge from which continental drift had occurred. Although separation along a line is possible on a flat surface, the stresses set up on the curved surface of a globe cause bifurcations of the spreading ridge, giving rise to triple junctions and creating a situation more complex than that envisaged by Menard. The crustal plates delineated by this process may not move uniformly over the whole of their surfaces, and the stresses set up may be relieved by the development of transform faults parallel to the direction of movement of the plate. Differential movement can then take place on either side of the fault. Approximate dates for the plate movements were indicated by the fact that, apart from a small area of Jurassic age, the whole of the floor of the North Pacific is covered by deposits of Cretaceous or later age; and that of the South Pacific is covered by Tertiary deposits (Menard 1964). Much more precise dating became possible after the discovery that the earth's magnetic field is periodically reversed and that bands of normal and reversed magnetism parallel to the spreading center can be detected in the extruded rocks and dated by radioisotope techniques. Past attempts at continental reconstructions have been almost entirely based on data from single disciplines. Geologists were often unwilling to place much reliance on paleontological or neontological evidence. Now, with the development of plate tectonics and the acceptance of continental drift, it is no longer possible to say, "what do a few plants matter"? It is a question of rafting entire floras and faunas on moving plates, so that biological evidence cannot be ignored and must take its place side by side with evidence from geology, geophysics, and other relevant disciplines. In attempting a reconstruction of Pacifica, I have taken into account evidence from a variety of sources and disciplines.

Reconstruction of Pacifica

Holmes' account (1965:1135) of the sequence of geological events in Japan reads as a description of the uplift of a continental area and its subsequent disruption. Uplift started in the Triassic and was followed by the development of a geosyncline on the eastern side of Japan as the rift-valley stage was reached, and by the deposition of a great thickness of sediments in the Jurassic and Cretaceous after drift had started. Early in the Tertiary smaller transverse geosynclines and faults developed, culminating in the Miocene and Pliocene with the development of the Sea of Japan as the country was pushed away obliquely from the Asiatic continent. Separation took place along existing faults to form the island arc. Thus the opening of the marginal basin and the formation of the island arc were events that took place a considerable time after the disruption of the North Pacific continent. Similarly, the other peripheral basins off the eastern coast of Asia all were formed during the Tertiary (Segawa and Oshima 1975; Karig 1971). The first operation for the reconstruction of Pacifica, therefore, is to slide the island arcs back onto the Asiatic continent following the lines of the transform faults along which the separation originally took place. On the eastern side of the Pacific, the Gulf of California is lined with oceanic crust, and the coastal strip to the west of the San Andreas fault up to Cape Mendocino is moving slowly in a northwesterly direction, which may lead—in perhaps another 15 million years—to a Californian island arc. According to Larson et al. (1968) the Gulf of California began to open about 4 million years ago (4 Ma), although the fault started 8–10 Ma. It is necessary to slide this coastal strip back into its original position so that the southern tip of Lower California contacts Cape Corrientes in Mexico. When this is done, there is a very close fit between the reconstructed coast lines on either side of the North Pacific (figure 6.1). A very similar fit for the two continents, supported by much geological evidence, was obtained by Hughes (1975).

South Pacifica

Later authors have added little to Hooker's (1860) speculations on landbridges between South America, Antarctica, and Australia. Seeking an explanation, I discovered that Chile and Patagonia did not suffer glaciation in the Permo-Carboniferous ice age as did adjacent parts of Brazil and Argentina (Holmes 1965). This paleoclimatic evidence suggested that the Chile + Patagonia sector, which I will call Magellania, was not in contact with the present mainland of South America in Permo-Carboniferous times. Paleogeological maps of South America (Stose 1950) show that a band of marine Jurassic strata stretches from 33° S. on the Chilean coast to the Golfo San Jorge on the Atlantic coast of Argentina, thus indicating that Magellania was not originally part of South America. A similar band of marine Jurassic rock marks off Peru. Thus it appears likely that these two sectors of South America drifted eastward from some position in the Pacific where they had been close to New Zealand.

Confirmation for the position of Magellania in the Pacific is provided by a paleomagnetic pole for the mid-Jurassic of Patagonia (Valencio and Vilas 1970). The lavas investigated came from the Chou Aike formation near Puerto Deseado, 66°W, 48°S, which lies to the south of the Golfo San Jorge and within the Magellanic sector of South America. Valencio and Vilas considered this evidence for the opening of the South Atlantic in the Jurassic, an interpretation conflicting with extensive and widely accepted evidence for the initiation of drift between South America and Africa about 112 Ma in the early Cretaceous (Larson and Ladd 1973; Funnell and Smith 1968).

New Zealand is situated on a submerged continental platform, which has three finger-like peninsulas projecting northwest-to-north from it. Lord Howe Island, New Caledonia, and Fiji are situated on these submerged ridges. For the reconstruction of the southern Pacific land mass, the triangular base of the New Zealand platform has been brought against the flank of

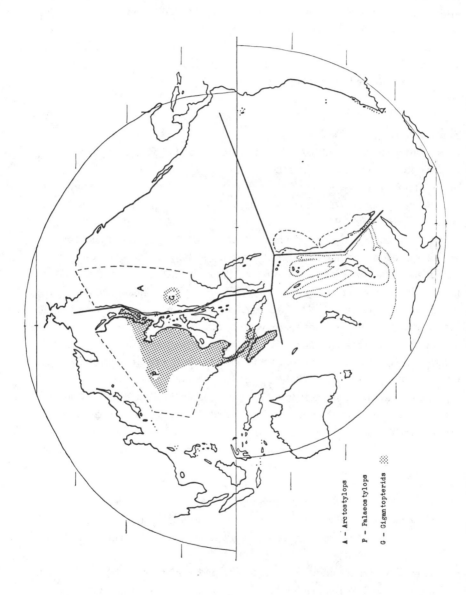

Figure 6.1. Reconstruction of the continent *Pacifica*, with distributions of *Arctostylops* (A), *Palaeostylops* (P), and (stippled) *Gigantopteris* (G).

A – Arctostylops

P – Palaeostylops

G – Gigantopterids

the South Pacific Rise so that the eastern side of the triangle is in line with the Eltanin Fracture Zone (figure 6.2). The Fiji ridge then runs northward and with the Eltanin Fracture Zone forms an angle that probably marks the site of a triple junction. The third arm of this junction would then be in line with the great Alpine Fault of New Zealand (figure 6.1). Peru and Magellania, with its southern tip on the center of the Southeast Pacific Rise, can then be brought against the two arms of the triple junction on the eastern side, and the western Antarctic peninsula can be placed along the Southeast Pacific Rise with its tip in contact with Cape Horn. The South Pacific continent thus reconstituted would consist of an arm of Gondwanaland centered on longitude 150°W and extending northward into the area of the present Pacific.

Controversy exists over the interpretation of the sea-floor topography in the New Zealand region. Barker (1967) has interpreted the Kermadec Ridge as part of the world-wide oceanic ridge system. Summerhayes (1967) and Cullen (1967) rejected this concept and claimed that the Kermadec Ridge is part of an island-arc complex. The two ideas are in harmony if the Kermadec Ridge was part of the ocean-ridge system in the early Cretaceous and if the South Fiji Basin was formed as the result of secondary drift in the Tertiary, like the other marginal basins of the western Pacific enclosed within the andesite line.

Geophysical Evidence
The central point for the assembly of Pacifica is the triple junction between the Kula, Farallon, and Pacific Plates, which was estimated to be at about 12°S, 170°W early in the Cretaceous (Larson and Chase 1972). The central spreading ridge of the North Pacific was then aligned on Laysan Island at the northwestern end of the Hawaiian Archipelago (figure 6.1). The positions of the principal fracture zones were next inserted. It then appeared that the Marquesas Fracture Zone forms the southern boundary of the Farallon Plate. Drift of the Farallon Plate appears to have been relatively uncomplicated until late in the sequence, when the Southeast Pacific Rise altered its direction, and the minor Cocos Plate was formed in connection with the final closure of the Panama Isthmus. The positions of the fracture zones in the Kula Plate are only partially known, but at the level of the Hawaiian Archipelago they run roughly parallel with those of the Farallon Plate. Recorded in this area are magnetic lineations that date back to 150 Ma and indicate that drift had already started in the late Jurassic (Larson and Pitman 1972). Toward the southern border of the plate, north of the equator and east of the Gilbert

Figure 6.2. The Pacific Ocean with its mid-ocean spreading ridge, the present Southeast Pacific Rise (solid line) and its former position (double lines), the principal fracture zones, the tectonic plates, and the Hawaiian and Phoenix magnetic lineations.

Islands, lies another sequence of magnetic lineations, the Phoenix sequence, that is approximately at right angles to the Hawaiian sequence. These lineations indicate that a local readjustment took place from 122 to 112 Ma, which was some time after the start of the main orogeny. Reference to the reconstruction (figure 6.1) indicates that this minor drift must have affected New Guinea, which must have been separated from all other parts of Pacifica during this period. The separation of New Guinea was an event of the highest biological significance to which I shall again refer.

Fracture zones are not yet recorded for the Pacific Plate, but to the north of Fiji is a small submerged platform, the Manihiki Plateau, which bears the islands of Manihiki and Nassau. This plateau would have helped to bridge the gap between North and South Pacifica during the rift valley phase of the orogeny. It is probable that for much of its history New Zealand was an offshore island on a continental platform, a circumstance that would explain the great discrepancies between the floras of Australia and New Zealand and the absence of marsupials from New Zealand. The history of the Phoenix Plate, also, is imperfectly known, but was evidently complex. The present Southeast Pacific Rise dates back only to 20–25 Ma, when it replaced an earlier ridge, trending roughly NNW-SSE (Herron 1972), which began about 50–65 Ma. Both ridges were active between 9–20 Ma with the result that fragments of the old ridge have drifted away from the present ridge (figure 6.2). It is assumed that a still earlier phase of drift must have occurred, presumably in the Cretaceous, when the rift valley of North Pacifica spread southward and began the disjunction of the South Pacific peninsula. The injection of granite intrusions in New Zealand between 90–120 Ma (Landis and Coombs 1967) lends support to this interpretation. With the dating of the Phoenix lineations, it is likely that New Zealand and Peru were drifting by about 115 Ma. The start of the drift of the Antarctic peninsula began about 80 Ma (Dalziel and Elliot 1971). The reconstruction shows that the angle of divergence between the original and present positions of the Antarctic peninsula is about 30°. Similarly, the angle between the present position of Tasmania and its pre-drift situation in the Ross Sea area is about 30°. This implies a rotation of the Antarctic continent of 30°, which is independently confirmed by paleomagnetic data (Blundell 1962). Although the Antarctic peninsula began to drift at 80 Ma, Australia did not separate from Antarctica until 50 Ma. During that interval, Australia must have been under compressional stress, which sent it into a synclinal fold that allowed a marine transgression to take place, almost splitting the continent in two. This epicontinental sea lasted from the late Cretaceous until the Eocene (Andrews

1916), when isostatic readjustment had taken place following the separation of Australia. The effect of this marine interlude is reflected in numerous vicarious and bimodal distributions in the Australian flora, such as the Epacridaceae (Melville 1975) and as among Australian *Gossypium* (Fryxell 1965a).

Paleontological Evidence

Numerous paleontological distributions have a bearing on the existence of Pacifica. The Cathaysian flora of the Permian was dominated by a group of pteridosperms, the Gigantopteridae, which occupied much of China, Japan, Indochina, Sumatra, and the western end of New Guinea (figure 6.1; Gothan and Weyland 1964; Asama 1959; Asama et al. 1975). They are also represented in parts of Oklahoma, Texas, and New Mexico in western North America (Read and Mamay 1964).

The late Paleocene Gashato fauna of Mongolia is of considerable interest, for it contained marsupials, insectivores, and notoungulates. In this period, after the breakup of Pacifica, the notoungulate *Palaeostylops* was present in Mongolia, and the related *Arctostylops* was vicariously living in Wyoming (Colbert 1973). Marsupials, notoungulates, and other groups represented in the Gashato fauna were present also in western North America, and they were able to migrate into South America. The land bridge that made this possible was broken early in the Eocene, and South America became an island continent for about 50 million years, until the present Central American isthmus was completed in the Pliocene. In the interval, marsupials died out in North America, but diversified in South America and reinvaded the north after the present Panamanian link was established. They were accompanied in their migration by giant sloths, the armadillo, and the armorplated glyptodonts. The problem of how the marsupials reached Australia in the Oligocene—when they first appear as fossils—without any of the South American mammals, is an outstanding puzzle for zoologists. Martin (1970) has suggested that they may have entered from New Guinea when Australia made contact with it in the Oligocene. According to the present reconstruction of Pacifica, early marsupials could have migrated into New Guinea by the early Cretaceous, before it was isolated by the local sea floor spreading alluded to above. That New Guinea had been in land connection with the Chinese mainland is indicated by the presence of Gigantopteridae in both areas in the Permian. The period of about 70 million years during which New Guinea was isolated would have been sufficient for the diversification of the marsupials before they were able to enter Australia, and their progenitors must have been present in the western half of Pacifica before drift began.

Central America

The nature of the land bridge between western North America and South America during the Paleocene has remained a problem. That a land bridge must have existed appears substantiated by abundant paleontological evidence. In my first attempt to reconstruct Pacifica (Melville 1966), I paid no special attention to the Greater Antilles, but it will be noted (figure 6.3) that, if the islands are moved into contact with one another and with the tip of the Yucatan Peninsula, the peninsula thus formed would be of the same length as the present Central American isthmus. The boundary used for the eastern side of the western North American sector of Pacifica is the zone of marine Jurassic strata shown by Schuchert (1955) on his paleogeographical maps. By the time that the Antillean peninsula made contact with South America, the Pacific and Atlantic sectors of North America were probably already in contact in the north, but may not have been fully united in the south. The fauna that was able to migrate into South America would have been, on the whole, similar to the Mongolian Gashato fauna. The land connection probably held up drift for a time, but when it was broken drift continued until the Greater Antilles reached their present positions and the Isthmus of Panama was closed in the Pliocene.

The hypothesis that the Greater Antilles formed a land bridge between North and South America in the Paleocene and part of the Cretaceous is supported by paleomagnetic evidence. The paleomagnetism of some Cretaceous lavas from Jamaica indicates that it was then situated about 1000 km to the southwest (Steinhauser et al. 1972). This position places Jamaica on the present isthmus. Other paleomagnetic evidence of about the same period indicates that Yucatan was then situated to the west in the Pacific (Gose and Swartz 1977). The correlation between these data is consistent with the simultaneous movement of the Greater Antilles and Yucatan, but conflicts with other theories of movement of the Antilles within the Caribbean area (Freeland and Dietz 1971; Mattson 1972).

If the above hypothesis is valid, there should be biological evidence to support it. A detailed analysis of the floras of the Greater Antilles, of Central America, and of the adjacent parts of South America will be necessary. In the

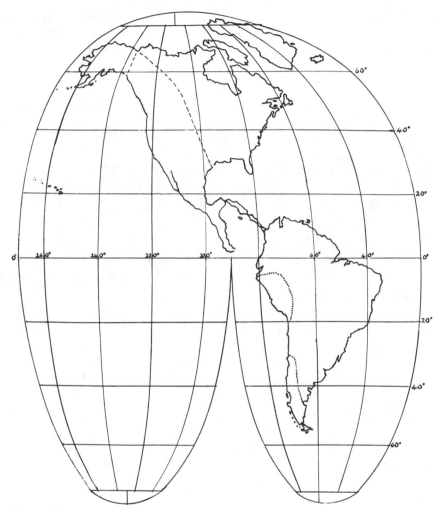

Figure 6.3. America in the Paleocene, showing the temporary land bridge formed by the Greater Antilles.

meantime, *Bontia*, a monotypic genus of Myoporaceae, exemplifies the anticipated distribution pattern. *Bontia daphnoides* occurs throughout the Greater Antilles and extends into the Bahamas and British Guiana. Vegetatively it closely resembles a *Myoporum* such as *M. sandwichense*, but the two-lipped corolla is zygomorphic and adapted to a more specialized pollinator than *Myoporum*. The ovary of *Myoporum* varies from 2–10 loculi with one or sometimes two ovules per loculus. In *Bontia* the ovary is bilocular with two ovules per loculus; it may be considered a specialized vicariant offshoot of a Pacific *Myoporum* such as *M. rapense* (G. 3–6) or of M. stokesii (G. 3–4) of the Austral Islands.

Island Archipelagoes

Galapagos

Of the numerous archipelagoes of the Pacific, the Galapagos, Marquesas, and Hawaii are of outstanding interest. The Galapagos are noteworthy for their animal life, especially the Darwin finches, the lizards, and the tortoises, but also for the part they played in the evolution of cotton. The Galapagos straddle the equator just to the south of a displaced sector of the Galapagos Fracture Zone (figure 6.2). It is inferred that the islands are a group of volcanoes initiated at the time that Peru was close to South America and approaching the end of its drift. Direct connection was made with the Peruvian microcontinent, allowing overland migration of plants and animals. Tortoises, which soon drown in water, would have been able to cross unimpeded. As Peru continued its drift, the sector of the Galapagos Fracture Zone was first pulled out of line and then, as Peru contacted the body of South America, it would have rotated counterclockwise into its present position, thereby shearing off the Galapagos. If this interpretation is correct, a very close relationship would exist between the Galapagos and Peru. Porter (1976) has analyzed the Galapagan flora and its relationship to Central and South America. Disregarding introduced species, he found that there were 228 endemic and 286 indigenous (non-endemic) species. Of the latter he found that 99 percent were present in Peru and Ecuador and only one percent was present in Central America and Mexico. It is difficult to imagine how this situation could have developed without direct contact with Peru because the Galapagos are about equidistant from the closest parts of Central America and Peru. If the island biota had made the sea crossing, about equal proportions should have been contributed by the two areas.

Marquesas

Reference to the map (figure 6.2) will show that the Marquesas Archipelago lies just north of the Marquesas Fracture Zone at a point where a change in direction of the fault occurred. It is inferred that the tip of the Panamanian peninsula of Pacifica made contact with the Marquesas at the time of their inception, creating a situation comparable with that between Peru and the Galapagos. Continuation of the drift of the American sector of Pacifica with a change in direction would have severed this connection, and later the Marquesas would have subsided about 2 km—in common with the rest of the Central Pacific. This interpretation is supported by the unusually rich flora for such an isolated group of islands, with its 80 endemic species and close links with the flora of the Hawaiian Archipelago. For phytogeography, the importance of the Marquesas is comparable with that of the Galapagos for zoogeography.

Hawaii

In my reconstruction of Pacifica the line of junction between the Chinese and American sector (the Kula and Farallon Plates) was aligned on Laysan Island. Midway Island, at the northwestern end of the Hawaiian group, probably should have been used. The Hawaiian lineations as presently known (Larson and Pitman 1972) would then be juxtaposed to the spreading line. On the evidence of these lineations, sea floor spreading began in this area about 150 Ma and finished at 112 Ma. It is generally accepted that starting at Midway the oldest islands of the group are at the northwestern end and that the Island of Hawaii is the youngest at the southeastern end. Sinking of the sea floor began at the northwestern end and progressed gradually toward the southeast (Menard 1964). Many of the northwestern islands are now submerged seamounts. Dredgings from the Necker Ridge and the mid-Pacific seamounts to the west of Hawaii indicate that this region has sunk about 2 km since the early Cretaceous on the evidence of fossil corals and other reef organisms of that age. The conclusion is that the northwestern islands must have originated by volcanic activity early in the drift process. It is probable that at first a long narrow island bearing a string of volcanoes was produced. This was colonized by a limited number of plant species while the water gap between the island and the drifting continental fragments was narrow. From his study of Pacific floras, Guppy (1906) concluded that most of the Hawaiian flora was originally adapted for bird dispersal although the birds were no longer effective vectors for transoceanic dispersal. Under the conditions existing in the early phases of drift, both birds (if they were sufficiently advanced) and wind could have been effective vectors for the small number of species that Fosberg (1948) envisaged as the early colonizers.

The nature of the history of the archipelago can be judged from the bathymetry around the major islands. For simplicity in the map (figure 6.4),

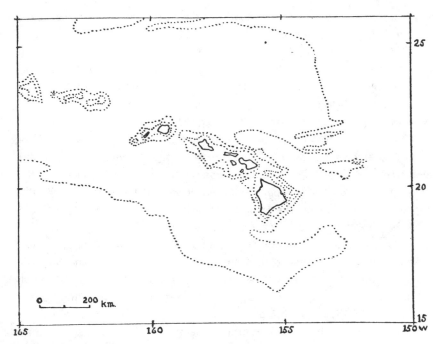

Figure 6.4. Bathymetry of the southeastern end of the Hawaiian Archipelago. The 1-3-, and 5-km isobaths are shown.

only the 1-, 3-, and 5-km isobaths are drawn. Oahu, Molokai, and Maui are all united somewhere above the 1-km contour, and Hawaii is only just separated. The vast quantities of volcanic material ejected on Hawaii have caused it to sink in isostatic readjustment, and the effect of the sinking is indicated by the moat at the 5-km contour partly surrounding the islands (Menard 1964). At a not very distant date Hawaii must have been united with the other islands northwest to Oahu. Borings on Oahu have demonstrated successive stages in sinking with a Miocene shore line at 500 m (Stearns and Chamberlain 1967). It is probable that from Oahu to Hawaii there was a single island in early Miocene and that at an earlier date Kauai was also attached. The process continued back to the early stages of drift before the origin of the southeastern islands. Thus migration across water barriers may have played an insignificant part in the evolution of the modern biota. Only about one percent of the present indigenous flora consists of plants capable of transoceanic dispersal, and these have a pan-Pacific distribution. The remaining 99 percent must have come overland or have crossed only very narrow water barriers. The chances of long-distance transoceanic dispersal are infinitesimal for plants not specially adapted for water transport. If this were not so, why is there no evidence for transoceanic dispersal of any of the numerous Hawaiian endemics?

If the Hawaiian Archipelago was formed in the manner here postulated, the question arises why the islands were not swept away by sea-floor spreading, leaving the oldest islands nearest to the drifted continent as in the South Atlantic (Wilson 1963). In the North Pacific the early stages of drift were accompanied by immense outpourings of basaltic lava, which formed a vast archipelagic apron enclosing the islands and straddling the spreading ridge. The archipelagic apron behaved as a minor continent, became decoupled from the spreading convection streams, but remained subject to their drag. The drag on the archipelagic apron introduced tensional stresses that began to tear it asunder. The event that finally sealed the fate of Hawaii was a change in the direction of sea-floor spreading of the Farallon Plate. Between the Molokai and Clarion Fracture Zones, this change imposed oblique stresses that severed the connection between Hawaii and the drifting continent. East of Hawaii the ocean now plunges to a depth of nearly 6000 m, and matching contours occur at the edge of the continental slope at depths of 4500–5000 m. The spreading ridge is now fossil and aseismic, leaving Hawaii on its submerged platform connected by the Necker Ridge to the mid-Pacific mountains submerged on the eastern half of the archipelagic apron.

One common circumstance attended the isolation of the three major archipelagoes: a change in the condition of sea-floor spreading. In the case of Hawaii and the Marquesas it was a change in the spreading direction, evidence of which can be seen in the transform faults. For the Galapagos, it was change in the motion of the continental fragment—Peru. In each case, oblique stresses caused the shearing off of the island group and so preserved a sample of its biota, which subsequently proceeded on a separate evolutionary path.

Significance of Pacifica for Biogeography

The reconstruction of the Pacific continent focuses attention on a number of factors of great biogeographical significance. Croizat's two Pacific "gates of angiospermy" merge into one, and they connect directly with the Gondwana continent. It is clear that the Pacific continent was one of the major migration routes of early angiosperms northward from Gondwanaland into the northern hemisphere. The early initiation of drift in the North Pacific (150 Ma) brings into question the part played by birds as plant vectors at a period contemporaneous with *Archeopteryx*. If primitive birds had already developed the migratory habit, only one north-south route would have been possible. Drift was well advanced by the mid-Cretaceous, when birds may have been effective vectors, but two parallel migration routes would then have been available. If birds had been effective dispersal agents for plants at an early period, as claimed by Guppy (1906), their present ineffectiveness among the islands of the Central Pacific could be due to the wide separation of the island archipelagoes consequent on drift.

The hypothesis that the angiosperms orginated in southeastern Asia has been accepted by many authors (Thorne 1963; Takhtajan 1969; Smith 1970) on account of the relatively large number of species surviving in that region with characters considered primitive. Takhtajan (1969) gives the limits, between Assam and Fiji, which encompass that large area of Pacifica into which early angiosperms first migrated and where primitive members could be expected to survive. The eastern border is given as Fiji, although Van Balgooy (1960) gives reasons for placing it at Samoa and Tonga, beyond which Malaysian elements disappear from the island floras. The line indicated is part of the spreading ridge of South Pacifica; to the east of it there are no major islands that have continental rocks. The thinning out of the Malaysian element is consistent with the decreasing size of the continental fragments in the eastward direction and with the reconstruction of Pacifica. The fragmentation of Pacifica provides a simple explanation of vicarious plant distributions, both east to west and north to south. Stages in the drift account for the compositon and relationships of the floras of the major island archipelagoes, some examples of which are given below.

Pacific Distributions

Fagus and Nothofagus. It has been suggested that *Nothofagus* is a test case for phytogeographical distributions (Van Steenis 1971) because the seeds sink in, and are rapidly killed by, sea water. I previously described the vicarious distribution of species pairs and groups of species on either side of the South Pacific and need not enter into details here (Melville 1973). It will now be interesting to link the distributions of *Fagus* and *Nothofagus*.

It is generally agreed that *Fagus* and *Nothofagus* are closely related genera; at first the southern beeches were all placed in *Fagus*. One of the characters distinguishing *Nothofagus* is its hexacolporate pollen grains, which first appear in the fossil record early in the Cretaceous. Although it is likely that *Fagus* and *Nothofagus* had begun to diverge from a common proto-*Fagus* ancestor by the Middle Jurassic, the sharing of tricolporate or possibly tricolpate pollen of a generalized early angiosperm type would not permit their discrimination on microspore characters. From the timing of the breakup of Pacifica in the Jurassic, it is probable that *Fagus* was migrating northward along the mountains of the rift-valley system in company with many early angiosperms requiring the temperate conditions of higher altitudes. After the drift, groups of *Fagus* were separated on either side of the Pacific and began to differentiate. In contrast with *Nothofagus*, only minor divergences developed in cupule and seed characters, but on the Asiatic side a cline in leaf characters evolved.

Among the extant species of *Nothofagus*, *N. alessandri* has the most primitive leaves and inflorescence. Its leaves are relatively large, thinly textured, and closest in appearance to those of the northern beeches. The margin is sharply dentate, each tooth with one or two secondary denticles. In these characters the North American *Fagus grandifolia* comes closest (figure 6.5). It is a variable species exhibiting many of the characters found in Asiatic species, but gene interchange appears to have prevented diversification to the species level. *F. mexicana* has smaller teeth on its leaves than *F. grandifolia* with which it forms a species pair, matched on the Asiatic side by a vicarious pair comprising *F. lucida* and *F. chienii*. The leaves of these Chinese species are more advanced than those of their North American counterparts and mark the beginning of the Eurasian cline in leaf characters. The teeth are much reduced in size, and between them the margin bulges out to form shallow crenations with the teeth in the sinuses. From this point two evolutionary lines radiate, one developing long slender penducles to the cupules up to 6–7 cm long and the other retaining short penduncles generally 1.0–1.5 cm long.

In the longipedunculate group, *F. longipetiolata* has very small blunt teeth, which are overtopped by the crenations of the margin. The other two, *F. japonica* and *F. engleriana*, have sinuately crenate margins which are edentate. They form a vicarious pair in Japan and China in which *F. japonica* is distinguished by a reduction in the relative size of the cupule lobes, which are only half to one third as long as the nuts. In the second, brevipedunculate group, the leaves of adult trees are edentate, and the lateral veins no longer reach the base of the sinus but curve round parallel with the margin. *F. sieboldii* and *F. multinervis* form a vicarious pair, respectively in Japan and Korea, with sinuate crenate margins.

FAGUS

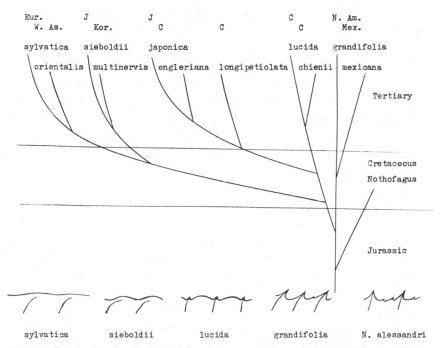

Figure 6.5. Dendrogram of phylogenetic relationships in *Fagus*, placed on a geological time scale, showing vicarious distributions, and, at the base, the cline in leaf characters: Eur., Europe; W. As., western Asia; J., Japan; Kor., Korea; C., China; N. Am., North America; Mex., Mexico.

The series is completed by *F. sylvatica* in Europe and *F. orientalis* in the Near East with distributions overlapping in the Balkans. The margin is shallowly sinuate crenate in *F. orientalis*, but only slightly sinuous or simple and unmodulated in *F. sylvatica*. The leaf characters form a simple cline from east to west across Eurasia without complication by secondary centers of diversification. The distribution pattern exhibited by *Fagus* is fairly representative of many other genera that started their evolution in the South Pacific or have close relatives there. As in *Nothofagus*, the most advanced members of the series are farthest from the point of origin.

Oreomyrrhis.   *Oreomyrrhis* (Umbelliferae) is a genus of 23 species of small carrot-like plants widely distributed across the southern Pacific (Mathias and Constance 1955). The most generalized species is *O. andicola*, found at high elevations along the Andes from Colombia to the northern Argentine. Its range of variation is almost as great as that of the entire genus, but it has not been possible to segregate it into species. In Central America to the north, three species occur, which probably recently originated by migration and speciation following the Miocene closure of the Panamanian Isthmus. To the south, after a gap in its distribution, the genus is represented in Fuegia and the Falklands by *O. hookeri* (figure 6.6), which can be regarded as an isolated segment of the *O. andicola* complex. *O. ramosa* in New Zealand is closely related to *O. hookeri* with which it forms a vicarious species pair. In Australia and Tasmania there are seven species that form a closely knit group allied with *O. hookeri*. The progenitors of these and of *O. ramosa* probably migrated from their Fuegian homeland in the late Jurassic, when the rift-valley phase of the orogeny had broadened the previously existing Antarctic continental connection and had made a land link with New Zealand.

Prior to the link, New Zealand and New Caledonia had been isolated islands on a continental shelf. The orogenic upwarping created mountain ranges high enough to provide temperate conditions suited to these cold adapted plants. They were able to migrate from New Zealand via New Caledonia to New Guinea and on to Borneo and Taiwan. With isostatic readjustment in the post-orogenic phase, parts of these migration routes either were submerged or were at too low an altitude to provide temperate conditions in the tropics. Thus *Oreomyrrhis* has not survived in New Caledonia and only at altitudes over 4000 m on Mt. Kinabalu in Borneo. As a result of migration and the climatic changes during the orogeny, we now are left in the western Pacific with four more vicarious species pairs: *buwaldiana* (New Guinea) + *colensoi* (New Zealand); *borneensis* (Borneo) + *rigida* (New Zealand); *invoucrata* (Taiwan) + *papuana* (New Guinea); *taiwaniana* (Taiwan) + *pumila* (New Guinea). An interesting parallel with *Nothofagus* is that the most advanced species in the genus, *O. azorellacea* and *O. linearis*, are found on the mountains of New Guinea.

Mathias and Constance show about equal extension north and south from the Peruvian enclave of the *O. andicola* complex into Colombia and into northern Argentina. There is then a gap in the distribution until *O. hookeri* appears in Fuegia. Disjunct distributions along the Andes in South America are known from many genera and can be accounted for by the divergent paths taken by the Peruvian and Magellanic sectors of South Pacifica. The intervening gap in northern and central Chile is opposite to the deepest part of the Peru-Chile Trench, where, presumably, only oceanic crust was subducted. Of the three closely related genera of Scrophulariaceae, *Porodittia*, *Jovellana*, and *Calceolaria*, the first two are separated by the gap and *Calceo-*

OREOMYRRHIS

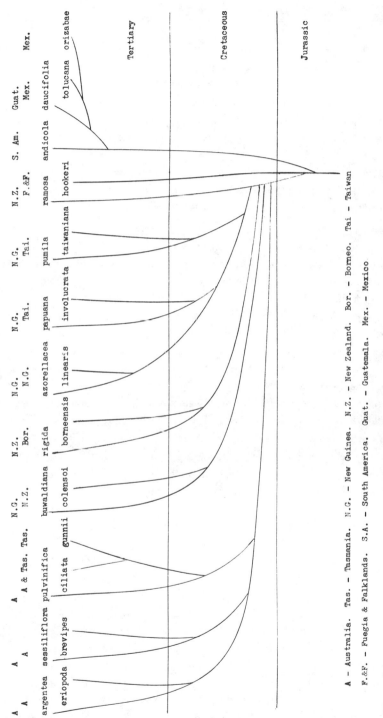

A – Australia. Tas. – Tasmania. N.G. – New Guinea. N.Z. – New Zealand. Bor. – Borneo. Tai – Taiwan

F.&F. – Fuegia & Falklands. S.A. – South America. Guat. – Guatemala. Mex. – Mexico

Figure 6.6. Dendrogram of phylogenetic relationships in *Oreomyrrhis*, placed on a geological time scale, showing vicarious distributions.

laria bridges it. The most primitive of the three, represented only by *Porodittia triandra*, is confined to a small area in Peru. *Jovellana* is absent from Peru, but has two pairs of sibling species in New Zealand and southern Chile (*J. sinclairii*, NZ + *J. punctata*, C and *J. repens*, NZ + *J. violacea* C). *Calceolaria* is absent from New Zealand, but, with numerous species, extends from southern Mexico along the Central American isthmus and down the whole length of the Andes, bridging the mid-Chile gap. A more complete study of the phylogeny of *Calceolaria* would probably shed some light on how the Chilean gap was bridged. The genus passed through a period of rapid evolution during the Tertiary, expanding into nearly every available ecological niche.

Coriaria.   By contrast with *Calceolaria*, *Coriaria*—sole genus of the Coriariaceae—is an example of a slowly evolving taxon. The range of variation in both vegetative and floral characters is comparatively small and this, added to a facility for forming hybrids, creates difficulties for the taxonomist. The most generalized species is *C. ruscifolia* L., which occurs in both Chile and New Zealand, suggesting that little morphological change has taken place in the last fifty million years. Although the New Zealand populations are treated as a separate species, *C. arborea*, I have been unable to find any constant characters to separate them from the Chilean populations. Closely related to *C. ruscifolia* is *C. sarmontosa* of New Zealand, which probably gave rise to the small leaved complexes now vicariously separated in New Zealand and Peru to Mexico (figure 6.7). The American complex, *C. thymifolia*, has not been satisfactorily resolved into separate species, but three species—*C. angustissima*, *C. kingiana*, and *C. pteridoides*—can be recognized in New Zealand. Their limits have been confused, however, by recent hybridization due to human interference with the habitat.

Forms of *C. ruscifolia* in the Kermadecs, Fiji, and Tahiti link the New Zealand populations with the northern Pacific. The distributions suggest that the migration route was confined to the western side of the rift valley through the former Pacific continent. Forms of *C. ruscifolia* probably reached the New Hebrides and Solomons during late stages of the drift, when these volcanic islands were formed. *C. papuana* in New Guinea and *C. intermedia* in Taiwan and the northern Philippines can be regarded as a vicariant pair separated from the *C. ruscifolia* stock during the breakup of Pacifica. Related to *C. intermedia*, *C. sinica* and *C. japonica* comprise another vicarious pair in China and Japan. The remaining Eurasiatic species appear to have arisen from the *C. sinica* stock. *C. nepalensis* from the Himalayas and western China forms a vicarious pair with *C. myrtifolia* around the borders of the Mediter-

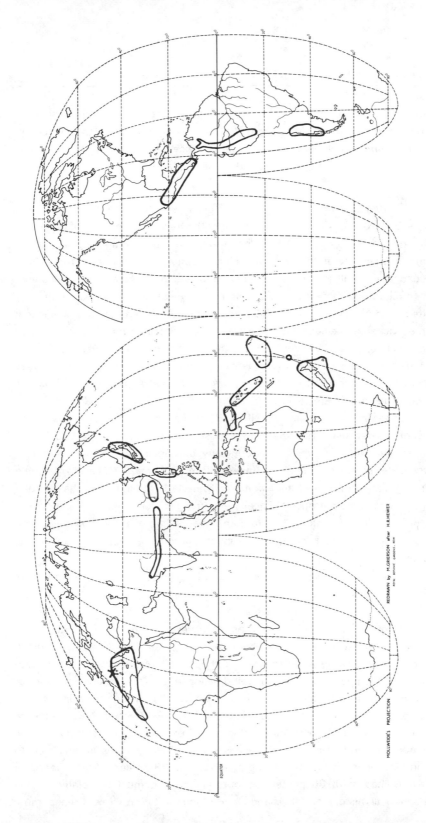

Figure 6.7. Distribution of *Coriaria* (Coriariaceae). X, site of the Oligocene fossil *C. longaeva*.

MOLLWEIDE'S PROJECTION

EQUATOR

REDRAWN by M.GRIERSON after H.B.HEWER
ROYAL BOTANIC GARDENS, KEW

ranean. *C. terminalis*, which is sympatric with *C. nepalensis*, stands apart in having terminal racemes. It appears to be closely related to the Oligocene fossil *C. longaeva* Saporta from southern France, indicating that the *C. terminalis* offshoot also reached the Mediterranean (Saporta 1865).

Ranunculaceae. Among the numerous floristic relationships between New Zealand and South America, some of the Ranunculaceae are of outstanding interest. Fisher (1965) has drawn attention to a number of similarities among members of the Trollianthoideae section of *Ranunculus* from Peru, Ecuador, and Bolivia and alpine members of section *Epirotes* in New Zealand. With regard to the development of an androgynophore and elaborate nectary pits on the petals, the Trollianthoideae can be considered the more advanced. Three vicariant species pairs are noteworthy for their extremely primitive leaf architecture. *R. godleyanus* (NZ) has the most primitive leaf venation in the genus and is closest to *R. macropetalus* (Peru). *R. insignis* (NZ) and *R. gigas* (Peru) have orbicular cordate leaves, and in *R. lyallii* (NZ) and *R. clypeatus* (Peru) the leaves are peltate. In all of these species the midrib is poorly developed (or not present at all in *R. godleyanus*), and the venation is dichotomo-reticulate. *R. godleyanus* is closest in its leaf architecture to *Laccopetalum giganteum*, which was originally described as a *Ranunculus*, and which also comes from the high Andes of Peru. *Laccopetalum* leaves resemble the Permian form genus *Gangamopteris* (Melville 1969) in shape, absence of a midrib, and in the presence of flabellately arranged dichotomo-reticulate veins. It differs in the dentate leaf margin and the infilling of the major areoli by a secondary minor venation, but the aspect still remains that of a *Gangamopteris*.

Although *Ranunculus* has a worldwide distribution, leaves as primitive as those mentioned above are confined to Peru and New Zealand. Evolutionary stages slightly more advanced than *R. insignis* occur occasionally across northern Asia and into Europe, as for example *R. thora*. Another relatively primitive leaf type is much more widespread. This I call flammuloid, using *R. flammula* as an example. The shape varies from ovate to lanceolate or linear, the midrib is poorly to well developed, and the venation is more or less dichotomo-reticulate or intermediate toward polygono-reticulate types. The proportion of flammuloid leaf types in the New Zealand *Ranuncults* flora (table 6.1) is only 14 percent, but it is only 9 percent in Australia (table 6.1). In tropical South America, where this group of *Ranunculus* is restricted to high elevations on the Andes, the proportion is 23 percent. The situation in New Guinea, with 60 percent, is outstanding and must be related to the geophysical history of the island. In our interpretation, New Guinea must

Table 6.1 Distribution of Flammuloid Leaves in *Ranunculus*

	No./Total	Percentage	Authority
New Zealand	6/43	14	Fisher
Australia	3/32	9	Herb. Kew
Temperate South America	7/28	25	Lourteig
Tropical South America	8/35	23	Lourteig
New Guinea	14/24	60	Eichler
Taiwan	2/11	18	Li et al.
China	4/18	21	Ic. Cormoph.
Japan	3/25	12	Ohwi
Central & Northern United States	5/36	14	Gray
California	4/30	13	Munz
Europe	17/131	13	Fl. Europ.
Great Britain	4/23	17	C.T. & W.
Africa	0/23	0	Herb. Kew

have received its ranunculi by migration from South Pacifica early in the orogeny and afterwards was isolated until contact was made with Australia in the Oligocene. Long isolation may account, in part, for the large proportion of relatively primitive species surviving, but more important is the presence of high mountain ranges that have provided suitable habitats for cool-adapted species in the tropics. A few species occur at elevations of 2000 m, but the majority are found between 3000–5000 m. These altitudinal requirements account for the absence of ranunculi from numerous low-lying islands in the tropics, and they also throw much light upon the Pacific migration route of the angiosperms. An altitudinal limit of 2000 m would prevent migration through the tropical Pacific at present. The widespread evidence of a subsidence of the floor of the Pacific by approximately 2000 m since the Cretaceous (Menard 1964) implies that any pre-existing land surface along the line of the rift valley would have been upraised by at least this amount. Suitable altitudes would therefore have existed during the period of maximum uplift to enable temperate plants to migrate from the southern into the northern hemisphere. The converse is the absence of *Ranunculus* at the present time from islands that would have been on or adjacent to the migration route in the past and have more recently subsided below the critical level. These include Norfolk Island (310 m), Fiji (1300 m), Tonga (1000 m), Kermadecs (520 m), and Marquesas (1400 m). Altitudes are sufficient in the Hawaiian Archipelago, but the early history was different. There are two closely allied modern species, which are probably derived from one species that reached Hawaii over a narrow water gap.

    Caltha is another of the cold loving Ranunculaceae that managed to cross the equator. The genus is divided into two sections of which *Populago* has a pan-boreal distribution, and *Psychrophila* is confined to alpine and subalpine moorlands in Australia, New Zealand, Peru, and Magellania. The vascular structure of the flower in *Psychrophila* is one of the most primitive in the family, with simple follicles supported by a single vascular strand. In *Populago* the three traces of the follicle are more or less disjunct, as they are in the majority of the Helleboroideae. Because of these differences an argument could be made in favor of separating *Psychrophila* at the generic level. The only other closely comparable genus is *Asteropyrum* with two species in China. *Psychrophila* and *Asteropyrum* then constitute a vicarious pair of genera to the south and north of the Pacific.

The basic leaf shape in *Psychrophila* is sagittate, with the basal lobes turned upward as in *C. sagittata* (figure 6.8), so that the fold makes an angle of 90° with the midrib. In different species this fold is rotated to various extents, and in the extreme case, *C. appendiculata*, it is rotated 180°, with the bases of the lobes parallel with the midrib (figure 6.8*F*). Vicariant pairs can be recognized among the intermediate species. Thus, in *C. phylloptera* (Tasmania) and *C. alata* (Peru) the petioles are 3-trace and bifacial, and the basal angle is about 150°. Two vicarious species have unifacial petioles with 4–8 traces and the basal angle of 90°–100°, viz., *C. sagittata* (Peru and Chile) and *C. introloba* (Australia). For *Caltha* in the wide sense, there are vicarious pairs north to south and east to west.

Marquesan Flora

The Marquesas Archipelago is a group of volcanic islands situated at 8–10° south of the equator at longitude 139–140°W. They are very isolated; the nearest land consists of the atolls of the Tuamotu group 300 miles to the south. Hawaii lies 2,000 miles to the northwest over trackless ocean; and Mexico, the nearest continental point, is nearly 3,000 miles away. Despite their isolation the Marquesas have a relatively rich flora with 80 endemics, most of which are either rare or endangered species. The islands lie on a submerged platform that shelves steeply to a depth of 4 km. At a depth of 2 km (figure 6.9) lies a narrow col, which divides the islands into a northern and a southern group. The partial separation of the islands at this depth is reflected in the distribution of the flora. Nukuhiva, the largest island of the northern subgroup, supports 42 of the endemic species, and 24 of these are confined to Nukuhiva. All but one (17) of the remainder are shared with Hivaoa, the largest island of the southern subgroup. Hivaoa supports 34 of the endemics, 13 of which are confined to Hivaoa. The situation here outlined has led to numerous vicarious distributions among the islands of the archipelago and has been

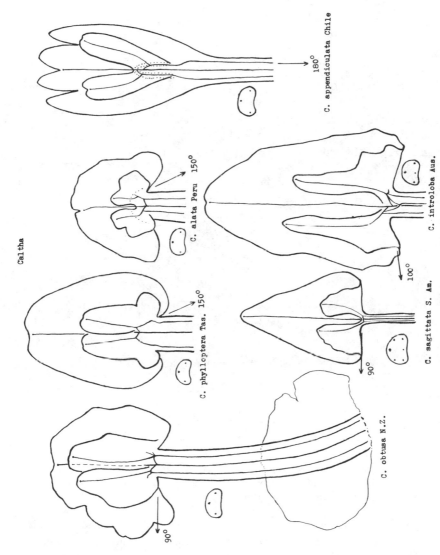

Figure 6.8. Leaves of *Caltha*, subgenus *Psychrophylla*, showing the rotation of the upturned basal lobes and two vicarious sister species.

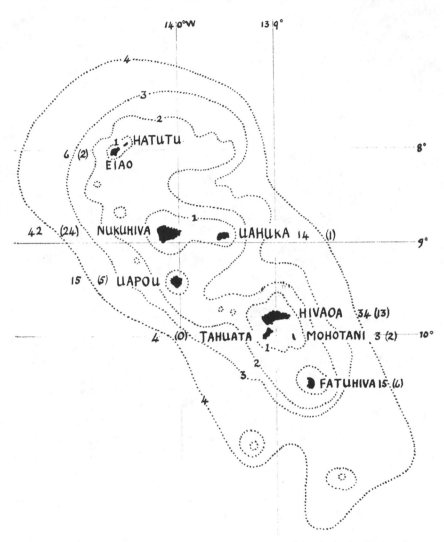

Figure 6.9. Marquesas Archipelago with 1-, 2-, 3-, and 4-km isobaths. Numerals show the number of Marquesan endemics on each island and, in brackets, the number of endemics confined to the island.

brought about by a gradual sinking of the ocean floor since the Cretaceous. It seems probable that the subsidence of the Marquesan platform has been of the order of 2 km, but no firm data on this point are yet available. Sinking of the Tuamotu Archipelago by at least 1 km since the Eocene is already proved by the dredging of corals of that age in their vicinity.

One of the interesting features of the Marquesan flora is the presence of eight species of *Bidens*. One of these, *B. beckiana*, is confined to the northern island Eiao. Four are endemic to Nukuhiva (*B. polycephala, B. cordifolia, B. jardinii,* and *B. serrulata*), one is endemic to Uapou (*B. uapensis*), and two are endemic to Hivaoa (*B. collina, B. henryi*). *B. uapensis* appears to be the most primitive of the group and closest to *B. cordifolia. B. beckiana* is morphologically near *B. cordifolia; B. jardinii,* is near *B. collina.* Between individual island pairs and between the northern and southern halves of the archipelago, there are vicarious distributions that can be accounted for by subsidence. All of the Marquesan species of *Bidens* belong to the section *Campylotheca,* which is distributed through the Pacific from Marotiri in the south to the Hawaiian Archipelago in the north and involves wide-ranging vicariance. *B. st. johniana* (Sherff 1937a) is unique both in its habitat and in having the most primitive leaf architecture in the genus. It was collected by St. John on the Mangarevan expedition (St. John 1935; Fosberg 1962), on one of the now almost submerged basaltic stacks that constitute Marotiri (143°W, 28°S). This *Bidens* and its associates represent the last remnants of the montane flora of an island like Uapou, which has volcanic plugs rising as vertical pinnacles for up to 2,000 feet above the ridge on which they stand. The venation is subflabellate with dichotomo-reticulate secondary veins and represents a relatively early stage in the evoluton of modern leaves from *Gangamopteris,* all stages of which can be demonstrated in other genera of Compositae. Elsewhere in the South Pacific, *B. hendersonensis* on Henderson Island, with a variety on the adjacent Oeno Island, and *B. mathewsii* on Pitcairn Island are closely related to the Marquesan species. In the Society Islands sibling species survive vicariously on Tahiti (*B. orofenensis*) and Moorea (*B. paniculata*). These are more advanced in their leaf architecture than the Marquesan species and appear to be more closely allied with the Hawaiian *B. amplectens* and *B. skottsbergii.*

The section *Campylotheca* is not represented on the continental mainlands of either Asia or America, but *B. monticola* (Section *Clomptonia*) from Peru is close to *B. australis* of Tahiti and Tonga and to *B. hawaiensis* of Maui and Hawaii (Sherff 1937a). The section *Greenmannia* includes the relatively primitive *B. shrevei* from Jamaica as well as other species in the Greater Antilles, Central America, and Peru, thus repeating the distributional pattern of the New World cottons. Section *Platycarpaea* includes *B. tripartita* and *B. cernua,* which occur in North America and extend across Eurasia from Japan to the Atlantic seaboard. Taken together, the sections of *Bidens* have followed the same paths as *Ranunculus, Coriaria,* and other genera that have followed the Pacific migration route.

The genus *Coreopsis* is considered closely related to *Bidens* and has a number of species distributed throughout the Americas. The two genera are usually discriminated by the presence of winged exaristate achenes in *Coreopsis* and awned exalate achenes in *Bidens*. These distinctions break down in the Marquesan species of *Bidens*. The achenes are neither awned nor winged in *B. beckiana*, *B. polycephala*, and *B. uapensis*. *B. cordifolia* is either awnless or has two minute deciduous awns; *B. serrulata* is narrowly winged and has a crown of minute cuspidate teeth, while *B. henryi* is narrowly winged but has two smooth awns. It is evident that these southern *Bidens* species constitute a variable and primitive complex, which may be a relict of the original complex that gave rise to the more typical sections of *Bidens* and to the American *Coreopsis* by stabilization of the fruit characters. Although a primitive species of *Bidens* has survived on Marotiri, it is significant that there is none on Rapa, the nearest island. Instead on Rapa there are three species of *Oparanthus*, another closely related genus with alate and aristate achenes (Sherff 1937b). The only other species (*O. albus*) is vicariously distributed on Hivaoa in the Marquesas. Thus there are three vicariously distributed genera in this alliance, one confined to two southern islands, one widespread across the Pacific, and the third on the American continent.

The genus *Coreopsis*, as usually accepted, includes a number of African species, but there is none on the main body of South America. Although morphologically similar, the African group may have had a separate origin, and a critical reappraisal of it is needed. The South American group is confined to the western fringe of the continent and conforms to the distributional pattern characteristic of plants with Pacific relationships. Thus there is one species in Chile separated by a wide gap from one species in Bolivia, then seven species in Peru, and four species in Ecuador. The genus continues up through Central America with 16 species, into the United States with 41 species. The distribution thus ties in closely with that of *Bidens*.

Links between the Marquesas and Hawaii

Vicarious links between the floras of the Marquesan and Hawaiian Archipelagos, like those in *Bidens*, are repeated in a number of other genera. Two genera of Araliaceae occur in the Marquesas. *Reynoldia marchionensis* occurs on Hivaoa and Fatuhiva and appears to be closely related to *R. sandwichensis* in Hawaii. Another four species occur in Hawaii, and there are two vicarious species in Samoa and one in Tahiti. The second genus, *Cheirodendron*, is represented by *C. marquesense* on five of the islands of the Marquesas and by six species on Hawaii. Of the Hawaiian species, *C.*

platyphyllum from Kauai and Oahu appears to be closest to the Marquesan species.

Among the Malvaceae the tribe Gossypieae is of exceptional interest. It is represented in the Marquesas by the monotypic genus *Lebronnecia* (Fosberg and Sachet 1966) and by *Gossypium hirsutum* var. *taitense*. The single tree of *L. kokioides* originally discovered (Fosberg and Sachet 1966) on the island of Tahuata is now dead, but several colonies have since been found on Mohotani. The closest ally and vicariant genus is *Kokia*, of which four species occur in Hawaii.

Gossypium provides another link between the floras of the Marquesan and Hawaiian Archipelagos. *G. tomentosum* is confined to Hawaii, but its sibling species, *G. taitense*, occurs in the Marquesas, Tahiti, and Samoa. *G. taitense* is now (Fryxell 1965a) regarded as a variety of the more widespread *G. hirsutum*, which in turn is related to *G. barbadense*. These three species are amphidiploids, combining the A- and D-genomes of cotton. *G. tomentosum* has played no part in the development of modern cottons, but both *G. hirsutum* and *G. barbadense* have been important sources of modern crop plants. Due to cultivation, breeding, selection by man, and the escape to the wild of cultivars, there is considerable difficulty in deciding which forms are truly survivors of the original wild stocks. I shall consider here only those accepted as such by Fryxell (1965a, 1965b).

In addition to the Tahitian variety of *G. hirsutum*, there is another on Socorro Island off the Pacific coast of Mexico (figure 6.10), a third in the Jaqui Valley of Sonora, Mexico, and a fourth near Progreso at the tip of the Yucatan Peninsula. All of these varieties and their distribution are consistent with their drift *in situ* after the breakup of Pacifica. In addition, the Marie-galante variety occurs in Venezuela, which could have been reached by migration from the Isthmus of Panama, but a form of it is on St. Kitts in the Lesser Antilles, and another island form is on Key Vaca off the Florida Coast. Cotton seeds are capable of floating in sea water and also surviving for short periods of time, so that transport by water between the lesser islands of the Caribbean is possible. It is significant, however, that although seeds of *G. tomentosum* can float for a year, this species has never been found outside the Hawaiian Archipelago. The bulk of the evidence suggests that the present distributions of the forms mentioned here are due to continental drift.

The third amphidiploid, *G. barbadense*, has a wild variety (*v. darwinii*) on the Galapagos Islands, and the Tumbo wild form occurs in northern Peru and Ecuador. In the later stages of drift, the Peruvian craton must have been in contact with the Galapagos, which were probably upraised by volcanic action

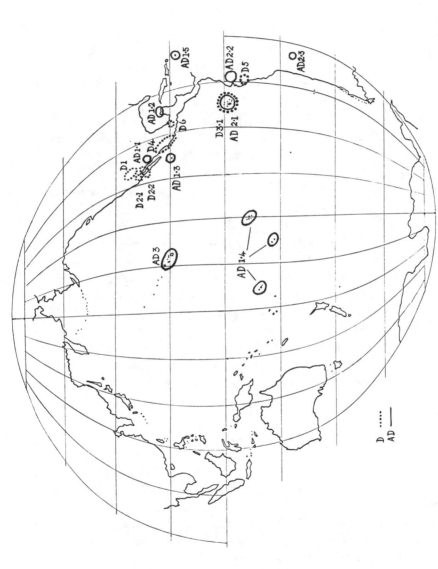

Figure 6.10. Distribution of cottons (*Gossypium*) in the Pacific region. D-genome (diploids): D1, *G. thurberi*; D2.1, *G. armourianum*; D2.2, *G. harknessii*; D3.1, *G. klotschianum*; D4, *G. aridum*; (D5), *G. raimondii*; D6, *G. gossypioides*. AD-genome (allotetraploids): AD1, *G. hirsutum*; AD1.1, *G. h. var. morrillii*; AD1.2, Yucatan var.; AD1.3, Socorro var.; AD1.4, *G. h. var. taitense*; AD1.5, Marie Galante var.; AD2, *G. barbadense*; AD2.1, *G. b. var. darwinii*; AD2.2, Tumbo wild var.; AD2.3, Wild River var.; AD3, *G. tomentosum*.

at this time. Various biota, including Darwin's cotton, then were able to transfer to the islands, and Peru drifted to its present position with what is now the Tumbo wild variety of *G. barbadense*. Thus the vicarious distribution of these two varieties would have originated. Subsequently the Tumbo variety, or its progenitors, must have spread down into northern Argentina to give rise to the present river variety after following a migration path common to many other genera (e.g., *Oreomyrrhis, Coreopsis*).

The origin of the amphidiploid cottons is a problem that has puzzled cotton geneticists for a long time. No wild A-genome cottons occur in the Pacific region, nor is there any evidence of the cultivation of any of them there. Species with the D-genome occur in the Galapagos, Peru, Central America, and north into California. Fryxell recognizes *G. armourianum* from Marcos Island and *G. harknessii* from Baja California as sibling species, as well as *G. thurberi* from Arizona and northern Mexico, and *G. trilobum* from Mexico. *G. klotschianum* from the Galapagos has a vicariant variety, var. *davidsonii*, in Baja California. As with *G. barbadense* var. *darwinii*, *G. klotschianum* probably reached the Galapagos during the drift of Peru, and a sister species, *G. raimondii*, remained behind in Peru. The general situation in regard to vicariance is very similar in both the D- and the AD-genome cottons. Both are consistent with the continental drift theory and an origin in the south Pacific peninsula of Gondwanaland.

Northern Trans-Pacific Vicariants

Trans-oceanic vicariants in the North Pacific region are very numerous and occur in most families that have members in eastern Asia and North America. Some of these have clearly migrated from the south—e.g., *Fagus-Nothofagus, Oreomyrrhis, Ranunculus*, and *Caltha*—and their most advanced taxa are at the farthest fringes of their distribution. Among smaller genera there are commonly vicarious species or groups of species on either side of the Pacific. In the Ranunculaceae, *Anemone canadensis* from Canada and the eastern United States, is a close match for *A. dichotoma* of northern China; and *Trautvetteria japonica* from Manchuria and Japan has close relatives in *T. carolinensis* of the eastern United States and *T. grandis* of the western seaboard of California. Among Magnoliaceae the evergreen, *Magnolia grandiflora* of the eastern United States has its counterpart in *M. delavayi* in southwestern China; one species of *Liriodendron* (*L. chinense*) is in China and the other species (*L. tulipifera*) is in the United States.

That many of these vicariant species occur on the eastern side of North America rather than on the western side, where they would be closer to their Asiatic relatives, was first noted by Asa Gray (1859) and has been discussed more recently by Li (1952). At first these distributions may appear discordant with the continental-drift theory because the eastern half of North America was formerly part of a North Atlantic continent. The explanation lies in the climatic changes resulting from the upraising of the Rocky Mountains during the Miocene. The Redwood (*Sequoia sempervivens*) and the Big Tree (*Sequoiadendron giganteum*) migrated in the reverse directions and their origins are documented by fossils (Florin 1963). Their presumed ancestor, "*Sequoia*" *couttsiae*, was present in western Europe and eastern North America early in the Cretaceous, probably having originated in the mist forests of the mountain ranges of the Atlantic continent before its disjunction. By the late Cretaceous, *Sequoia* had migrated into the Pacific sector of the United States and by the Miocene was close to its present location, having died out elsewhere in North America. The upraising of the Rockies recreated the mist forest conditions favored by *Sequoia*, but it also caused a rain shadow and altered the ecology of the western half of the continent so that many species were able to survive only by migrating to the east. Some, with distributions extending into Central America, now cross over from the eastern United States through Mexico. An example is *Liquidambar styraciflua*, which extends as far south as Honduras and has a vicariant relative in *L. formosana* in China and Taiwan. The presence of a third species, *L. orientalis*, in western Asia suggests that the distribution of *Liquidambar* is a relict of the common type exemplified by *Fagus* and *Coriaria*. *Osmanthus americanus* has a similar distribution in North America (Carolina, Georgia, Florida, and Mexico), but has a vicariant link in Hawaii (*O. sandwichensis*), bridging the Pacific gap to *O. minor* in China.

Bering Land Bridge

It has been customary in the past to assume that vicarious distributions across the North Pacific were due to migration via the Bering land bridge. This assumption was adopted because there did not appear to be any other possible explanation, rather than because of positive evidence in its favor. There is evidence that land connection was made at the beginning of the Quaternary via the Aleutian Islands and that this connection was interrupted from time to time during the Pleistocene, probably as a result of isostatic readjustment as the ice load on the adjacent continents fluctuated (Hultén 1937a). Tundra conditions existed during this period, and only the hardiest of plants could have used this migration route (Colinvaux 1964). The list of plants common to America and eastern Siberia (Hultén 1928) is brief and does not indicate any substantial interchanges. If the Bering bridge had been an important migration route, chains of species with cladistic relationships linking China and North America could be expected, comparable to those discussed in *Fagus, Nothofagus, Coriaria*, and *Oreomyrrhis*. I have not been able to find a single example of this phenomenon across the Beringian link. The conclusion is inevitable that the Bering bridge has played only an insignificant role in plant migration. Croizat (1952) arrived independently at the same conclusion.

Pacifica as Migration Route

From his phylogenetic and biogeographical studies, Croizat (1952) realized that the angiosperms had migrated northward from the regions he called the "gates of angiospermy." The migration routes appear to point back to the Antarctic, a fact that was also realized by Skottsberg (1960). The evidence collected together here for the existence of a Pacific continent in the Mesozoic is consistent with these earlier theories, but Croizat's interpretation is simplified by the fusion of his Polynesian and Magellanic gates into a single migration route along the Pacific continent. The various episodes in the orogeny and their timing, from the initial bridging of the sea gap between Pacifica and the Gondwanian peninsula of the south Pacific, to the isolation of New Guinea, the origin of the Hawaiian, Marquesan, and Galapagos Archipelagoes, the making and breaking of the Central American isthmus, and the drifting of the Peruvian and Magellanic enclaves of South America are all attested for by geological and geophysical evidence. The botanical evidence is extensive, and only a few examples of representative distribution patterns have been touched upon here with some of the vicariant species involved.

With the available evidence it appears that land connection had been made between the northern Pacific continent and the southern peninsula of Gondwanaland by the early Jurassic. It is possible that intermittent contact was made in the late Permian and was sufficient to allow a few species of

Glossopteris to make their way north into New Guinea and Thailand during the early phase of the orogeny (Asama et al. 1975). Other reports of *Glossopteris* from China have been rejected and need reinvestigation. By the Jurassic, however, angiosperms had evolved from the Glossopteridae and early angiosperms made their way northward when the land bridge was finally formed. Isolation preserved primitive forms of *Bidens* in the Marquesas, and in the Ranunculaceae primitive leaf types were left behind vicariously in New Zealand and Peru. Among Compositae, primitive leaf types have survived in New Zealand (*Celmisia, Senecio*), Juan Fernandez (*Robinsonia*), and Hawaii (*Debautia, Raillardia*). Continental relatives of these genera are generally more advanced. Only in *Raillardiella*, vicarious sister genus of *Raillardia* in the United States, have some examples of primitive leaf architecture survived.

Through the sequence of events in the orogeny, it is evident that land connections were made successively and then broken. The migration paths were severed before sufficient time had elapsed for much diversification to take place in newly colonized regions. Backward migration of more advanced species thus was prevented, and the migrational path was unidirectional. The constraints imposed by the migration route had a tendency to cause orthogenetic evolution. At any stage, only a part of the syngamion extended the range, to be modified and subjected to natural selection for changing ecology and climate. The effect of progressive changes brought about by this mechanism is exemplified in *Fagus, Nothofagus*, and *Oreomyrrhis*. The most advanced members of these series are at the ends of their migration paths, farthest away from the centers of origin. There is no possibility of reading these series in the reverse direction because they are intimately interlocked with the sequence and timing of successive stages of the drift. The final outcome is the reverse of that proposed by Matthew (1915) for animals. Whereas it may be possible for a vertebrate to drive away its less efficient ancestors, so that they are banished to the periphery of the distribution area, this is not possible with plants. The individual plant is immobile, and only its propagules are dispersed. Moreover, the relative efficiency of the means of dispersal of their propagules is one of the characters tending to cause the more advanced members of a genus to outstrip their congeners.

The peculiar circumstances of disjunction of the migration route and isolation on islands of no great size did not afford much opportunity for adaptive radiation in the Pacific region itself. The genera *Clermontia* and *Cyanea* in Hawaii are exceptions to this rule, but the general picture is of simple phylogenetic relationships and uncomplicated vicarious distributions. Much greater scope for adaptive radiation developed on the continents to which the two main segments of Pacifica are now attached. *Fagus* has diversified to a minor degree in China, but the interrelationships of the numerous species of *Ranunculus* remain to be worked out. Babcock (1947) has studied the intricate relationships of *Crepis*, which radiate from the Altai-Tianshan region of central Asia to Europe, Africa, India, and eastern Asia. The chromosome numbers range from $N=6$ to $N=3$, with $N=4$ the most frequent. *Dubyaea* and *Soroseris*, with $N=8$, are considered by Stebbins (1940) to be the nearest relatives and the most primitive surviving genera of the Cichorieae. *Dubyaea* has a distribution in western China and eastern Himalaya; and *Soroseris*, from Szechuan and Yunnan to the western Himalayas and Tibet. *Prenanthes*, another related genus, is widespread in eastern Asia and eastern North America. Together these genera have a distribution pattern similar to that of many other genera, such as *Coriaria*, that have followed the Pacific migration route. It seems probable, therefore, that *Crepis* originated from ancestors that had followed the Pacific migration route, but that failed to survive in the Pacific region. The reason for their demise is probably the same as that for *Ranunculus*—unsuitable ecological conditions on the islands after the subsidence of the Pacific floor.

In the pre-drift context of the world of the Carboniferous and Permian, Pacifica supported one of three distinct floras of the northern hemisphere—the Cathaysian or *Gigantopteris* flora. The Angara flora was isolated in eastern Siberia (Sahni 1936; Meyen 1971), separated from the Euramerican coal flora in the North Atlantic continent by a broad sea, later to be closed as China, Angaraland, and Europe drifted together in the Cretaceous to form the Eurasian continent. The super-continent of Gondwanaland occupied much of the southern hemisphere with its *Glossopteris* flora. Between the northern continents and Gondwanaland was a circum-global sea, the Tethys, which appears to have been constricted into a relatively narrow strait to the south of Pacifica. This strait was closed by regional uplift during the early stages of the orogeny, providing one of the major angiosperm migration routes and accounting for Croizat's Polynesian and Magellanic "gates." Africa and South America began to drift in the Triassic (Creer 1964) and probably made contact with the North Atlantic continent some time in the Jurassic. The second major migration route of the angiosperms was thus established before the breakup of the Atlantic continent and accounts for Croizat's African "gate." The data presented in this way do not support the idea of a Mesozoic Pangea, nor does there appear to be any support for Wegener's concept for any period during the

Phanerozoic. Yet most geologists and many biologists have accepted the existence of a Pangea.

As Hughes (1975) has so much geological evidence in favor of Pacifica, let us consider his reconstructions of Pangea. When his reconstructions are placed on the surface of a globe it is difficult to see how they can be related to the evidence supplied by ocean-floor topography and the positions of the transform faults that indicate the direction of drift. In offering the present solution to the Pacific problem, I have taken account of such facts, with the result that the data now form an interlocking plexus supporting the interpretation, at least in its main outlines. The harmonization of apparently conflicting facts, as in the case of the Kermadec Ridge and the paleomagnetism of Central America, also supports the validity of the reconstruction. In the biogeographical field, this solution appears to offer a more satisfactory explanation of distribution patterns than any theory hitherto advanced.

Discussion

B. N. Haugh

THAT THE WESTERN third of North America and Central America en masse, along with Peru and Magellania (Chile + Patagonia), formed part of an ancient continent called Pacifica, located several thousand kilometers to the west of their present position, is an assertion that is not only astounding, based on the meager geological information presented, but naive in terms of the known geology of these regions. Further, the timing of the purported breakup of Pacifica—the vicarious barrier event—and the subsequent drift history of the fragments make it extremely doubtful that the mega-Noah's arcs, after docking with circum-Pacific continents, could account for the biogeography of the organisms cited by Dr. Melville. More geologically rigorous and more philosophically parsimonious explanations are available to explain observed distributions by means of (1) vicarious biotic separation brought about by the breakup of Gondwanaland and the formation of other geologically documented barriers, and (2) floral and faunal dispersal and migration in the classical sense.

A primary rationale for suturing western North America and Central America to eastern and southeastern Asia is the "very close fit between the reconstructed coast lines on either side of the North Pacific." This idea apparently is derived in part from Hughes (1975), who illustrated the closeness of fit with several bathymetric contour matches. Significantly, both

Melville and Hughes either ignore or are unaware of the fact that the Pacific margins of these continents were generated by large scale Tertiary-to-Recent tectonic events. Thus, any fit based on present day bathymetrics is irrelevant and can have little if any resemblance to the bathymetry of the coasts of these land masses as they appeared in the Paleozoic, when they were purportedly sutured into Pacifica (e.g., Dott and Batten 1976: paleogeographical maps). In western North America, for example, the Coast Ranges, the Sierra Nevadas, and the Rocky Mountains were not extant during the proposed Paleozoic suturing of Pacifica. As a prime example of impossible historical geology, Melville takes great care to point out that for a good fit of western North America with Asia, Baja and southern California must be pushed south along the San Andreas Fault to their Tertiary position. These land areas and the fault did not exist at the time of the proposed Paleozoic suture.

Melville places the eastern continental boundary of the cordilleran portion of his Pacifica along the edge of the marine Jurassic (Oxfordian) as drawn by Schuchert (1955). Figure 6.11 illustrates Schuchert's map and also delimits the eastern boundary of Melville's cordilleran Pacifica (heavy dashes), which in fact cuts across much of Schuchert's proposed marine Jurassic. For whatever reason Melville chose this particular continental boundary, it is ludicrous in the light of known geology.

Geological cross-sections that transect Melville's boundary (figure 6.11, section A-A'; figure 6.12; also Mallory 1972; AAPG 1966–73) for the geological interval during which cordilleran Pacifica was supposedly separated from the remainder of North America reveal geological violations of the following continuities: (1) laterally continuous marine sedimentation across the proposed continental boundary; (2) well documented and geographically well delimited epicontinental marine depositional basins; (3) laterally continuous terrestrial sedimentation across the proposed boundary; (4) laterally continuous unconformities across the proposed continental boundary; (5) laterally continuous faunal zones across the proposed boundary; and (6) the absence of tectonic disturbance such as mountain building, thrust faulting, and associated igneous activity that would be expected from a continental collision of cordilleran Pacifica with North America along this boundary. Furthermore, the presence of Franciscan rocks along the west coast indicates a Jurassic-to-Cretaceous subduction zone in the area where Melville's reconstruction requires a spreading zone. Thus, the notion that western North America, as delimited by Melville's Line, formed a major portion of a Pacifica continent and served as a mega-Noah's arc that

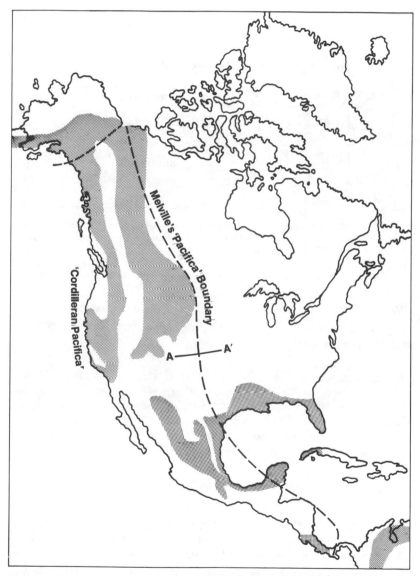

Figure 6.11. Distribution of Jurassic sediments (stippled) with the boundary of Melville's cordilleran Pacifica fragment (heavy dashes) and the location of cross section A-A' in figure 6.1. Adapted from Schuchert (1955).

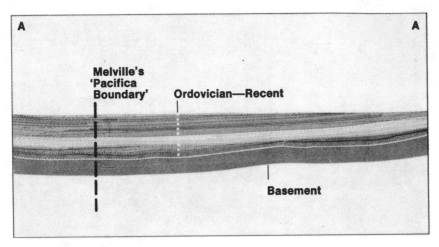

Figure 6.12. Geological cross section through western Kansas and eastern Colorado across Melville's pacifica boundary. See Figure 6.11 for location. Adapted from AAPG (1966–73).

vicariously distributed organisms by docking in the early Tertiary can be rejected unequivocally.

With regard to the two mega-Noah's arcs of southern Pacifica, Peru, and Magellania (figure 6.13), Melville's geological reasoning is equally naive. For example, he states that:

A band of marine Jurassic strata stretches from 33° S on the Chilean coast to the Golfo San Jorge on the Atlantic coast of Argentina [in fact it does not go anywhere near the Atlantic coast], *thus indicating that Magellania was not originally part of South America.* A similar band of marine Jurassic rock *marks off Peru.* Thus it appears likely that these two sectors of South America drifted eastward from some position in the Pacific where they had been close to New Zealand (emphasis added).

I fail to see any sound geological basis for suturing these areas based solely on the occurrence of marine Jurassic, Bajocian-Oxfordian age, strata. Strata of these ages also occur in many other areas of the world. Perhaps Melville could enlighten us on this point. Melville goes on to state that "*confirmation* [emphasis added] for the position of Magellania in the Pacific is provided by a paleomagnetic pole for the mid-Jurassic of Patagonia," citing Valencio and Vilas (1970) as a source. Melville clearly fails to understand that paleomagnetic pole data can not resolve paleolongitude; furthermore, this statement is a blatant misrepresentation of Valencio and Vilas' findings.

With regard to the paleomagnetic poles for the Triassic, Jurassic, and Cretaceous of Patagonia, Valencio and Vilas state that:

The circle of confidence of the middle Jurassic pole (SA8) overlaps a small part of the circle of confidence of (SA7) [Triassic] and half the area of the circle of confidence of the mid-Cretaceous pole (SA9). Then apparently, it would not be clear from the available data whether there is any real difference between the middle Jurassic pole and either the Triassic population or the middle Cretaceous pole.

This would not, of course, discount possible major longitudinal (i.e., east-west) movement during the interval from the Triassic to the Middle Cretaceous *unless* an independent paleomagnetic pole reference—specifically that of Africa—is considered in conjunction with data about South Atlantic sea-floor spreading. Valencio and Vilas do just that: "The circles of confidence of the mean of African Mesozoic poles (Af 6–14) and the mean of

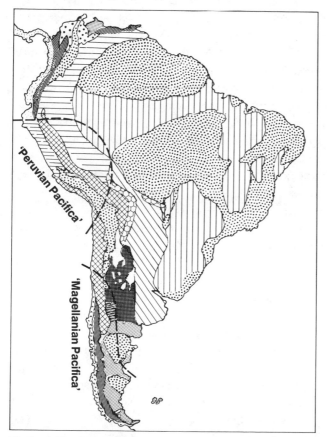

Figure 6.13. Major geological provinces of South America with the boundaries of Melville's Peruvian and Magellanic Pacifica fragments. Adapted from Jenks (1956a).

the South American Triassic poles (SA7) overlap." Hence the two continents were likely coupled and shared the same pole. Continuing, Valencio and Vilas state: "The middle Jurassic pole of South America (SA8) is *out of these populations* [emphasis added], which indicates that in the middle Jurassic (160–7Ma) Africa and South America were drifting apart." Clearly, these data indicate that South America and specifically Melville's Magellania were sutured to Africa and the remainder of Gondwanaland through the Triassic and had only begun to separate in the Lower-Middle Jurassic.

According to Valencio and Vilas' data and spreading ridge data, Magellania *could not have been part of a Pacifica continent* that lay thousands of kilometers away from Gondwanaland. Furthermore, the band of marine Jurassic that connects Peru with Bolivia, Chile, and Argentina (figure 6.14A) indicates geographical continuity among these areas in the Jurassic, and in turn, through sea-floor spreading data, also indicates geographical continuity with African Gondwanaland as is now commonly accepted by geologists. Paleogeographical maps of South America for other geological periods—Devonian, Permo-Carboniferous, Triassic—also demonstrate that Melville's Peruvian Pacifica and Magellanian Pacifica (dashed lines, figures 14B–D) were part of the South American continent. We can see that the proposed Pacifica boundaries cut through many geological trends (figure 6.13). Hence, the same general geological objections cited against Melville's cordilleran Pacifica also apply here. My conclusion is that the mega-Noah's arcs of Melville's Pacifica are mere geofantasy and should join mythical Atlantis as a purely fictional lost continent.

My purpose here is to explore the crucial timing of vicariance events that would affect any *Pacifica theory*, no matter how large or how many continental fragments are involved. I use the work of Larson and Chase (1972) and Larson and Pitman (1972) on sea-floor spreading in the Pacific as a geological temporal standard for these events.

It is fundamental to the theory of vicariance biogeography that the organisms that suffer disjunction exist as a geographically contiguous population *prior* to the creation of some sort of barrier that partitions their geographical range. Whether the coherent ancestral population is inferred on the basis of some systematic theory that relates the ancestry of now disjunct taxa (e.g., Platnick and Nelson 1978), or whether the inferred coherent ancestral population is represented by fossils, and its subsequent disjunction is historically traceable through inferred fossil descendants (e.g., McKenna 1973), is theoretically irrelevant. Evaluation of specific cases of biogeo-

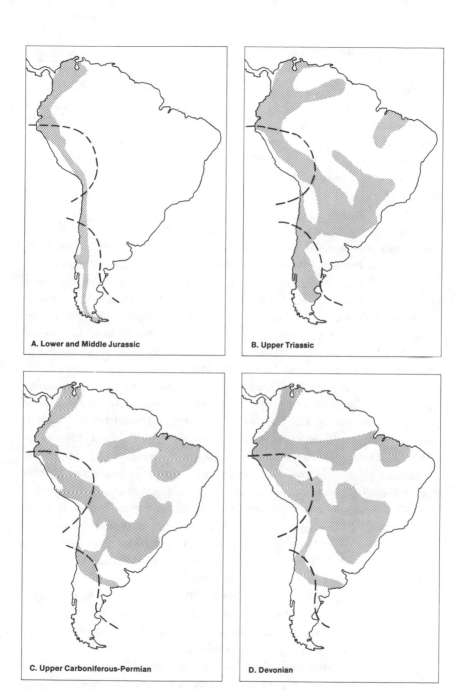

Figure 6.14. Paleogeographical sedimentary provinces of South America (stippled) at four geological times prior to the proposed rifting of Pacifica. The Peruvian and Magellanic fragments, outlined, are alleged by Melville to have been several thousand kilometers to the west at these times Adapted from Weeks (1947).

graphical vicariance depends on: (1) the specific systematic theory purporting to relate the ancestry of now disjunct taxa; (2) the timing of barrier formation relative to the inferred coherent ancestral population; and (3) the timing of possible barrier breakdown allowing mixing of descendant populations (docking of Noah's arcs in the case of Pacifica). Evaluation of Melville's taxonomic examples on the basis of these timing criteria creates serious doubts in my mind that the proposed rifting of Pacifica can account for their present observed distribution.

Assuming, for the sake of analysis, that Melville's Pacifica existed and that it was situated over the fracture zones that delimited the Pacific, Kula, Farallon, and Phoenix Plates of the Mesozoic Pacific Basin as defined by Larson and Chase (1972) and Larson and Pitman (1972), physical rifting would have begun in the Middle Jurassic (150 Ma). Using these authors' spreading rates, a separation of cordilleran Pacifica from Asiatic Pacifica from 1200 km to 1800 km would have existed by the earliest Cretaceous (130–120 Ma). An oceanic separation from 3200 km to 3800 km would be expected by the Middle Cretaceous (100 Ma). McKenna (1973) has pointed out that a given physical barrier may become biologically effective some time before or after physical rifting of a continent into two oceanically separated pieces. In this specific example, effective faunal and floral oceanic barriers likely would have existed at least as early as the earliest Cretaceous (130–120 Ma), and perhaps as early as the latest Jurassic (140 Ma). Barrier breakdown, docking of the mega-Noah's arcs with their respective circum-Pacific continents, would have occurred in the early Tertiary—Paleocene (70–60 Ma) for cordilleran Pacifica and perhaps as late as Eocene (50 Ma) for Peruvian and Megallanian Pacifica. Melville's Pacifican mega-Noah's arcs would have been isolated from one another and from their prospective continental docks for at least all of the Cretaceous, and perhaps even for the latest Jurassic and early Tertiary. Consequently, all biological examples must have systematically reasonable ancestors on Pacifica prior to latest Jurassic-earliest Cretaceous; and the resulting vicariously disjunct circum-Pacific continental descendant taxa cannot appear prior to the Paleocene or Eocene without invoking ancillary dispersal hypotheses.

The notoungulates mentioned by Melville (family Arctostylopidae) do not fit these timing criteria because systematically reasonable ancestors would not have come into existence until the latest Cretaceous to earliest Paleocene. This evolutionary timing would require independent evolution of the ancestral notoungulates on three isolated fragments of Pacifica in order to account for the known biogeography of fossil notoungulates. McKenna (personal communication) believes that the notoungulates originated in South America and that one family (Arctostylopidae) migrated northward across the Panamanian land bridge to North America, and from there migrated with other mammals to Asia via the Bering land bridge in the Paleocene.

The angiosperms are a classic case of explosive evolution and biotic replacement during a comparatively short period of geological time (Beck 1976). It is the particular timing of both the origin and the radiation of the angiosperms relative to geological events in the Pacific Basin that is a major difficulty in Melville's floral vicariance biogeography. If Pacifica is to serve as a "gate of angiospermy," then systematically reasonable hypothetical ancestral angiosperms, or their actual fossil remains, must have been extant there *prior* to the Middle Jurassic. In fact, no angiosperm pollen is known anywhere prior to the early Cretaceous (125 Ma). Thus, either the first angiosperms are of Cretaceous age, or the fossil record of Jurassic angiosperm pollen is lost. The latter possibility seems unlikely because gymnosperm pollen is well known for that time, and selective destruction of coeval angiosperm pollen would seem an unrealistic hypothesis. Nevertheless, Melville states: "From the timing of the breakup of Pacifica in the Jurassic, it is probable that *Fagus* [beech] was migrating northward along the mountains of the rift-valley system [of Pacifica] *in company with many early angiosperms* [emphasis added] requiring the temperate conditions of higher altitudes." The fossil pollen record for the beeches, Family Fagaceae, ranges only from Upper Cretaceous to Recent. Further, it can be shown that the vast majority of the taxonomic orders of angiosperms, as defined by pollen, do not appear in the fossil record until the late Cretaceous (70–80 Ma). Raven and Axelrod (1975) go so far as to state: ". . . there is no evidence that any of the existing orders of angiosperms appeared until the mid-Cretaceous, about 110 million years ago." In my view Melville does not present a convincing systematic theory (e.g., figure 6.5) that would compel us to support a theoretical ancestry of angiosperms in the early Jurassic.

Based on the known palynological record it would seem that angiosperms originated in the latest Jurassic to early Cretaceous (140–130 Ma) and had become taxonomically diverse and geographically world-wide by the mid-to-late Cretaceous (110–70 Ma; summary in Beck 1976; Raven and Axelrod 1974). By the late Cretaceous to early Tertiary, angiosperms had become dominent over gymnosperms in many areas. If Pacifica is upheld as a gate of angiospermy, then once again we must invoke several independent origins for major orders of angiosperms on isolated fragments of Pacifica.

From drift rates, the stratigraphic palynological record, and biogeographical data, it is an inescapable conclusion that *if* Pacifican mega-Noah's arcs docked with circum-Pacific continents in the early Tertiary, a diverse angiosperm flora was already on hand to greet them at the shore. We can resolve this temporal dilemma only by resorting to transoceanic dispersal from Pacifica. For example, how can Pacifican vicariance account for the occurrence of angiosperms in the Canadian Arctic Islands in the Middle Cretaceous (Albian, 105 Ma)?

Finally I wish to comment briefly on several of Melville's floral examples of Pacifican vicariance biogeography. The disjunct biogeography of the southern beech, *Nothofagus*, and its relationship to the breakup of Gondwanaland is a classic textbook example of vicariance biogeography, as well as of dispersal. Its fossil remains appear in the latest Cretaceous (Senonian, 80–70 Ma) in southern South America, Antarctica, eastern Australia, and New Caledonia, and in the late Miocene on New Guinea. A polar projection of the Gondwanaland continents for the late Cretaceous (figure 6.15) indicates that all areas that have a late Cretaceous record of *Nothofagus* were either very close, or were in land contact with one another. In fact, Raven and Axelrod (1972, 1974) believe that direct overland dispersal between South America and Australia was possible until the Middle Eocene (50–45 Ma). This reconstruction seems to offer the most parsimonious explanation for the biogeography of *Nothofagus* (Schuster 1976). Melville's Pacifica hypothesis would encounter difficulty in explaining the appearance of *Nothofagus* in Australia in the late Cretaceous because it is improbable that New Zealand could have drifted westward from its proposed original mid-Pacific location by that date. Australia was far south, attached to Antarctica at that time, and had not yet begun to drift northward. The argument is academic anyway, because there is good geological evidence that New Zealand, the Campbell Plateau, and New Caledonia were attached to the eastern margin of Australia (figure 6.1) until the late Cretaceous to Paleocene (80–60 Ma), when rifting created the Tasman Sea (Hayes and Ringis 1973; Kennett and Houtz, 1973; Griffiths 1971). Hence, these areas could not have been part of Pacifica as Melville asserts. The same problem is encountered in the purported vicarious transfer of *Nothofagus* from Magellania to Antarctica by the late Cretaceous (figure 6.15). Furthermore, the appearance of *Nothofagus* on New Guinea would have to be explained by northward migration from Australia in the Miocene (figure 6.15). The stratigraphic palynological record of Australia appears to support this contention. *Nothofagus* pollen appears in successively younger strata in a northerly direction from the

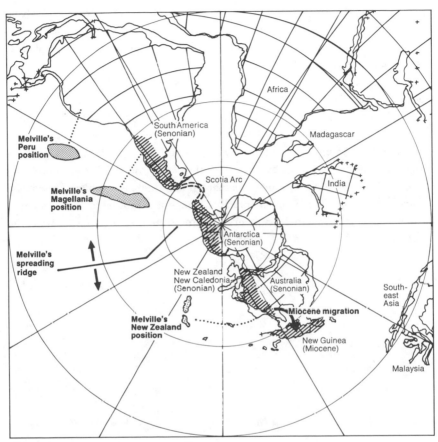

▨ Northofagus occurrence   .... Future drift path

Figure 6.15. Polar projection of the Gondwanian continents in late Cretaceous time, with distribution and time of earliest known appearance of the southern beech, *Nothofagus*, as generally accepted by geologists and paleobotanists. The approximate positions of Melville's Pacifica fragments (stippled) and spreading ridge are also shown. Adapted from Smith and Briden (1977).

Senonian to the Eocene (Dettmann and Playford 1969). New Guinea probably emerged as dry land beginning in the Miocene.

A number of Melville's floral examples turn out to be cold-adapted high altitude plants that botanists have long used as examples of extreme biogeographical disjunction. *Oreomyrrhis*, a small carrot-like plant of the family Umbelliferae (range: Paleocene-to-Recent), as well as *Ranunculus* and *Caltha*, buttercups of the family Ranunculaceae (range: Oligocene-to-Recent), fit this category. Many paleobotanists believe that these groups of plants are not descendants from ancient indigenous (Cretaceous) floras as Melville states, but rather that they were introduced in late Pliocene to Pleistocene times (5–10 Ma) via wind dispersal coeval with mountain uplift in Malaysia, New Guinea, and New Zealand.

In summary, I do not believe that Melville's Pacifica is geologically possible. Nor do I believe that it could serve as a gate of angiospermy as framed within the concepts of vicariance biogeography. In fact, it is probable that southeastern Asia, Australasia, New Caledonia, etc.—the home of many of Melville's floral examples—likewise cannot be regarded as a gate of angiospermy as proposed by Croizat, Smith, and others. Certain floral elements of this region very likely represent only primitive survivorship, not the place of origin. Other paleobotanists present arguments that western Gondwanaland represents the point of origin of the angiosperms (summary in Schuster 1976; Raven and Axelrod 1974).

Discussion

G. F. Edmunds, Jr.

DR. MELVILLE DESCRIBES vicariant disjunct patterns for a relatively large number of taxa of angiosperms. For some of these plants phylogenetic models are proposed. Melville proposes no sequence for the breakup of Pacifica that corresponds precisely with splits in the phylogeny of the plants, but he shows a number of interesting vicariant pairs. He presents some evidence that long-distance dispersal across barriers is not a viable explanation for the plants considered. Nevertheless, I feel that long-distance dispersal deserves greater attention for many of the groups. I appreciate the fact, however, that everything cannot be given detailed consideration in a comprehensive manuscript of limited size. It is interesting to contrast Melville's paper with Carlquist's (1965), where distributions of many of the plants on Pacific islands are explained by overwater dispersals. Confronted with the problem that many of the vicariant distributions he describes are inadequately explained either by the old fixed continent hypothesis or by the widely published Pangea model, Melville examines the geological evidence for clues to a Pacific continent that will most adequately explain his data. We thus are offered a new hypothesis to explain Pacific Basin biogeography.

The proposed fragmentation of a Pacific continent to explain the distribution of plants around and within the Pacific Basin is a substantial departure from conventional continental-drift models. The majority of geologists do not interpret these data in the same way as does Melville. It is easy to dismiss Melville's theory because it does not conform to the widely accepted new dogma of plate tectonics. But if the recent past history of biogeography exemplifies one thing, it is that widely accepted or conventional models of earth history are not models to be accepted but instead are models to be tested. Science is not a popularity contest, and no solution comes from accepting the opinions of the majority of geologists or biogeographers.

My task is critically to evaluate Melville's findings. My efforts point out a serious problem in attempts to arrive at a general biogeography; I lack the knowledge to evaluate the quality of the underlying biology and relationships of the plants considered in the paper. I know the genus *Bidens* when I see it in the Rockies, and I have picked its clinging seeds from my clothes, but I do not know if the seeds of Marquesan and Hawaiian species cling, especially to birds. Even though I have wandered among *Nothofagus* trees in a number of their disjunct homes, I do not feel competent to evaluate data on angiosperms or any other group for which I do not know the biology. My evaluation will be based on the degree to which data from my specialty, aquatic insects of the order Ephemeroptera (mayflies), fit the patterns of the angiosperms. Only by such comparisons do we proceed from special cases to the general patterns that have scientific meaning.

The Ephemeroptera are insects whose larvae (or nymphs) are aquatic and whose adults are usually short-lived (usually 2–3 days). Eight or nine separate lineages have a derived ultrashort life of less than three hours for both subimago and imago. In two genera, *Callibaetis* and *Cloeon*, the females of at least some species retain the eggs until they are ready to hatch; these forms have a longer adult life. The mayflies are one of two surviving orders of primitive winged insects, the Paleoptera. They were abundant and diverse in the Permian, and several mayfly specialists regard the Upper Carboniferous *Lithoneura* as a mayfly. Existing distribution patterns indicate that mayflies are conservative in dispersing across barriers. The order is fairly well known on a world-wide basis. The larvae are known for a high percentage of the genera, but outside Europe and North America the larvae of most species are not described. Phylogenies can be reconstructed with considerably confidence if egg, larval, and adult characters are analyzed; for most lineages, studies are in progress but not complete. In general, the age of the group should be useful for determining the generality of the patterns that Melville reports in angiosperms.

Two classes of mayfly genera are uninformative to biogeography. Some species are clustered into a genus on the basis of shared characters primitive to the family or a substantial part of the family. It is probable that the widespread genera *Baetis* of the family Baetidae and *Caenis* of the family Caenidae as presently used are defined largely on the basis of plesiomorphic characters. Detailed systematic study of reared specimens is needed to make the group biogeographically informative. Another class of genera of little biogeographical value are those defined by reductional characters such as the loss of hind wings. The danger of polyphyletic genera is high, and again the solution to the problem is additional study and reared specimens. Distributions of reductionally defined mayfly genera such as *Cloeon* and *Pseudocloeon* are thus of little biogeographical value.

I will review the trans-Pacific mayfly distributions, starting in the northern Pacific region and proceeding to the southern patterns. More than half of the genera and subgenera of mayflies in North America north of Mexico are found also in Eurasia. The mayfly faunas of China, Taiwan, and Korea are poorly known, and the Japanese and Siberian faunas are only moderately well known. The vicariant patterns may prove to be more numerous than we know. In addition, a number of North American endemics have their closest relatives in Eurasia. For some of these the evidence favors Atlantic vicariant patterns; for others strong Pacific vicariant patterns are suggested, but for most of them the data do not allow decisions as to whether the vicariant patterns are Pacific, Atlantic, or both. This is true especially when allowances are made for climatically caused extinctions in Europe and western North America. The detailed phyletics of species within the genera is necessary for such analysis; for mayflies, this frequently requires that the larvae are known. There are, nevertheless, vicariant species pairs of mayflies in Asia and western North America in genera such as *Rhithrogena* and *Heptagenia*. The mayfly genus *Habrophlebiodes* (Leptophlebiidae) with species in China and eastern and central North America, and *Acanthametropus* with one species in the Amur and one in Illinois and South Carolina are similar to well known distribution patterns of plants. Several subgenera of *Ephemerella* (*Drunella, Serratella,* and *Attenella;* Ephemerellidae) occur in both eastern and western North America and Asia. Similarly the heptageniids *Cinygma, Cinygmula,* and the subgenera *Iron* and *Ironopsis* of *Epeorus,* show strong trans-Pacific patterns.

My answer to whether or not I believe that mayflies require a Pacifica to account for vicariant patterns in western North America and eastern Asia is, simply, no. If the American plate extends to the Verkhoyansk range of Siberia, and variations in level of an epicontinental Bering Sea allow land connections up to 2000 km wide, the Bering area and the North Atlantic closure seem adequate to account for the North American-Eurasian patterns in mayflies. Because of the role of warm ocean currents, the climate of a closed North Pacific may have been less severe than it is at present. A divided Pacifica continent, however, is clearly consistent with existing distribution patterns.

Problems of distribution—as in the plant family Lardizabalaceae with representatives in China-Japan and Chile—do not occur in the Ephemeroptera. Some groups are found as disjuncts in the cool temperate and warm temperate, but are not also trans-Pacific. The most primitive mayfly family, Siphlonuridae, has a markedly disjunct distribution; the subfamily Acanthametropodinae is Holarctic, the subfamily Siphlonurinae has Holarctic and amphinotic distributions (Magellania, Australia, and New Zealand), and two other subfamilies are wholly amphinotic. These disjunctions could conceivably be the result of a dispersed Pacific continent, but the breakup of a Pacific continent is an explanation no better than the breakup of Pangea. Edmunds et al. (1976) list 13 genera of mayflies of five families that occur in North America and that they believed are of South American origin. Can any of these be explained by a Pacific continent? None is represented anywhere except in North, Central, and South America, and none has sister groups in the Pacific. The genera themselves and their sister groups are predominantly South American. Only two of the genera are known west of the Sierra Nevada, but eight are known from Texas, and most or all of the others probably occur there. No one has identified a Peruvian endemic element in Ephemeroptera. In fact, none of the Andean Ephemeroptera has close relatives in the Pacific except in Australia, Tasmania, New Zealand, New Caledonia, and nearby islands.

More than 40 genera of mayflies occur in eastern tropical Asia (south of China, including the Sunda Shelf and the Philippines), and more than 50 genera are reported from tropical South America (see table 6.2). Only eight genera are common to the two regions. Of these, two are almost certainly the result of errors of generic identity (*Hexagenia*, Ephemeridae, in the Philippines; and *Habrophlebiodes*, Leptophlebiidae, in South America), and four other genera present problematical data. *Baetis* (Baetidae) and *Caenis* (Caenidae) are, as explained above, poor material for biogeography because they are plesiomorphic. *Pseudocloeon* and *Cloeon* (Baetidae) are reductionally defined genera with great danger of polyphyly; they are poorly known in South America. *Centroptilum* (Baetidae) is poorly understood in both areas. *Choroterpes* is represented by the subgenus *Euthraulus* in tropical Asia and is poorly known (but not represented by *Euthraulus*) in South America.

Table 6.2 Tropical Mayfly Taxa in Asia and South America

	Southeast Asian genera	Tropical South American genera	Remarks
Baetidae	4+	7+	4 common genera
Oligoneuriidae	1	6	no common subfamilies
Heptageniidae	9	1 doubtful	
Leptophlebiidae	8	14+	2 common genera
Potamanthidae	2	0	
Euthyplociidae	1	3	relationship uncertain
Palingeniidae	2	0	
Emphemeridae	Ephemera Hexagenia? Eatonigenia	Hexagenia	
Polymitarcyidae:			
Polymitarcyinae	Ephoron	0	
Campsurinae	0	2	
Asthenopodinae	1 -	2	possibly trans-Pacific
Ephemerellidae	4+	1	no common subfamilies
Tricorythidae	2	6	no common subfamilies
Neoephemeridae	2	0	
Caenidae	4	3	Caenis common
Prosopistomatidae	Prosopistoma	0	

The differences between South America and tropical Asia are emphasized by noting that four families (Potamanthidae, Palingeniidae, Prosopistomatidae, and Neoephemeridae) are in tropical Asia but absent from South America, and the Heptageniidae are abundant and diverse in Asia and known in South America only from a dubious record from Brazil. Five subfamilies present in tropical Asia are absent from South America; three other subfamilies are in South America, but not in tropical Asia. In three of the families common to both areas, there are no subfamilies in common to both areas. Even in the one case where there is a trans-Pacific vicariant pair (Polymitarcyidae, Asthenopodinae, *Asthenopus* in South America; *Povilla* in tropical Asia), I previously considered this a South American-African pair, but there is no way that the likelihood of either geography for the pair can be judged without analyzing the cladistic relationships of all species. Among the primarily tropical groups the relationships of South America are predominantly with Africa; relationships of tropical Asia are with Africa and Madagascar. These groups tend to be less diverse in tropical Asia than in Africa, but for most the evolutionary pathways and geography have not been investigated in detail. Table 6.2 summarizes the data for all families present in either area. I consider the lack of any reliable vicariant group across the tropical Pacific quite remarkable if a Pacifica was involved in mayfly distribution.

The tropical Oriental mayfly fauna extends in a rather attenuated form to New Guinea. The endemic New Guinea mayfly genus *Plethogenesia* is a palingeniid, a family predominantly Oriental and Palearctic. Other genera in New Guinea (*Prosopistoma, Thraulus, Caenomedea*) are found also in the Oriental Region. The Baetidae are diverse (there are several undescribed endemic genera), but the facts that hind wings are absent from all, and that all the larvae lack gills on segment one, suggest that probability of *in situ* evolution from a single ancestor. A remarkable fact is that to date no one has reported mayflies common to New Guinea and Australia, although there must be common genera and perhaps species. The Solomon Islands fauna appears to be a continuation of the New Guinea fauna (with one species of *Prosopistoma* common to the Solomon Islands and New Guinea). This pattern appears to be common in insects (Gressitt 1974). The Australian mayflies (*Cloeon, Centroptilum, Austremerella*) of Oriental affinity, which appear to be absent from New Guinea, probably entered Australia from the more southerly route through Timor. Although there are rather clear relationships of some insects, and of the flora between New Guinea and New Caledonia or New Zealand and New Guinea and Borneo, no such relationships exist in the Ephemeroptera. Possibly some plants and insects have crossed narrow water gaps.

Mt. Kinabalu on the northern tip of Borneo does not have, to my knowledge, any south temperate mayflies. In the Liwagu River near Park Headquarters (elevation 1620 m) only five species occur, and all are clearly Oriental; down the Liwagu toward Ranau the species diversity increases markedly, and the fauna remains typically Oriental. The mayflies of Mt. Kinabalu are thus consistent with geological evidence that this mountain is relatively young, having arisen in the Pliocene. Most plants and insects in the higher zones of Mt. Kinabalu are related to those in the Himalayas.

The relationships of Ephemeroptera of Magellania, New Zealand, and Australia are remarkably clear. Three subfamilies of Siphlonuridae are present on these land masses. The phylogenetic sequence has been independently examined in each lineage, and they conform; the New Zealand genus is a sister group of the Australian-Magellanic pair as shown by figure 6.16. The Oligoneuriid subfamily Coloburiscinae also has a set of three genera; again the Australian-Magellanic pair of genera share derived characters that show them cladistically nearer to each other than either is to the New Zealand

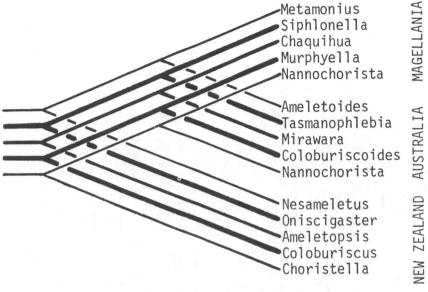

Figure 6.16. Phylogeny of mayflies and Nannochoristinae (Mecoptera).

genus[1]. These cool adapted complexes do not occur in New Caledonia. The mayfly family Leptophlebiidae also occurs in this area. Several complexes of genera are found in Australia, Magellania, and New Zealand; at least some of these repeat the pattern noted above. The analyses of these diverse groups are still in progress in studies centered at Florida A & M University and involving W. L. Peters, J. G. Peters, Manuel Pescador, David Towns, Harry Savage, Michael Hubbard, E. F. Riek, and G. F. Edmunds, Jr. One result to date is that the New Caledonia Leptophlebiidae mayflies are almost entirely sister groups of New Zealand mayflies. Publication of the New Caledonia mayfly study has only started (Peters et al. 1979). The isolation of the Magellaniac Ephemeroptera is remarkable. The relationships tend to be very strong with Australia and quite weak with the rest of South America. Two genera, *Callibaetis* and *Caenis*, appear to be relatively recent arrivals of the typical South American fauna (*Baetis* may have the same affinity, but its rela-

[1] The question concerning the degree to which concordant cladograms were selected or "plucked" came up both in the auditorum and in private discussions. To allow persons to judge this in the cases cited above I present a cladogram (figure 6.17) of the members of a highly paraphyletic group. considered to be one family at the time of analysis. Three other families—Baetidae, Caenidae, and Leptophlebiidae—remain to be analyzed. The Nanno-choristidae (figure 6.16) (Insecta: Mecoptera) are a *selected* example suggesting that entire cool adapted lotic water communities were vicariated.

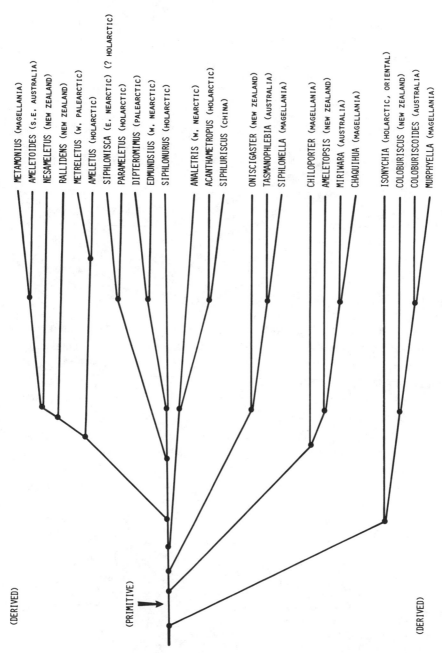

Figure 6.17. Cladogram of mayfly family Siphlonuridae and part of family Oligoneuriidae.

tionships with Australian and other South American *Baetis* need study). Chilean Siphlonuridae or Oligoneuriidae are known only to about La Serena (30°S), but the Magellanic leptophlebiid genera are found in the Andes west of Tucuman, Argentina (ca. 26°S). This conforms to the way the families are limited in the New Zealand-New Caledonia area; the Siphlonuridae and Oligoneuriidae are limited to New Zealand, but Leptophlebiidae extend north to New Caledonia.

I do not expect that each lineage of Leptophlebiidae that is being analyzed will be present in Australia, New Zealand, and Magellania and will show the same phyletic branching sequence as the Siphlonuridae and coloburiscine Oligoneuriidae. The groups that will conform to the multiple cladogram pattern that I have shown must have (1) been cosmopolitan to all of the areas being analyzed, (2) survived in all areas under consideration, and (3) been collected and come into the hands of the right biologist. The analyst must have worked with single cosmopolitan groups that exclude evolutionary branching prior to the sequence of barrier establishment that broke up the original range, and he must be astute enough to recognize all members that belong to the group despite differing evolutionary rates (Edmunds 1975). This strongly defined pattern is consistent with widely accepted earth-history models of the region; the Pacifica pattern is consistent in a broad sense but not in detail.

Little attention has been paid to the Ephemeroptera of Pacific islands. There are remarkably few records, probably because there are few mayflies living on the islands. Generally if it is known, few biologists report that the mayflies are absent. The Hawaiian Archipelago has a single introduced species. The Galapagos Archipelago has no mayflies. Mayflies occur on Yap, Fiji, and Samoa. These are Baetidae (usually *Cloeon*) or Caenidae. They are not well known groups, and even their generic assignment is dubious in the absence of larvae. Baetidae also occur on New Caledonia (W. L. Peters, personal communication), but the specimens are not adequate to determine possible relationships with Fiji or New Guinea. The Pacifica model is inconsistent with the essential absence of Ephemeroptera from Pacific islands.

In summary, mayfly distributions in and around the Pacific Basin are consistent with the hypothesized Pacifica continent because they have numerous vicariant groups in Asia and North America and because the Magellanic mayflies have strong affinities with forms in Australia, New Zealand, and New Caledonia. There are no reliable vicariant patterns linking the tropics of South America with tropical southeastern Asia despite the occurrence of a rich mayfly fauna in both areas. There is equally no evidence of vicariance between New Caledonia and New Guinea. The New Guinea mayfly fauna has Oriental relationships, but is not diverse; the most diverse group (Baetidae) may have evolved from a single ancestor. Most Pacific islands are without mayflies. The distribution of mayflies in and around the tropical Pacific does not support the concept of a Pacifica continent. In both the south and the north they are just as easily explained with a more conventional Gondwana-Laurasia pattern even though they do fit a Pacifica pattern.

Obviously the Ephemeroptera alone do not test the generality of the distribution patterns of angiosperms shown by Melville. My purpose in including the aquatic scorpionfly larvae (*Nannochorista, Choristella*) with my amphinotic mayfly phylogenies is to illustrate the fact that the amphinotic pattern suggests that entire communities of aquatic insects were broken into vicarious disjuncts by the breaking of land masses in the southern Pacific. Other aquatic insects have representatives in Australia and Magellania, but not in New Zealand (e.g., Diptera: Blepharoceridae, *Edwardsina* and Plecoptera: Eustheniidae, *Eusthenia*; Zwick 1979). No one has done the studies necessary to determine to what extent vicarious groups are linked into tight aquatic communities, but my observations suggest that the communities will prove to be only loosely linked.

This leads me to suggest that there is a stronger test of the Pacifica angiosperm patterns than simple concordance with distributions of other organisms. Many angiosperms have associated and coevolved organisms. If these angiosperms undergo long-distance dispersal, it is improbable that many of the associated or coevolved organisms would be dispersed in the same pattern. *Eucalyptus* dispersed as seeds by man to California, Chile, Madagascar, etc., have undamaged leaves and contrast strongly with *Eucalyptus* in Australia, where they are attacked by an array of chewing and sucking insects. A rich arthropod fauna resides under the loose bark of some Australian *Eucalyptus*, but collecting insects under the bark of the same species in California is unrewarding.

If an angiosperm lineage disperses gradually over an area and is subsequently disrupted by a newly formed barrier, however, it should retain many associated and coevolved groups in both vicariant populations. As an example, Schlinger (1974) has noted the occurrence of the *Neuquenaphis-Sensoriaphis* lineage of aphids on *Nothofagus* in Magellania, New Zealand, Australia, and New Guinea. Braconid wasps parasitize the aphids; one of these parasitoids, in turn, is secondarily parasitized by a cynipid wasp. Schlinger's study is incomplete, but it clearly shows the potential value of widespread biogeographical study of associated organisms.

Botanists have frequently complained to me that they have few characters of value for reconstructing phylogenies. Whether or not this is true, phylogenies of all organisms are in need of independent testing. The phylogenetic study of a set of coevolved organisms might require several cooperating specialists, but it should yield a robust set of data. A robust set of phylogenetic data for a group posing problems in biogeography would be especially valuable. Biogeographers show considerable preoccupation with the degree to which propagules can survive in the sea, the weight of propagules if they might be airborne, the possibility of dispersal by active locomotion, etc. But dispersal is not in and of itself adequate for *effective* dispersal, i.e., arrival *and establishment*. Under the right air-mass movements butterflies regularly and predictably arrive in New Zealand from Australia; they do not establish themselves because their food plants do not grow in New Zealand. These butterflies are specialists, and their survival is therefore unlikely; when generalist insects are dispersed they are more likely to establish themselves. It should be equally true that angiosperms dependent on specialized pollinators will tend to fail to establish themselves when dispersed, but seed plants dependent only on generalized pollinators should be more successful. Hence, if long-distance dispersal explains the angiosperm patterns in Pacific islands we should expect an excess of plants with generalist pollinators and generalist herbivores. Plants with Pacific disjuncts as remarkable as New Guinea-Borneo-Taiwan or Marquesas-Hawaii deserve closer study of coevolved and associated organisms.

Response

R. Melville

DR. HAUGH PRESENTS a chaotic account of the sequence of geological events in the Pacific region and their effects on biological distributions, in which he neglects some of the essential evidence and misconstrues part of the remainder. My reconstruction of Pacifica is based on an earlier attempt (Melville 1966), with errors corrected and later evidence integrated. I disagree with Hughes (1975) when he forces the evidence to fit Pacifica to Pangea. It is remarkable that geologists continue to accept Wegener's hypothesis of Pangea in the face of evidence for three separate floras in the northern hemisphere in the Carboniferous (Sahni 1936). If these floras had existed on a single continent there should be evidence of mingling. The disjunction of one of these northern continents (Atlantica) is now accepted on the evidence for continental drift in the Atlantic, which resulted in the separation of the Carboniferous coal flora of western Europe and eastern North America. Little attention has been paid to the exactly parallel case of the Cathaysian (*Gigantopteris*) flora now separated in eastern Asia and western North America. This evidence has been overlooked by geologists and geophysicists, who have assumed that North America consisted of a single craton of Pangea. It focuses attention on the need to reconsider whether any of the existing continents has received accretions of minor or major cratons during the latest cycle of orogenesis. According to Holmes (1965), the earth has passed through at least eight cycles of orogenesis, each lasting about 200 million years (280 million years according to Steiner 1967), which have resulted in the accretion of blocks of various ages on the present continents during the history of the earth. For our present purpose we are concerned only with what took place during the last orogenic cycle.

The existence of two distinct Paleozoic floras, separated by a sea that lasted into the Jurassic, is evidence that North America consists of two cratons that were brought together by continental drift. The drawing of the boundary of the western craton, based on Schuchert's (1955) map for the Jurassic (Bajocian), is approximate; it did not seem justifiable to attempt greater precision until controversies over details have been resolved. The general trend of this boundary is supported by Schuchert's maps for the mid-Permian and for the Upper Triassic (his maps 56, 57, 62), in which these strata are not represented in eastern North America. They do, however, show a gap extending from 40°N in a southwesterly direction to Baja California. Haugh chooses to illustrate a geological section in this gap (his figure 6.12), thus proving that there is no geological discontinuity where none is shown on the map. A more critical examination of the evidence is necessary to elucidate the causes of the lack of continuity of the boundary of eastern Pacifica in this region. Haugh's section lies further to the east of the Pacifica boundary (his figure 6.11) and is irrelevant to the discussion.

In South America, the floras of Peru and Magellania have a considerable number of elements related to those of Australia, but the relationships for the rest of the continent are with Africa. The African relationships can be expected from the geophysical evidence for the former unity of South America and Africa, but the floras of Peru and Magellania are then incongruous. For example, the Proteaceae of South America are almost confined to the latter two regions, and the genera are related to Australian genera. *Lomatia* is shared with Australia, but it is absent from Africa. Relationships of this kind are significant when repeated many times in a number of unrelated families. In a search for a geophysical explanation, the evidence for the absence of Permo-Carboniferous glaciation in Magellania (Holmes 1965) is significant; that of the single pole of Valencio and Vilas (1970) is at best only ancillary. Haugh, quoting from Valencio and Vilas, notes that the circles of confidence of the mean of African Mesozoic poles and the mean of the South American Triassic poles overlap. I agree that this is consistent with the relationships existing between the floras of Africa and the major portion of South America. It is irrelevant to the critical point at issue, which is the former position of Magellania. The significant comparison, which is yet to be made, is between the mean of the Carboniferous to Triassic poles of *Africa south of the Sahara* with the mean pole for the same period of the *particular minor craton of South America* involved in the argument, i.e., Magellania. A similar lack of precision applies to the distribution of the marine Jurassic strata of South America. Haugh (his figure 6.14) depicts this as a broad continuous band, and bases his map on the approximate and generalized maps of Weeks (1948), which show no marine Jurassic near the Golfo de San Jorge. Reference to Stose's (1950) map shows the marine Jurassic as a narrow interrupted band turning out to the coast north of Valparaiso near 32°S and veering toward the coast near the Golfo de San Jorge at its southern end. The marine strata are flanked at intervals by Jurassic volcanics, which occur on both the northern and southern shores of the gulf and indicate the general trend of the marine beds. The boundary of Magellania is indicated with some degree of precision.

The problem of the distribution of *Nothofagus*, as of many other genera, is linked with Magellania. Haugh gives his interpretation on a polar projection of the southern hemisphere, allegedly of the situation at 80 Ma (his Figure 6.15). This is a hotchpotch of misinformation. The positions of Peru and Magellania are not those that I indicated against the spreading ridge. The position of New Zealand attributed to me appears to be its present day position. New Guinea is depicted in contact with Australia, but contact was not made until the Oligocene, long after Australia had separated from Antarctica. The allegedly original position of New Zealand against Australia conflicts with a vast amount of biological data, and the geophysical views cited by Haugh are based on slender evidence that needs critical re-examination. On his map Haugh shows South America and Antarctica in their present positions and argues from this the possibility of the migration of *Nothofagus* from South America to Australia via Antarctica. Up to 80 Ma the Antarctic Peninsula was against the Southeast Pacific Rise (Dalziel and Elliot 1971; Blundell 1962), when the drift began that resulted in the rotation of the Antarctic continent into its present position. Prior to this, there would have been a considerable water gap that would have prevented the migration of *Nothofagus* and for that matter the supposed migration of marsupials along this route. The reconstruction of South Pacifica on the lines I have proposed takes account of this evidence and also of the paleoclimatic evidence that Magellania was not attached to South America at the time. The Antarctic land bridge can have operated only when Magellania was in the position shown in my reconstruction, and this rules out the possibility of marsupial migration from South America to Australia. Haugh's suggestion that the appearance of *Nothofagus* in New Guinea can be explained by northward migration from Australia in the Miocene is contrary to botanical evidence. The evolutionary sequence of species passes from New Zealand via New Caledonia to New Guinea, where the most advanced forms in the genus occur (Melville 1973), and this is consistent with the reconstruction of Pacifica.

Another of Haugh's misconceptions is that ancillary dispersal hypotheses are necessary to account for vicariously disjunct circum-Pacific taxa. This is certainly not true for angiosperms. According to the evidence available to me, angiosperms began their evolution on the Gondwana continent. During the period of uplift in the rift valley stage of the orogeny, contact was made between South and North Pacifica. The land bridge thus formed provided a migration route to the north for early angiosperms. Angiosperm distributions indicate that they must have dispersed widely in Pacifica before the final disjunction, which would have separated some related species and cut into two parts the territory of others. In either event, evolution would have continued during the drift, and the "Noah's arks" would have arrived at their final destinations with sets of vicarious species already in existence. There is no need to invoke any other mechanism, and there would have been no other angiosperms "to greet them at the shore," for this would have been their first arrival in western North America. This Pacific migration route was only one of the gates of Angiospermy. Croizat's interpretation gives the Pacific two gates, but the Pacifica hypothesis simplifies them into a single gate. Croizat's third gate was in or adjacent to South Africa, which indicates a source of angiosperms from a different part of Gondwanaland. His third gate accounts for the angiosperms of Africa and South America, excluding Peru and Magellania, but the African gate was not relevant to a discussion of vicariance in the Pacific region.

Dr. Edmund's account of the biogeography of the Ephemeroptera is of great interest, dealing as it does with a very ancient group of insects that have achieved a world-wide distribution. The two major migration routes of the angiosperms, the African and Pacific gates, appear to have been utilized. The primarily tropical groups with relationships between Africa and South America and among tropical Asia, Madagascar, and Africa seem to point to an African origin. The wide distribution of the primitive family Siphlonuridae appears consistent with an African origin for the order; dispersal would be both northward and southward to the Antarctic part of Gondwanaland and then eastward to Australia, New Zealand, and Magellania. Distribution of the three subfamilies of Siphlonuridae in the latter territories compares closely with that of angiosperm genera in the South Pacific, but the absence of any endemics from Peru is striking. Angiosperm species and sometimes genera may be found in Peru or Magellania or both, or they may have extended their ranges. Brundin (1966) found similar types of distribution for chironomid midges, with sister species in either Australia or New Zealand. In the Ephemeroptera, Peru appears to be omitted from the sequence. Vicariant distributions across the North Pacific parallel those of angiosperms with some of the species in western or eastern North America. It is likely that the changes of climate and ecology consequent to the upraising of the Rockies may have been responsible for this distribution pattern, as occurred with plants. Trans-Atlantic vicariants, however, may have been the result of migration into the North Atlantic continent from Africa before the opening of the North Atlantic. On the whole, the Ephemeroptera appear to parallel rather closely angiosperm distributions that have been linked with continental drift.

I fully endorse Edmunds' plea for more extensive collaboration among specialists in working out the phylogeny of coevolved organisms. The distribution and relationships of fungal parasites of *Nothofagus* have been studied, and it would be valuable to have further evidence from the aphids attacking *Nothofagus* and their parasites. The problems arising from Pacific distributions are so varied and so extensive that they cannot be solved by the data of any one discipline. Knowledge has now advanced to the point where discussion and collaboration among geologists, geophysicists, botanists, zoologists, and paleontologists could be fruitful in solving outstanding problems.

I am fully aware that my reconstruction of Pacifica calls into question certain widely accepted dogmas of geology, and that for my failure to accept them I am accused of naïveté. However, I suspect that in the final analysis it will be the geologist who is proved naïve for his gullibility in swallowing these dogmas—hook, bait, and sinker.

7

Relative Importance of Plate Movements, Eustasy, and Climate in Controlling Major Biogeographical Changes Since the Early Mesozoic

A. Hallam

IT IS DIFFICULT to see how a paleontologist could be anything but a sup-
porter of the vicariance model of biogeography outlined by Croizat et al.
(1974) insofar as the methodology involves taking geological history fully
into account. Furthermore, it appears self-evident that one should consider
information from whole faunas and floras to produce the so-called "generalized tracks." On the other hand, I cannot see the matter as a simple
"either-or" situation. In many cases it can readily be demonstrated from the
fossil record that ancestral biotas have geographically subdivided (vicariated)
into descendent biotas, but for some groups the alternative model involving
centers of origin cannot be rigorously excluded. Paleontologists can confidently argue, for instance, that proboscideans and, for that matter, hominids
originally evolved in Africa and subsequently expanded their area of distribution to other parts of the world.

The overwhelming acceptance of plate tectonics by geologists and
geophysicists, implying that the continents originated from the breakup of the
supercontinent Pangea in the Mesozoic and Cenozoic, has decisively shifted
the balance in favor of the vicariance model to account for present-day
biogeographical distributions, although continental suturing as well as
separation must be taken into account. The great majority of recent research
articles in pre-Quaternary paleobiogeography concern themselves principally

or exclusively with lateral movements of lithospheric plates. Important though these are, the changing distribution of land and sea through time is also controlled by transgressions and regressions of epicontinental seas related at least partly to eustatic changes of sea level. It is, after all, a matter of indifference to a terrestrial organism whether the marine barrier preventing contact with relatives on another landmass has been created by spreading ocean floor or a shallow transgression over continental crust.

A principal concern of this article is to evaluate the respective importance of these two different phenomena in Mesozoic and Cenozoic biogeography. In addition, there is a brief outline of the influence of climate throughout this time. I shall endeavor as far as possible to avoid repetition of material contained in my earlier reviews (Hallam, 1967a, 1973b, 1974). Initially, the geophysical and geological evidence for plate movements and eustasy is summarized, and then the organic response is considered.

Plate Movements

The most powerful aid to reconstruction of the former positions of continents is the recognition of sets of magnetic anomalies on the intervening ocean floor. By this means successive positions can be established with a high degree of confidence back to about 80 Ma. Before this time, in the mid-Cretaceous, the anomaly record is much poorer during a so-called magnetic quiet interval, but a good set of anomalies reappears in the early Cretaceous and late Jurassic, before which there was another quiet interval. Extensive deep-ocean drilling has failed to reveal evidence of ocean crust older than late Jurassic, and reconstructions prior to this time depend upon reasonable extrapolation of data. Information on the timing of initial breakup is provided also by geological data on rifting and associated vulcanicity and sedimentation.

Location of the position of continents prior to breakup can be established by several methods. For the younger part of the record the sea-floor spreading data are generally sufficient, but further back in time other phenomena have to be taken into account, such as the position of ocean-floor fracture zones and geological matches between continents. In addition, computer fits of continental margins at the 1000-m isobath, using the least-squares method, have proved a valuable aid, and results from continental paleomagnetism give a broad check both on relative positions and the time of dispersal of the Pangean components.

Smith and Briden's (1977) series of world maps in several projections, dating back to the start of the Mesozoic, are an invaluable general guide to former continental positions, although details of fitting and timing of events are open to dispute. Their widely accepted pre-drift reconstruction (figure 7.1) shows two major components of Pangea: Laurasia in the northern hemisphere and Gondwanaland in the southern hemisphere, partly separated by the Tethys Ocean widening eastward from a closure in the present-day Mediterranean region. The subsequent changes can be dealt with successively in terms of the splitting of Laurasia by opening of the North Atlantic, the breakup of Gondwanaland by opening of the South Atlantic and Indian Oceans, and the closure of Tethys by suturing of Africa-Arabia and India with Eurasia.

I follow Smith and Briden in ignoring plate movements in eastern Asia as not directly relevant to the story I shall outline, but it should be noted that a continental collision probably took place in the region of the Verkhoyansk Mountains of eastern Siberia during the Lower Cretaceous. Audley-Charles (1978) gives an able review of possible movements involving the islands of

Figure 7.1. Continental relationships and approximate extent of sea in the early Jurassic. Continental areas stippled.

southeastern Asia. I shall, however, have something to say about the concept of a Pacific continent because it is a major subject of this symposium. I also restrict myself to events since the start of the Mesozoic, but one should recognize that plate-tectonic movements in the Paleozoic had an important influence on organic distributions; the best documented example is the closure of the Iapetus Ocean in the Lower Paleozoic (Ziegler et al. 1977).

Opening of North Atlantic

The story of the creation of the Atlantic is complex and involves several distinct opening phases. There is general agreement that the earliest phase of opening was in the central sector between Africa and North America, with Africa sliding eastward relative to Europe along a fracture zone (Pitman and Talwani 1972; Sclater et al. 1977). Estimates of the timing of this initial event differ considerably. Earlier interpretations correlate it with rifting and vulcanicity in eastern North America and northwestern Africa (e.g., Dietz and Holden 1970), but a consensus has now developed favoring a Jurassic date. Pitman and Talwani (1972) and Sclater et al. (1977) extrapolate back in time from ocean-floor magnetic anomalies to argue respectively for early Jurassic (180 Ma) or early Middle Jurassic (165 Ma), on the assumption that the so-called magnetic quiet zone of the opposed continental margins is true oceanic crust generated during a time of few or no magnetic reversals. Jansa and Wade (1975) cite geological evidence from the continental margins to support an early Middle Jurassic date, but Hallam (1977b) favors a late Middle Jurassic or early Upper Jurassic date on several grounds: the probability that part or all of the magnetic quiet zone is subsided continental crust, the age of oldest proven oceanic crust, and data from marine molluscs suggesting restrictions to free intermigration between the Pacific margins of the Americas and Europe before this time.

The next sector of the North Atlantic to open was between Newfoundland and Ireland. The current best estimate based on ocean-floor magnetic-anomaly data indicates a commencement in the Middle Cretaceous (90–95 Ma), when a line of opening ranged from the Azores-Gibraltar Ridge northward into the Rockall Trough (Kristoffersen 1978). Between this time and 80 Ma (late Santonian) the Rockall Trough opened, Newfoundland and Ireland separated, and Spain rotated in counterclockwise direction, opening the Bay of Biscay (Ries 1978). Just before 80 Ma the line of opening jumped to the west of the Rockall Trough and initiated the Charlie Gibbs Fracture Zone. This new pattern persisted until the start of the Tertiary, when the Norwegian Sea began to form. Spreading extended into the Labrador Sea in the late Cretaceous.

The youngest phase of opening was studied in detail by Talwani and Eldholm (1977). Opening of the Norwegian Sea commenced in the Paleocene (60–63 Ma). From this time to the end of the Eocene the Labrador Sea was also opening, and the motion of Greenland was northwestward relative to Eurasia; Greenland slid past the Barents Shelf and Svalbard in transcurrent fashion. A land connection persisted between Svalbard and Greenland until the end of the Eocene (38 Ma), after which the Greenland Sea began to form. Since this time the opening of the Norwegian-Greenland Sea can be described simply in terms of the separation of the Eurasian and North American plates.

Breakup of Gondwanaland

Based on the occurrence of shallow marine sediments in eastern Africa, Madagascar, and western Australia, and extensive basic lavas and sills in southern Africa and elsewhere, it is widely assumed that the Indian Ocean began to form in the Jurassic. Dietz and Holden (1970) infer an even earlier breakup during the Triassic. Evidence from continental paleomagnetism concerning the divergence of polar wandering paths indicates very clearly, however, that active disintegration of the Gondwana components (in the sense of "drifting" rather than rifting) did not start before the Cretaceous (McElhinny 1973a). Convincing support for this comes from sea-floor spreading data and modest extrapolations back through time where the magnetic-anomaly record becomes unclear (Norton and Sclater 1979).

The oldest magnetic anomalies (125–130 Ma) are recognized in the Cape Basin off the west coast of South Africa (Larson and Ladd 1973) and off southwestern Australia (Markl 1978), and indicate a Valanginian commencement of breakup. A clear pattern of magnetic anomalies indicating spreading along the whole length of the South Atlantic is present only from 80 Ma (Le Pichon and Hayes 1971). Not until about this time was there a free ocean connection with the North Atlantic, when the transverse Rio Grande-Walvis Ridge sank below 1-km depth; a 4-km deep water channel was established by the end of the Cretaceous (Van Andel et al. 1977).

There remains some uncertainty about the creation of ocean in the early and mid-Cretaceous. Cande and Rabinowitz (1978) assume rigid plate tectonics and argue that spreading started between Brazil and Angola at the same time that it started further south, but at a much lower rate because of the narrower oceanic gap. There is, however, no clear anomaly sequence prior to anomaly 34 (80 Ma); hence the possibility of a land link between Africa and South America until the mid-Cretaceous cannot be discounted (see figure 7.2). The Aptian of the Angolan and Brazilian margins is characterized by thick evaporite sequences extending well offshore, deposited on continental crust that probably subsided below sea level as a graben before an inrush of marine water in the Albian (Evans 1978).

In the Indian Ocean, India began to separate from Antarctica-Australia in the Valanginian (Markl 1978) and from Madagascar in the late Cretaceous (80–90 Ma) as indicated by a lava sequence on the eastern side of Madagascar. India then commenced a rapid northward movement in the later Cretaceous of up to 13 cm/year half-rate (Norton and Sclater 1979). The same authors indicate that Madagascar probably separated from Africa in the Middle Cretaceous, with relative movement between the two land-masses ceasing before the end of the period. The magnetic-anomaly record shows that Australia began to separate from Antarctica in the Eocene (53 Ma;

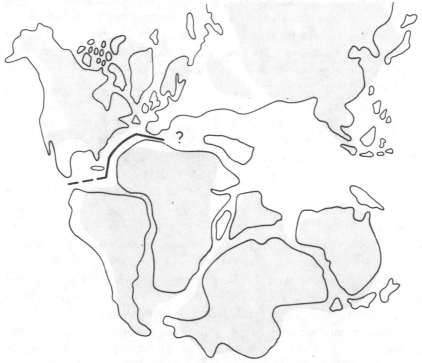

Figure 7.2. Continental relationships in the late Jurassic. Continental areas stippled. Thick line indicates spreading axis and associated fracture zones in Atlantic.

Weissel and Hayes 1972; Weissel et al. 1977), and Australia became attached to the Indian Plate. As a result of spreading in the Tasman Sea, New Zealand began to break away from Australia-Antarctica much earlier, about 80 Ma (Molnar et al. 1975; Weissel et al. 1977). Separation of South America from West Antarctica occurred when the Drake Passage opened in the Oligocene, allowing the creation of a circum-Antarctic polar ocean current system (Barker and Burrel 1977). The Scotia Arc is widely considered a Tertiary creation, but Dalziel (1979) maintains that there might have been an oroclinal bend in this region since the early Mesozoic. There has been no major change in continent-ocean relationships since the Oligocene except northward movement of Australia to meet Indonesia (figure 7.5).

Closure of Tethys

According to some widely quoted reconstructions, oceanic separation, although narrow in the western Mediterranean, existed between Laurasia and Gondwanaland from the Middle Jurassic through the Cretaceous. Whereas movement between Africa and Europe was predominantly transcurrent during this time, it changed to convergent motion in the early Tertiary. The Tethys seaway was finally closed as Africa-Arabia and India collided with Eurasia (Dewey et al. 1973; Smith and Briden 1977). Considerable uncertainty remains, however, about the precise timing of this major plate-tectonic event. The best evidence for continental collision comes from the occurrence of obducted ophiolite complexes.

Let us first consider the collision of India with Asia along the line of the Himalayas. According to Smith and Briden's maps this did not take place until about the early Miocene, but Powell and Conaghan (1973) infer from the dating of ophiolite obduction and associated sedimentation that it must have occurred shortly before the Middle Eocene. This interpretation is supported by Molnar and Tapponnier (1975), who point out a sharp reduction in sea-floor spreading rate in the plate carrying India subsequent to the late Eocene. Continued spreading at a reduced rate after Eocene collision produced further convergence of India against continental crust, which has caused extensive deformation by strike-slip faulting over a large area of the Asian land mass.

Similarly, Dewey et al. (1973) maintain that a continuous sialic connection from Arabia to Asia was not established until as late as Pliocene times, as the northern margin of Arabia collided with a trench-arc complex on the southern margin of Iran, and the Zagros Crush Zone was initiated. Yet there

Figure 7.3. Continental relationships in the early Cretaceous. Continental areas stippled. Thick lines indicate spreading axes and associated fracture zones.

is unequivocal evidence along a zone extending from the Oman through southern Iran and Turkey to the eastern Mediterranean of ophiolite obduction in the Maastrichtian, shortly before the end of the Cretaceous, after which sedimentation patterns changed drastically (Glennie et al. 1973; Hall 1976; Hallam 1976). There was probably another subduction zone through the Mesozoic further north, along the line of the Caucasus and Pontide ranges of northern Turkey, so that a marine strait could have existed until quite late in the Tertiary, but no convincing story of continental collision has yet been put forward for this region (see figure 7.4).

A further disparity is apparent in the Mediterranean region, which presents a very complex kinematic jigsaw puzzle that is as yet far from adequately resolved. Dewey et al. (1973) argue for Miocene collision of northern Africa with the Iberian Peninsula along the line of the Betic Cordillera, and for the conversion of several oceanic straits into collisional sutures in the Alpine-

Apennine region at this time. On the other hand, Laubscher and Bernoulli (1977) criticize many details of the Dewey scheme and indicate the ubiquity of evidence of compressive tectonic movements from the Apennines and Alps to Turkey and beyond, from Middle Cretaceous times. Milnes' (1978) detailed analysis of the Alps suggests that the final stages of continental underthrusting, leading to locking together of the separate land masses, had been completed by the early Oligocene.

Relationships at the western end of the Tethys, between North and South America, have been analyzed by Ladd (1976) on the basis of the implications of Atlantic spreading data and consideration of Caribbean tectonics. According to Ladd, convergent motion between the two continents did not take place until the late Eocene to Miocene, with consequent uplift of

Figure 7.4. Continental relationships in the late Cretaceous. Continental areas stippled. Thick lines indicate spreading axes and associated fracture zones.

the Greater Antilles and development of the Lesser Antilles arc. The youngest plate-tectonic event was the opening of the Red Sea and the Gulf of Aden. There has been controversy about how much of the floor of the Red Sea is genuinely oceanic as opposed to thinned continental crust. Although uncertainties remain, geological and geophysical evidence now seems to favor the view that the zone of true ocean crust is no wider than 70 km and did not start to form until the Pliocene (3.5 Ma) after a long precursory phase of rifting and vulcanicity (Le Pichon and Francheteau 1978).

In a broader context it seems evident that Middle Cretaceous commencement of convergent motion between Africa-Arabia and India on the one hand, and Eurasia on the other, is more consistent with the story of the disintegration of Gondwanaland and the creation of the South Atlantic and Indian Oceans than is the Tertiary alternative. In particular, paleomagnetic results indicate northward motion of Africa since Middle Cretaceous times (Norton and Sclater 1979). Once collision had been accomplished, the driving forces within the upper mantle must have been severely affected. One important consequence was the formation of a new spreading axis in the Gulf of Aden and the Red Sea. Figures 7.1–7.5 give a general indication of the relative positions of continents from the Triassic to the early Tertiary.

Pacific ocean and margins.   The Tertiary history of the Pacific Ocean is now comparatively well understood as a result of extensive mapping of magnetic anomalies, analysis of regional depth and heat-flow distribution, and dating basement in deep-sea drilling holes (Atwater 1973). The principal, Pacific, plate is limited on the east by the East Pacific Rise, which has taken on its present configuration during the last 5–10 million years. During this time north-south spreading began between the Cocos and Nazca Plates to the east of the rise, and uplift of the Isthmus of Panama linking North and South America appears to be a biogeographically important consequence. The history of the southwestern Pacific is outlined by Molnar et al. (1975).

Back in the Cretaceous (there is no earlier record) the plate configuration was considerably different (Larson and Chase 1972). The Pacific Plate is the sole survivor of four major plates; the others (Farallon, Kula, and Phoenix) were almost totally destroyed by subduction beneath the Pacific margins: the Kula beneath Asia, the Farallon beneath North America, and the Phoenix beneath South America. At about 30 Ma, parts of the Pacific-Farallon spreading center became entangled with the subduction zone of the western edge of North America, leading to the cessation of both spreading and subduction in that region. Subduction beneath South America and the

Figure 7.5. Continental relationships in the late Oligocene. Continental areas stippled. Thick lines indicate spreading axes and associated fracture zones.

western margins of the Pacific has continued to the present. Evidence of compressional fold structures in Alaska suggests a convergence of North America on northeastern Eurasia in the Bering Strait region, starting in mid-to-late Cretaceous time. This correlates with the second North Atlantic opening phase (Patton and Tailleur 1977).

Interest has recently been provoked among biogeographers by a speculative reconstruction of a former continent termed Pacifica (Nur and Ben-Avraham 1977). Pacifica is claimed to have broken up in the Mesozoic and dispersed from a site northeast of Australia, the component fragments travelling on the migrating Kula, Farallon, and Phoenix Plates, and colliding with the margins of Asia and North and South America. This novel interpretation is based partly on the geology of these margins and partly on biogeographical studies. The authors maintain that the combined evidence makes a compelling case. On the contrary I believe that their evidence is extremely tenuous.

The authors' principal argument is that various parts of the Pacific margins contain old continental crust on the oceanward side of geosynclinal "mobile belts," implying continental collision, and the geosynclinal zone representing a highly compressed sector of old ocean. Most of their evidence comes from the western margins of the Americas, from Alaska to Patagonia. Besides the geological evidence, paleomagnetic data are cited to suggest that the area of the Wrangell Mountains of Alaska was much closer to the equator in Triassic times. It can readily be shown that Nur and Ben-Avraham have insufficient knowledge of the relevant geology, that they fail to take into account other, less extravagant, interpretations of the facts, and that they get involved in a circular argument.

There are no indications from detailed geological investigations that old continental crust has migrated across the Pacific to become welded, as claimed, onto Peru. On the contrary, a subduction zone has been in more or less continuous existence to the west of the coast since the early Mesozoic, and a western Peruvian geosyncline developed *within* continental crust in the mid-Cretaceous (Cobbing 1978). Long-continued marginal subduction is inferred also for the southern Andes, and the entire Patagonia-Scotia Arc geosynclinal region occurs on the Pacific side of any undoubted Precambrian basement rocks (Dalziel 1979). For parts of western North America a consistent geological pattern emerges through Phanerozoic time of the development by extension of marginal basins bordered oceanward by arc-trench systems, followed by compression of these basins and closure of the arc-trench systems onto the main continental mass (Churkin 1974). None of this need involve significant continental displacement.

Granitic continental crust certainly occurs oceanward of a mélange zone suggestive of material deposited on the true ocean floor in California south of San Francisco (Hsü and Ohrbom 1969), but this clearly is the consequence of transcurrent displacement parallel to the coast along the San Andreas Fault. Displacement of this type is not taken into account by Nur and Ben-Avraham, although it could help provide an alternative explanation of low-latitude Triassic basalts in Alaska. The apparent northward movement of a geologically distinct entity extending from Oregon to southern Alaska, according to data from Triassic stratigraphy (Jones et al. 1977), depends strongly on paleomagnetic results for these basalts. Not only is there no need to invoke movement of this purported continent Wrangellia across the

Pacific, but the substantial Triassic basalts of the region imply an earlier phase of rifting, which is more consistent with the marginal basin model of Churkin (1974).

The location of Pacifica depends heavily on biogeographical data supplied by Martin (1970) and Melville (1966), but the interpretation fails to recognize that these authors depended, in turn, on a long-rejected geological interpretation of the region in question. Menard (1964) orginally postulated an oceanic rise (*not* a continent) in the mid-Pacific on the basis of evidence of subsidence of guyots and atolls since the early Cretaceous. Menard did not infer extensive emergence of this so-called Darwin Rise, and he abandoned his interpretation a few years later when extensive sea-floor spreading data became available. Subsidence of the ocean floor is now seen as a consequence of cooling from a spreading ridge generated elsewhere (Sclater et al. 1971). Furthermore, fragments of Pacifica supposedly reached continents several thousand miles away *before* the purported Darwin Rise began to subside.

Eustasy

Eustatic, or world-wide, changes of sea level have long been recognized in the Quaternary and related to alternating glacial and interglacial climatic episodes. Recognition of pre-Quaternary eustasy has been less universal, but the evidence for at least the grosser changes is now overwhelming. The frequency, timing, extent, and even existence of short-term or small-scale oscillations of sea level are still controversial, and much depends on the availability of good zone fossils allowing fine stratigraphic correlation across the world. This topic need not concern us here, except that short-lived regressive episodes in epicontinental regimes can temporarily restore land connections, but such restoration is no longer possible once sea-floor spreading has commenced to drive continents apart.

The grosser changes through the Mesozoic and Cenozoic can be studied in two different ways. First, the areal distribution of strata containing marine fossils can be plotted for successive time intervals on equal-area maps, and the percentage of continent flooded by sea can be estimated. Second, the stratigraphic sequence of shallow marine and non-marine deposits on the continents and continental shelves can be analyzed in terms of facies variations, onlap, and offlap—an approach much improved in recent years with the development of the new technique of seismic stratigraphy (Payton 1977). The results obtained by the two methods are broadly similar despite the complication of local tectonic uplift and subsidence, and they give confidence in the general correctness of the interpretation (Hallam 1977c; Vail et al. 1977; and figure 7.6).

From a low stand in the late Triassic and early Jurassic, sea level rose progressively to reach a peak early in the late Jurassic, after which there was a relatively sharp fall at the end of the period, persisting into the early Cretaceous. Then began a very significant rise in the Middle Cretaceous (late Aptian-Albian) reaching a peak in the Campanian, when over a third of the present continental area was flooded. Following a sharp end-of-Cretaceous fall, the sea never returned to its previous high level of the late Cretaceous. Despite an important Eocene transgression there was comparative stability throughout most of the Paleogene until the late Oligocene, when there was a major fall. A further significant fall at the end of the Miocene caused, among other things, the isolation of the Mediterranean. Early Miocene and Pliocene transgressions failed to cover more than a small fraction of the area of late Cretaceous and Paleogene seas. The Neogene record is generally regressive, culminating in the low stands of the Quaternary.

In terms of regional changes several biogeographically significant events can be recognized. An important transgression starting in the late early Jurassic (Toarcian) occurred in the Middle East and margins of the Indian Ocean, in eastern Africa, Madagascar, and western Australia (where the oldest marine rocks are early Middle Jurassic); the sea persisted in these regions throughout the remainder of the Mesozoic. In the late Middle Jurassic (Callovian) an Asian continent became separated from Europe by a linkup of the Arctic across the Russian Platform and West Siberian Depression as a result of transgression of an epicontinental sea, which was to persist until the Oligocene regression, when a Eurasian land link was re-established.

During the mid-to-late Cretaceous rise of sea level, two landmasses in North America became isolated by a mid-continent epicontinental seaway extending from the Gulf of Mexico to the Canadian Arctic. This sea began to retreat shortly before the end of the Cretaceous, by which time land links between east and west were re-established. Open-sea conditions first spread throughout the South Atlantic region in Albian-Cenomanian times, when, in addition, a broad Saharan epicontinental sea extended between the Mediterranean part of the Tethys and West Africa. The sea arrived at the southern margin of Africa somewhat earlier, in the Valanginian. Marine deposits in

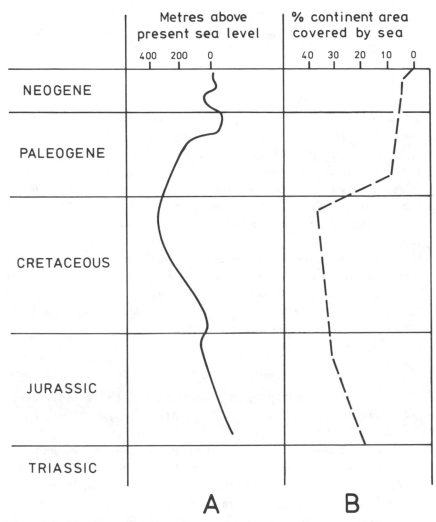

Figure 7.6. Major eustatic changes of sea level in the Mesozoic and Cenozoic: A, Estimate of position above present sea level, simplified from Vail et al. (1977); B, Approximate percentage of North America covered by sea, after Hallam (1977c).

Patagonia, West Antarctica, and southern Australia indicate that no free land communication existed in the late Cretaceous between South America and Australasia.

The entry of sea into the Indian Ocean region in the Jurassic and into the South Atlantic region in the Cretaceous is almost certainly bound initially with rise of sea level and marine transgression into narrow zones of streteched and thinned (and hence subsided) continental crust rather than with the creation of new ocean floor by spreading processes. The present continent-ocean relationships were substantially established by the time of the late Oligocene regression, when the formerly continuous Tethyan seaway was interrupted by the emergence above sea level of the Middle Eastern region.

Although I have written of plate motions and eustasy as independent phenomena, there is almost certainly a connection between them. During the whole of the Mesozoic and early Tertiary there is no evidence of polar ice caps, so that changes of sea level must be bound up with changes in the cubic capacity of the ocean basins. The most popular interpretation at present relates times of rapid sea-floor spreading to buoyant ocean ridges, hence to rise of sea level, and *vice versa* (Hays and Pitman 1973; Pitman 1978), implying that eustasy in non-glacial times is ultimately controlled by variations in heat flow from the mantle (Turcotte and Burke 1978). From Middle Miocene times onward, when an extensive Antarctic ice cap first developed, continental glaciation must have been a significant contributor to regression (for instance, the end-of-Miocene (Messinian) regression). Figures 7.1 to 7.5 indicate in a general way the considerable variation through time of flooding of the continents by shallow seas.

Biogeographical Response to Plate Movements and Changes of Sea Level

Clearly one can consider only a limited sample of the enormous amount of information available from the fossil record, but this sample will include terrestrial vertebrates and plants together with marine invertebrates, and hence should give a fair indication of some of the most important changes in biogeographical pathways that occurred during the Mesozoic and Cenozoic. At the very least, interpretive models can be constructed and tested by further detailed work on organisms of widely different types.

Triassic

It will not be necessary to deal more than cursorily with this period. The distribution of terrestrial reptiles indicates very positively that free migration was possible between all the present continents, and no endemism is recognizable. Evidently there were no major physical or climatic barriers to restrict movement (Cox 1974).

Jurassic

The only good dinosaur faunas are found in high Upper Jurassic deposits of the western interior of the United States and eastern Africa. The high degree of similarity of these faunas indicates more or less free land communication between the northern and southern hemispheres until quite late in the period (Charig 1973; Galton 1977). The only possible land routes would seem to be either Iberia-North Africa or Central America. The presence of marine Upper Jurassic rocks in southern Spain suggested to Galton (1977) that a Central and South American route from North America to Africa was more likely. Either way there is an apparent disparity between the biogeographical evidence and most continental reconstructions for the time in question, which indicate oceanic separation between Laurasia and Gondwanaland, albeit narrow in the west.

For marine faunas the most important feature is the regional differentiation of the Tethyan and Boreal Realms, notably among the ammonites and belemnites. Whatever the environmental causes responsible, which are still controversial, they appear to have had nothing directly to do with plate tectonics. Some sort of temperature control has been widely invoked because the fluctuating boundary of the two realms runs through the northern hemisphere roughly along lines of latitude. Strong arguments can be put forward against a simple temperature-control hypothesis (Hallam 1975), however, which is not to say that latitudinal factors are irrelevant, because even in the equable world of the Jurassic there must have been systematic changes of seasonality and diurnal illumination from the equator to the poles. One of the most attractive hypotheses involves the stability of trophic resources (Valentine 1971), and climatic factors might well have been limiting for some of the more stenothermal groups such as rudistid bivalves, more or less confined to the site of the ancient Tethys.

Much work remains to be done on this subject, but it is becoming increasingly apparent that paleogeographical changes bound up with either regional or world-wide marine transgressions were of considerable significance. Thus it can be demonstrated that times of low sea level correlate with high endemism among the bivalve molluscs, a phenomenon evidently associated with decreased freedom of communication between shelf seas (Hallam 1977a). Fürsich and Sykes (1977) argue plausibly for the importance of regional paleogeographical changes in the Oxfordian of Britain in accounting for differences in molluscan faunas of the Boreal Realm. It can hardly be a coincidence, furthermore, that times when the Tethyan-Boreal differentiation among the ammonites was most acute—in the Bathonian and Tithonian/Volgian—correspond with phases of marine regression. A major episode of withdrawal of the sea from much of the North Atlantic region took place early in the Middle Jurassic, and the end-of-Jurassic regression was apparently world-wide. Times of marine transgression, both among ammonites and bivalves, appear to correlate, as might be expected, with phases of faunal spread and radiation (Hallam 1978).

Despite the Tethyan-Boreal provinciality, which strongly affected only the ammonites and belemnites, Jurassic marine faunas are decidedly more cosmopolitan than those of the present day—a fact that should occasion little surprise because of the equability of the climate and the lack of major oceanic barriers between continents and their shelf seas. Plate-tectonic factors must be invoked, however, to account for the apparent lack of direct communication of molluscan faunas between Europe and the western part of the Americas until quite late in the period, when spreading began in the Central Atlantic region (Hallam 1977b). The comparatively late opening implied by this apparent lack of direct communication supports the evidence from dinosaurs.

Cretaceous

As Cox (1974) has pointed out, evidence for intercontinental connections can be inferred only for organisms that evolved during the period. Thus the tyrannosaur, ceratopsid, protoceratopsid, and hadrosaurian dinosaurs are known in the "Laurasian" continents but occur only doubtfully in Gondwanaland. The few possible occurrences could be explained by chance dispersal across the Tethys. The formation of the interior seaway in North America during the mid-Cretaceous was the most significant biogeographical event in the continents of the northern hemisphere because it created two separate land masses that Cox (1974) has called *Asiamerica* (eastern Asia and western North America, with a Bering link in the north) and *Euramerica* (Europe and eastern North America) separated from Asia by the so-called Turgai Sea. Tyrannosaurs and protoceratopsids occur only in Asiamerica, while iguanodonts and primitive ankylosaurs survived in Euramerica. The Cretaceous angiosperm floras of these two land masses are correspondingly different (Hickey 1979). Dinosaur faunas in the southern hemisphere are too rare and too poorly known adequately to evaluate relations with the northern hemisphere, but Raven (1979) argues that similarities in angiosperm floras point to relatively free migration across the Tethys. Either dispersal across ocean barriers was easier than botanists such as Raven think plausible, or the width of the Tethys portrayed in the maps of Smith and Briden is excessive.

A southern, Antarctic, migration route between Australasia and South America is geologically the most plausible way to account for the primitive mammal fauna and many plants of Australia and New Zealand (Cox 1974; Raven and Axelrod 1975; Raven 1979). What has not been explained is why only the marsupial and not the placental mammals succeeded in reaching Australia, because all plate-tectonic reconstructions put the severance of that continent well into the Tertiary. The explanation may be that marsupials evolved earlier and succeeded in making the crossing before the late Cretaceous transgression flooded West Antarctica and the southern margin of Australia, thereby isolating that continent. By the time that sea level again dropped significantly, sea-floor spreading insured isolation of Australia. Not until the late Tertiary when Australia-New Guinea impinged upon the Banda Arc of Indonesia were a limited number of placentals able to colonize from Asia.

As is well known, there are certain groups of organisms—such as ratite birds, the southern beach *Nothofagus*, and austral gynosperms—that are presently confined to the southern extremities of the continents from South America to New Zealand. According to Raven (1979) these must have used the Antarctic land-migration route because such groups do not disperse well across water barriers. A free land connection must have ceased by late Cretaceous times, as indicated above, and New Zealand was isolated by opening of the Tasman Sea.

The extensive creation of new ocean during the period had significant effects on marine invertebrate distribution. A progressive divergence of apparently stenothermal Tethyan faunas, such as the rudistid bivalves and large benthic Foraminifera between the Caribbean and Mediterranean regions, is well documented (Coates 1973; Kauffman 1973; Dilley 1973) and readily attributable to the continued widening of the intervening ocean. Similarly, endemism of ammonites in the western African region decreased from early Upper Albian times as connections between the South and North Atlantic improved (Förster 1978).

Comparison of faunas across the North Pacific suggests the reverse effect, according to Kauffman (1973), who partly attributes the reduced diversity and endemism of bivalve faunas in this region toward the end of the period to the shrinking gap between Asia and North America as North America migrated away from Europe. On the other hand, as we have seen, a Bering land connection well before the end of the Cretaceous seems required by dinosaur and angiosperm distributions. Kauffman also invokes eustasy to account for important changes in bivalve faunas. Thus the late Cretaceous creation of the North American interior seaway and flooding of Tethys continental margins led to increased diversity as new endemic faunas evolved in response to the creation of new areas for colonization. Conversely, episodes of regression promoted competition between newly evolved and already established faunas of the main Tethys; lowered diversity and endemism resulted. Although Kauffman's arguments appear plausible enough, his results are the reverse of those obtained by Hallam (1977a) for Jurassic bivalves.

An endemic ammonite fauna evolved also in the North American mid-continent seaway (Kennedy and Cobban 1976). Because this evolution is clearly bound with changing paleogeography influenced by rise of sea level, perhaps an analogy may be drawn with the evolution of ammonites endemic to the Boreal Realm in the Jurassic, thereby strengthening the view that climatic factors played at most only a subordinate role in the creation of this realm.

Tertiary

Until the Middle Eocene the mammal faunas of Europe and North America were very similar to each other, but different from those of Asia; subsequently a marked divergence is apparent (McKenna 1972, 1973). This evidence accords well with marine geophysical data indicating a severance of the Greenland-Svalbard land link shortly after this time (Talwani and Eldholm 1977). The subsequent withdrawal of the Turgai Sea in the Oligocene allowed free land migration across Eurasia for the remainder of the Tertiary. Similarly, the geological evidence suggesting that India collided with Asia shortly before Middle Eocene times at the latest is confirmed by the record of mammals in that subcontinent. According to Sahni and Kumar (1974) the earliest Indian mammals are of Middle Eocene age and constitute quite a rich fauna exhibiting strong affinities to the Mongolian fauna; a migration corridor, not a sweepstakes route, is required.

Coryndon and Savage (1973) point out that the Eocene mammals of Africa are wholly endemic, but decreasing endemism is exhibited through the Oligocene and Miocene into the Pliocene, with the most frequented (if not the only) migration route being to and from western Asia. One of the best known groups, the proboscideans, first migrated to Asia in about early Miocene times; the later Miocene marks the time of strongest links for the whole mammal fauna.

Relationships between land organisms in North and South America throughout the Tertiary are thoroughly discussed by Raven and Axelrod (1974) and Raven (1979). Although geological reconstructions indicate a significant oceanic gap in the early Tertiary (e.g., Ladd 1976), various mammals, lizards, the genus *Bufo*, and plants seem to have been dispersed between the two continents prior to the end of the Eocene. The Tertiary mammal fauna of South America is strongly endemic, however, and indicates marine isolation that broke down only with the establishment of the Central American isthmus in the Pliocene as a result of a changed pattern of plate movements in the East Pacific. Pronounced cross migration of mammals took place at this time. Webb's (1976) recent ecological study of this celebrated interchange reveals two major phases. The first, in the early Pliocene, was limited to a few broadly adapted herbivores and carnivores, which might have been able to cross water gaps. The second and more important phase occurred in the late Pliocene-early Pleistocene and involved a diversity of adaptive types including freshwater herbivores—a surer indication of land connection.

A valuable cross check on the timing of events comes from the record of marine organisms on the Pacific and Caribbean sides of the land bridge. As Ekman (1953) pointed out, the existence of numerous geminate species in these areas indicates recent derivation from common ancestors when no land barrier existed. Keigwin (1978) has established from his studies of planktonic Foraminifera that a significant divergence of faunas took place in the time interval 3.5-3.1 Ma, which must correspond to the time of formation of the Isthmus of Panama.

A further cross check on the timing of closure of Tethys in the Old World can be obtained by analysis of marine faunas. In the early Tertiary, invertebrate faunas exhibited a high degree of similarity throughout the length of Tethys, but in the late Oligocene or early Miocene this general unity was abruptly disrupted. Indian Ocean benthic foraminiferans and molluscs differ strikingly from those of the Mediterranean region, implying closure of the seaway in the Middle East by creation of a land corridor between Africa and Asia (Adams 1967; Hallam 1967a; cf. Coryndon and Savage 1973). At about the same time Atlantic and Mediterranean foraminiferan faunas diverged (Berggren and Phillips 1969), presumably as a consequence of suturing of North Africa with Spain.

The influence of Tertiary eustasy on organic distributions cannot be adequately evaluated until much more research is done, but it is apparent from data on mammals that, from Oligocene times onward, relations between Asia and North America (Colbert 1973), and Africa and Asia (Coryndon and Savage 1973), fluctuated between corridors and sweepstakes routes, in other words alternating "make or break" situations. This fluctuation can be interpreted only in terms of sea-level changes. The extent to which the initiation of free land migration between Africa and Eurasia relates to the Oligocene fall rather than continental collision is a subject well worthy of closer investigation. As already pointed out there is much geological and paleontological evidence to suggest that collision took place much earlier than the maps of Dewey et al. (1973) and Smith and Briden (1977) would suggest, but in any case a shallow marine strait must have persisted along the line of Tethys until the late Oligocene.

Influence of Climate

During the Quaternary, strong climatic fluctuations provide the leitmotif of geological and biological history. Ice caps advanced and retreated, sea level went down and up at a rapid rate, and atmospheric and oceanic circulation patterns changed drastically. The principal organic response both on the continents and in the oceans involved successive migrations with shifting climatic belts, with temporary isolation of continental organisms at times of high sea level. This subject has generated an immense amount of research, and the general story is comparatively well known; it need not be considered further here.

In complete contrast, evidence from terrestrial plants and vertebrates and sedimentary rocks indicates that the Mesozoic world had a warm equable climate lacking polar ice caps, with only a modest latitudinal zonation recognizable from the plant record (Barnard 1973; Hallam 1975; Krassilov 1975). Because the oceans are more equable than the continents, climatic influences should have been even slighter. Its importance remains controversial, but broad latitudinal zonation is apparent for some invertebrate groups (e.g., Kauffman 1973). What appears beyond serious dispute is that purely climatic effects cannot explain significant changes in organic distributions through Mesozoic time—changes that appear to be related dominantly if not entirely to plate movements and marine transgressions and regressions, at least some of which were world-wide.

Interest therefore focuses on the Tertiary as the time of transition from one climatic extreme to the other. There appears to have been a phase of slight climatic cooling, at least in the northern hemisphere, starting shortly before the end of the Cretaceous (Maastrichtian) and continuing into the earliest Tertiary. This phase is inferred both from changes in angiosperm floras across the Cretaceous-Tertiary boundary in the Euramerican Province (Krassilov 1975; Hickey 1979) and from oxygen-isotope results obtained from planktonic foraminiferans in the North Pacific (Savin et al. 1975).

The early Paleogene climate was evidently as equable as that of the Mesozoic, with warmth-loving plants extending into much higher latitudes than today, but an abrupt cooling at the end of the Eocene is recognizable both from terrestrial plants and foraminiferan isotope data (Kennett 1977; Wolfe 1978). This cooling seems to be connected with the establishment of a circum-Antarctic ocean current system and the growth of Antarctic sea ice. The plant record for the rest of the Tertiary does not show any further change of comparable importance until the Quaternary, but the foraminiferan isotope record shows a further sharp drop in ocean-surface temperatures in the Mid-

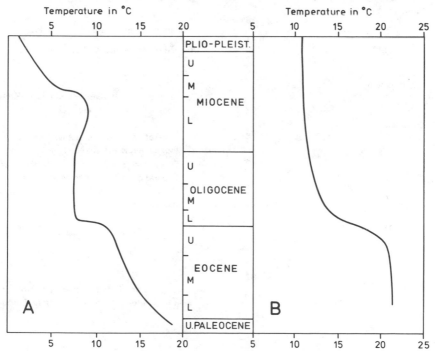

Figure 7.7. Major climatic trends in the Cenozoic: A, Estimate of mean annual temperature of Antarctic surface waters based on oxygen-isotope ratios of planktonic Foraminifera, simplified from Kennett (1977); B, Estimate of mean annual temperature of northwestern United States, based on percentage of plant species leaves with entire margins, simplified from Wolfe (1978).

Table 7.1 Significant Biogeographical Events Related to Plate Movements and Eustasy

Stratigraphic Subdivisions		Age in Ma'	Plate-tectonic Events
Pleistocene		2	Uplift of Central American isthmus
Pliocene		5	
Miocene	U	10	
	M	16	
	L	22.5	Suturing of N. Africa with Spain
Oligocene	U	30	Opening of Drake Passage
	L		Final closure of oceanic straits in Alpine region
		37.5	Opening of Greenland Sea commences
Eocene	U	43	
	M	49	Suturing of India with Asia
	L		Separation of Australia from Antarctica
		53.5	
Paleocene	U	60	Opening of Norwegian Sea commences
	L		
		65	
Maastrichtian			
		70	Closure of ocean between Arabia and Turkey-Iran but persistence of shallow sea
Campanian			
		78	Separation of Europe and N. America between Ireland and Newfoundland Opening of S. Atlantic along its whole length Separation of India from Madagascar Separation of New Zealand from Australia/Antarctica
Santonian			
Coniacian		82	
Turonian		86	
Cenomanian		92	
		100	? Separation of Madagascar from Africa; start of convergent motion of Africa on Europe
Albian		108	
Aptian		115	
Barremian		121	
Hauterivian		126	Spreading starts in Cape Basin of S. Atlantic Separation of India from Antarctica/Australia
Valanginian		131	

*Palaeogeographic Changes
Related to Eustasy*

Organic Response

Commencement of extensive cross migration of N. and S. American mammals;
Divergence of marine faunas on the two
sides of the Central American isthmus

Isolation and dessication of Mediterranean
Definitive closure of Tethys by (relative) uplift
  in Middle East

Extensive cross migration of mammals
between Africa and Eurasia;
Divergence of marine faunas of E. and W.
Tethyan remnants

Withdrawal of Turgai Sea in Eurasia

Divergence of N. American and European
  mammal faunas

Migration of Asian mammals into India

Withdrawal of N. American midcontinent seaway

Development of Euramerican and
Asiamerican dinosaur and angiosperm
provinces

Endemic faunas evolve in midcontinent
seaway of N. America

Isolation of Antarctica from S. America and
  Australia. Isolation of S. America from
  Africa by epicontinental seaway. Creation
  of two N. American land masses by transgression of interior seaway

Cosmopolitan ammonites replace
endemics in West African region

Migration of marsupials, ratites, austral
gymnosperms, and *Nothofagus* to
Australasia

Table 7.1   (continued)

Stratigraphic Subdivisions	Age in Ma'	Plate-tectonic Events
Berriasian	135	
Tithonian/Volgian	141	
Kimmeridgian	143	
Oxfordian	149	
Callovian	156	? Separation of Africa from N. America
Bathonian	165	
Bajocian	171	
Aalenian	174	
Toarcian	178	
Pliensbachian	183	
Sinemurian	189	
Hettangian	192	
TRIASSIC		

NOTE: Time scale based on Berggren (1972) and Van Hinte (1976a, 1976b).

dle Miocene, evidently related to the growth of a substantial Antarctic ice cap (figure 7.7; Savin et al. 1975; Kennett 1977).

The principal effect on this progressive climatic deterioration in the marine realm appears to have been to create a larger number of latitudinally zoned ecological niches. Because fine niche partitioning promotes speciation, a substantial increase in diversity of marine invertebrates occurred. Part of the diversity increase, however, is attributable to the creation of land barriers in the Middle East and Central America (Valentine 1973). Further climatic changes were induced in the late Cenozoic by an increase in continental relief, partly connected with lowering of sea level and partly with tectonic uplift of plateaus and orogenic belts. The formation of extensive arid zones, which apparently had not existed in the early Tertiary, was one important consequence, as has long been recognized from paleobotanical studies in western North America. Increased mammalian endemism in the Quaternary of Africa can be related to the climatic barrier of the Sahara (Coryndon and Savage 1973).

The only obvious interaction of climate and plate-tectonic processes is the creation of a circum-Antarctic current following separation of Australia and opening of the Drake Passage. The northward movement of Australia toward southeastern Asia resulted in a different pattern of climatic change from the rest of the world, with an apparent climatic optimum in the Miocene

Palaeogeographic Changes Related to Eustasy	Organic Response
	Free communication of marine molluscs between Europe and western N. & S. America
Separation of Asia and Europe by epi-continental sea	
Marine transgression on E. margin of Indian Ocean	
Marine transgression on W. margin of Indian Ocean	
	High endemism of marine bivalves at time of low sea level

(Hallam 1967a). Paleobotanical studies indicate that the climate changed from one of high humidity in the Eocene to a somewhat drier one in the Miocene, as shown by the occurrence of various scleromorphic plants (Kemp 1978). The creation of the Central American isthmus in the Pliocene also must have affected oceanic circulation, which might have influenced the formation of a North Polar ice cap (Berggren and Hollister 1977).

Conclusions

A summary of the biogeographically more significant events related to plate movements and eustasy, as discussed in the foregoing account, is presented in table 7.1. Plate-tectonic processes did not have any notable influence on organic distributions until the late Jurassic. They became increasingly important during the Cretaceous and into the early Tertiary as the old super-continent of Pangea progressively disintegrated. Rise of sea level also played an increasingly significant role in the creation of isolated land masses from the Middle Jurassic to the late Cretaceous. The combined effect generated a high degree of endemism in terrestrial organisms, in contrast to the cosmo-politanism characteristic of the early Mesozoic. This is well illustrated by early Tertiary mammals compared with Triassic reptiles (Kurtén 1967; Cox 1974).

The two most important events in the Tertiary involving a combination of plate-tectonic and eustatic events were the closure of Tethys in the Middle East at about the end of the Oligocene, and the uplift of the Central American land bridge in the Pliocene. Both resulted in reduced endemism of terrestrial organisms and increased endemism of marine organisms. The precise timing of Tethyan closure poses a major problem because of the wide disparity between what might now be called conventional plate-tectonic reconstructions, which indicate a late Tertiary date, and geological and biological evidence favoring closer juxtaposition of the Laurasian and Gondwana continents in the late Mesozoic, with convergence commencing in the Middle Cretaceous and collision events taking place from the Maastrichtian to the Oligocene. If a constant earth radius is assumed, this may mean that more continental crust has been lost under Eurasia then generally supposed, or that Africa was not as closely juxtaposed against South America as indicated in the Smith and Briden maps (Hallam 1977b).

Climatic influence on biogeographical changes was of minor importance throughout the Mesozoic but became increasingly significant through the Cenozoic to achieve its present dominant role. Other problems worthy of thorough multidisciplinary study are the precise timing of the establishment of a land link in the Cretaceous between Eurasia and North America, and a fuller elucidation of the changing paleographical character of the late Mesozoic-early Tertiary Antarctic migration route.

Discussion

R. A. Schweickert

PROFESSOR HALLAM is to be congratulated for providing a thoughtful and balanced synthesis of presently available data on the movements of major plates and on eustatic sea-level change during the Mesozoic, and for evaluating the effects of these phenomena on patterns of biogeographical change. Unlike many recent attempts to interpret biogeography according to the vicariance hypothesis, Hallam's contribution is firmly rooted in sound geological and geophysical data and will be of enduring value to biogeographers.

There are just three points on which I feel slight modifications of Hallam's interpretation are necessary, none of which seriously affects his overall conclusions. These are: (1) the fit of continents prior to the breakup of Pangea; (2) the timing of opening of the Central Atlantic in the Jurassic as related to the loss of a land connection between North and South America; and (3) the causes behind the formation of the Cretaceous seaway in western North America.

Hallam's Figure 7.1 shows the pre-drift reconstruction of Pangea by Smith and Briden (1977). At issue is the relation between South and North America, and by extension, between Laurasia and Gondwanaland. Paleomagnetic data presented by Van der Voo et al. (1976) suggest that during the Permian-Triassic, northern South America fit snugly against the southern margin of the United States, occupying the present position of the Gulf of Mexico (figure 7.8). This result requires a 20° clockwise rotation of Gondwanaland from the fit of Bullard et al. (1965), which is apparently nearly identical to Smith and Briden's (1977) solution. The solution of Van der Voo et al. (1976) better reconciles the geological evidence for a Carbo-niferous-Permian collisional orogeny (related to the Hercynian-Variscan-Appalachian assembly of Pangea) along the Ouachita-Marathon belts of the southern United States (Graham et al. 1975; Coney 1979). As noted by Van der Voo et al. (1976) and Coney (1979), the problem of overlap between South America and Central America produced by the above fit can be reconciled by restoring large displacements on a major NW-SE trending sinis-tral transcurrent fault in Mexico first proposed by Silver and Anderson (1974) to account for the apparent offset of Precambrian basement terranes. This structure, although embarrassingly hypothetical over most of its length, may indeed resolve another important problem addressed by Hallam.

From studies of magnetic anomalies in the Central Atlantic, Pitman and Talwani (1972) and Sclater et al. (1977) respectively have inferred an early Jurassic (ca. 180 Ma) or mid-Jurassic (ca. 165 Ma) opening of the Central Atlantic and separation of Africa from North America. Because South America and Africa were joined until the early Cretaceous, opening of the Central Atlantic implies opening within the Caribbean (assuming the fit of

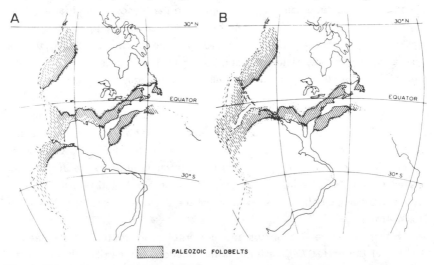

PALEOZOIC FOLDBELTS

Figure 7.8. A, Reconstruction of Pangea, as proposed by Bullard et al. (1965); B, Reconstruction of Pangea, as proposed by Van der Voo et al. (1976). From Van der Voo et al. (1976:fig. 1). Published with the permission of the authors and the Geological Society of America.

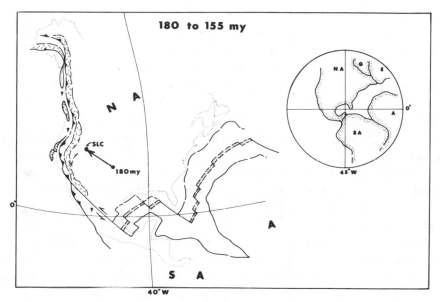

Figure 7.9. Early to mid-Jurassic configuration. From Coney (1979:fig. 2–3). Published with the permission of the author and the Geological Society of America.

Van der Voo et al. (1976)) and thus, apparently, separation of North and South America during the early or mid-Jurassic. Hallam notes a conflict between this apparent timing of separation as suggested by geophysical arguments and the biogeographical requirement for free land communication between North and South America until the late Jurassic.

This dilemma is possibly resolved by Coney's (1979) reconstruction of the opening of the Central Atlantic and Caribbean in the early to mid-Jurassic, which uses Silver and Anderson's (1974) "megashear" (figure 7.9). In Coney's (1979) analysis, the megashear approximates a small circle about the pole of opening for the Central Atlantic given by Pitman and Talwani (1972). The part of Mexico and Central America southwest of the fault initially moved with South America. The megashear thus developed within an isthmus connecting South America and North America through Mexico. Significantly, this geometry allows for the existence of a land bridge between the two continents long after the initial opening of the Central Atlantic, perhaps even until the end of the Jurassic, when separation to the south of Honduras must have severed the connection. Thus the presently accepted timing of opening of the Central Atlantic is consistent with the mammalian data cited by Hallam, because the early opening need not have immediately produced a separation between North and South America.

Hallam states that the development of the mid-Cretaceous seaway in North America (together with the Turgai Sea in eastern Europe) was the most important biogeographical event in the northern hemisphere continents. The formation of this seaway is ascribed primarily to eustatic rise in sea level, especially because a large eustatic rise during the mid-Cretaceous can be tied to a time of rapid sea-floor spreading documented by Hays and Pitman (1973). The implication is that eustatic sea-level change (albeit related to plate motions) was of greater consequence than continental plate motions themselves.

It is a minor yet important point that influences related to plate tectonics played an important role in the development of the Cretaceous interior seaway in North America. Dickinson (1976) has argued that the interior seaway in part occupied a foreland basin linked to a backarc fold and thrust belt (known as the Sevier orogenic belt) that evolved from late Jurassic to late Cretaceous time in concert with metamorphic and igneous activity to the west along the Pacific margin. The subsidence of such foreland basins is probably produced by backarc thrusting and tectonic loading of the continental lithosphere (Dickinson 1976). Alvarez et al. (1979) have presented paleomagnetic data for very rapid subduction at the Pacific margin of North America during the late Cretaceous. The interior seaway may thus have formed as a twofold response to the mid-Cretaceous pulse of fast spreading (Hays and Pitman 1973): (1) eustatic sea level rise and (2) intensified backarc thrusting and basin subsidence related to rapid subduction.

Discussion

M. C. McKenna

DR. HALLAM'S PAPER is a fascinating recitation of some of the main events in the earth's tectonic development during about the last 200 million years, a time during which about a tenth of the history of life leading up to the present has taken place. His conclusions are based mainly on geophysics, primarily marine magnetic anomaly data preserved on oceanic crust not yet destroyed by subduction or by other means. As a geologist and paleontologist he has more or less laid down the law concerning the most recent chapter in the history of the physical world, to which must conform that part of biological distribution that arises from the reordering of chunks of the earth's crust by plate-tectonic processes. Such reordering maintains vicariance once it occurs, but vicariance itself can arise from many causes.

    Hallam really does not come to grips with whether the methods and concepts of vicariance biogeography are useful, useless, or irrelevant for solving problems of historical biogeography, although at one point early in the paper he notes that they are useful but are not the only factors in biogeography. Thus his paper seems to say: "This is the way the present distribution of land and sea has come to be; adjust your biological distribution hypotheses accordingly." As a scientist with a primarily geological background, Hallam does not emphasize the data of vicariance biogeography as such to seek out what, if anything, biological distributions might have to say about geology. Rather, the information flow is one way, from the major events of geology to biology. I must hasten to say, however, that this coin has another side. Some vicariance biogeographers, from their side, seem to delve only superficially into the results of geology; if they mention geology at all, their outdated, inappropriate, or simply missing references reveal the shallowness of their geological understanding. For them, biological distributions interpreted as passively achieved are the true clue to the earth's history, and therefore the geologists must adjust *their* notions of continental jostlings accordingly.

Possibly it is a good thing for the practitioners of different divisions of science to hone their locally parsimonious hypotheses in private in order to avoid circular reason, and to emerge at conferences like this one for the purposes of Kuhnian confrontation, but I would like to push for greater future interchange and synthesis among the so-called subjects of botany, zoology, and geology. The real subject is natural history—not just geology, not just botany, not just zoology. All three subsumed areas of inquiry ought to produce generally congruent results—topologically congruent cladograms for instance—because we all agree that the world has had just one history. But where they are not congruent, I suspect that some of the most interesting and potentially fruitful research in the field of natural history lurks. If we want to deal with these interesting questions we must become ever more conversant with each other's subjects—not an easy task in a world increasingly devoted to intellectual fragmentation and its attendant arrogance and paranoia.

I would now like to deal with some specific issues that arise either directly or indirectly from Hallam's comments. Hallam primarily deals with the first-order phenomena of plate tectonics—the big separations, the big collisions, the big inundations. He is not much concerned with minor events—second-order effects such as aseismic oceanic ridges created on moving plates by underlying "hot spots" or long continental contact along transform faults by large crustal blocks that nevertheless are separating. Some of the second-order effects of plate-tectonic evolution of the earth are probably as important for the origin of biological distributions as are the first-order phenomena. For instance, a complication arises when continents collide: between converging continents there must be at least one subduction plate boundary, although transform-fault motion may remove some of the intervening crust to the side to make way for the approaching continental masses. If this subduction is continued long enough, an associated volcanic arc forms, either offshore or along the edge of one of the continents. The presence of such transform faults and arcs might allow terrestrial organisms to spread from one continent to another, either in both directions or in one direction only, long before the main collision occurs.

Elsewhere (McKenna 1975a) I have dealt with the effect of breaking up a continuous land area, Euramerica, during the Eocene. The faunal evidence from terrestrial fossil mammals in areas such as France and Wyoming indicates that a corridor (Simpson 1953 and references there; McKenna 1973) connected them somewhere in the North Atlantic area at the beginning of the Eocene, but during the early Eocene a water gap appeared at some point along the route, and they thereafter remained faunally separate. Hallam, on the other hand, cites a growing body of evidence that Svalbard, part of northern Scandinavia, was still tectonically in contact with Greenland, which in turn was structurally part of North America, as late as the end of the Eocene, 38 Ma. If so, and if the tectonic contact was not under a shallow epicontinental seaway, then one might hypothesize that Norway, Sweden, and the vast plains that have now sunk to form the Barents Shelf as far east as the mouth of the Turgai Straits in north-central Russia may well have had a mid-to-late Eocene biota with an essentially North American stamp at a time when Europe south of the Baltic was busy producing diversified endemic taxa at about the generic and subfamilial levels. Eocene vicariance somewhere along the Greenland-Iceland-Faeroes-Scotland aseismic ridge system may not have affected northern Scandinavia. At the end of the Eocene, however, Europe become more unified. Although the Eocene/ Oligocene Grande Coupure of European vertebrate paleontologists (Stehlin 1909; Brunet 1977) has always seemed a result of Asiamerican invasions, perhaps part of it resulted from the local time-delayed release of the northern Scandinavian biota.

With regard to the relative motion of North and South America, Hallam cites the main conclusion of Ladd (1976) but not the "fine print," wherein Ladd admitted that northward convergence at about the beginning of the Tertiary may have been imbedded in *net* dilation because the data points are well separated in time. Second-order tectonic effects created by such convergence may have allowed a certain amount of faunal and floral transfer in the earliest Tertiary between North and South America, but not at the present site of Panama.

Hallam takes proponents of "Pacifica" to task for various reasons with which I concur. Drs. Nur, Ben-Avraham, and Melville have their chance to defend the concept. Others will also present their ideas, so I wish to add only that the Pacific Ocean floor (Panthalassa) has been tectonically decoupled from its surrounding lands for at least 200 million years—perhaps even longer. If it originated by widening of a subcontinental rift, any separating continental fragments whose tops were above water would subsequently have been isolated for long periods as well, perhaps 100 million years, before colliding with other landmasses. Thus, if "Pacifica" existed above sea level, one would expect rather large morphological differences between any two resulting terrestrial sister taxa. The sister taxa would also be of high rank. One should not invoke Jurassic or earlier separations to account for cladogenesis within taxa that on generally parsimonious grounds were not yet in existence at the time. But if one persists, one should be prepared to defend *much* earlier existence than now known for various taxa whose fossil record is otherwise good and in which the morphocline polarities correspond well with the already-known sequence observed in the rocks.

A further problem with "Pacifica" is that the Pacific Ocean is a bit like a tank full of poisonous sheep-dip. As new ocean floor moves laterally away from a generating ridge, it also sinks because of cooling (Parsons and Sclater 1977). In the North Atlantic and North Pacific, for instance, the depth d in meters with respect to time t in millions of years is

$$d = 6400 - 3200\,e^{\frac{-t}{62.8}}$$

Put another way, after some time the depth of the ocean floor below sea level asymptotically reaches 6400 m. After about 70 million years of lateral transport, material formerly at a ridge crest will have subsided to within about 1000 m of that depth. Small continental blocks imbedded in such oceanic crust would rise a bit higher, of course, but during any long journey a small block, say the size of the Manihiki and Ontong Java plateaus, would sink to depths decidedly uncomfortable for terrestrially adapted organisms and would remain there a long time before emerging at the other side of the ocean in a collision with land. I suspect that any terrestrially derived original passengers would eventually stop holding their breath and would arrive at land as fossils on a Viking funeral ship rather than on a Noah's ark (McKenna 1973).

Response

A. Hallam

I WELCOME Dr. Schweickert's comments on the vexed question of the early Atlantic opening phase, which is undoubtedly one of the most complex parts of the story of the Pangean breakup. I have been reluctant to follow the Van der Voo reconstruction because of the problem of Central American overlap, but Schweickert may well be right to argue that the problem is soluble by invoking large transcurrent displacements. I am particularly interested in the possibility that an inter-American land bridge could possibly have existed through the entire Jurassic, and I am glad to have my attention drawn to Coney's analysis. With regard to the development of the North American mid-continent seaway in the late Cretaceous, I find very acceptable the argument that the effect of rise of sea level was reinforced by local tectonic subsidence.

Dr. McKenna takes me to task for laying down the law to biologists, but he distorts what I actually said. There are indeed many instances where the combined weight of sound geological and geophysical evidence is such that a biogeographer would be foolhardy to ignore it. I endeavor to point out, however, that there are other instances where the earth-science data are incomplete, ambiguous, or contradictory, and in these instances paleo-biogeographical data have a major role to play in unraveling geological history. The most important instances I refer to are the early opening of the

Atlantic, the closure of Tethys, the existence of an Antarctic migration route, and the Bering land connection.

As for not coming to grips with the methods and concepts of vicariance biogeography, I do not consider this part of my brief, although I make allusions to the subject. McKenna's remarks give me the opportunity to outline my view, which in essence is that I regard vicariance and dispersal as equally important phenomena and two sides of the same coin. Thus the creation of the Central American isthmus and Middle Eastern closure of Tethys promoted vicariance among marine organisms and dispersal among terrestrial organisms. I do not feel it necessary to reply to McKenna's other comments because I am not in disagreement with them.

8

Lost Pacifica Continent:
A Mobilistic Speculation

A. Nur and Z. Ben-Avraham

There are two puzzling phenomena associated with the crust in the western
Pacific Ocean and the circum-Pacific continental margins: (1) a large number
of old allochthonous continental fragments throughout the entire Pacific
continental rim, and (2) submerged thick crusted platforms in the western
Pacific Ocean. We first review the evidence for the continental nature of the
fragments embedded in the circum-Pacific, and the paleomagnetic and
geological data related to their origins and age. We then reconstruct a possible migration of these fragments with Cenozoic and Mesozoic plate motion in
the Pacific. Independently, we review the evidence for the continental
character of the western Pacific platforms that may have originated, like the
other fragments, in a large, ancient, continental mass in the paleo-Pacific—a
mass that we call Pacifica. We then consider some implications of the Pacifica speculation, among them the origin of spreading and the nature of
continental collision.

Continental Fragments in Pacific Margins

In figure 8.1 we summarize evidence to support past continental masses in
the Pacific Ocean. Holmes (1965) presented a compelling case for late

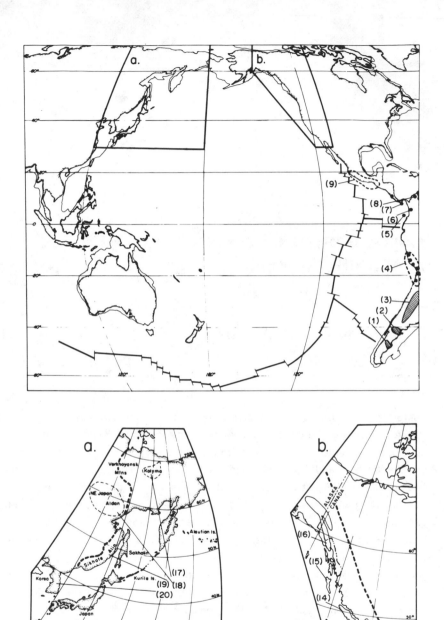

Paleozoic to early Tertiary continental land forms, such as Cascadia and Lla-
noria, to the west of present-day North America (Schuchert and Dunbar
1950). The land includes conglomerates derived from crystalline sialic rocks
that have since disappeared. Hamilton (1969) refined this notion, specifying
that "old arcs presumably have been swept into the (North American)
continent." This is necessary to explain, for example, the Klamath-Sierran
arc geology (Burchfiel and Davis 1975; Schweickert and Cowan 1975;
Anderson 1976). Most recently, Davis and Armstrong (in Fischer 1976) suggested "that the Klamaths were originally some distance off shore to the
west and that the Permo-Triassic Sonoma Orogeny results from an arc-
continent collision."

Several investigators (Monger and Ross 1971; Jones et al. 1972;
Richards 1974) have suggested a large-scale collision of Alaska with a
continental fragment during the Paleozoic and early Mesozoic, while masses
finally coalesced in late Jurassic-to-early Cretaceous time. Hamilton (1969)

←

Figure 8.1. Distribution of some of the old continental masses around the
Pacific Ocean. Insets a and b mark the location of enlarged maps on the
bottom. (1) Deseado massif (Herrero-Ducloux 1963); (2) Patagonian massif
(Herrero-Ducloux 1963); (3) Pampean massif (Herrero-Ducloux 1963); (4)
Small blocks in the coastal range of Peru and Chile (James 1971a); (5)
Gorgona Island and the continental shelf off Colombia (MacDonald and Hurley
1969; Case et al. 1971; Meyer et al. 1976; Lloyd 1963; Guzman and Cserna
1963); (6) Small blocks in the Serrania de Baudo in Colombia (MacDonald and
Hurley 1969; Case et al 1971; Meyer et al 1976; Lloyd 1963; Guzman and
Cserna 1963); (7) Nicoya complex in Costa Rica and Panama (MacDonald and
Hurley 1969; Case et al 1971; Meyer et al 1976; Lloyd 1963; Guzman and
Cserna 1963); (8) Santa Marta Mountain in Colombia (MacDonald and Hurley
1969; Case et al. 1971; Meyer et al. 1976; Lloyd 1963; Guzman and Cserna
1963); (9) Small block in the Sierra Madre del Sur in Mexico (MacDonald and
Hurley 1969; Case et al. 1971; Meyer et al 1976; Lloyd 1963; Guzman and
Cserna 1963).
Inset a (Far East): (17) Kolyma block in Siberia (McElhinny 1973a; Hamilton
1970); (18) Aldan block in Siberia (McElhinny 1973a; Hamilton 1970); (19)
Sikhote Alin in Siberia (McElhinny 1973a; Hamilton 1970); (20) The
Precambrian in Korea (Kawai et al. 1969); Inset b (northwestern America):
(10) Plumas Terrane, Sierra Nevada, California (Churkin and Eberlein 1977);
(11) Eastern Klamath Mountains (Hamilton 1969); (12) Hells Canyon in
eastern Oregon, western Idaho, and southeastern Washington (Jones et al
1977), Suplee-Izee areas, central Oregon (Churkin and Eberlein 1977), the
Ochoo terrane; (13) San Juan and northern Cascade Treanes Butte area and
the Juan Island, Washington (Churkin and Eberlein 1977); (14) Vancouver
Island (Churkin and Eberlein 1977); (15) Queen Charlotte Islands (Jones et al.
1977); (16) Alexander Archipelago, Alaska (Churkin and Eberlein 1977) and
the Wrangell Mountains, Alaska (Jones et al. 1977). The dashed line in insert b
indicates limit of Triassic continental shelf (Jones et al. 1977).

has proposed that Permian terranes bearing Tethyan fusulinids may have formed in the Central Pacific, on island arcs that subsequently were swept into the North American continent. These North American terranes share Jurassic and Cretaceous faunas and floras with New Zealand, New Caledonia, the Antarctica peninsula, and Chile (Hamilton 1969). This is consistent with several paleomagnetic studies that suggest that large fragments in the western United States, Canada, and Alaska were located near the equator, perhaps during Triassic times (Symons 1971; Irving and Yole 1972). Hillhouse (1977) found that tholeiitic flows in the Wrangell mountain area were formed 15° north of the equator during Triassic time. Other paleomagnetic evidence is summarized in table 8.1.

Jones et al. (1977) have shown convincingly that a large continental block, Wrangellia, was incorporated into northwestern North America in late Mesozoic time. The block or blocks extending over 2000 km from Alaska to Oregon could not have been contiguous to central Alaska in the Jurassic. Warm water carbonate rocks, with no evidence of faunas, have been found at high latitudes in western Canada. This is typical of North American or nothern Asian regions. Most remarkably, Jones et al. (1977) have pointed out that the displaced Wrangellia block received "enormous quantities of Triassic tholeiitic basalts—to become one of the largest domains of non oceanic basalts. . . . Presumably, rifting initiated this volcanism, but where it occurred and what was rifted remain enigmatic." This rifting, as well as the subsequent synchronous subsidence through Wrangellia, could be the result of a pre-Triassic continental breakup in the South Pacific.

In Central and South America, there are numerous old basement inclusions within the mobile belts, some of which extend well into the Pacific Ocean itself and suggest past continental accretion. In Argentina the Pampean, Patagonian, and Deseado massifs are composed of igneous and metamorphic rocks of Precambrian and lower Paleozoic age (Herrero-Ducloux 1963). The Pampean massif, for example, is flanked by continental deposits ranging in origin from the Permo-Carboniferous to the Tertiary (Herrero-Ducloux 1963). We do not know the original positions of these massifs, but Windhausen (1931) and Morrison (1962) have suggested that Patagonia was a separate continental fragment before Cretaceous time. During the Jurassic, South America was bounded on the west by volcanic rocks "resting on strongly folded and metamorphosed rocks" off Ecuador, Peru, and Bolivia (Weeks 1947; Marks 1956; Tschopp 1956; Jenks 1956b). Old Precambrian continental basement fragments of unknown origins have been identified in the Santa Marta Mountains in Columbia, the Pacific Ocean off Peru, and the

Table 8.1   Paleomagnetic Evidence for Large-scale Migration of Continental Fragments Now Embedded in Pacific Margins

Region	Position and Age	References
Part of eastern Siberia	*U. Carb.-Perm.*—50° away from computed pole; 20° farther from pole	Creer (1973)
eastern Siberia	*Triassic*—Distance to pole ∼ 30° further away than computed. *Jurassic*—Poles coincide. Implies a 3000 km northward migration in Triassic time, at a rate of 30°/30 MY = 10 cm/y	Creer (1973)
Sikhote-Alin	*Permian*—50° away from computed pole. *Cretaceous*—10° away from computed pole. Moved 4000 km (40°) in ∼50 MY or 8 cm/y	McElhinny (1973b)
Kolyma	*Permo-Triassic*—45° away from computed pole. *Cretaceous*—5° away from computed pole. Implies a 4000 km northward migration between Permo-Triassic and Cretaceous	McElhinny (1973b)
Insular belt, western Canada	Insular belt has moved 4000 km northward since Triassic	Irving and Yole (1972)
Southern Alaska	Low paleolatitudes in *Triassic* time Upper Triassic Nikolai Greenstone was 15°N or 15°S of paleo-equator—thus 3000 or 6000 km south of computed position. Has moved 3000 or 6000 km since Upper Triassic times	Hillhouse (1977)
	Ordovic-Pennsylv.—Prince Wales Is. was at least 25° farther south than computed	Jones et al. (1977)
	Triassic or Mid-Cenozoic—Queen Charlotte Is. has moved northward 25°	Hicken and Irving (1977)
Japan	*Permian*—Southern Japan was situated near the paleoequator, and drifted northward during early Permian-late Cretaceous	Minato and Fujiwara (1964) Adachi (1976)

Sierra Madre del Sur in Mexico (MacDonald and Hurley 1969; Case et al. 1971; Meyer et al. 1976; Lloyd 1963; Guzman and Cserna 1963). The situation is perhaps best summarized by James (1973):

> Jurassic volcanic rocks in southern Peru are wedged in among crystalline metamorphic rocks at least 400 m.y. old. Just what these remnants of ancient sialic crust are doing some 300 kilometers west of the currently exposed geosynclinal rocks of the continental margin is unknown. These rocks could be part of the paleozoic microcontinent that lay to the west of the South American coastline.

In northeastern Asia, paleomagnetic data (McElhinny 1973a) suggest that the Kolyma block and the Sikhote Alin region have been welded onto the Asian continent, probably in late Jurassic or Cretaceous time. The Verkhoyansk and Sikhote mountain belts therefore represent probable sites of continental collisions (Hamilton 1970). Other possible continental fragments from the Pacific Ocean are the Sea of Okhotzk and surrounding areas, almost all of China south of 40°, and Korea (Kawai et al. 1969; Hurley 1971). All this suggests that large fragments have collided with mainland Asia from the Triassic through the Cretaceous. Churkin and Eberlein (1977) point out that

> Permian . . . rocks lie outbound of poorly known Paleozoic and Precambrian rocks in the Alaska range. Ancient rocks reappear west of the Bering Sea along the northwest rim of the Pacific, where similar terranes of Paleozoic age occur in northeastern USSR, in Japan, and discontinuously father south along the west Pacific rim.

North America, the Andes, Japan, eastern Siberia, and China all show traces of mysterious continental masses in the Pacific.

Dickinson (1971) suggests that "for western N. America . . . we are forced to contemplate the possiblity of . . . several collisions of the main North American Craton with other continents, microcontinents, or island arcs, and the initiation of several arc-trench systems. . . ." We may conclude that numerous fragments of the aforementioned land masses have been incorporated into the entire borders of the circum-Pacific continents.

Pacifica Continent

Three processes have been proposed to account for the presence of old continental crust in the circum-Pacific belts: (1) separation, subsequent return, and collision of continental slivers; (2) the transverse motion of irregular continental slivers along transform faults such as the San Andreas fault; and (3) collision with an incorporation of island arcs. We envision a fourth process: collision of large continental chunks with the circum-Pacific continents over at least the past few hundred million years. These chunks were parts of a continental mass that disaggregated in the manner of Gonda-wana and, currently, of Africa.

We posit the following parallel sequence for the Indian Ocean and Africa: If the Carlsberg Ridge continues to spread, India may eventually be consumed by the Himalayas, and a trench may develop south of India to accommodate the continuously forming ocean plate. With this configuration, the Tibet-Himalaya-India orogen would become quite similar to a circum-Pacific orogen: a trench and ocean adjacent to the collision belts.

As an alternative to random migration of island arcs or haphazard recoa-lescence of continents, we suggest that the circum-Pacific fragments were embedded in, and moved with, the major plates of the Pacific Ocean. We may roughly reconstruct the motion of such fragments back to 190 Ma, by the paleomagentically derived motions of the Kula, Farallon, Phoenix, and Pacific Plates (Larson and Chase 1972; Hilde et al. 1976). In figure 8.2, we remove continental blocks from Alaska, western North America, the Andes, Kamchatka, and Japan, attaching them in a cartoon fashion to their cor-responding plates. We note that the various fragments, as they migrate toward their respective spreading ridges, also approach each other. In fact, it appears that by late Jurassic time, the earliest time for which magnetic data are available, these fragments are well on their way toward coalescing into a single continental mass. We suggest that such a mass actually existed by approximately mid-Permian times.

We thus propose that a continental mass, intact before early Mesozoic time, was broken up by the complex spreading (Larson and Chase 1972) that separated the Kula, Farallon, Pacific, and Phoenix Plates. The fragments, divided into four groups associated with these plates, were presumably car-ried toward subduction zones and eventually reached continental margins. Roughly speaking, the Kula fragments collided with Alaska and eastern Siberia; the Farallon fragments collided with North America; and the Phoenix fragments collided with South America. There is no major continental colli-sion region associated with the Pacific Plate of Larson and Chase (1972); this fact may be related to the submerged platforms in the western Pacific Ocean (figure 8.3).

The oldest magnetic anomalies and sediments in the Pacific Ocean sug-gest that the continental fragments of Pacifica were already fully separated

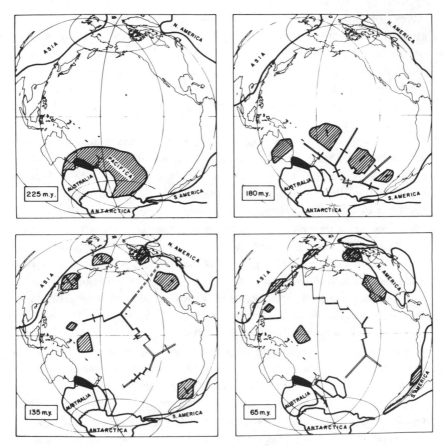

Figure 8.2. Schematic model of the breakup of Pacifica and the resulting collision events. Possible ages of the reconstruction stages: (a) 225 Ma; (b) 180 Ma; (c) 135 Ma; (d) 65 Ma. Fine lines mark the present-day continental outline. Heavy lines mark the location of the various continental areas through the geological evolution (after Dietz and Holden 1970). Position of spreading centers simplified from Larson and Chase (1972), Uyeda and Ben-Avraham (1972), Ben-Avraham and Uyeda (1973), Hilde et al. (1976), and Hayes and Ringis (1973). New Guinea is shown in black. Schematic continental blocks in the western Pacific are also shown.

by late Jurassic or early Cretaceous times, approximately 120 Ma (Larson and Chase 1972). It is quite likely that major continental collisions were already in advanced stages, and that at this time a large part of the Pacific Ocean had been swept clean of continental fragments. By reconstructing the spreading junction, we may locate early Pacifica northeast of today's Australia (Hilde et al. 1976). The continent either was a distinct mass in the middle of the Pacific Ocean, or was originally attached to Pangea. A hypothetical configuration of Pacifica near Pangea, some time during or before the Permian, is shown in figure 8.2a.

We may estimate the time scale for migration of fragments to the circum-Pacific continental margins by taking typical distances as 4000, 6000, and 9000 km, and typical plate convergence rates as the current Pacific 10 cm/yr; resultant durations are 40, 60, and 90 million years, respectively. These durations can easily be accommodated in the period from the Traissic to the Cretaceous.

We propose the following gross sequences of breakups and collisions:

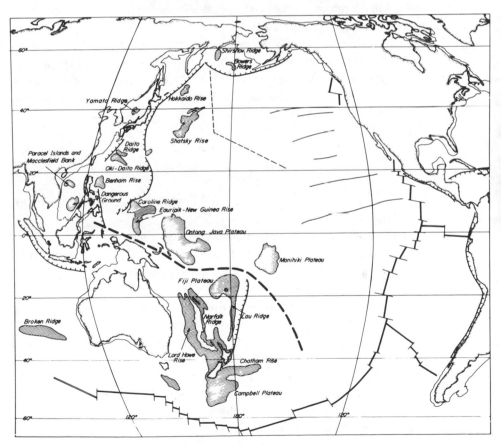

Figure 8.3. Submarine plateaus and ridges in the western Pacific Ocean. The dashed line marks the boundary between highs that were part of Australia to the south and those that may have been part of Pacifica to the north.

by late Permian to Triassic time, rifting and spreading developed sufficiently to define the Kula, Farallon, and Phoenix Plates (figure 8.2b). Each one of these plates then carried one or more fragments of the original Pacifica continent. In the course of subduction near proto-North America, South America, Alaska, and East Asia, the three plates were consumed at their converging boundaries.

Toward late Jurassic time, the Pacifica fragments began to collide with the surrounding continents. We assume that collision replaces subduction when a continental fragment approaches a subduction zone adjacent to a continent. In the proto-Japanese and South American areas, a Pacifica fragment totally coalesced with the continent. In Alaska and North America, the bulk of the continental mass was approaching rapidly; some collisions were already taking place (figure 8.2c).

By Cretaceous time, massive collisions took place in North America. New subduction zones developed behind the various Pacifica segments, now part of their respective continental masses. In Cenozoic time, all continental fragments in the eastern and northern Pacific coalesced with their respective continents; left behind was a purely oceanic crust with spreading centers (figure 8.2d).

Western Pacific Ocean Floor

One of the attractions of this hypothesis is that it may account for some of the submerged platforms in today's western Pacific Ocean. Typically, these platforms and blocks (figure 8.3) are shallowly submerged and rise perhaps 2–3 km above the surrounding sea floor. Unlike the sea floor, they are devoid of magnetic lineations, and exhibit strikingly thicker crusts. In some places, these crusts have compressional velocity structures that approach continental values (table 8.2). Of particular interest is the example of the Ontong Java Plateau in the southwestern Pacific Ocean; the thick crust ranges from 36–43 km. Remarkably, seismic velocity to a depth of 20 km is only 6.3 km/sec, typical of granitic basement (figure 8.4). The western margin of the plateau is rifted, whereas Joides drill-holes penetrated through shallow-water Cretaceous-to-Recent sediments.

A number of authors (Milson and Smith 1975; Winterer 1974) have suggested that the Ontong Java Plateau, among others, consists of piles of

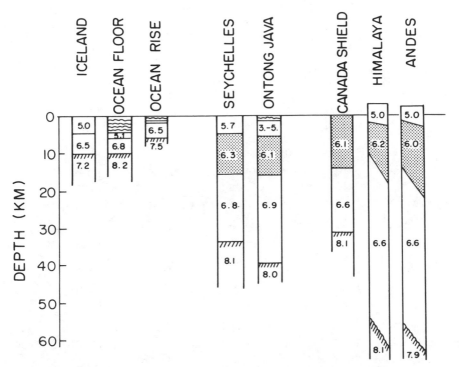

Figure 8.4. Comparison of oceanic and continental crustal structures. Although morphologically slightly similar, the enigmatic Ontong-Java platform is totally dissimilar to Iceland (Furomoto et al. 1973; Pálmason 1971) or to typical oceanic crust. It is, however, remarkably similar to typical shield structures, with thick 6.1 km/s upper crust, and to the Seychelles banks, known to be continental (Laughton et al. 1970). Typical orogenic crusts are even thicker, given Himalaya (Narain 1973) with known continental collision. Note the similarity with the Andes (James 1971b), where no collision is presently known. Past collisions with Pacifica fragments may be the explanation.

volcanic flows, similar to present-day Iceland. As shown in figure 8.4, the crustal velocity structures of Ontong Java and Iceland (Furumoto et al. 1973; Pálmason 1971) are drastically different. Iceland resembles a typical ocean floor and rise; the Ontong Java structure resembles a shield. The granite layer is 10–20 km thick and has a seismic velocity of 6.1 km/sec. It is unlikely that basaltic piles at a depth of 15–20 km would have such a low velocity.

We propose that these platforms are continental crustal fragments of Pacifica. They are grossly similar to known submerged continental platforms in Melanesia (table 8.1) and in the Indian Ocean. The exposed granitic base-

Table 8.2 Characteristics of Several Submerged Platforms in Western Pacific Ocean

Area	Water Depth	Mantle Depth	Sialic Velocity (km/sec)	Depth of Sialic Layer	Notes	References
Kermadac Ridge	.7–2.5	16–19			Generally assumed to be submerged continental fragments	Shor et al. (1971)
Norfolk Ridge	1–2	~22				
Lord Howe Rise	1.2–1.6	18–29	6.0	16		Woollard (1975)
Coville Ridge	1.7–2.3	14–20				Murauchi et al. (1973)
Ontong Java Plateau	2–2.5	40–42	6.1	17	Rifted margin to the west	Furumoto et al. (1976)
Manihiki Rise	2.5	>13.5	6.1	13	Moho not reached	Sutton et al. (1971)
Oki Daito Ridge	2.5	>15	6.0	12	Moho not reached	Murauchi et al. (1968)
Eauripik-New Guinea Rise	2–3	20(?)	(6.9?)	?	Velocity data uncertain	Den et al. (1971)
Bismark Archipelago	1–2	25–35	6.1	10–15		Woollard (1975)
Shatski Rise	1.4	>24	(7.0)	(25)	Water depth is, but velocity is not, consistent with continental crust	Den et al. (1969)

ment of the Seychelles bank, for example, indicates its continental origin, as do the P velocities of 6.1–6.3 km/s, which are typical of shallow "sialic" continental crust (Kanaev and Turko 1976).

Collision and Orogenic Deformation

It can be shown (Nur and Ben-Avraham 1978) that even relatively simple continental collision leads to very complex geology like that in parts of the circum-Pacific mountain belts. In the past it was assumed that immobile sediment-filled geosynclines led to mountain building or orogeny by means of upheaval and deformation. This hypothesis could not quite explain the great crustal shortening implied by the deformation observed in mountain belts. It was plate tectonics that explained this essential element. Several investigators (Dewey and Bird 1970; Smith 1976) have journalized the general features of orogeny in terms of continental collision, subduction, and rifting. As a result, the Alpine mountain chain is now generally considered the product of continent-continent collisions. In this belt, particularly in the Tibetan and Iranian segments (Ben-Avraham and Nur 1976), the zone of recent tectonic activity is over 2000 km wide. Crustal thicknesses are 1.5–2 times as great as the average continental crust; the light continental material presumably has been pushed into the asthenosphere. Under the Himalayas, for example, the crust is 70 km thick (Narain 1973). The active collision zone, as indicated by seismicity, includes not only the highly deformed Himalaya belt, but also the entire width of the Tibetan Plateau. This great width (figure 8.5) is not accounted for at present, but may be closely related to the collision process.

The circum-Pacific mountain belts, with width and morphology similar to the Alpine belt, clearly do not experience continental collisions today. The crust in western North America, Alaska, eastern Siberia, and the Andes, is often as thick as 70 km (figure 8.4; James 1971a). Even morphologically, the elevated parts of the western United States, Alaska, and to some extent South America, Japan, and Kamchatka resemble the segments of the Alpine belts. All are seismically active, wide, highly deformed, and marked by high plateaus of various sizes. The Pacifica hypothesis provides an explanation for the similarities and suggests that the more complex *circum-Pacific* mountain belts may be in part the result of past continental collisions similar to those associated with the Alpine belt.

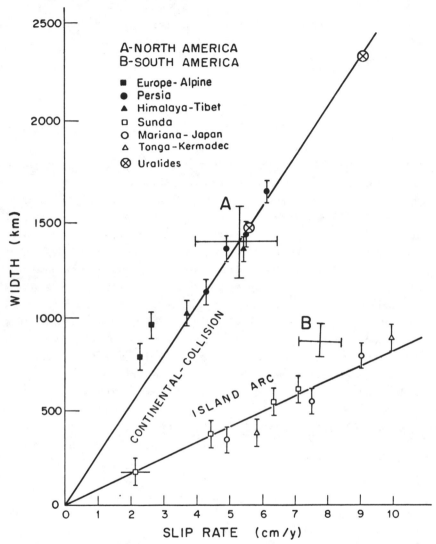

Figure 8.5. Width of known continental collison zones and other continental mountain belts vs. the rate of consumption. Island arc values are shown for comparison. From Ben-Avraham and Nur (1976).

Biogeography and Trans-Pacific Connection

A curious and possibly very important aspect of the drifting of the Pacifica fragments, is the trans-Pacific connection for fauna and flora. In this section we briefly and incompletely mention a few of the published works on the distribution of flora and fauna that suggest the existence of some sort of continental link between southeastern Asia and western North America (table 8.3).

Following Wegener's publication of *The Origin of Continents and Oceans*, Gregory (1925) stated: "There is however similar (to the Atlantic) evidence of land connection across the pacific." This is required to explain the distribution of the alligator, some lizards, amphibians, earthworms, and various plants. Hallier (1912), following earlier studies, had already suggested "the birthplace of the angiosperms in the basin of the Pacific Ocean on the hypothetical continent of Pacifica" (Takhtajan 1969). This early suggestion for a Pacifica continent, preceding Wegener's (1915) continental drift theory, was abandoned because, as Gregory (1925) pointed out, "The existence of a land connection from America westward across the pacific is . . . wholly inconsistent with the present form of (Wegener's continental) displacement theory." Several decades later, Melville (1966, 1967) forcefully resurrected the Pacifica continent notion, occupying the Central Pacific over Menard's (1964) Darwin Rise. Here the land connection was required to explain the distribution of *Gigantopteris* flora. Melville (1967) suggested: "During the Carboniferous there were three continents in the Northern Hemisphere: Atlantica consisting of western Europe and eastern North America, Pacifica consisting of western North America and eastern Asia with the adjacent island arcs and Angaraland (Siberia). . . . The upraising of the Darwin rise produced a land bridge which connected Pacifica with the New Zealand platform in the Triassic. . . ."

Melville's suggestion was immediately challenged by Hallam (1967b) and others. Most important is the conclusion by Menard and Hamilton (1963) that "there is no possibility that sunken continents could have been in the area (of the Darwin Rise) since the Middle Mesozoic. . . ." Takhtajan (1969) pointed out on the basis of Menard and Hamilton's (1963) conclusions that a Pacifica land connection would be very attractive, but the marine geophysical evidence does not support this idea. Obviously, Takhtajan was not aware in 1969 that the structure and history of the Pacific Ocean floor have been totally reevaluated since Menard's earlier static interpretation. The measurement, interpretation, and analysis of the magnetic anomalies in the Pacific established the mobilistic nature of its sea floor, with migrating spreading centers (Vine 1966; Heirtzler et al. 1968), and led to the conclusion that most parts of the Pacific floor have been in motion since late Jurassic time or earlier.

Our version of the Pacifica notion, namely that a late Paleozoic continental mass has disaggregated, with fragments moving with the various

Table 8.3 Examples of Biogeographical Problems Associated with Pacific Basin and Pacifica

Problem	Proposed Source Region	Reference	Notes
Origin of angiosperms	Southwest Pacific region (New Guinea, New Caledonia, China, etc.)	Hallier (1912)	Suggested a *Pacifica* continental bridge
Origin of angiosperms *Glosopteris* and *Gigantopteris* flora	Southwest Pacific region (New Guinea, New Caledonia, China, etc.)	Melville (1966)	Differences between European and eastern North American to western North American coals
Coal floras	Cathasia	Melville (1966)	Tropical in southern Alaska
Marsupial biogeography	New Guinea/New Caledonia in early Mesozoic	Martin (1977)	
Multituberculata	Migration from eastern Asia to North America in early Mesozoic	Kielan-Jaworowska (1974)	Migration only from Asia to America, not reversed
Lizards, alligators	Migration from China to America	Wegener (1924); Gregory (1925)	Suggested a continental trans-Pacific link
Subtropical broad-leaf forest in Western U.S. & China, Japan (Tertiary)	S.W. Asia?	Leopold & MacGinitie (1972)	Trans-Pacific link

Mesozoic plates, therefore provides a renewed possibility for a continental trans-Pacific link. The link is much more mobile than previous models and does not involve major inconsistencies with plate tectonics as known today. In fact, the motion of the fragments of Pacifica is estimated on the basis of the motion of the plates, and therefore is generally consistent with plate tectonics. Thus a mobile trans-Pacific land connection could have existed, and may have played a role in determining the distribution of floras and faunas around the Pacific Basin. This may help to resolve some aspects of the bitter debate among biogeographers concerning not only the Pacific Basin, but also the dominance of vicariance or dispersal in evolution in general (e.g., Nelson 1976).

Conclusion

The mass that we call Pacifica, to emphasize its centrality in Pacific geological history, could have been part of the Pangean supercontinent adjacent to Australia and Antarctica. The breakup of this continent and the drift of its fragments resulted in continental collision with South America, North America, Alaska, Kamchatka, Japan, and eastern Asia. Submerged platforms in the Pacific Ocean, such as the Ontong Java area, the Shatsky rise, and the Manihiki Plateau, may be further remnants of Pacifica. The thick crusts of these plateaus, with seismic velocities typical of continents, are thus predicted to be continental crusts.

Although the details of the breakup and collision of Pacifica cannot be resolved very well at present, we suggest that Pacifica disaggregated in a manner similar to the current breakup of Africa, producing continental slivers that eventually may appear in the collision zone as allochthonous fragments. The notion of Pacifica and its breakup provides an attractive explanation for the similarities of faunas and rock sequences in widely separated locations in the mountain belts around the Pacific, and may tie in divergent paleomagnetic data. It may explain the curious geological history of Wrangellia (Jones et al. 1977), where flood basalts and Triassic continental deposits are supplemented by strong evidence for continental rifting in an unknown location near the equator. The submergence of this fragment, and its subsequent emergence upon collision with North America, is an almost perfect example of the history we envision for the fragments of Pacifica.

The greatest difficulty that our hypothesis encounters is the scarcity of direct evidence. By the very nature of plate consumption, older lithosphere becomes very rare in the oceans and highly deformed and distorted in continental mountain belts. The validity of the proposed plate processes in the pre-Mesozoic Pacific can be tested only through essentially second order effects that survive the subduction and consumption of older crusts. The Pacifica notion will remain speculative until the physical and geological nature of the submerged platforms in the western Pacific are revealed by geophysical and drilling activities. We have a general working hypothesis for reassessing the geological evidence in deformed orogenic belts: How strong is the evidence for the incorporation of large continental masses in the circum-Pacific and other mountain belts? Can some of the apparent complexity be resolved by the multiplicity of collisions? At present, we lack a basic understanding of the mechanics of continental collisions. We do not know what happens to lithospheric slabs below the colliding crusts. Do they, for example, override one another, or deform viscously into a thick fluid-like blob? We must investigate the role of small density variations between colliding continents, variations due either to different thermal histories or to rock types.

There is little doubt that the thermal history of continental regions is of the greatest importance in understanding the mechanics of plate motions. Major problems remain unresolved. Why do some large continental areas, such as the Canadian Shield, remain immobile for long periods of time while some small blocks spread, as in the western Mediterranean? The Pacifica speculation leads to exciting generalizations about the nature and history of plate tectonics on earth; these generalizations in turn provide working hypotheses and experiments that address major questions about the nature of geological processes.

Acknowledgments

We are greatly indebted to G. Thompson for important discussions on crustal velocities, and to W. Dickinson for critical and insightful comments. The responsibility for the ideas and conclusions of this paper, however, are solely ours, and no one else should be blamed for them. Research was supported in part by grant #NSF DES 75-04874 from the Earth Science Division, U.S. National Science Foundation, and by a grant from the Arthur L. Day Fund of the U.S. National Academy of Sciences.

Discussion

R. L. Batten and R. A. Schweickert

WE PROPOSE to test the hypothesis that fragments of a displaced Pacifica continent have been incorporated into the present rim of circum-Pacific continents and to test whether or not these fragments help to explain the zoogeographical distribution of displaced faunas by examining the nature of the basement rocks of the allochthonous terranes of western North America and the distribution of Middle Permian Tethyan fusulinid Foraminifera.

It is critical to the Pacifica hypothesis to be able to identify exotic continental fragments now lodged in circum-Pacific mountain belts. Nur and Ben-Avraham implicitly assume that the existence of terranes with "continental crust" guarantees the viability of a former continental land mass. This assumption is questionable on several counts. "Continental crust" as usually defined simply means relatively thick (ca 40 km), low density (ρ = 2.85 g/cm^3), and therefore low velocity (V_ρ = 5.0–6.8 km/sec), crust. In addition to continents, mature island arcs such as the Aleutians contain thick crust of this character (Jacob and Hamada 1972), and it is therefore important to recognize that thick "continental crust" alone carries no significant information about the former existence of continental land masses. Instead, geological data must be examined; here their analysis does not stand up to careful examination, and also disregards relevant information. All of the present continents are cored by ancient ($>$ one billion years old) crystalline rocks. Surely, if the notion of Pacifica is to merit acceptance, terrances of ancient crystalline rocks should be evident throughout the circum-Pacific mountain belts. Such complexes are lacking in North America and to a large extent in South America.

Nur and Ben-Avraham assert that terranes in North America such as the Klamath-Sierra in California, the Alexander terrane in southeastern Alaska, and Wrangellia in Alaska, British Columbia, and Oregon are exotic continental blocks—pieces of Pacifica (figure 8.6). In fact, none of these terranes contains any evidence for ancient (1 b.y.) crystalline basement. The Klamath-Sierra terrane contains, as its basement, an Ordovician peridotite considered by some to represent oceanic crust (Hamilton 1969) and an undated sequence of feebly metamorphosed sedimentary rocks that resembles lower Paleozoic sediments derived from the North American continental margin (d'Allura et al. 1977). As they note, many investigators interpret the Klamath-Sierra terrane as a Paleozoic island-arc complex.

The Alexander terrane on Prince of Wales Island contains a sequence of deformed volcanic and sedimentary rocks intruded by a 730 Ma granitic body (Churkin and Eberlein 1977). The rocks are overlain by an extensive, thick sequence of volcanic and sedimentary rocks ranging in age from Ordovician to Carboniferous. The Alexander terrane thus provides no evidence of ancient crystalline rocks and again probably represents island arcs that developed during Eocambrian and Paleozoic time. Nor does Wrangellia, a large, displaced terrane along the Pacific margin of North America, contain evidence for ancient crystalline basement. As noted by Jones et al. (1977), the distinctive Triassic rocks that characterize Wrangellia rest upon a Pennsylvanian-Permian island-arc sequence.

Aside from the question whether or not exotic terranes in western North America represent continental crust or fragments of Pacifica, many geologists working in the cordillera believe such terranes did not originate in their present positions with respect to North America. If they were transported, when did they arrive in their present positions? Nur and Ben-Avraham's figure 8.2 suggests that a fragment (Alexander terrane and Wrangellia?) arrived in Alaska in late Jurassic or early Cretaceous time, a result consistent with available data (Jones et al. 1977). Surprisingly, their figure shows a similar fragment (the Klamath-Sierra terrane?) riding the Farallon plate and colliding with the western United States in Cretaceous or early Tertiary time, an interpretation ignoring the fact that the Franciscan terrane in coastal California and Oregon indicates an actively subducting plate margin during the late Jurassic, Cretaceous, and Paleogene. The Franciscan terrane lies 100 km

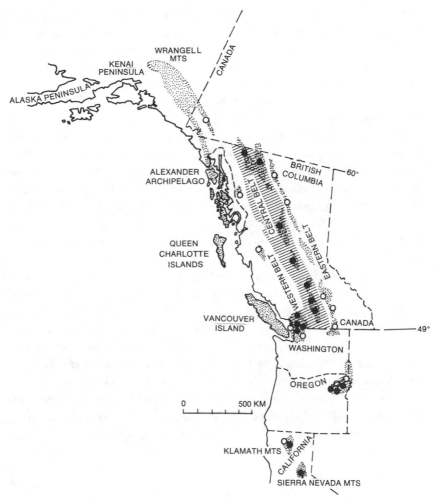

Figure 8.6. Map of cordilleran North America showing allochthonous terranes. Stippled areas have Paleozoic island-arc basement complexes. Hachured areas have Paleozoic ocean-crust basement complexes. Solid circles are localities of Middle Permian Tethyan fusulinids, Open circles are localities of Middle Permian non-Tethyan fusulinids. Redrawn from Jones et al. (1977).

west and outboard of the Klamath-Sierra terrane, with several additional Paleozoic and Mesozoic terranes between them, indicating that this "fragment" accreted far earlier, probably during the Triassic when Pacifica supposedly was still a single landmass in the southwestern Pacific.

We now turn to the problem of fusulinid foraminiferal distributions. In particular, we analyze a Middle Permian fauna that is dominated by members of the family Verbeekinidae that identifies the Middle Permian Tethys faunal realm (Ross 1967). The Tethyan fusulinid fauna (composed of some 180 species and 15 genera) is known from hundreds of localities in a narrow tropical band about 15° wide between latitudes 30° and 45° North and stretching eastward from Tunisia through the Mediterranean, the Middle East, and the Himalayas to eastern Asia. In that region, that band bifurcates with a south limb traceable through the Malaysian Peninsula southeast to the North Island of New Zealand. This has been called the Tethyan gap and can be explained by rotation during continent displacement (Dott and Batten 1976). A northeast trending limb extends through eastern China and Japan and abruptly changes direction in western and southern Alaska to the south-southeast through British Columbia to central California (figure 8.7). Most noteworthy is the fact that this Tethyan fauna is found mostly in the terranes identified by Nur and Ben-Avraham as fragments of Pacifica in North America.

To the north and east of this Tethyan band there is a worldwide province of what we here term the non-Tethyan fusulinid faunal realm, which can be divided into a number of sub-provinces ultimately derived from a Carbo-niferous fauna based on the families Fusulinidae and Schwagerinidae. Exam-ples of these regional provinces are the McCloud fauna of the northwestern United States and southwestern British Columbia and the mid-continental fauna found in Nevada, Texas, Central America, and elsewhere.

The Tethyan fauna is found in thick, poorly bedded limestones that are crinoidal or oolitic and represent reef or Bahama-type bank deposits, interpreted as high energy environments. In western North America these limestones are found in thick sequences containing volcanic rocks in

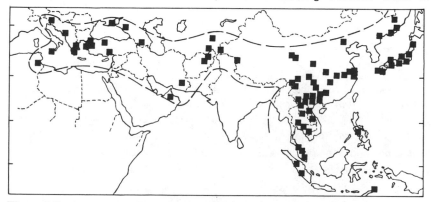

Figure 8.7. Eurasian distribution of the Middle Permian Tethyan fusulinids (Verbeekinidae only are plotted). Redrawn from Gobbett (1967).

structurally complex allochthonous terranes in the cordillera thought by Nur and Ben-Avraham (this symposium) and others (Jones et al. 1977) to be fragments of a Pacific continent (figure 8.1). The limestones occur in thick sedimentary rocks that in some areas contain ribbon cherts, basic volcanic rocks such as tholeiitic basalts, and ultramafic rocks that are thought to have formed on the oceanic crust. The western cordilleran Central Belt of British Columbia is one example.

In other anomalous terranes having different geological histories, these limestones overlie Pennsylvanian or older crumpled and altered rocks containing acidic flow rocks and sediments suggesting deposition in and around island arcs (Jones et al. 1977). Areas that are most similar in tectonics and stratigraphy are the Wrangell mountains of southeastern Alaska, Queen Charlotte Islands, Vancouver Island, and eastern Oregon (figure 8.6). Jones et al. (1972) considered these areas as portions of a once continuous land mass. All the areas contain thick Triassic sediments and tholeiitic basalts and carbonates, which contain ammonites and bivalves that differ from those found in North American cratonic Triassic sequences containing clastics derived from the North American craton and located at least 500 km to the east.

These areas have nearly identical geological histories. In the Wallowa and Blue Mountains of eastern Oregon there are five localities where limestones occur in lenses in argillites. At three localities there are non-Tethyan (McCloud type) fusulinids in argillaceous limestones, but in two other sequences the limestones contain Tethyan fusulinids. Hence it would appear that both of the major faunal realms are found in the same terrane. Jones et al. (1972) attempted to resolve this dilemma by adjusting the edge of the Wrangellian continent to exclude the non-Tethyan limestone localities, but structural complications prevent reconstruction of the relationship of these limestones. A similar juxtaposing of Tethyan and non-Tethyan limestones is seen also in northwestern Washington, where they are again found essentially in the same areas in a series of thrust sheets.

The picture is somewhat clearer in British Columbia, where the Tethyan localities are in the clearly delineated Central Belt, which contains Tethyan fusulinids (Monger and Ross 1971). Immediately to the west the Alexander Archipelago has Paleozoic rocks intruded by granites and with sandstones and argillaceous limestones containing non-Tethyan fusulinids. The adjacent Eastern Belt is separated from the Central Belt by blue shists and ophiolites indicating a suture zone. The Eastern Belt also has sandstones, argillites along with acidic flow rocks and pyroclastics, and thin bedded argillaceous limestones with non-Tethyan fusulinids identical to those found in the Western Belt. Hence the history and development of the British Columbian belts are quite different from the Wrangellian terranes.

On Honshu Island of Japan also, Permian limestones are found in terranes containing both acidic and basaltic volcanic rocks. Igo (1964) has shown that the Tethyan fusulinids in the Nyukawa district of central Honshu are in carbonate bank deposits representing a high energy environment, while adjacent non-Tethyan fusulinids occur in argillaceous limestone deposited in a low energy, closed basin. The suggestion is that these faunas represent separate, but contiguous, onshore-offshore environments of local situations. Importantly, many of the Japanese species are found in the allochthonous terranes of North America. Danner (1965) and Bostwick and Nestell (1967) believe that these faunas may be "environmental facies" rather than distantly separated faunal realms. We take the position that the McCloud non-Tethyan fauna is distinct from the mid-continent faunas and that both the Tethyan and McCloud assemblages could have originated and indeed did originate, to the south, away from the North American continent.

It is instructive to look again at the cordillera of British Columbia. Monger and Ross (1971) have suggested several models to account for the presence of the Western Belt, which is identical to the Eastern Belt. The most likely model shows that the Western Belt is a sliver of the Eastern Belt that has been brought up from the south by a right lateral transform fault, and that the Central Belt was likewise displaced northward and from further southwest. Large scale transform motion is probable for several of the other allochthonous terranes, based on geological and paleomagnetic data, such as those identified for Wrangellia (Hillhouse 1977). For example, Jones et al. (1977) have shown that the allochthonous Wrangell Mountains of southeastern Alaska were formed within 15° of the paleoequator and probably in the southern hemisphere. Paleomagnetic determinations of a lower Permian sandstone in northern Honshu, Japan, indicate a paleolatitude of 13°.

The Middle Permian paleoequator was located near San Francisco and tilted at about 40° relative to modern latitude so that most of the Tethyan fusulinid localities of Japan and North America could have formed within 30° of the paleoequator *without* any movement of present positions. To explain fusulinid distributions using current reconstructions of continental placement, however, would require that Japan, New Zealand, and eastern China be in very high latitudes; hence we should postulate a very broad and warm sea belt ranging from 70° north to 60° south. In light of the very close cohesiveness of the present verbeekinid distribution in a narrow belt from Tunisia east to Oregon, it is difficult to account for this by a repetition of local conditions over so vast a distance, or to account for the same species occurring in Japan and North America. The major problem is the broad sweep of the band into high northern latitudes, which must be explained by extensive drifting for which there is little firm geological evidence (Gobbett 1967).

For the most part, the South America fusulinid faunas are derived from a fusulinid-schwagerinid faunal realm that is widespread throughout continental North America, Central America, and down through the Andean geosyncline. At its southernmost occurrence in Chile (Isla Madre de Dios) there are advanced Upper Carboniferous and Lower Permian species of Fusulinidae similar to those found in Brazil and Guatemala (Douglass and Nestell 1972), and thus the South American faunas are of no help in assessing the Pacifica continent problem. In South America, the Deseado, Patagonian, and Pampean massifs are identified as fragments of Pacifica by Nur and Ben-Avraham even though they are distinctly *east* of the Andes Mountains, which geological evidence indicates were the site of a convergent plate boundary from late Jurassic to the present time.

In summary, an important observation resulting from this review is that the Tethyan fusulinid fauna found in reefal or bank deposit types of limestone in Japan and North America is confined to those allochthonous terranes having a basement complex of oceanic crust. The non-Tethyan, McCloud type assemblage and other derived mid-continental assemblages of fusulinids are confined to those terranes having island-arc basements. The most parsimonious hypothesis to explain Middle Permian fusulinid distributions and the allochthonous terranes of North America is one in which Permian sediments accumulated on the ocean crust on seamounts or other non-continental positive areas or on islands arcs possibly in a relatively narrow belt across portions of the Pacific.

We argue that the notion of a fragmented former continent, Pacifica, that may have rafted a fauna and flora once indigenous to the southwestern Pacific to the far reaches of the circum-Pacific should not be accepted uncritically by biogeographers. Rather, evidence from the North American cordillera suggests that island arcs and other small land masses may have docked repeatedly throughout the Paleozoic and the Mesozoic. It seems clear that they must, in most cases, have moved separately and independently. However, where these small terranes originated—the western, southwestern, or southeastern Pacific, or even along the margins of the Americas—cannot be told with certainty at present for any of them, but the exciting prospect exists that faunal data may eventually help limit some of the possible alternatives and may account for pre-drift Paleozoic distribution patterns in allochthonous terranes of the present-day circum-Pacific continents.

Discussion

R. H. Tedford

DRS. NUR AND BEN-AVRAHAM speculate that fragments of a "lost Pacific Continent" can be recognized imbedded in the marginal terranes of the Pacific Basin, and implaced in their present sites as the result of the development of the Pacific Basin spreading centers during Mesozoic time. They assemble the fragments in the South Pacific following the reconstruction of crustal history advocated by Larson and Chase (1972) and Hilde et al. (1977). Using a series of cartoons to depict the history of the "lost continent," they speculate that Pacifica probably constituted the margin of the Australian part of the late Permian Australo-Antarctic segment of Gondwana, and that the ridge triple junction that initiated the Mesozoic history of the Pacific developed beneath the blanket of continental crust forming Pacifica. Subsequently, in Triassic and Jurassic time, Pacifica was rifted, and its fragments drifted west on the Pacific Plate, northwest on the Kula Plate, northeast on the Farallon Plate, and southeast on the Phoenix Plate to collide with the continents of the Pacific margin in late Jurassic and early Cretaceous time. They do not propose any specific geological tests of their hypothesis aimed at falsifying its predictions; therefore in the remarks that follow, I briefly suggest some possible tests.

If the Pacifica hypothesis is true, the origin of the dispersed fragments in a continental block should be reflected in some common geological characteristics among the fragments—the shared features, unique to them all, that specifically indicate a former union. Perhaps it is too much to expect to detect such common characters in composition, history, structure, etc., that would constitute evidence for a unique union at this stage in our knowledge of Pacific geology, and I found no such clues in the literature. Some of the postulated fragments—for example, the southern South American massifs—are overlapped by early Paleozoic sediments and are thus incorporated in the continental stratigraphy as South American cratonic nuclei (Herrero-Ducloux 1963) rather than as exotic blocks. These South American massifs lack garlands of ophiolite or other ultramafics that would give evidence of the subducted oceanic crust on which they were supposed to have been translated. Evidence of subduction along the Pacific margin of southern South America prior to Jurassic time has recently been identified by Forsythe and Mpodozis (1979) in the outer archipelago of southern Chile. There fusulinid-bearing, pelagic carbonates, radiolarian chert, and pillow basalt of oceanic origin have been accreted to a late Paleozoic continental margin west of the massifs. There is more convincing evidence of the importance of allochthonous terranes in the composition of western North America, where paleomagnetics and geological history indicate formation in oceanic sites removed from the continental margin. Batten and Schweickert examine the North American examples for this symposium.

In Nur and Ben-Avraham's reconstruction, Pacifica of the Triassic shows that the "lost continent" extends far to the east of the New Zealand-Campbell Plateau region. A Pacifica continent in this position can hardly have been continental because the Permian and Triassic stratigraphy (Brown et al. 1968) of this region is dominated by basic volcanics, ultramafics, and graywackes representing a subduction-zone association, backed to the west by andesitic volcanoes of an island arc. The distribution of these rocks indicates that the eastern border of early Triassic New Zealand was a plate boundary between the proto-Pacific and the Australian peninsula of Gondwana.

It is doubtful that the loosely formulated Pacifica hypothesis either explains or gains support from what little is known about the oceanic plateaus and rises on the Pacific Plate. The best studied are the Ontong Java Plateau (Packham and Andrews 1975) north of the Solomon Islands, the Shatsky Rise (Lancelot and Larson 1975) east of Japan, and the Eauripick Rise (Weissel and Anderson 1978) in the Caroline Basin. The ages of the basal sediments and directly underlying oceanic basalts indicate contemporaneity of these features with the surrounding ocean floor. Furthermore, the Ontong Java Plateau is crossed by low amplitude magnetic lineations

(Andrews et al. 1975) roughly parallel with the Jurassic Phoenix anomalies (Cande et al. 1978) on the adjacent sea floor to the northeast. Lancelot's (1978) study of the drift history of these features indicates travel with the developing Pacific Plate from a southern-hemisphere position 30–40°S in the mid-southern Pacific in the early Cretaceous in a site very different than indicated by Nur and Ben-Avraham for Pacifica fragments on the Pacific Plate. The roughly parallel drift pattens demanded by coupling to the Pacific Plate show no convergence when projected into the early Cretaceous. Unless the plateaus were uncoupled from the Pacific Plate in earlier times, there seems to be no mechanism for gathering them together as Pacifica fragments on the Pacific Plate.

The Cretaceous and Cenozoic histories of these plateaus involve the accumulation of thick sedimentary blankets on oceanic basalt basement. In the case of the Ontong Java Plateau, oceanic ridge-type tholeiite of 109 Ma (Hammond et al. 1975) was overlain by volcaniclastics derived from a nearby ridge. Just after sedimentation began in the early Cretaceous, water depth increased to below the carbonate compensation depth. As the site crossed into equatorial latitudes in the late Cretaceous, shallowing and/or decreasing carbonate solution resulted in the development and preservation of a thick (over 1200 m) carbonate blanket despite erosional intervals presumably representing scouring by bottom currents. Thus the Ontong Java Plateau has been in a deep oceanic environment at least from early Cretaceous time to the present. The similarity in stratigraphy of the plateau with the exposed sections in the nonvolcanic northern Solomon Islands suggests that these islands may represent the uplifted edge of the plateau adjacent to the Solomon volcanic arc. If this view is correct, part of the plateau was elevated above sea level only in late Cenozoic time after existing at bathyl depths for at least 150 million years.

Nur and Ben-Avraham point out that in its seismic structure the Ontong Java Plateau is more comparable to continents, or known continental fragments such as the Seychelles Islands, than to oceanic plates, and that this similarity is evidence of continental origin. If so, the plateau has behaved in an anomalous fashion if in fact its crustal structure is inherited. The composition of this crust is not directly known beyond the fact that it is mantled by ocean floor basalts. The hypothesis that such thick crust may originate in a tensional environment has been proposed by Milson and Smith (1975) for southeastern Papua, where injection of potassic rocks may have thickened oceanic crust to continental proportions. Similarly, Weissel and Anderson (1978) have suggested that the thick crust of the Eauripik Rise may be the result of crustal generation along a "leaky" transform fault in the Caroline Plate. Thus it is possible that some present oceanic plateaus owe their dilated crust and shallower depths to some crustal differentiation later in their history. The Ontong Java Plateau may have been developed in Cenozoic time as that part of the Pacific floor moved into the plate boundary north of Australia.

If such rises are representative of Pacifica fragments, they make poor vehicles for the trans-Pacific dispersal of terrestrial organisms. Those cited are too small to have remained above sea level at any distance from the ridge crest. Even if some of the fragments were large enough to resist submergence, and were thus able to act as ferry boats for terrestrial organisms, biogeographical hypotheses incorporating such events seem less parsimonious than the better supported distribution of ancestral biota on a Pangea of the Triassic followed by vicariance in response to the established history of fragmentation of Gondwana.

9

Aspects of Neotropical Bird Speciation During the Cenozoic

J. Haffer

MOST CONTRIBUTIONS to this symposium are concerned with broad theoretical or worldwide biogeographical problems. I restrict my discussion to the Neotropical Region, which is inhabited by the most diversified fauna on earth. A number of avian families, some of them with over 200 component species, are restricted to this region, where they presumably developed since the separation of South America from Africa during the Cretaceous. As examples, I mention the passeriform spinetails and relatives (Furnariidae) and the antbirds (Formicariidae); 20 to 45 species of each of these families coexist at individual sites in the Neotropical lowland forest. Up to eight or even ten species of the sympatric antbirds may belong to the same genus, as is the case for the antwrens, *Myrmotherula*. Vertical stratification of the main feeding zones in the forest and corresponding morphological adaptations of the birds are among the means that have been suggested to minimize competition among these ecologically and taxonomically closely similar species.

Here I investigate some aspects of the geological causes of avian speciation in the Neotropical Region during the Cenozoic, i.e., the Tertiary and Quaternary periods. My basic assumptions are that avian speciation in the

Neotropics was mostly allopatric,[1] and that the speciation process may, under certain conditions, be completed in a comparatively short period of time. This applies to members of "plastic" groups of animals such as many passerine birds and small mammals. Restricted and effectively isolated populations of these animals may reach species status in 10,000 to 50,000 years or less (Selander 1971). Therefore, periods of geographical isolation of short duration on the geological time scale, say on the order of 100,000 years, are potentially important for the evolution of subspecies and species.

In South America, the paucity of conspicuous orographic, vegetational, and climatic barriers (except in the Andean region to the west) posed a challenge to biologists attempting to explain the origin of the large diversity of life in this region on the basis of the theory of geographical speciation. Authors proposed the development of barriers to faunal interchange by (1) paleogeographical changes in the distribution of land and sea during the Tertiary period, or (2) development of the river system in Amazonia at the turn of the Tertiary/Quaternary, or (3) vegetational fluctuations following climatic reversals during the late Tertiary and especially during the course of the Quaternary. All of these kinds of barriers probably have been important for the biotic evolution in the Neotropical Region. As a basis for the following discussion of biogeographical patterns I first describe briefly the geological history of South America during the Tertiary and Quaternary periods.

Cenozoic History of Neotropical Region

Tertiary

South America represents the western portion of the Paleozoic-Mesozoic Gondwana continent, which drifted toward its present position during the late Cretaceous and the Tertiary. A connection with North America via the Middle American land bridge developed during the late Tertiary (Pliocene). The geological "basement" of South America is the combined Guayana Shield plus Brazilian Shield, which consist of Precambrian metamorphic and igneous rocks (figure 9.1). These shield areas have been above sea level since Paleozoic times, forming low-lying lands under the hot arid climate of the Mesozoic. Continued uplift of the shield areas occurred during the course

---

[1] It is generally agreed that the speciation process in most sexually reproducing animals follows the allopatric (geographical) mode (Mayr 1963). Parapatric and sympatric speciation probably occur mainly in certain groups of plants and animals with low vagility, e.g., some flightless insects, rodents, snails, parasites (Bush 1975b). The statements of Endler (1977) and White (1978), as to the frequent occurrence of parapatric speciation, even in vertebrates, and the development of avian "hybrid zones" by primary intergradation, need verification.

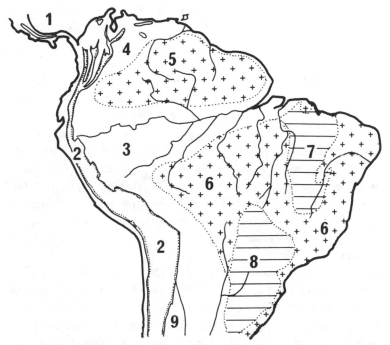

Figure 9.1. Geotectonic elements of tropical South America: 1, South Central American orogen; 2, Andes; 3, Amazon Basin; 4, Llanos Basin; 5, Guayana Shield; 6, Brazilian Shield; 7, Parnaiba-São Francisco Basin; 8, Paraná Basin; 9, Pampean ranges massif.

of the Tertiary, when the Amazon Basin subsided and the table mountains of southern Venezuela and Guyana reached their present elevation of up to 2800–3000 m above sea level. These mountains consist of Precambrian sandstone (Roraima Formation) and were modeled down to erosional remnants during the course of the Tertiary.

The Amazon Basin received mainly lagoonal and fluvial sediments. Brackish and saltwater fossils found in the upper Amazon valley indicate occasional marine ingressions from the Atlantic and Pacific Oceans during the early Tertiary. Sediments were deposited in Amazonia, probably in large swamps and marshes, and on vast flood plains crossed by numerous irregularly meandering streams flowing into a huge inland sea that connected with the sub-Andean basin to the west and with the Atlantic Ocean to the east. As a result of the petroleum drilling activity on the continental shelf near the mouth of the Amazon, geologists suspect in this and other areas of eastern Brazil the existence of a stable carbonate shelf and rather limited depositon of clastic sediments until the Middle Miocene; from the late Miocene on, the Amazon River began to build a large delta over and beyond the older carbonate shelf. Toward the end of the Tertiary, the Amazon Valley probably was covered by a large lake with a narrow eastern outlet (Belterra Lake).

The last major uplift of the Andes during the late Miocene to the Pliocene and the emergence of the upper Amazonian lowlands led to the establishment of the eastward directed drainage pattern in Amazonia during the late Pliocene and early Quaternary. Portions of the tropical Andes as well as the Venezuelan coastal mountain ranges were raised above sea level as narrow low-lying islands at the end of the Cretaceous and during the early Tertiary. Marine ingressions from the Pacific Ocean into the sub-Andean basin east of the Andes occurred until the middle Tertiary (Oligocene), after which time the rising Ecuadorian and Peruvian Andes were connected, thereby closing the last portal to the Pacific Ocean. Uplift of the mountains continued during the Tertiary and in some areas may have reached 1500 to 2000 m above sea level during the Miocene.

The later uplift of an additional 2000 to 3000 m occurred during the Pliocene and Quaternary and led to the emergence of the lowlands immediately surrounding the Andes. The formation of the Amazon delta during the late Miocene and its rapid seaward growth (delta progradation) during the Pliocene indicate the periods of major uplift and erosion of the Andes. Vertical movements of these mountains continued during the Pleistocene into Recent times as indicated by uplifted river terraces, tilted or faulted gravel and fan deposits, and heavy earthquakes.

A wide ocean gap separated North America (south to central Nicaragua) and South America throughout most of the Mesozoic into the Paleocene (Haffer 1970a; Malfait and Dinkelman 1972; Dengo 1973). Early archipelagoes possibly facilitated some faunal interchange (Webb 1978). A volcanic arc developed in the area of southern Central America (Costa Rica-Panama) during the Eocene. The Tertiary uplift of this arc was progressively more pronounced until a continuous land bridge was eventually formed during the late Pliocene (Savage 1974; Webb 1978). No continuous land bridge connecting North and South America existed in the Pacific Ocean or in the Caribbean Sea during the Tertiary until nearly the end of this period.

Mountain building in southern Middle America and northwestern South America occurred at the beginning of the late Eocene and of the late Miocene, and during the late Pliocene. Sedimentation in the basins continued during the intervening periods when erosion and partial sinking of previously uplifted areas occurred. Water gaps that connected the Caribbean Sea and Pacific Ocean during most of the Tertiary are the Nicaraguan, the Panamanian, and the Colombian portals. All of them seem to have been closed or almost closed for short periods during the Tertiary, although probably not simultaneously. The Colombian portal, for example, may have been closed briefly during the period of volcanic activity at the beginning of the late Eocene. The same was probably the case at the beginning of the late Miocene, when pronounced uplift of all mountain ranges took place in the area of Middle America and the Andes. The entire region of southern Middle America and northwestern Colombia was one large barrier zone, consisting of differentially rising and subsiding islands and peninsulas.

The Tertiary climate in the Neotropical Region probably was fairly uniform and generally warm, reaching far to the north and south of the present tropics. Moist woodland and forest probably existed in large portions of South America, growing along the slopes of the tropical Andean hills, on the lower parts of the rivers flowing into the Amazon Basin, and extending for varying distances into the interior of the basin. Vegetation similar to the present woodland savanna (cerrado) probably covered the shield areas in central South America. Forests slowly retreated northward in temperate South America during the second half of the Tertiary, when the Andes were gradually uplifted and the climate became cooler and drier. An analysis of fossil vertebrates indicates the same trend of increasingly arid conditions in temperate South America and the existence of various forest and woodland communities in tropical South America (Webb 1978).

Quaternary

Alternating humid and dry climatic periods in the tropics caused by the periodicity of Pleistocene world climate resulted in periodic shrinkage and expansion of forest and nonforest vegetation. Extensive continental shelf areas emerged during the dry glacial periods of lowered world sea level, when vast polar glaciers advanced toward lower latitudes and extensive mountain glaciers covered the higher slopes of tropical mountains. Interglacial seas flooded shelf areas and coastal lowlands and also covered a huge portion of the Amazon valley.

Although the temperatures in the tropical lowlands remained "tropical" during glacial periods (yet were 3–5°C lower than today), forests broke into isolated remnants during cool dry periods (glacial phases). The blocks of forest expanded and coalesced during warm humid periods (interglacial phases). Conversely, nonforest vegetation expanded during glacials and retreated during interglacial phases (as at present). Climatic-vegetational fluctuations probably have been more complex than this simplified scheme indicates. Detailed studies have demonstrated not only cold-dry and warm-humid periods, but also cold-humid and warm-dry periods (Van der Hammen

1974). Geoscience data so far are insufficient to map the changing distribution of forest and nonforest vegetation during the various climatic periods and, in particular, to locate accurately areas of remnant forests that during arid phases presumably served as "refugia" for animal populations. From the location of current rainfall maxima and the topographic relief (already in existence during most of the Pleistocene) as well as detailed geomorphological studies, Ab'Saber (1977) reconstructed the distribution of major vegetation types during the dry climatic phase of the last glacial period. The lowland tropical forests are shown to be restricted to a number of isolated areas (forest "refugia") separated by extensive regions of nonforest vegetation. Additional evidence for the generalizations about the Pleistocene climatic-vegetational fluctuations in the Neotropical Region is derived from palynological, geomorphological, geological, and climatological studies (reviews by Haffer 1974; Garner 1974, 1975; Brown 1976, 1977; Simpson and Haffer 1978; Brown and Ab'Saber 1979; Colinvaux 1979).

Vicariance Events During the Cenozoic

Reviewing the geological history of the Neotropics during the last 60 million years as described above, we may list various events that led to the fragmentation of biotas and potentially to the differentiation of portions of their components. These events or processes are in descending order of geological significance:

Continental Breakup and Drift

The separation of South America from Africa/Antarctica during the Cretaceous and earliest Tertiary isolated the western portion of the Gondwana fauna, which included many ancestral groups of the contemporary South American fauna. Perhaps included among the birds were primitive members of the parrots (Psittacidae), barbets (Capitonidae), and trogons (Trogonidae), the ancestors of the curassows (Cracidae), jacamars (Galbulidae), toucans (Ramphastidae), and of several families of suboscine Passeriformes (Cracraft 1973). These groups differentiated extensively within South America during the course of the Cenozoic.

Mountain Building

The final uplift of the Andes toward the end of the Tertiary led to the formation of a discontinuous corridor between the north and south temperate faunas of the western hemisphere and to the emergence of the lowlands adjacent to the Andes Mountains. The Andes formed an effective barrier to the interchange of trans- and cis-Andean lowland faunas. These faunas communicated mainly in the lowlands of northern Colombia and northwestern Venezuela during the Quaternary. In this region the northern Andes terminate in the form of low hilly ranges. Some interchange of the trans-Andean fauna of Pacific Colombia and Middle America with the cis-Andean fauna of Amazonia probably took place also in the area where the low Eastern Cordillera of Colombia joins the Central Cordillera at the head of the Rio Magdalena Valley as well as in the region of the low Porculla Pass (2150 m) in northern Peru (Chapman 1917; Haffer 1967).

Differential Erosion
The differential destruction of uplifted areas by erosion continuing over millions of years may lead to the isolation of portions of an upland fauna on mountain massifs that lag behind the regional leveling process. The erosional isolation of individual table mountains of southern Venezuela and of their faunas during the Tertiary has been used to explain the origin of certain endemic taxa among the Recent amphibian fauna of these mesa mountains (Rivero 1970).

Epicontinental Seas
Regional subsidence due to epeirogenic movements often leads to the formation or change in extent of epicontinental seas and the concomitant separation of portions of a previously continuous biota. Such isolation of major portions of the Neotropical fauna occurred repeatedly during the Tertiary paleogeographical development of South America as mapped by Harrington (1962). The widening of the Amazon Basin during the earliest Tertiary separated the fauna of the Guayana Shield from that of the Brazilian Shield. This event may have isolated the ancestors of certain contemporary birds that, mostly as monotypic genera, survive in the area of the Guayana Shield (*Rupicola rupicola, Perissocephalus tricolor, Haematoderus militaris*) and the Brazilian Shield (*Rhea americana, Cariama cristata, Chunga burmeisteri*), and numerous genera in the southeastern Brazilian region (figure 9.2).

Partial sinking of previously uplifted areas in the Andean region during the unstable history of the Tertiary isolated faunas on low lying or hilly islands of varying extent and probably led to the differentiation of the early Andean fauna.

Figure 9.2. Distribution of selected birds whose ranges are restricted to the Guayana Shield (north of the Amazon) or to the Brazilian Shield (south of the Amazon). These species are taxonomically isolated representatives of Tertiary faunas and form mostly monotypic genera. North of the Amazon: *Rupicola rupicola* (solid line), *Perissocephalus tricolor* (dashed line), *Cyanicterus cyanicterus* (stippled line). South of the Amazon: *Chunga burmeisteri* (solid line), *Cariama cristata* (dashed line), *Rhea americana* (stippled line).

Climatic-Vegetational Fluctuations

Habitat changes following climatic reversals in South America during the Cretaceous, Tertiary, and especially the Quaternary led to alternating forest and savanna fragmentation. Ecological barriers disappeared during subsequent favorable climatic periods leading to renewed habitat continuity. During cold periods, expanding mountain glaciers and pluvial lakes in the tropical Andes probably also separated animal populations that were reunited after the retreat of the glaciers and/or lakes (for reviews see Müller 1973; Haffer 1974).

Changes of World Sea Level

During glacial periods of lowered world sea level, coastal lowlands were periodically enlarged, and islands on continental shelves became interconnected or connected with the mainland, e.g., some islands along the north coast of South America and along the coast of southeastern Brazil. Additional islands formed when portions of the present lowlands were flooded during the height of the interglacial periods, when sea level was approximately 50 to 60 m higher than at present.

Formation of Major River System

Some authors have assumed that the developing network of rivers in an extensive lowland region, such as in Amazonia toward the end of the Tertiary, fragmented a pre-existing continuous biota. The populations on opposite river banks presumably differentiated to the level of subspecies or even species. This theory has been invoked on various occasions to explain species differentiation in Amazonia, but the theory has never been formally proposed or quantitatively tested (review by Haffer 1974).

Avian Speciation Patterns

Given the geological history and especially the various types of barriers as described above, we may expect certain kinds of biogeographical patterns if indeed these barriers affected the differentiation of the bird fauna. We may expect a certain amount of clustering of endemic and restricted species in areas of Quaternary refugia and the occurrence of secondary contact zones, that may be clustered in areas between such refugia.

Lowland Forest Birds

Distribution. Systematic studies have revealed the fact that, in certain families at least, most species are members of superspecies ("monophyletic groups of entirely or largely allopatric species," Mayr 1969): Cracidae—75 percent, Ramphastidae—85 percent, Galbulidae—75 percent (Haffer 1974), Pipridae—75 percent (Snow 1975). In each superspecies, the combined distributional ranges of the parapatric or allopatric allospecies esti-

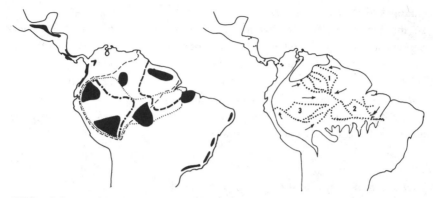

Figure 9.3. Aspects of the distribution of Neotropical forest birds. *Left:* Distribution patterns in the humid lowlands: centers of species endemism formed by clusters of endemic species with fairly restricted ranges (solid); upper Amazonian birds (dash-dotted line); lower Amazonian birds (heavy dashes); widespread Amazonian birds missing from southeastern Amazonia (thin dashes), widespread Amazonian birds missing from northeastern Amazonia (stippled line). Ranges of northern and southern Amazonian birds as well as varyingly extensive ranges in middle America and southeastern Brazil are not shown. The outlines of the patterns illustrated follow contour lines in regional gradients of species numbers as mapped by Haffer (1978). *Right:* Location of contact zones of forest birds in Amazonia. Adapted from Haffer (1974). Contact zones (dotted lines)—arrows denote expanding forest faunas; 1, northcentral Amazonian suture zone; 2, southcentral Amazonian suture zone; 3, upper Amazonian suture zone. Thin line indicates limits of Amazonian forest.

mate the range of their common ancestor. In many other species the geographical representatives hybridize along the contact zones, inasmuch as they did not reach species status prior to establishing contact. As I will discuss, studies of these contact zones and of the distribution of localized endemic species permit two kinds of biogeographical analysis: (1) mapping of *faunal suture zones*, which probably reveal the approximate location of previous barrier zones; and (2) mapping of *centers of species endemism*, which, in conjunction with geoscientific interpretations, may indicate areas where at least a portion of the localized species originated in geographical isolation.

Secondary contact zones of Neotropical forest birds are clustered, forming faunal suture zones in the following areas (Haffer 1974): northern Honduras, eastern Caribbean Costa Rica, northwestern Colombia, central Amazonia, and upper Amazonia south of the Marañón-Solimões River (figure 9.3). In these faunal contact areas we encounter stepped clines, evidence of hybridization, or competitive exclusion of parapatric species. These situations are usually interpreted as areas where formerly isolated populations have recently met (Mayr 1963). Endler (1977) questioned the generality of this interpretation, arguing that at least some of these contact zones originated *in situ* as a result of differentiation across ecological gradients. It remains to be seen whether this alternative interpretation applies to any of the conspicuous contact zones in Neotropical birds.

In the areas between Amazonian faunal suture zones, clusters of endemic species with rather restricted and largely congruent ranges form several major *"centers of species endemism"* (biogeographical core areas), each characterized by 10 to 50 species (figure 9.3). The number of these fairly localized sympatric species mapped by contour lines decreases away from each center (where all species of a particular cluster coexist). The total number of forest birds present between the six Amazonian "centers" is more or less held constant, however, by species of a neighboring center or by species with extensive ranges (Haffer 1978). The six Amazonian clusters together are characterized by a total of around 150 species or about 25 percent of the Amazonian forest bird fauna (which comprises a total of about 600 species). Close biogeographical relations exist among the various Amazonian centers as well as between Amazonia as a whole and the forest region of southeastern Brazil (figure 9.4).

Vanzolini and Williams (1970) analyzed the geographical variation of the Neotropical lizard *Anolis chrysolepis*. These authors found extensive areas of uniform character expression (core areas), which are separated by regions where complex character variation suggests hybridization and introgression along zones of secondary contact. Dixon (1979) and Lynch (1979) mapped clusters of reptilian and amphibian species endemic to upper and lower Amazonia. The locations of these clusters coincide with similar centers mapped for the forest avifauna of Amazonia. Brown (1976, 1977) carried out detailed analyses of the speciation patterns in butterflies and also found distinct centers of endemism in the Neotropics. He recently mapped these centers and intervening areas of faunal mixing and interbreeding by contour lines delineating average hybrid levels of species populations (Brown and Ab'Saber 1979; Brown 1979).

In summary, biogeographical studies of Neotropical forest animals as diverse as birds, reptiles, insects, and also plants (Prance 1973) yield similar results regarding the existence and location of centers of species endemism, which are separated by zones of faunal overlap and interbreeding. Differences include the greater number of centers mapped in insects and plants compared to other groups studied.

Historical interpretation. The central portion of tropical South America (Guayana Shield and Brazilian Shield) formed stable units during the

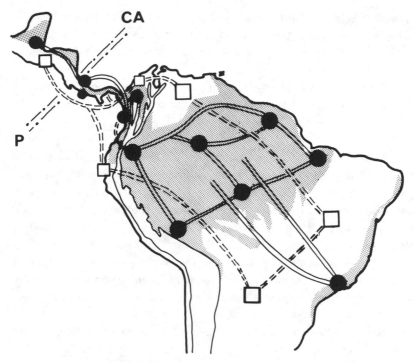

Figure 9.4. Relations between various avifaunal centers of species endemism in the Neotropical lowlands. Schematic representation. Forest areas (shaded): centers are shown as circles and relations are indicated by continuous lines; nonforest areas (blank): centers are shown as squares and relations are indicated by dashed lines. Relations between the marine biotas of the Pacific Ocean (P) and the Caribbean Sea-Atlantic Ocean (CA) across the Middle American land bridge are illustrated by dashed-dotted lines. Observe the frequent occurrence of "cross-over" in the regional biogeographical relations.

Tertiary. Their geographical extent and outline varied little during epeirogenic movements (mainly regional uplift) and sea level fluctuations. No conspicuous geological changes (tectonic events) are known that could have led to the geographical isolation of the regions corresponding to biogeographical core areas on the shields and to the differentiation of their respective biotas. A comparison of figures 9.1 and 9.3 shows that the centers of species endemism in tropical South America are located on the shield areas and in the foothill regions of the Andes mountains, i.e., on stable regions and in geologically youthful areas.

Data sets derived independently from geoscientific studies, especially geomorphological analyses, led to correlative results and support the interpretation that the core areas (centers of species endemism) of the

Neotropical biota indicate the approximate location of forest refugia during adverse climatic-vegetational phases of the Quaternary (Simpson and Haffer 1978; Brown and Ab'Saber 1979). Few large centers have been analyzed for birds; more have been analyzed for butterflies and plants. Many remnant forests probably existed and have acted as refugia for the forest fauna during peaks of arid phases. The gradients of decreasing species numbers around each biogeographical center probably are at least partially explained historically by varying dispersal distances of species from core areas, which have acted as past centers of dispersal.

Populations of plants and animals isolated in the refugia could have (1) become extinct, (2) survived without much change, or (3) differentiated. In the third case, they could have reached subspecies or species status before coming into secondary contact with previously conspecific populations of other forest refugia during a subsequent period of forest expansion. Estimation of the varying percentages of these outcomes for different refugia or different groups of animals and plants will be one of the major tasks of future biogeographical studies.

Pleistocene environmental changes probably caused the extinction of numerous species, and thus led to the elimination of entire evolutionary lines. No means exist, however, to measure directly the amount of extinction. The presence of several groups within a major region probably dates from the Tertiary or even the Cretaceous, and some of the species merely survived in the forest refugia. That is to say, some of the Pleistocene "centers of differentiation and dispersal" are necessarily located within old Cretaceous and Tertiary centers of evolution (e.g., the Quaternary Guayana forest refuge on the old Guayana Shield, and the Quaternary Serra do Mar forest refugia along the southeastern Brazilian mountains). The strong effect of the Quaternary bursts of speciation partly obscures the previous pattern of differentiation in the areas where the Pleistocene forest refugia were later located. Therefore, a direct causal correlation of distribution patterns in certain avian subspecies or butterfly species with Tertiary paleogeographical changes in South America (as suggested by Schauensee 1952 and Emsley 1965, respectively) appears unconvincing in view of the possibility that these patterns might correlate instead with later environmental changes of the Quaternary.

Results of future cladistic studies of groups of related bird species might yield data to determine the percentage of species that merely survived in Quaternary refugia after having originated during the Tertiary. If it is confirmed that all Quaternary forest refugia in the tropical lowlands of a particular continental region were formed more or less at the same time during the beginning of each dry period, then no cladistic branching sequence for the formation of isolated forest patches may be reconstructed in an area cladogram (see Rosen 1978 and Platnick and Nelson 1978 for a discussion of area cladograms). This probably would contrast with the results of analyses of the species groups, each of which will yield a particular cladistic branching pattern. No congruence of these branching patterns among the various species groups as to areas of origin of the species would constitute a positive test of the action and evolutionary significance of the Quaternary refugia, the latter having been formed three or four times, more or less simultaneously, i.e., with no sequence. On the other hand, if the forest refugia were formed following a particular sequence during the repeated dry climatic periods, congruence of the cladistic branching patterns of groups of Amazonian forest animals and plants with the area cladogram might be expected (assuming differentiation did indeed occur in the refugia rather than during earlier periods of isolation).

Lowland Nonforest Birds

Distribution.   Extensive areas of dry open habitats occur in tropical South America north of Amazonia in the Llanos plains of eastern Colombia to central Venezuela, and south of Amazonia from northeastern Brazil to the Argentine pampas. In the latter nonforest region two centers of differentiation may be recognized (figure 9.4), based on the discussions and range maps published by Short (1975) and Fitzpatrick (1980): northeastern to central Brazil, and eastern Bolivia-Paraguay to Argentina. Contact zones with or without hybridization, or with range overlap of allied species, are clustered in the intervening areas between the centers. The northeastern chaco is particularly important in this respect because a large number of geographical representatives are in contact in this region.

The nonforest avifauna of northern South America is closely related to that of central Brazil despite their wide separation (numerous species occur both to the north and to the south of the Amazon forest). Isolated savanna enclaves in the forests of lower Amazonia are inhabited by characteristic nonforest bird communities and indicate a contemporary or previous pathway of communication between the northern and southern nonforest regions. Close relations at the species level also connect the Brazilian nonforest avifauna with that of the arid Pacific lowlands of western Ecuador and northwestern Peru.

Figure 9.5. Combined distribution of the six species of mountain toucanets, genus *Aulacorhynchus*. Five species occur in the northern Andes (solid); two to three of them are regionally sympatric but are often separated altitudinally; of the Andean species, only *A. prasinus* inhabits the montane forests of Middle America and the foothills of the Andes in Peru and Bolivia (stippled); only the *A. sulcatus* superspecies inhabits the mountains south of the Orinoco River (*A. derbianus*, also widespread in the Andes) and near the Caribbean coast (*A. sulcatus*, crosses).

Historical interpretation. The biogeographical relations between widely separated nonforest faunas may be explained at least partially by Quaternary vegetational changes, which established direct communication between northern and southern nonforest habitats across Amazonia. The same applies to an interpretation of the relations between the nonforest fauna of Caribbean northern Colombia and Pacific Middle America. On the other hand, temporary forest connections between Amazonia and the southeastern Brazilian forest region across central Brazil probably fragmented the nonforest fauna of central South America, causing the differentiation of northern (or eastern) and southern (or western) representatives.

Highland Birds

Distribution. Among montane Neotropical birds there exist many wideranging species and superspecies, whose component subspecies and allospecies, respectively, inhabit variously extensive areas (Chapman 1917, 1926; Vuilleumier 1969, 1970, 1971, 1980; Vuilleumier and Simberloff 1980; Fitzpatrick 1973; Paynter 1972, 1978). Habitat discontinuities subdivide the species ranges and in many cases coincide with ecogeographical barriers such as deep valleys or generally lower mountain ranges. In other instances allospecies are in direct contact without hybridization, and no barriers are immediately obvious. Vuilleumier (1969) suggested on the basis of his studies of about 30 percent of the high Andean fauna (a total of about 880 species) that "speciation is presently favored . . . wherever any kind of habitat discontinuity breaks up the range of species, centrally or peripherally." Analyses of montane birds have not been carried out to determine the existence of centers of endemism in certain areas of narrow but laterally extensive vegetation belts along the slopes of the Andes.

The six species of mountain toucanets, genus *Aulacorhynchus*, are mainly green with blue marks on the head. They inhabit humid montane forests of the tropical Andes (figure 9.5) where two to three species coexist, although often separated altitudinally. One species, *A. prasinus*, extended its range in Middle America north to Mexico. Another species, *A. derbianus*, reached the isolated table mountains of the Guayana Highlands as well as northern Venezuela; the latter populations (*sulcatus, erythrognathus, calorhynchus*) form a separate species. Because most mountain toucanets occur in the tropical Andes, the genus *Aulacorhynchus* probably originated in this general region from a lowland toucanet during the late Tertiary. The ancestor was further differentiated during the Quaternary, when one species reached Middle America, and another colonized isolated mountains in northern South America (Haffer 1974).

The montane avifauna of the Guayana Highlands (*Pantepui*) consists of 96 species. Of those 30 percent are endemic, and 57 percent are subspecifically differentiated; only 13 percent are undifferentiated. About 30 percent of the avifauna are related to, and probably derived as altitudinal representatives from, members of the surrounding lowland fauna. Of the montane birds, 50 percent are related to the montane avifaunas of the Andes and the northern Venezuelan cordilleras (Mayr and Phelps 1967). In contrast to the bird fauna, the relationships of the flora of the Guayana Highlands are primarily with the highlands of southeastern Brazil or even with Africa. Only 11 percent of the 459 plant genera known from the summit of Pantepui are related to Andean plant genera (Steyermarck 1979b).

Historical interpretation.   The early Tertiary proto-Andes formed low hilly ranges emerging from the waters of the Andean geosynclinal basin west of the Guayana and Brazilian Shields. The uplift of the Andes and Middle American mountains during the course of the Tertiary took place during several more or less well defined episodes of vertical movement—episodes which did not necessarily occur simultaneously along these mountain ranges. These phases of uplift were separated by periods of quiescence and erosion or even partial sinking of previously uplifted areas. The lowlands surrounding the present Andes emerged at the end of the Tertiary (Pliocene) when these mountains experienced the last major uplift, the high montane biota started its evolution, and the Middle American land bridge was finally completed.

The lowland fauna of the chains of islands forming the nascent Andes during early Tertiary times probably immigrated mainly from central South America at times when land connections permitted range expansions. As the hills were further uplifted and as they locally reached montane conditions, some populations from the adjoining lower levels colonized the newly available habitat and differentiated in geographical isolation (figure 9.6). Horizontal range expansion of these newly differentiated montane species probably took place when the ecological montane life zones reached lateral continuity through continued uplift of the mountains. South temperate faunal elements probably also immigrated, following their respective habitat zone along the mountains north into tropical latitudes. The high Andean biota as a whole (not necessarily all of its elements) evolved only since the late Tertiary and early Quaternary, when the mountains had reached a sufficient elevation (e.g., Chapman 1926; Simpson 1975, 1979). The Quaternary temperature fluctuations during glacial and interglacial periods led to repeated upward and downward displacements of the montane zones along the Andean slopes. Lateral range extension and faunal interchange were facilitated during glacial periods, when upper montane zones and their faunas were located along less dissected lower mountain slopes. Conversely, the upward shift of the climatic zones during interglacial periods led to an increasing dissection of montane forests and other habitat zones along the higher slopes, where speciation again occurred in small isolated populations (Vuilleumier 1969; Simpson Vuilleumier 1971; Haffer 1970b, 1974). A special situation may have existed in the large altiplano region of the central Andes (Vuilleumier and Simberloff 1980). In this region speciation possibly occurred predominantly during the glacial (rather than the interglacial) phases when enlarged glaciers and glacial lakes in the high plains fragmented species ranges. These were reconnected during interglacial periods when the glaciers and lakes retreated.

The direct ancestors of many contemporary montane species in the Andes and in the Pantepui table mountains of southern Venezuela probably

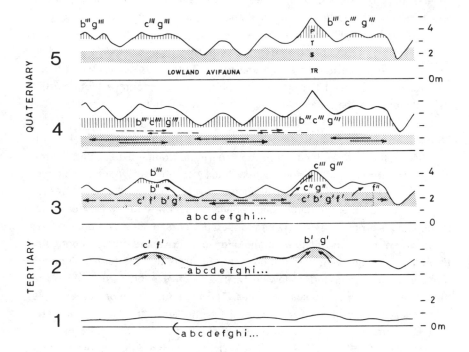

Figure 9.6. Origin of the montane avifauna on a growing tropical mountain range during the Cenozoic. Schematic representation. 1, Uniform tropical lowland biota with ancestral species a to i on initial hills. 2, Areas of most pronounced uplift have reached lower montane zone (s, stippled) and are colonized by some populations derived from ancestral species in the lowlands. Species differentiation (b', c', f', g') occurs through adaptation in geographical isolation. 3, Mountain peaks have reached higher zones (upper montane, T = blank; paramo, P = hatched) leading to further differentiation of new species from ancestors which are now dispersed widely in lower montaine life zones and which, in part, have immigrated from the temperate zones in northern and southern latitudes. 4, Temperature reduction during glacial phases of the Pleistocene led to downward displacement of montane vegetation zones (together with their faunas) which thereby became more continuous permitting extensive lateral dispersal. 5, During interglacial periods (as today) montane vegetation zones and their faunas were displaced upward again and strongly disrupted along the higher slopes. Erosion of mountains causing range fragmentations in upper montane faunas is unlikely as a general explanation in the case of geologically young (Tertiary) mountains like the Andes, but possible for older table mountains. Vertical scale in thousand meters.

originated from species inhabiting the adjacent lowlands when these mountains were uplifted during middle or late Tertiary times, or they may have
originated later during the Pleistocene. The occurrence of the same montane
bird species in the Andes and in Pantepui (both are geologically independent)
is considered evidence for dispersal from one area (of origin) to the other
region after both were sufficiently uplifted to offer montane conditions. It is
inconceivable that a montane species could have been independently differentiated from a lowland ancestor twice in these two mountain regions.
Dispersal across the lowlands between the Andes and Pantepui took place
either by "hopping" across the lowland barrier (active dispersal; Mayr and
Phelps 1967) or through lowland forests during periods of barrier reduction
when montane life zones were lowered. Small mountains between the Andes
and Pantepui in southeastern Colombia with an elevation as low as 500 m
may have had a montane (subtropical) summit during cool periods and
probably served as stepping stones for montane species to reach far distant
mountains.

Individual colonizing flights may not have been longer than 20 to 150
km in northern South America. The largely unexplored low table mountains
of the forested southeastern Colombian lowlands may have facilitated the
immigration of many Andean birds into the southern Venezuelan highlands
during glacial periods (Haffer 1970b, 1974). A few montane birds of the
forest interior may have reached widely isolated mountains through the lowland forests. The isolated mountains served as refugia upon the return of
warm and adverse conditions in the lowlands. The varying rate of differentiation of isolated bird populations on far distant mountains subsequently may
have concealed the fact that the immigrating portion of the fauna was
acquired during several more or less well defined periods when the tropical
climate was somewhat cooler.

Discussion

It has been known since the days of Charles Darwin and Moritz Wagner that
spatial isolation of animal populations is the prerequisite for the speciation
process in many or most sexually reproducing groups (Mayr 1963).
Zoogeographers pointed out that geographical isolation of populations
originates from two basically different processes: (1) fragmentation (subdivision, "vicariance") of a pre-existing continuous species range, or (2) crossing
of a pre-existing barrier by some dispersing individuals that establish a

founder population (Mayr 1954, 1963). In both cases the isolated populations may reach subspecies or species status by continued genetic-mor-
phological differentiation, with the rate of change depending mainly upon the
degree of geographical isolation, the size of the isolated population, and the
"plasticity" of the various systematic groups of animals and plants. Mayr
(1954) speculated that differences in the species composition of animal
groups, such as many similar (often sibling) species in contrast to conspic-
uously different species, many of which are placed in monotypic genera, may
be due to their mode of allopatric speciation (range subdivision or founder
effect, respectively). Possibly chromosome evolution is always associated
with speciation in restricted founder populations and does not occur or only
rarely occurs in speciation resulting from range fragmentation. The general
proportion of incipient species due to the founder effect and to range subdivision in continental faunas remains unknown, however, because no comparative systematic studies have yet been attempted.

Mayr's historic biogeographical interpretations, earlier discussed in part,
take into account both fragmentation of species ranges (vicariance) and dispersal of founder individuals, with the relative importance of these models of
allopatric speciation depending upon biological characteristics of the various
animals and upon geological aspects of the regions concerned. For the differentiation of world faunas Mayr (1963) emphasized the importance of fragmentation of species ranges due to geological and climatic-vegetational
changes as well as widespread active dispersal (e.g., between oceanic islands
and between continents that, until about twenty years ago, were considered
independent units by a majority of geological authors).

Croizat's historic biogeographical interpretations (1958, 1976) are more
restrictive because he admits only tectonic vicariance events as causal factors for faunal differentiation at the regional, continental, and intercontinental
levels. In view of recent widespread support of the theory of continental drift,
a vicariance interpretation of a number of basic biogeographical patterns at
the intercontinental level appears more likely than dispersal interpretations
(unless the young age of a group of organisms argues otherwise). At the
regional level and in the case of individual continents with fringing islands,
biogeographical interpretations probably should take into account the possibility of both vicariance and dispersal. Tests should be designed to establish
the relative significance of these models for different regions and/or different
groups of animals. Croizat (1958, 1976) mapped the ranges of many
Neotropical birds and attempted to explain certain distribution patterns at the
species and subspecies levels on the basis of tectonic movements in offshore

regions of South America as well as the erosion of mountain systems. While Tertiary paleogeographical changes certainly determined the early evolution of contemporary groups, subsequent vegetational shifts probably influenced the differentiation at the level of species and subspecies.

Considerations of the geological history of South America during the Cenozoic and an analysis of various biogeographical aspects of the land bird fauna have led me to a predominantly vicariant interpretation of differentiation patterns except for certain montane birds found on geologically independent mountain systems. Future studies should make an effort to sort out the timing or age of various differentiation events whose results we notice in the taxonomic composition of the extant bird fauna. In recent years I have placed emphasis on the conspicuous Pleistocene environmental changes in the tropics and their potential effects on speciation in birds and other animals, mainly because it was long assumed that tropical faunas were unaffected by Pleistocene climatic-vegetational fluctuations and that all tropical species are old, i.e., Tertiary. It is my intent here to place this interpretation in perspective by stressing the almost continuous formation of various kinds of barriers and the disappearance of some of them throughout the Cenozoic history of the Neotropical Region. Most or all of the barriers probably contributed through speciation events to the taxonomic composition of the extant bird faunas of South America.

The models of avian geographical speciation in the Neotropical Region during the Cenozoic assume a series of range fragmentations (vicariant events) leading to extensive speciation in isolated populations. Periods of disjunction were caused by geological-tectonic processes (paleogeographical changes in the distribution of land and sea) as well as by climatic-vegetational fluctuations during the Tertiary and especially during the Quaternary. Passive dispersal of the biota occurred during expansive phases of their respective habitat zones. Species that had reached reproductive and ecological isolation from their geographical representatives during the preceding period of geographical isolation possibly dispersed more widely through continuous forest or savanna regions.

A well known example of extensive dispersal is the great American faunal interchange during the late Cenozoic. Webb (1978) reviewed the known facts on the basis of the fossil mammal record. Some 20 North American mammal genera, most of them savanna-adapted, had reached temperate South America by the early Pleistocene. A few additional ones arrived later. Extensive differentiation took place among the newcomers in South America, leading to the evolution of new genera and numerous new species. The extinction among South American savanna vertebrates probably was a result of the faunal interchange with North America at the beginning of the Pleistocene and presumably was due to competitive interactions among members of the immigrating and established groups. No comparable extinction of savanna vertebrates in North America seems to have resulted from the very restricted immigration of South American vertebrates.

In view of the paleogeographical stability of central South America it appears difficult to explain the origin of the various avifaunal "centers" in this region and the faunal diversity at the species level on the basis of true tectonic vicariant events, for which there are no indications in the geological record. One needs to invoke range fragmentations due to historical causes other than geological-tectonic processes—e.g., vegetational shifts following climatic reversals. The frequency of crossed "tracks" (relations) among Neotropical biographical regions (figure 9.4) also points in this direction as mentioned by Cracraft (1975a:237–38) for the generalized track connecting the land biotas of South and Central America and for that connecting the marine biotas of the Caribbean Sea and the Pacific Ocean. "Crossed relations" (tracks) may indicate the past occurrence of widespread dispersal in one or the other of the biotas involved in the "cross-over."

In a general sense, pre-Quaternary speciation in the Neotropics probably occurred under environments more equable and/or more slowly changing than those that resulted from the constantly changing climates of the last two million years. Evolution of many genera and higher taxonomic levels probably took place during the Tertiary and resulted from paleogeographical and vegetational changes. In some slowly evolving groups such as the primitive Protura insects, however, the contemporary pattern of species distributions may directly reflect vicariance due to continental drift (Tuxen 1978).

The refuge theory combines aspects of the seemingly incompatible biogeographical models based on active dispersal across preexisting barriers and vicariance due to fragmentation of existing species ranges. Dispersal of the biotas during favorable periods of habitat expansion and habitat continuity was, in a sense, "passive," because it did not occur across barriers.

Summary

Processes that determine geographical changes of the earth include vicariant events at different levels of geological significance: continental fragmentation due to rifting and subsequent drift; mountain building (uplift) and erosion of uplifted areas; epeirogenic movements leading to the formation, or changes in extent, of epicontinental seas; and climatic-vegetational fluctuations causing shrinkage and expansion of forest and nonforest habitat. The fusion of drifting continents such as North and South America leads to large-scale biotic interchange and dispersal.

Paleogeographical changes within the Neotropical Region, including the development of the Andes mountains and of the Middle American land bridge, provided the stage for extensive organic evolution during the Cretaceous and Tertiary periods. Because of the large land masses of tropical South America and their relative paleogeographical stability during the Cenozoic (except for the Andean region in the west), it appears difficult to explain the origin of the various avifaunal centers of species endemism in these regions on the basis of a series of geological-tectonic vicariant events. Fragmentation of species ranges in the lowlands and mountains, and subsequent differentiation of isolated populations in many groups of animals due to vegetational changes following climatic reversals of the Tertiary and especially the Quaternary, appear to have played a major role. Periods of range fragmentation and the formation of ecological "refugia" during adverse conditions alternated with periods of habitat expansion and habitat continuity under favorable conditions. Passive dispersal of the biota occurred during expansive phases of their respective habitat zones. This refuge theory attempts to explain the origin of biogeographical centers of endemism and of many existing avian species. The theory combines aspects of the seemingly incompatible biogeographical models based, respectively, on dispersal and vicariance.

Acknowledgments

I gratefully acknowledge the many privileges and help received from all members of the Ornithology Department of the American Museum of Natural History during repeated visits to the museum in conjunction with my work on the Neotropical avifauna. Francois Vuilleumier, New York, kindly read this manuscript and made several helpful suggestions.

Discussion

G. T. Prance

I AGREE with most of what Dr. Haffer has written with regard to bird speciation, and I can best use this opportunity to comment on his paper by
emphasizing the similarities and differences in the study of Neotropical
plants. Both are apparent. There is no need to discuss Haffer's factual and
useful review of the Cenozoic geological history of South America.

Exactly the same situation as in the antbirds cited by Haffer occurs in
many large genera of lowland plants where numerous closely related species
coexist at individual sites (for example, the 12 species of *Eschweilera*
(Lecythidaceae) cited by Prance et al. (1976) on a single hectare of rain
forest near Manaus). Botanists, too, would make the same assumption of
allopatric speciation as the predominant means of speciation, although in
plants there are several examples of sympatric speciation by allopolyploidy,
following hybridization of two species. Chromosome data indicate, however,
that this is not important in the rain forest habitat. For example, all species of
Eschweilera cited earlier and related genera have the same chromosome
number of $n = 17$. The tropical flora is less well known than the bird fauna
and does not enable botanists to differentiate between plant superspecies as
ornithologists can between bird superspecies. The relationships within most
genera are much less clear. Nevertheless, obviously closely related species
occur sympatrically. Haffer assumes also that the speciation process may be

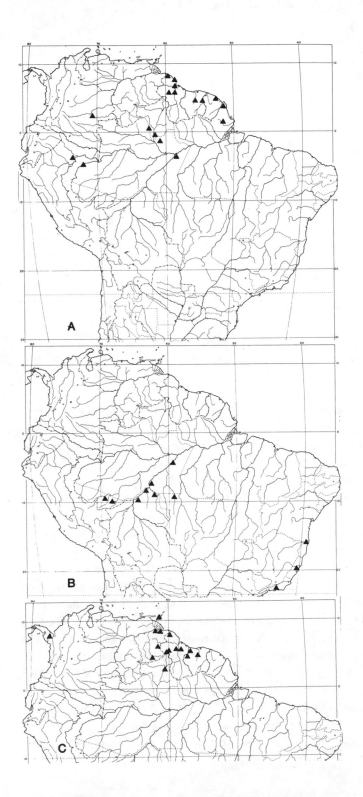

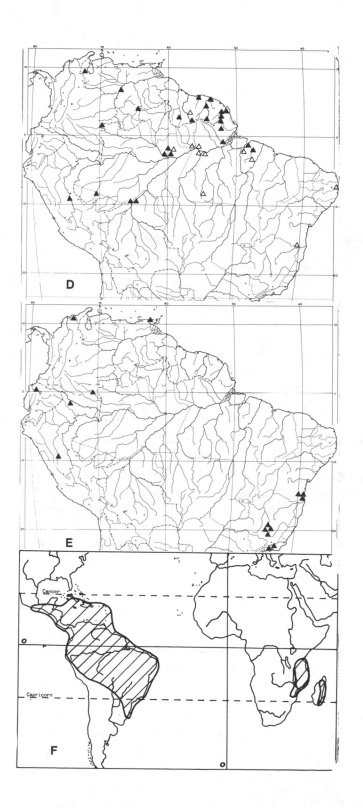

D

E

F

Figure 9.7. (pp. 396–97). Disjunct distribution of various taxa of woody angiosperms which resulted from various vicariant events. A, *Couepia parillo* DC (Chrysobalanaceae) with separate populations in the Guianas, central Amazonia, and western Amazonia; B, *Couratari macrosperma* A.C. Smith (Lecythidaceae), a species with a southern Amazonia-Atlantic coastal disjunction; C, *Caryocar nuciferum* L. (Caryocaraceae), a species with a Panama-Guiana disjunction; D, *Hirtella bicornis* Mart. and Zucc. (Chrysobalanaceae) with a Amazonian-Atlantic coastal disjunction (closed triangles represent variety *pubescens*, open triangles variety *bicornis* which differ in stature and habitat; this species is also disjunct in the Catatumbo refugium area); E, distribution of the nine species of *Stephanopodium* (Dichapetalaceae), a genus which is distributed in northwestern South America and Atlantic coastal Brazil, but absent from the intervening Amazonia; F, distribution of the genus *Hirtella*, which is widespread in the neotropics (85 species) and present in West Africa and Madagascar (one species).

completed in comparatively short periods of time. This is certainly true in birds with a short generation time. It may be different in the case of rain forest trees, where each generation is usually over 30 years. We might expect differences between tree species and short-lived annual plants. This is a subject for future study and has really not been considered to date. Ten thousand years represents only 350 generations of many tree species. There were at least three dry periods in the Pleistocene, however, so the total time span of refugia was longer.

Haffer recognizes the importance of the various vicariant events in South America beginning with the breakup of Gondwanaland. These earlier vicariances are just as important as the effect of the more recent Pleistocene climate changes. Haffer puts them all into a balanced perspective. Figure 9.7 illustrates some of the variation at different levels of the taxonomic hierarchy of the Chrysobalanaceae and Dichapetalaceae caused by different vicariant events in the history of South America. Both families are pantropical and presumably date back to the time of united continents. The separation of the genus *Hirtella* (figure 9.7f) into African and Neotropical representatives relates to the breakup of Gondwana. The separation of *Stephanopodium* (figure 9.7e) into northern and southern groups of species relates to later occurrences in South America. The four species disjunctions shown in Figures 9.7a–d relate to different times. Presumably, *Couratari macrosperma* and *Hirtella bicornis* divided into two populations earlier than the Pleistocene because the continuous connection between the Amazon forest and Atlantic coastal Brazil occurred prior to that time. The two species *Caryocar*

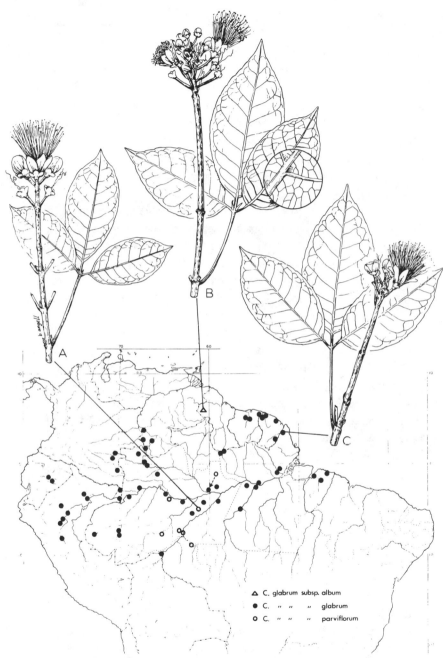

Figure 9.8. *Caryocar glabrum* (Aubl.) Pers. (Caryocaraceae), an example of a woody tree species that has diversified slightly in two regions, but is still a single rather polymorphic species with a wide distribution throughout Amazonia: A, subsp. *parviflorum* (Prance et al. 22842); B, Subsp. *album* (Maguire & Fanshawe 32326); C, subsp. *glabrum* (Irwin 48707).

nuciferum and *Couepia parillo* were divided into two populations by the more recent Pleistocene breakup of the forest and have not yet differentiated morphologically. This is the commonest situation in woody plants. Figure 9.8 illustrates *Caryocar glabrum*, a widely dispersed tree species, which like other polymorphic ochlospecies shows some morphological variation, but not enough to form a separate species. This also has occurred in many cases as a result of the Pleistocene breakup of the forest. Haffer puts these different vicariances into perspective by covering the Cenozoic rather than just the more recent times.

Haffer points out that the estimation of the various percentages of the outcomes of isolation in refugia (extinction, survival without change, or differentiation) is one of the major tasks of future biogeographical studies. I concur with this point of view and add that in the case of plants it is important to establish the degree of differentiation that has occurred. With a small number of generations we might expect much more differentiation at the subspecific level, as illustrated in Figure 9.8. The fact that hybridization data are lacking for lowland forest species poses a problem and a challenge for both plant geographers and experimental systematists.

One of the differences between plants and birds and other animals is that plants tend to be less vagile. Low vagility is especially true of rain forest species, for which long-distance dispersal mechanisms are rare, and tends to give vicariant events a greater significance for plants. Redistribution can be much slower, and a comparatively small barrier can isolate two separate populations. Low vagility in some way compensates for the larger generation span and partially accounts for similar distributions between the plants studied by me and the birds studied by Haffer.

In his summary of Quaternary events Haffer cites the geomorphological studies of Ab'Saber (1977) and his reconstruction of the distribution of major vegetation types during the dry climatic phase of the last glacial period. This is a dubious model because of its over-simplification of the vegetational diversity. Ab'Saber mentions only four vegetation types in his geoscientific model: caatingas, cerrados, tropical forest, and gallery forest. He ignores many other vegetation types and all the transition types of forests (see Prance 1978, 1979). It is unlikely that most of Amazonia became a uniform vegetation type as dry as the caatinga 12,000 years ago as is suggested in the Ab'Saber model. Other vegetation types, such a dry forest, transition forest, liana forest, and bamboo forest, would break up the distribution of many species and would be equally effective as a cause of vicariance. Mapping the occurrence of plant endemism shows that centers of species

SOUTH AMERICA

Figure 9.9. Forest refugia, based on distribution of woody angiosperm families: 1,
Panama-Darien; 2, Chocó; 3, Rio Magdalena; 4, Santa Marta; 5, Catatumbo; 6,
Apure; 7, Rancho Grande; 8, Paria; 9, Imataca; 10, W. Guiana; 11, E. Guiana; 12,
Imerí; 13, Napo; 14, São Paulo de Olivenca; 15, Tefé; 16, Manaus; 17, Trombetas;
18, Belém; 19, Tapajós; 20, Aripuanã; 21, E. Peru-Acre; 22, Beni; 23, Pernambuco;
24, Bahia; 25, Rio-Espírito Santo; 26, Araguaia.

diversity (endemism) occur also in lowland plants (figure 9.9; Prance 1973, 1978). These correspond closely to the endemism centers pointed out by Haffer for birds, and by other authors for many groups of organisms (e.g., Brown 1976, for butterflies). These centers of endemism within the lowland forest indicate that the forest is not a uniform habitat with a uniform history.

Plant data confirm Haffer's conclusion that the forest was broken up. Haffer makes the important observation that many remnant forests probably existed in addition to the large refugia. I am sorry that he does not comment on the role of gallery forest. Botanical data of present-day distributions in savanna areas, such as the cerrados of central Brazil, show that gallery forests are also important as refugia and as corridors for a more continuous distribution of some species, as is the case in *Cariniana estrellensis* illustrated in figure 9.10. In drier times the gallery along the principal rivers in lowland Amazonia must have had a similar role. Most authors who have discussed the Pleistocene history of Amazonia have tended to ignore the role of gallery forest.

Haffer discusses the lowland non-forest birds in the arid regions of tropical South America. The relationship among birds is found also in the vegetation. The arid vegetation types of the llanos region of Colombia are paralleled and closely related to those of northeastern Brazil. The number of related species and genera indicates a closer contact in the past during drier spells, and is good evidence of the breakup of the continuous rain forest (e.g., in the genera *Caesalpinia*, *Capparis*, *Opuntia*, etc.). There is an important difference between typical forest species of plants and those of savannas and other open types of vegetation. The dispersal capacity of plants of open vegetation types if far greater than those of the forest; for example, Macedo and Prance (1978) showed that 75.67 percent of the woody species of an Amazonian campina have a capacity for long-distance dispersal (bird, bat, or wind dispersal) in marked contrast to most rain forest species, which are gravity dispersed. This is an interesting difference that tends to make the present-day islands of savanna and other open vegetation isolated less than a forest refugium would have been in the dry climate periods.

Another important aspect of the non-forest habitats is the distribution of present-day forest refugia. In addition to the gallery forests there are other forest refugia in the arid northeast of Brazil. The hilltops have a forest vegetation locally called *brejo*. The humidity and temperature differences caused by elevation allow forest with trees up to 25 m to occur on the brejos. This was described in more detail by Andrade-Lima (1976, 1981). These areas merit much further study in order to obtain data about similar situations in Amazonia during the Pleistocene.

Figure 9.10. Distribution of *Cariniana estrellensis* (Raddi) Kuntze, a forest species that occurs in southwestern Amazonia in Acre and in the forests of Atlantic coastal Brazil. These two remote areas are connected by a continuous distribution of this species through the gallery forests of the planalto of central Brazil and of Bolivia. This distribution is repeated in many other plant species.

Haffer tries to balance different theories and to show the importance of a varied approach to biogeography. It is refreshing to read a paper that accepts different possibilities for speciation and not just one model, and that discusses both vicariance and dispersal across pre-existing barriers. Long-distance dispersal is important but cannot account for all the disjunction and clusters of endemism in lowland plant species. I do not agree with Haffer's claim that refuge theory combines both vicariance and dispersal models. Redispersal is an important part of refuge theory—not across barriers of other vegetation types such as savanna, but by the gradual redispersal of the forest. This is very different from the dispersal of organisms across a barrier such as the sea to an island, or a rain forest between islands of savanna. Refuge theory is certainly an example of vicariance rather than dispersal, and it would be wrong to claim that it also includes dispersal. The example of the relationship of highland birds between the Andes and Pantepui, however, shows that dispersal over barriers does occur in birds. Haffer himself points out the difference between birds and plants when he cites Steyermark's data. Steyermark (1979, 1981) has shown that the Pantepui vegetation is little related to the vegetation of the Andes. The differences between the plants and the birds can be accounted for by the birds' greater vagility. The Pantepui vegetation is closely related to the vegetation of the lowlands and to a much lesser extent to that of the cerrado region of the Brazilian shield.

Table 9.1 lists the species of the predominantly lowland plant family Lecythidaceae that occur at altitudes of over 1000 m. This is an assemblage of not particularly close relatives that have been able to move upward with the various uplifts of mountains discussed by Haffer. There is no close relationship between the Andean and Pantepui high altitude plants, which confirms Haffer's contention that the birds that have crossed from one highland area to the other have done so by their greater vagility, rather than by closely related species evolving in the two areas. The less vagile plants have been unable to disperse from Pantepui to the Andes.

Elsewhere (Prance 1979) I have commented on the isolated nature of both the Pacific coastal refugium in Colombia and the Atlantic coastal refugia of Brazil. These areas today have a species complement much more distinct

Table 9.1 Species of Lecythidaceae Known to Occur at Altitudes Over 1000 m

Species	Distribution
Eschweilera antioquensis Dugand and Daniel	Colombia, Antioquia
E. cabrerana Philipson	Colombia, Sierra de la Macarena
E. cauliflora Cuatr.	Colombia, Magdalena, Sierra Nevada Santa Marta
E. ciroana R. Knuth	Colombia, Valle, Cordillera Occidental
E. montana Cuatr.	Guyana, Akarai Mountains
E. papillata Uribe	Colombia, Cundinamarca, Guaduas
E. perumbonata Pittier	Venezuela, Aragua, Rancho Grande, cloud forest
E. sessilis A. C. Smith	Colombia, Mt. Chapón
E. tenax Moritz ex Berg	Venezuela, Tovar, coastal cordillera
E. trinitensis Smith and Beard	Trinidad, montane rain forest
E. violacea	Colombia, Valle, Cordillera Occidental
Lecythis karuaiensis Steyerm.	Venezuela, Pantepuí, Sororopán-Tepuí
Gustavia macarensis Philipson subsp. paucisperma Mori*	Venezuelan Andes, W. of Merida
Gustavia speciosa (Knuth) Berg subsp. occidentalis (Cuatr.) Mori	Colombia, Valle, Pacific slopes of western Cordillera Occidental

* The second subspecies of this species occurs on Sierra de La Macarena and south through lowland Ecuador into Amazonian Peru.

and isolated than that of other central Amazonian refugia, indicating a greater isolation. Apparently this is not so marked in birds with a greater ability for dispersal. Haffer emphasizes the importance of the dispersal corridor north of the Andes in Colombia. This corridor does not appear so important in the case of plants. The Chocó refugium has remained rather isolated and has not contributed much to the coalescing forest of other lowland areas. The woody angiosperms are rather isolated distinct species, which have remained isolated even today in an area that continues to be a refugium. Plant distributions and relationships indicate that this area certainly remained largely forested during the Pleistocene refugium periods, but that vicariance took place earlier with the uplift of the Andes. Similarly, the Atlantic coastal forests of Brazil have a large number of extremely isolated species, as well as many common Amazonian species, such as those listed by Andrade-Lima (1953). Isolation of this area took place in the Tertiary; some species have remained unchanged, some dispersed into the region from Amazonia, and others have differentiated considerably. The Atlantic coastal refugia (three according to my data) have contributed little to the species diversity of the recoalesced Amazon forest.

I am sorry that Haffer has no space to discuss more of the ecological problems concerning how so many species live sympatrically. This is a subject that needs discussion in future forums and much emphasis in research programs. The omission of ecological problems here avoids the issue of yet another reason for diversity, i.e., niche specialization. Various authors (e.g., Richards 1969; Ashton 1969) have proposed this as the major source of species diversity in tropical forests. It is thus important to consider why the vicariance model is better. There are many different niches within a small area of forest, but it would be hard to believe that sufficient isolation occurs—for example, between the various strata of the canopy—for sympatric speciation to occur frequently. The refuge model is helpful here. Speciation takes place in refugia and as a result of other vicariant events. After the return of the forest and the resultant mixture of closely related but reproductively isolated species, there is strong competition. At this time it is easy to imagine these competing species adapting themselves to the different niches, i.e., different levels of the strata, different phenology to avoid competition for pollinators, etc. This is not dissimilar to the adaptation to various altitudinal levels that Haffer discusses.

Haffer's paper is based on refuge theory. Refuge theory is a case of vicariance and supports vicariance explanations rather than dispersal as discussed above. Haffer's paper is a useful review of the theory and its importance in context with other earlier happenings in the region.

Discussion

I. Tattersall

AS A PERSON who is not an ornithologist, nor a biogeographer, nor a specialist in any aspect of the Neotropical biota, I feel eminently qualified to claim objectivity on this topic. And as thoughtful and persuasive as I found Dr. Haffer's paper, I have to concede in all objectivity that it largely avoids what I consider the central issue of this symposium. Despite his quite lengthy excursions into the Tertiary paleogeography of South America, Haffer's concern lies almost exclusively with the explanation of modern biotic diversity at low taxonomic levels. I find little indeed about either the origin or the identity of the various Neotropical avifauna, or perhaps more properly, the ecological groups discussed. Any flora or fauna ultimately resolves down to a collection of taxa, but Haffer rarely mentions an actual taxon, or even specifies a taxonomic rank when discussing "relatedness." While I am sure that this avoidance presents no problem to the ornithologist familiar with the avifauna of the region, the nonspecialist must contend with a series of statements to be uncritically accepted at their face value or, equally uncritically, not accepted at all.

I may be unfair to fault the lack of substantiating detail in Haffer's general review of a problem not strictly of historical biogeography. But because Haffer indicates his belief that refugia theory falls within the realm of vicariance explanations, and because any such explanation demands as a prerequisite that the relationships of the taxa under consideration be demonstrated, I regret that at least some hypotheses of relationship are not presented and compared with actual distributions. I would do so even if I accept, and it is by no means clear to me that I should, Haffer's reasoning that it is not possible to test an area cladogram against a taxic cladogram when an original species range has been fragmented into several parts simultaneously.

Such cavalier quibbles aside, how plausibly does Haffer's theory of Pleistocene refugia explain modern faunal distributions and diversity within the Neotropics? First, there is no question that the evidence for large-scale climatic fluctuations in South America during the Pleistocene, with recurrent cooling and aridification leading to the disappearance of forest from vast areas of the Amazon Basin, followed by re-expansion of tropical forest as the climate ameliorated, is at least as strong as Haffer claims (see references in Colinvaux 1979).

The idea that the humid lowland tropical forest, together with its fauna, was periodically restricted to isolated remnants is thus compelling. Any explanation of modern faunal distributions and diversity in the region must take these well documented climatic fluctuations into account even if it seeks to reject them as primary influencing factors.

Second, Haffer's avowed assumption that among birds speciation is mostly allopatric and may take place rapidly is certainly reasonable and would, I think, meet with the approval of most avian biologists. The underlying assumption that speciation is a probable outcome of short periods of isolation seems less secure, and I would ideally wish to have some way to confirm that a relative faunal uniformity did indeed precede the creation of the refugia.

Third, Haffer's identification of centers of endemism provides a strong argument in favor of his hypothesis because such centers are predicted by the refugia model. I wonder, however, if the centers of endemism in the relatively continuous present-day habitat are the same for all the various groups comprising the modern forest fauna. At least one avian biologist (Vuilleumier, personal communication) is less than convinced. If centers of endemism for particular groups are not concordant across the biota as a whole, then delineation of refugia on biotic grounds becomes difficult at the very least.

To the extent that Haffer limits his analysis to generalized bird faunas, it is impossible to judge how real this potential problem actually is. In a study of the distributions of certain Neotropical Primates, my colleague Dr. Warren Kinzey (1979) found that the refugia model fits his data well; but in the process he was obliged to postulate a new center of endemism (the Rio Doce) that had gone unrecognized in studies of the distributions of other vertebrates. His study suggests that comparison across the biotic board of the centers of endemism postulated for different taxa will provide the ultimate test of the former existence of refugia as well-defined geographical entities.

None of this, of course, does violence to the basic concept that range contractions and disjunctions must have occurred, for many taxa at least, as a result of the geological and climatic changes discussed by Haffer. Indeed, it seems likely that different taxa would have been differently affected by, and would have differentially responded to, these events. If a fauna as a whole thus may fail to respond in a unified manner to environmental changes, one might expect a certain amount of variation in, or even the absence of, centers of endemism according to the environmental tolerance of the organisms under consideration.

Implicit in the concept of former refugia within a now-continuous forest environment is the modern existence of suture zones: areas of secondary contact between at least slightly differentiated biotas. In theory, such zones should indicate, if not define, the limits of former refugia; I suppose that the fit between the refugia and the suture zones shown in the two parts of Haffer's figure 9.2 is about as good as one might expect of the notoriously intractable real world. In absolute terms the fit is not particularly good, however, and alternative interpretations of at least some of these zones of high diversity seem worth pursuing. For instance, Endler (1977) has suggested that a pattern of variability "identical to that of coalesced refugia" may occur through a process of differentiation along environmental gradients, and that the time scale reflected in the clines so produced may yet be shorter than those involved in Pleistocene climatic fluctuations. Haffer notes, but neglects to deal with these observations; indeed, if there is one major potential weakness in his approach it is his failure to consider the effects of modern, or at least post-Pleistocene, ecology upon modern distributions.

It may then be that in his concern to contrast a relatively monolithic modern Neotropical environment (which nonetheless shelters a remarkably diverse fauna) with dramatic environmental modification and disruption at points in the past, Haffer underestimates the amount of floral and climatic diversity that actually occurs in today's Neotropics. Biogeographical filters may exist which are less dramatically marked than the broad swaths of grassland postulated for the arid parts of the Pleistocene, but which nevertheless act as the partial barriers that Endler believes would produce "stepped clines" indistinguishable from zones of secondary intergradation. Given the relative paucity of our knowledge, it thus may be too early to abandon the idea that at least some of the causes of modern Neotropical faunal distribution and diversity are to be sought in features of present-day topography and ecology.

What are the implications of Haffer's model of avian differentiation in the Neotropics for the issue of vicariance biogeography? In one sense, it provides a prime example of vicariance; the fragmentation of ranges into refugia is a vicariant event par excellence, emphasizing differentiation as a passive result of external events. On the other hand, as a cyclic phenomenon, the refugia model also postulates episodes of dispersal. While the formation of barriers within the range of an organism undoubtedly qualifies as vicariance, their disappearance and the subsequent geographical expansion of the isolates obviously must equally count as dispersal. This harmonious combination of vicariant with dispersal events is possibly the most attractive general aspect of Haffer's study, for it should be clear to anyone familiar with the organic world that to dichotomize biogeographical studies into vicariance versus dispersal would be fatuous. Vicariant events certainly have occurred—perhaps the best example is the breakup of Gondwanaland—and must have affected the evolutionary histories of almost every major group of organisms, certainly to a greater degree than was traditionally realized. But so indubitably has dispersal occurred; and Haffer has been obliged by the distribution of the highland birds of the Neotropics to supplement the refugia model, involving "passive" dispersal, with "active" dispersal across pre-existing barriers. I, for one, would have been surprised if this had not been the case, for I am hard put to think of organisms better equipped to disperse than are birds.

If dispersal can occur, then there is no necessary relationship between geography and phylogeny, and objectively testable historical biogeographical models are impossible to construct. Effectively, biogeographical hypotheses must exist at the level of complexity of what has been called the evolutionary "scenario" (see, for instance, Tattersall and Eldredge 1977); the scenario is testable only by the criterion of plausibility. I find Haffer's scenario plausible in many respects. It is clear that the historical factors that Haffer emphasizes cannot be ignored in explaining the present pattern of diversity in the Neotropical fauna; it is clear also that many aspects of that pattern support his hypothesis. It will be interesting to observe how the scenario fares as more is learned of the ecology, adaptations, and distribution of the modern Neotropical fauna; meanwhile, Haffer's contribution seems likely to appeal more to those who view biogeography as a set of real-world problems seeking solutions than to those who regard it as a science in search of a paradigm.

Response

J. Haffer

ASSUMING THE CENTRAL ISSUE of this symposium to be the definition of regional biogeographical patterns and their discussion in the light of vicariance and dispersal explanations, I believe (*contra* Dr. Tattersall) I have contributed by predicting a regional biogeographical pattern from the Cenozoic history of the Neotropics. This prediction was born out by ornithogeographical data supporting a vicariance interpretation (paleogeographical changes and vegetational shifts). A future test of this interpretation was suggested by a comparison of area cladograms and taxic cladograms. By emphasizing vicariance as well as dispersal across barriers (at least in certain montane birds), I offered broad interpretations and pointed out, as Tattersall notes, that the refuge theory combines aspects of both vicariance and dispersal interpretations even though "passive" redispersal occurred within continuous habitat zones, rather than "active" dispersal across pre-existing barriers.

Forest and nonforest refugia should not be identified only on the basis of biological data such as centers of endemism, but rather on the basis of geoscientific data. The difference or coincidence in location of the geoscientific refugia and biogeographical core areas (or between centers of endemism for various groups of organisms) should be established and discussed. A correlation between the location of centers of endemism and geoscientific refugia suggests, but does not prove, a causal relationship between both. More data are required to map core areas and contact zones of taxa in different unrelated groups of Neotropical organisms so as to establish the existence of such patterns and their possible significance and causation. In this respect it is interesting to note that Dr. Prance agrees from a botanist's point of view with many biogeographical aspects and interpretations of avifaunal data of the Neotropical Region.

It has been my intention to emphasize the importance of historical factors for an understanding of major biogeographical features observed today without, however, entirely denying the influence of modern ecological diversity. I agree with Tattersall that ecological diversity in the Neotropical lowlands is probably more complex than currently known and may eventually be shown to determine some of the observed patterns. Until evidence to the contrary is forthcoming, however, the conspicuous avian "hybrid zones," known from many parts of the world and used in my historical biogeographical interpretations of the Neotropical avifauna, will be considered as "secondary" rather than "primary," particularly in view of convincing geoscientific evidence for large scale habitat changes during the Cenozoic.

10

Vicariance Biogeography
of Angiosperms
in Relation to Paleobotanical Data

J. A. Wolfe

THE INCREASING ACCEPTANCE of plate-tectonic models during the last two decades has justifiably led to reappraisals of the relation of past continental movements to the past and present distribution patterns of plants, particularly angiosperms. An analysis of fossil-plant distribution by Axelrod in 1963 sought to deny past continental movements, but by 1970, faced with substantial geological data in favor of continental movements, he attempted to explain the present and past distributions of virtually all major angiosperm alliances in terms of rifting of plates, i.e., in terms of vicariance biogeography. Between these two extremes, Raven and Axelrod (1974), using more firmly based paleobotanical evidence, suggested that the distribution of only some angiospermous alliances was the consequence of rifting. Aubréville (1976) suggested a more complex history, involving both continental movements and high-latitude migration routes, to explain the distribution of the present tropical angiosperm flora. Thorne (1978) suggested a cautious approach to the relation between continental rifting and the distribution of angiosperms.

In this report, I will discuss several present patterns of angiosperm distribution and how these relations probably came about. In the first basic pattern—the vicariance of the northern hemisphere broad-leaved deciduous woody flora—much paleobotanical information is available and consequently allows a more detailed understanding of the origins of this pattern.

Arcto-Tertiary Geoflora

The classic example of vicariance biogeography, although it was not labeled as such, is the concept of an "Arcto-Tertiary Geoflora." "A Geoflora is defined as a group of plants that has maintained itself with only minor changes in composition for several epochs or periods of earth history . . . The Arcto-Tertiary Geoflora . . . has spread southward through Eurasia and North America in response to progressive changes in climate. . . ." (Chaney 1959:12). This geoflora concept arose in an attempt to explain the floristic similarities between eastern Asia and eastern North America, similarities that were recognized long ago by Asa Gray (1878). The concept envisioned that a common biota once occupied high latitudes of Eurasia and North America and that this biota became fragmented as it was pushed south by secular cooling during the Tertiary. Much of the biota became extinct in Europe because of glaciation and in western North America because of a trend to summer drought. This is indeed a highly parsimonious concept. It calls for but one major dispersal and one major and two minor vicariant events to explain vicariant relationships in Eurasia and North America.

Systematics and Distribution of Maples (*Acer*)

One of the most conspicuous broadleaved deciduous tree genera in Eurasia and North America is *Acer*, which includes the maples and boxelder. The approximately 140 species are centered largely in eastern Asia and eastern North America. Ogata (1967) recognized five major groups or subgenera and 26 sections within *Acer*. Three sections (*Macrantha, Spicata, Rubra*) have an eastern American-eastern Asian vicariant pattern. Additionally, two other sections (*Negundo* and *Cissifolia*) are closely related, as are *Arguta* and *Glabra*. One other section (*Palmata*) is vicariant between eastern Asia and western North America, and *Macrophylla* of western North America is closely related to three Asian sections. Of the remaining sections, three are endemic to Europe and the Middle East, seven to eastern Asia, one to North America, and three are both western and eastern Eurasian.

Members of Ogata's Group A (11 sections) are diverse, and their apparent phylogenetic relationships are not clear. Ogata (1967:159), however, considered the eastern Asian-eastern American section *Macrantha* "nearest to the ancestor of this group," and three other sections somewhat more advanced; these are the endemic eastern Asian *Distyla*, *Parviflora*, and the eastern Asian-eastern American *Spicata*. Morphologically somewhat isolated is *Palmata*, which is exclusively Asian except for one western American species. A third subgroup is composed of two sister sections, the Asian *Arguta* and the western American *Glabra*. A fourth subgroup is composed of the Eurasian *Trilobata* and the eastern Asian-eastern American *Rubra*. A fifth subgroup, which some workers recognize as a distinct genus, is composed of the North American *Negundo* and the eastern Asian *Cissifolia*. From Ogata's discussion, I infer that he considered all five subgroups to have had a common ancestor. Pojarkova's (1933) interpretation is in basic agreement, although she considered *Spicata* to have to the ancestral stock a relation more direct than has *Macrantha*.

Fossil Record

The fossil record of *Acer* is based on both abundant foliage and seeds. Most of the data given here result from a joint effort by Professor Toshimasa Tanai and me on the North American fossils and by Professor Tanai on the Asian fossils. I emphasize that, in contrast to the typically sparse record of fossil vertebrates, the record of plant megafossils is generally excellent. For example, the western American history of section *Rubra* is based on 74 occurrences in western North America, and ten of these occurrences are in Alaska. Indeed, the increasing knowledge of the Tertiary floras from Alaska, Kamchatka, and Chukotka is making the floristic history of this critical area one of the best known in the northern hemisphere. The Neogene localities or floras within the Cook Inlet basin alone now number over 70 and give us excellent knowledge of the woody flora.

General support for the interpretations of both Ogata (1967) and Pojarkova (1933) can be inferred from paleobotany. Members of *Distyla* are known in the Paleocene and Eocene of western conterminous United States

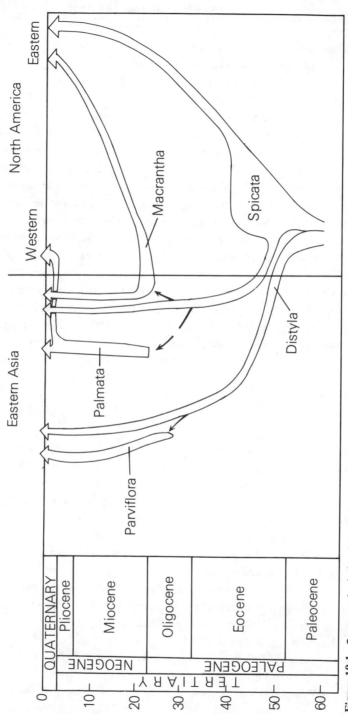

Figure 10.1. Suggested relationships in time and space of sections *Spicata, Distyla, Macrantha, Parviflora,* and *Palmata.*

and the Eocene of Japan (figure 10.1). *Spicata* is known from the Paleocene and Eocene of Alaska, as well as from the Eocene in both the conterminous United States and Japan. Such data seemingly support a vicariance "Arcto-Tertiary" distributional hypothesis: *Acer* originated at middle-to-high latitudes and became an integral part of a high-latitude broad-leaved deciduous forest, which has since been fragmented by various vicariant events. This hypothesis must presume that the various vicariant groups of *Acer* (both groups vicariant now and groups vicariant during the Neogene) had evolved to become part of an "Arcto-Tertiary Geoflora" by the end of the Eocene. Just a gross examination of the paleobotanical data indicates problems, as the following emphasizes:

Epoch	Number of Groups	Number of Sections
Miocene	5	16
Oligocene	3	11
Eocene	3	7
Paleocene	1	2

Macrantha, despite its supposed antiquity, does not have any Paleogene occurrences. It appeared at about the same time (early Miocene) in Japan, Alaska, and the conterminous United States. Such a pattern can indicate that the group evolved only recently (possibly from a primitive stock of *Distyla* or *Spicata* such as *Acer arcticum*) and rapidly dispersed.

Of the five subgroups in Ogata's Group A, each has a different history. The *Macrantha-Distyla-Spicata* subgroup does appear in part to fit the classic "Arcto-Tertiary" pattern. Not so the subgroup represented by *Palmata*, the only fossil record of which is in the Neogene of eastern Asia (figure 10.2). The present abundance and wide distribution of the extant western American *Acer circinnatum* Pursh makes very puzzling the lack of a fossil record of *Palmata* in North America.[1] The fact that *A. circinnatum* is morphologically very close to extant Japanese species, however, leads me to suggest that *A. circinnatum's* ancestor landed in North America via long-distance dispersal during the Pliocene or even the Quaternary.

The third subgroup of *Arguta-Glabra* is apparently old. *Glabra* extends back to the latest Eocene in Colorado. Specimens indicate a close relation-

[1] Prakash and Barghoorn (1961) compared a Miocene wood from Washington to *A. circinnatum*. Other than the differences they cited, it is significant that the fossil has rays one-to-five cells wide whereas woods of *Palmata* have rays that are typically five or more cells wide (Ogata 1967).

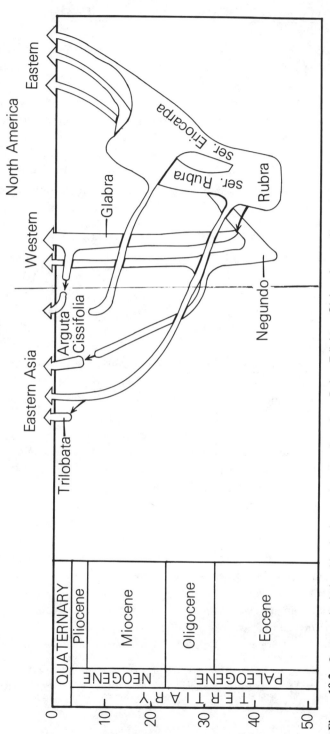

Figure 10.2. Suggested relationships in time and space of sections *Rubra, Trilobata, Glabra, Arguta, Negundo,* and *Cissiflora.*

ship to the fourth subgroup, and may be close in time to the origin of the *Arguta-Glabra* stock. In any case, this stock has no fossil record in the Miocene of eastern Asia. In western North America, the *Glabra* stock occurred originally in broad-leaved forest and adapted to coniferous forest. In eastern Asia, *Arguta* is largely, if not entirely, confined to coniferous forest. These facts may indicate that during the late Neogene, *Glabra* migrated through Beringia (the present distribution of *Acer glabrum* is almost to 60°N in Alaska), and evolved into *Arguta*, which then spread south in the montane coniferous forests.

The fourth subgroup, *Trilobata-Rubra*, has a record extending into the Eocene of the conterminous United States. *Rubra* appeared in Alaska and then in eastern Asia in the Oligocene and gave rise to *Acer pycnanthum* and possibly also to *Trilobata* in the late Neogene. Yet another dispersal of *Rubra* to Asia must, however, be suggested. The Oligocene and Miocene record of the *Acer saccharinum* type is extensive in western North America, and this type lasted into the mid-Miocene in Alaska. The *Acer saccharinum* type then, following the warm mid-Miocene, appeared for the first and only time in the late Miocene of Japan.

The fifth subgroup, *Negundo-Cissifolia*, also has an extensive record in North America from the Eocene through the Holocene. In Asia, *Negundo* first appeared in the Oligocene and lasted into the Miocene; presumably *Cissifolia* is a late Neogene derivative.

Ogata's Group B is composed of three sections, all now exclusively Eurasian (*Platanoidea, Campestria, Pubescentia*). Two sections are, however, known from fossils in North America; *Platanoidea* is known in the Oligocene through the late Miocene, and *Campestria* is known in the Miocene. The oldest record of Group B is a species of *Campestria* from the Eocene and Oligocene of Japan, and *Platanoidea* is known from the Oligocene of Kazakhstan. *Platanoidea* then dispersed into North America in the early Oligocene; and *Campestria* first appeared in Alaska and then in the Pacific Northwest (figure 10.3).

Ogata's Group C has a vicariant distribution between Europe-Asia Minor (sections *Acer* and *Goniocarpa*) and North America (section *Sacharina*). The oldest records of this group are in the Oligocene of France. In North America, the section *Sacharina* appeared in the early Miocene, and at least two lineages are recognizably distinct. In Japan, yet a third lineage of *Sacharina* appeared in the early Miocene and disappeared at the end of the Middle Miocene; the Japanese species is closely related to *A. saccharum* of eastern North America, but to neither of the two lineages of *Sacharina* that were

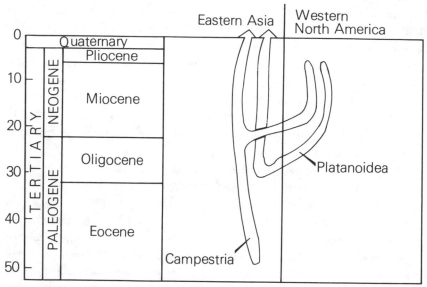

Figure 10.3. Suggested relationships in time and space of sections *Campestria* and *Platanoidea*.

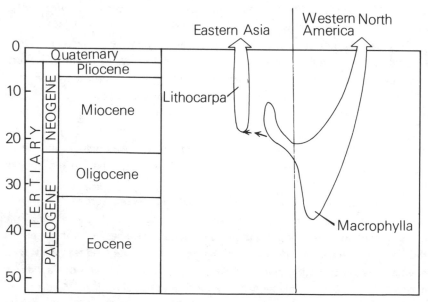

Figure 10.4. Suggested relationships in time and space of sections *Macrophylla* and *Lithocarpa*.

present in the Neogene of western North America. No records of Group C are known at high latitudes during the Tertiary. Such a distribution strongly indicates an origin of Group C during the Oligocene in Europe, evolution of *Sacharina* also in that region, spreading east to Japan and spreading west—via long-distance dispersal—across the Atlantic to North America.

Ogata's Group D is now and apparently always has been endemic to Eurasia; the oldest known record of this group is mid-Miocene.

Ogata's Group (or subgenus) E contains three sections endemic to eastern Asia (*Lithocarpa, Laurina,* and *Decandra*) and one section endemic to western North America (*Macrophylla*). Macrophylla and *Lithocarpa* are both represented in the early Miocene of Japan, and it would be tempting to suggest an origin of *Macrophylla* in Asia. The oldest record of *Macrophylla*, however, is in the late Eocene of western North America, and indicates a dispersal across Beringia, where *Macrophylla* appears during the early Miocene, and a derivation of the other sections from an early member of *Macrophylla* (figure 10.4).

Vicariance and Dispersal of *Acer*

Of the 12 sections of *Acer* that had or now have Asian-American disjunctions, seven may be attributable to vicariance from climatic separation. Two are certainly attributable to long-distance dispersal. The disjunctions of three other groups, however, may be the result of elimination due to competition rather than the direct result of environmental change. None of the disjunctions appears to be the result of plate tectonics.

It can certainly be said that the distribution patterns of fossil *Acer* do not support the hypothesis of an "Arcto-Tertiary Geoflora." And these patterns do not support the concept of fragmentation of one biota. The fragmentation of the mid-Miocene mixed northern hardwood forest in Alaska did result in some vicariant distributions in *Acer* and other genera, but few of these vicariant distributions still remain (Wolfe and Tanai 1980).

Even allowing for the fact that the Eocene floras of eastern Asia are not as well known as those of North America, a maximum of five vicariant distributions could have resulted from the climatic deterioration at the end of the Eocene, but two of these were not vicariant until much later.In fact, only the vicariance of *Spicata* might be attributed to the terminal Eocene event. Again, the well-documented mid-Miocene warming and subsequent cooling could have resulted in vicariance, and certainly the late Miocene vicariant distributions of series *Eriocarpa* of *Rubra*, series *Rubra* of *Rubra*, *Negundo*, *Macrophylla-Lithocarpa*, and *Campestria* are probably related to this climatic fluctuation. It is conceivable also that the Quaternary fluctuations resulted in vicariance in *Glabra-Arguta*.

Thus detailed analysis of the historical biogeography of *Acer* does not, in general, support a concept of vicariance biogeography for the entire genus. There was no ancestral series of populations that vicariated and that, through allopatric speciation, evolved into the various and now endemic sections of *Acer*. And the present vicariant sections do not appear to have attained such distributional patterns by means of a major vicariant event. Rather, the history of *Acer* is replete with repeated dispersals and vicariant events through a period of about 60 million years. Some of the sectional endemism has apparently resulted from sympatric speciation, with one of the descendant groups dispersing to another region and becoming extinct in its region of origin (figure 10.5).

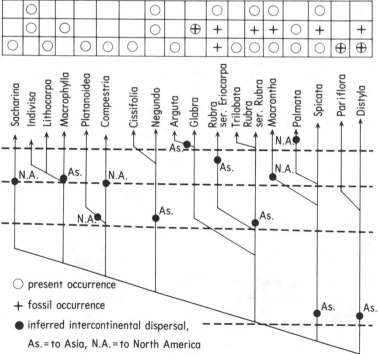

Figure 10.5. Hypothetical phylogeny of seventeen of the twenty-six sections of *Acer*.

Table 10.1 Suggested First Appearance of Angiosperms

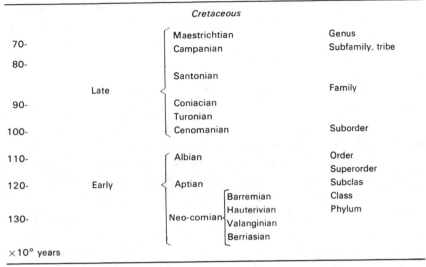

		Cretaceous		
70-		Maestrichtian		Genus
		Campanian		Subfamily, tribe
80-				
		Santonian		
	Late			Family
90-		Coniacian		
		Turonian		
100-		Cenomanian		Suborder
110-		Albian		Order
				Superorder
120-	Early	Aptian		Subclas
			Barremian	Class
			Hauterivian	Phylum
130-		Neo-comian	Valanginian	
			Berriasian	

×10⁹ years

NOTE: Suggested first appearance of organisms assignable to *some* extant groups of particular taxonomic levels of the phylum Angiospermae. The fact that, for example, a particular extant order first appeared in the Albian does not mean that all extant orders had appeared.

Vicariance and Dispersal of Tropical Angiosperms

Does the well-documented African-South American floristic relationship fit a pattern of vicariance biogeography? I emphasize that I am not ignoring the significance for plant distribution of the divergent movement of South America relative to Africa. Raven and Axelrod (1974) have stressed the fact that dispersal between the two continents would have been increasingly difficult as the two continents became more distant. Nevertheless, land-plant dispersal, whether across a water barrier of 800 km (as during the Paleocene) or across 1400 km (as today), is still dispersal. The central question that must not be ignored is: Have the present floristic relationships between South America and Africa primarily resulted from separation of a common ancestral biota or from dispersal?

In order meaningfully to discuss this topic, the time of diversification of the angiosperms must be briefly analyzed. Table 10.1 shows the generalized first appearance of angiosperms that can be relegated with some confidence to extant groupings of organisms of particular taxonomic levels (cf. Muller 1970; Doyle 1977; Hickey and Doyle 1977). I emphasize that these represent first appearances of organisms assignable to a particular taxonomic level and do not represent the first appearances of all extant groups of that level. For example, in the Lower Albian some angiosperms were probably assignable to the superorder Magnolianae, but organisms assignable to the superorders Hamamelidanae, Caryophyllanae, Dillenianae, Rosanae, etc., were not yet evident. Indeed, the first evidence for subclass Rosidae is in the Middle-to-Upper Albian (Wolfe et al. 1975), and even these rosids would probably not be assignable to any extant superorder of the subclass.

The discussion of South American-African floristic relationships has generally operated on too low a taxonomic level. If the last direct connection between the two continents was during the Cenomanian, then it follows that the disjunctions of families and lower levels were the result of dispersal and not of biotic disjunctions called for by vicariance biogeography. A discussion of the disjunction of genera and families is not relevant to the problem. Rather, sister families within the same suborder (or perhaps even in higher taxonomic levels) are taxa at the relevant levels. Within such a framework, only one example is apparent—that of Canellaceae and Myristicaceae. These two families, along with Annonaceae, comprise the suborder Annonineae (Walker 1976), which is one of the two suborders of the primitive order Magnoliales; all three families presumably had a common origin. In foliar morphology, the more primitive Canellaceae are South American (including Caribbean), and the more advanced are African; with Myristicaceae, the reverse is true. This pattern indicates that primitive Annonineae became disjunct with the separation of South America from Africa; the African stock evolved into Myristicaceae, and the South American stock evolved into Canellaceae (and also Annonaceae; cf., Walker 1971). The dispersal of the three families then occurred in the Coniacian or perhaps somewhat later. It is possible that Annonaceae actually evolved by the Cenomanian, in which case some of the trans-Atlantic vicarism in this family is properly the result of a vicariant event. Thorne (1974:166) validly surmised that these three families—alone among extant families—might have been involved in the rifting of South America from Africa.

If other groups of dicotyledons are examined, the origins of most of the various suborders, and even orders, appear to be too young to have been present prior to the separation of South America from Africa. This point is well emphasized in the analysis of Raven and Axelrod (1974).

Raven and Axelrod (1974:601) suggested that migration of land plants between South America and Africa was so easy until the Eocene that it was comparable to "direct overland migration." They reasoned that the 800 km or less separating South America from Africa prior to the Eocene "is a third more than the distance between Yucatan and Jamaica [actually Yucatan and the Cayman Islands], which has in about 15 m.y. acquired a flora of some 2,888 species of angiosperms." Jamaica is, of course, only about 145 km from Cuba, which is 180 km from Yucatan, and these distances were greatly reduced during the lowered sea levels of the Quaternary.

Raven and Axelrod (1974:602) further stated that the extant pollen floras of Africa have more "marked differences" from those of South America than in the past. Of the pollen discussed by Germeraad et al. (1968), 55 percent of the species of the late Cretaceous *Proteacidites dehaani* Zone occurs in both South America and Africa; for the Pleistocene the figure is 58 percent.

The paleobotanical data indicate that dispersals have occurred with regularity across the South Atlantic. The fact that such dispersals have continued to occur despite the increasing distance is perhaps a function of the fact that at least some of the more highly (and later) evolved angiosperm families of class Asteridae also have more efficient dispersal mechanisms (e.g., in Compositae). That all the distributions of Asteridae must have been attained during the Tertiary is clearly indicated by the palynological record (Muller 1970); none of the families is known in the Cretaceous, only one in the Paleocene, and large and predominantly tropical families such as Rubiaceae and Acanthaceae are not known until mid-Tertiary time. Distributions of some of these groups have been interpreted as the result of Cretaceous vicariant events, but clearly the distributions must largely be the result of dispersals, many of which occurred over long distances. While the distributions of some tropical groups appear to be the result of dispersals across moderate-to-long distances, in other instances it now seems clear that dispersals of some megathermal groups have occurred on land and via high latitude connections (Wolfe 1972, 1975, 1977; Aubréville 1976). Such connections occurred several times during the latest Cretaceous and early Tertiary (Wolfe 1977), and the various resulting disjunctions probably are also of differing ages.

One aspect of plate tectonics that bears on early angiosperm distribution has been generally overlooked: the apparent proximity (about 800 km) of Australasia to southeastern Asia during the Cenomanian, a proximity not again attained until the Eocene (Smith and Briden 1977). If, at a distance of 800 km, South America and Africa exchanged floristic elements, it seems reasonable that Australasia and southeastern Asia could also have exchanged floras.

One of the problems of the present distribution of angiosperm families that have retained some primitive characters is that four are clearly southeast

Asian while the remainder now either have ambiguous distributions or (the majority) are clearly centered in fragments of Gondwana. Thus, some workers (e.g., Takhtajan 1969; Thorne 1976) argue for a southeast Asian center of early diversification while others (e.g., Bailey 1949; Raven and Axelrod 1974) argue for a Gondwana center of diversification. Alternatively, the southeast Asian families could simply be relicts of the primitive early Cretaceous Laurasian angiosperms that reached Laurasia from Gondwana.

The four southeast Asian families are Magnoliaceae, Calycanthaceae, Illiciaceae, and Schisandraceae. According to the classification of Walker (1976), the Magnoliaceae are comembers of suborder Magnoliinae (order Magnoliales) with the Australasian Degeneriaceae and Eupomatiaceae. The Calycanthaceae are comembers of suborder Calycanthineae (order Laurales) with the Australasian Idiospermataceae. The Illiciaceae and Schisandraceae are members of suborder Illiciineae, which is, along with the Australasian Winterineae, one of the two suborders of Winterales. Recalling (table 10.1) that the ordinal and subordinal diversification of the subclass Magnoliidae was probably achieved in the Albian and Cenomanian, I suggest that ancestors of the Magnoliaceae, Calycanthaceae, and Illiciineae were dispersed from Australasia to southeastern Asia during that time interval. This interpretation would thus favor an early diversification of the angiosperms on the Gondwana fragments, an interpretation that would be in accord with palynological evidence (Doyle et al. 1977).

My interpretation that some presently southeast Asian primitive Magnoliidae arrived there from Australasia does not, however, indicate that the early diversification of the angiosperms was in East Gondwana (Australasia/Antarctica). Palynological data indicate that the arrival of angiosperms in East Gondwana was during the Middle Albian—substantially later than their first occurrence in West Gondwana (Doyle et al. 1977).

The timing of angiosperm origin and diversification is too late for there to have been on Pangea an ancient angiosperm flora that subsequently fragmented. The present floristic similarities between the two fragments of West Gondwana are at the specific, generic, and familial levels—again too late in most instances to have resulted from a common biota (Thorne 1978). The present disjunct distributions of various northern hemisphere deciduous woody groups could be attributed to vicariant events, but analysis of a genus such as *Acer* indicates such a complexity in space and time that a simplistic vicariance model (such as an "Arcto-Tertiary Geoflora") is contradicted by available data. Without paleobotanical evidence, it would be difficult, if not impossible, to determine when and how various disjunctions have been attained.

Concluding Remarks

The complexity of the history of a genus such as *Acer* is the result of a number of factors, including Cenozoic climatic history and the changing tolerances of individual lineages. In other words, the continuous flux of the environment and its impact on the distribution of populations and resulting genetic-physiological changes lead to complex patterns of distribution. The ranges of *Acer macrophyllum* and *Acer circinnatum* largely overlap, and both species have their closest relatives in eastern Asia. The vicariant relation in one instance does fit a model of vicariance biogeography, but it does not in the other instance. The current overlap and similar biogeographical relations are thus historically a coincidence.

Even before plate tectonics became widely accepted, paleobotanical data were negating one classical concept of vicariance biogeography: the "Arcto-Tertiary Geoflora" (MacGinitie 1962). Mason (1947:205) had, in fact, predicted this situation:

Such concepts of floristic organization and development demand unity and stability of communities in time and space beyond what is possible in the light of the nature of floristic dynamics such as are bound up with the genetics of the population, the physiology of the individual, and the diversity and fluctuation of the environment.

With the increasing documentation and the acceptance of plate-tectonic models, one should not, as Thorne (1978:299) has aptly cautioned, ignore "the realities of timing and direction of continental displacements, timing of origins of taxa and their dispersal, and the often rapid and distant dissemination of organisms about the world."

Some angiospermous disjunctions are the result of vicariant events, but other disjunctions are not. The current distributions of angiosperms have been so obscured by a variety of vicariant and non-vicariant events during the last 100 million years (or longer) that the fossil record is a clear necessity in evaluating the biogeographical significance of disjunctions within this phylum.

Discussion

K. J. Niklas

THE GEOFLORA CONCEPT has until recently been the framework within which the Tertiary history of vegetation has been interpreted. Chaney (1947, 1959) argued that some plant communities are recognizable as distinct associations within extended periods of geological time: "A Geoflora is defined as a group of plants which has maintained itself with only minor changes in composition for several epochs or periods of earth history, during which time its distribution has been profoundly altered although the area it has covered at any one time may not have varied greatly in size" (Chaney 1959:12). Four basic geofloras were recognized: the Neotropical-Tertiary and the Paleotropical-Tertiary Geoflora (prominent in western North American since the Pliocene), and the Arcto-Tertiary Geoflora (characterizing northern latitudes of the late Oligocene-Miocene). Research by Wolfe (1966, 1969, 1971, 1972) and others (e.g., Davis 1976) has, however, shown inherent weaknesses in the geoflora concept: (1) lower Tertiary communities of the Pacific Northwest do not show a zonation or biotic affinity pattern implied by the geoflora concept (e.g., lower Tertiary floras of Alaska show a tropical element); (2) the Neotropical-Tertiary Geoflora on the Pacific coast is predominantly paleotropical in affinity; (3) many of the genera common in Tertiary deposits (e.g., *Nyssa*, *Smilax*, *Juglans*, *Platanus*, *Carya*, *Myrica*) have broad ecological tolerances (temperate to tropical) suggesting that "commonly associated taxa" may not be taxocenes and that the present species ranges are poor indicators of potential range and/or ecological amplitude; and (4) the mixed mesophytic forest becomes recognizable only in the Miocene. Similarly, field ecology studies are inconsistent with the a priori cohesive geoflora concept (Mason 1949; Whittaker 1967; Levandowsky and White 1977). In contrast to the geoflora concept, paleobotanical data indicate that the origin of floristic affinities among Asia, North America, and Europe is a complex phytogeographical and evolutionary issue amenable to analysis only by a rigorous treatment of each taxon's history.

Wolfe's treatment (this volume) of the paleobiogeography of angiosperms is partitioned into two lines of reasoning: (1) the fossil and neogenic data known for *Acer* are discussed within the context of the vicariant event of the Arcto-Tertiary Geoflora hypothesis; and (2) the general paleofloristic relationships among Africa, South America, southeastern Asia, and Australia are summarized and conclusions drawn about the general applicability of vicariant models. Thus specific and general case studies are made. Wolfe has shown in this treatment that the paleobiogeography of *Acer* is consistent with both episodic long-distance dispersal and with climatic vicariance. In the general analysis of geographical distributions of Tertiary angiosperms, the occurrence of vicariant events is shown to be infrequent. Various logical and biological *a priori* difficulties may, however, be shown to mitigate the vigor with which some of these conclusions are stressed. Recent revisions of *Acer* (Ogata 1965, 1967; Murray 1970; Tanai 1978a, 1978b) collectively indicate a high level of phenotypic variation within and among species, as well as conflicting conclusions about "primitive" versus "advanced" character states. Specific difficulties pertinent to the use of the fossil record of *Acer* come to light in the treatment of each author. Ogata's (1965, 1967) revisions are based on admittedly incomplete collections; consequently his proposed sections and series of species are partly biased. Similarly, the issue of "primitive" versus "advanced" characters is not raised in these studies. Jong's (1976) revisions emphasize floral physiology, which has little utility in the fossil record. Tanai's (1978a, 1978b) various sections of *Acer* are of necessity based on an incomplete fossil record. Similarly, many contemporary species of *Acer* would not, if found as fossils, be recognized as assignable to this genus given classical paleobotanical techniques of identification (e.g., *A. oblungum, A. cissifolium, A. buergerianum*).

Phytochemical work (Bate-Smith 1978) suggesting *Macrantha* as the most primitive section is based on the as yet unsubstantiated view that trihydroxy tannic acids are *a priori* "primitive" characters, while paleophytochemical data indicate a high level of chemical homogeneity and conservatism in the genus. A major difficulty inherent in all of these studies is that many of the most "primitive" taxa are the most morphologically distinct, while more "advanced" sections show considerable morphological introgression. The recognition of paleospecies in fossil *Acer* is not in question here, but rather the qualitative/quantitative expression of phylogenetic and taxonomic relationships. Until apomorphic and plesiomorphic characters can be assigned, the cladistic relationships among sections of *Acer* will remain a moot point in testing vicariant events.

Another difficulty with the *Acer* "test case" is the taxon's relative recency in the fossil record, compounded by its potential for efficient long-distance dispersal. A vicariant "event" can be recognized as such only retrospective to an appropriate analysis, at which time innumerable climatic, tectonic, and/or geographical events may be proposed or identified as the referable vicariant barrier(s). Plate tectonics and continental drift are neither necessary nor sufficient components of vicariant analysis. Once a minimum 3-(or more) area system, comprising a cladistically dichotomized 3-taxon group, is proposed, a reiterative dichotomized analysis of other taxa provides the basis for assessing the generality of the pattern of area connections (cf. Platnick and Nelson 1978; Rosen 1978). Regrettably, the current fossil record for many angiosperm fossil taxa may preclude such a vigorous testing.

The data and conclusions presented by Wolfe (this volume) indicate that, within the context of the fossil history of *Acer*, a polarized view of the long-distance dispersal and vicariant models is inappropriate (e.g., seven of 12 sections of *Acer* may have shown climatic vicariance). This is clearly a truism because dispersal must precede vicariant events.

The application of the vicariant hypothesis to plant evolution as a whole is at least in theory germane to a number of instances: the Permo-Carboniferous "*Glossopteris* flora" (Sahni 1939; Schopf 1970a, 1970b); the Mesozoic history of the gymnosperms (Florin 1963); distribution patterns in the bryophytes (Schuster 1972b; F. E. Smith 1972); early angiosperm evolution (Schuster 1976); and the Tertiary history of the Neotropical flora in North America (Axelrod 1975). The fact that the first recognizable appearance of angiosperms preceded the disjunction of the Australasian land complex indicates the applicability of vicariant biogeographical techniques to the analysis of the consequences of plate movements resulting in the breakup of supercontinents and correlated disjunctions of floras. Difficulties arise, however, from three areas: (1) the taxonomic status and fidelity of early angiosperm groups (i.e., early angiosperm groups are predominantly extinct and are consequently difficult to relate to subsequent lineages); (2) the ability of plants to disperse across physical barriers, sometimes over considerable distances, may dilute the recognition of vicariant events within disjunct flora; and (3) neither the dispersal nor the vicariant models is amenable to falsification by statements about the age of a particular disjunction or the age of a taxon.

Critical to the supposition that vicariant events occurred in early (Cretaceous) angiosperm evolution is the problem of the respective appearance of angiosperms and the position and subsequent pattern of continental plate migration. Until at least the Middle Cretaceous an apparently significant level of cosmopolitanism existed in Gondwanaland along with a similar cosmopolitanism in Laurasia (Schuster 1976). These two geographical areas most probably had a limited biotic exchange, because taxa with presumed ineffective long-distance dispersal are seen to have migrated between these two supercontinents (e.g., Fagaceae, Marsupialia). Similarly, the relict distribution of putatively primitive, woody, ranalean, angiosperm families, which suggests considerable antiquity and limited dispersability, segregates into basically Laurasian and Gondwanian patterns. In contrast to more modern families, the primitive members of these ranalean plant groups apparently lacked efficient long-distance dispersal, and so it appears reasonable to assume that "plate migration" formed a significant phenomenon whereby floristic units were vicariated. Superimposed upon this primary trend was a "filtering" that depleted some of the "old elements" because of plate migration through inhospitable climatic regions, and the appearance of some *bona fide* dispersed taxa. Floristic structures must of necessity, therefore, contain some elements of vicariance and some of dispersal because plant taxa have a wide range of dispersability potential.

In agreement with Wolfe, even though early angiosperms generally lacked effective long-distance dispersal mechanisms, there is considerable evidence that these taxa utilized stepwise migration. The apparently rapid and wide dispersal of angiosperms during the Cretaceous, in Laurasia and Gondwanaland, may reflect the prevalence of migratory routes. Extant woody ranalean taxa, particularly in the Winterales, Magnoliales, Trochodendrales, Eucommiales, and Cercidiphyllales, occur equally in both continental provinces. Overland and/or short-distance migration routes among the provinces of a long-disjunct Gondwanaland are clearly evidenced from the fossil history of conifers and taxads (Florin 1963), hepatics (Schuster 1972a), and marsupials (Cox 1973). Similarly, limited migration was possible from North America to Australasia by means of South America and Antarctica.

Schuster (1976) notes that some Laurasian taxa reached Australasia via this route at least prior to the Miocene. Until at least mid-Cretaceous times, over-land migration within the southern hemisphere was possible (Cracraft 1973). It is clear also that during the Tertiary, when South and North America were isolated, coevolutionary patterns among mammals, birds, and fruits of flower-ing plants became progressively re-inforced and potentially led to more effi-cient long-distance dispersal. Floristic relationships between tropical Africa and tropical America, as outlined by Thorne (1973), argue against continental drift as a significant aspect in the distribution of many seed plants found in these areas.[1] Continental disjunction had occurred well before the develop-ment of the present seed-plant floras. Land bridges, such as those that exist or have existed in Central America, Greenland (McKenna 1975a), and the Beringian area (Wolfe 1972), most probably play or played a major role for taxa characterized by short- or long-distance dispersal, while biotic disjunc-tion in evolutionarily recent taxa across oceanic gaps must have been effected by long-distance dispersal (Carlquist 1966a, 1966b, 1966c, 1966d, 1967; Gressitt et al. 1963). The contradistinctive nature of vicariant and dis-persal biogeography is therefore mitigated by significant temporal changes in both the mode and the routes of migration.

Statements concerning the utility of the vicariance model in explaining specific plant historical biogeography events must, in part, be cognizant of fundamental differences between animals and plants. Comparisons of higher plants with various groups of birds, mammals, and some insect taxa indicate that discrete biological species are less frequent and anomalous species con-ditions more prevalent in plants. It logically follows that the factors affecting speciation common to both animals and plants are operatively different in the two kingdoms. The high frequency of interspecific hybridization and of uniparental reproduction (e.g., agamospermy) found in plants may be accounted for by the commensurate open growth system of the typical autotroph. Correspondingly, it perhaps is not surprising that the lower level of organismic homeostatis found in plants, and the presumed simplicity of the referable genetic system (Stebbins 1959; Grant 1971), are associated with a greater tolerance to interspecific hybridization. These and other fundamental characteristics of plants have ramifications on micro- and macroevolutionary phenomena, and bear directly on the testability, frequency of occurrence, and level of detectability of the vicariant model. Germane to this issue are: (1) the evolution of plant dispersal mechanisms and their relative efficacy; (2) the

[1] The disjunct distributions of some taxa (e.g., ceroxyloid and chamaedoreoid palms; Moore 1973) may, however, be evidence of *bona fide* vicariads.

components, rates of gene flow, and isolation within a population as a biological function of a taxon's dispersal characteristics; (3) the mode of speciation (e.g., allopatric, sympatric) and its tempo as a function of environmental heterogeneity; and (4) the implications of (1) and (3) on the plant species concept and on phylogenetic relationships as deduced from paleo- and neobotanical studies.

Prevailing theories are in general based on the premise that animal breeding units are extensive and that there exists a basically homogeneous gene pool within the greater part of their populations. Such assumptions are inconsistent with information on the potential and actual gene flow in higher plants (Levin and Kerster 1974). Pollen and seed dispersal are in many taxa predominantly localized or highly leptokurtic. Discontinuities among neighboring populations within many plant species (e.g., *Galium pumilum*, Ehrendorfer 1953; *Potentilla erecta*, Watson 1970; *Anthoxanthum odoratum*, Davies and Snaydon 1973), particularly those species showing self-compatibility, may be as pronounced as those shown among greatly separated populations (cf. Snogerup 1967; Strid 1970; Morley 1972).

Thus many seed plant populations are composed of multiple isolated breeding units that vary in size. Each unit may show distinctive physiological-morphological adaptations to localized environmental conditions. Clearly, then, it is a mere assumption (perhaps ill-founded) that all speciation is allopatric in mode. This pheno- and genotypic variation within any given population has a bearing (both quantitatively and qualitatively) on the magnitude of an "isolating" barrier necessary to effect recognizable vicariant species; e.g., vicariance may occur within a very small geographical area that is below the detectability level within the fossil record. Similarly, the nature of the vicariance-inducing barrier may be such that it leaves no tangible remains in the fossil record. The level of heterogeneity within a species' population structure is in part a function of the efficacy of its disseminule dispersal mechanism, which is dictated by the relation between the quantity of pollen or seeds produced within a population and that contributed from other populations.

In self-fertilizing species bereft of long-distance dispersal mechanisms, effective gene exchange between populations may occur at levels approaching their mutation rates (Bradshaw 1971). Consequently, effective population size in some plant taxa may be measured in meters rather than in kilometers, while in panmictic units effective population size may be significantly smaller (Grant 1971). Genera characterized by more efficient long-distance dispersal mechanisms may show pronounced physiological-morphological homogeneity, making difficult the recognition of species in the fossil record. Collectively, the level of gene exchange among populations is influenced by population size and density and by plant height and breeding system, terminal velocity of pollen/seeds, and by pollen/seed vector foraging behavior. Similarly, these factors may vary in time; e.g., self-fertilization within many species varies as a function of genetic and environmental influences (Jain and Marshall 1968; Jain 1975).

Population genetic data indicate that seed plants may store genetic variability and permit localized adaptation to different habitats (Wright 1960), as well as rapid evolutionary transformation in time. The phylogeny of many if not most higher plant groups is seen as reticulate rather than dichotomous (Lotsy 1916; Stebbins 1950; Ehrendorfer 1959). The difficulties of a reticulate pattern of characters among angiosperm superorders are clearly outlined by Cronquist (1968) and may be extended to the genetic relationships found in plant species complexes.

The implications derived here from the aforementioned characteristics of plants in contradistinction to animals are: (1) plant populations demonstrating genotypic heterogeneity are susceptible to rapid microvicariant events and subsequent rapid species divergence; (2) increased efficacy in long-distance dispersal mechanisms may be associated with increased morphological introgression among populations as a function of increased gene flow; (3) the plant species and paleospecies concepts, and instances of reticulate seed-plant evolution; make the testing of vicariant events difficult, particularly in the fossil record, where "ghosts" may alter cladograms; (4) the nature of plant disseminules facilitates repeated dispersal events across various "isolating" barriers, where selective pressures do not necessarily operate during transport of the disseminules; and (5) dispersal mechanisms in particular plant groups have evolved such that greater and greater distances may be traversed through their history (Schuster 1976).

Another aspect of the applicability of the vicariant model to plants (viz., criteria for testability) must also be mentioned. Platnick and Nelson (1978) conclude that the vicariance model must be tested by examining the interrelationships among taxa such that the biogeographical areas under consideration are related to their common ancestral biotas.[2] Such an approach provides the necessary basis for outgroup comparisons. The usefulness of this methodical dictum rests in part, however, on: (1) the degree to which ecosystems appear to form coherent taxonomically distinct units due

[2] The vicariance analysis must begin with a three-area three-taxon problem comprising a cladistically dichotomizing scenario.

to holistic properties resulting from coadapted component species; (2) the differential response of these component taxa—both quantitatively and qualitatively—to selective pressures and speciation; and (3) the reliability of concordance in the light of stochastic phenomena. The latter aspect has been dealt with in terms of gene flow and breeding structure in populations.

Evidence from field ecology seems to indicate that individual species vary independently in abundance from sample to sample along environmental gradients (e.g., altitude, temperature, pH, salinity; Whittaker 1967; Levandowsky 1972; Allen and Koonce 1973). Similarly, multivariate techniques indicate little evidence for tight clusters of points representing ecologically coherent species. The lack of such clearcut taxocenes (Chodorowski 1959), along with evidence for a lack of genetic homogeneity even in geographically restricted populations, suggests that the vicariant model, at least when applied to plants, may be difficult to test. Plant taxa within recently vicariated geographical areas may in theory show radically different speciation modes and/or tempos, and the geographical heterogeneity in their original distributions may result in unique area-cladogram patterns for each taxon.

In conclusion, both the theoretical and empirical considerations based on plant biology and biogeography suggest that paleo- and/or neobotanical vicariant events may have occurred in conjunction with short- and long-distance episodes of dispersal. The nature of the open growth pattern and plastic genetic system of plants further suggests that if vicariant events occur they may do so within relatively restricted geographical areas. Similarly, the designation of "primitive" and "advanced" characters is subjective, and in plants the level of subjectivity is compounded by reticulate evolution. Such a hypothesis involves an ad hoc inference that vicarant events in plants will be difficult to assess or detect in the paleobotanical record. Clearly, however, just as the geoflora concept must be assessed by a rigorous treatment of individual taxa, so too the vicariant hypothesis must be properly tested against paleo- and neobotanical data.

Discussion

P. Mankiewicz

ACCEPTING THE INTENTION of this symposium as a critical evaluation of the methods and hypotheses fundamental to vicariance biogeography, I believe my discussion of the paper just presented should reflect the generality and specificity intrinsic to such an evaluation. There are at least two approaches to the discipline of biogeography: one may discuss the *correspondence* of the distribution of a taxon with the distribution of other taxa and with an independently determined set of past geological and climatic (vicariance) events; or, the whole pattern of distribution of several taxa may be taken as *contextual* evidence, from which one may construct likely geological, climatic, and dispersal scenarios to explain that distribution. In the first case, one uses the specific events of earth history to correlate the distribution of specific taxa. In the second case, one uses the context of distribution—with its similarities and dissimilarities, its grouped and ungrouped taxa—to impose a logical guide for reconstructing the events of the past. In practice, all biogeographers need both correspondence and contextual means to compare vicariance and dispersal biogeography because the context frames general questions, while vicariant correspondences yield specific answers.

The fundamental question here is one of similarity. Is taxon A more similar to taxon B or to taxon C? And, is area A more similar to area B or to area C? In biogeography we would like to ignore all convergent similarities and to include only those similarities and differences that embody the property of genealogical relatedness, of descent. Willard V. Quine, the set theoretician and philosopher of science, speaks directly to this issue when he states (1969:118):

> Certainly we cannot define 'a is more similar to b than to c' to mean that a and b belong jointly to more sets than a and c do. If properties are to support this line of definition where sets do not, it must be because properties do not, like sets, take things in every random combination. It must be that properties are shared only by things that are significantly similar. . . . Kinds can be seen as sets, determined by their members. It is just that not all sets are kinds.

All biogeographers implicitly know that kinds inform, while other sets do not. If we group organisms into kinds biogeographical, we would have in our groupings more information than we required to carry out the classification in the first place. John Stuart Mill lends the clarity of his own authority on this point (1887:97):

> A hundred generations have not exhausted the common properties of animals or of plants, of sulphur or of phosphorous; nor do we suppose them to be exhaustable, but proceed to new observations and experiments, in full confidence of discovering new properties which were by no means implied in what we previously knew. While, if anyone were to propose for investigation the common properties of all things which are the same color, the same shape, or the same specific gravity, the absurdity would be palpable.

All biologists could agree then that a description of the distribution of *related* organisms would be more valuable for understanding the history of life than for example, a description of the distribution of all organisms with the same humidity requirement. The question then arises, how closely related are the organisms?

In the paper under discussion, Dr. Wolfe compares the distributions of the sections of *Acer*, maples, in Asia and eastern and western North America. In the context of this large and relatively widely dispersed group of organisms, the fossil and present distributions of the sections of the genus are contrasted. An attempt is made, given the phylogeny, to sort out where vicariance events and where dispersal events, respectively, are most suited to account for the present pattern in terms of the time and place of the appearance of particular sections of the genus in the fossil record. This approach is extremely valuable because, by making his assumptions and criteria clear, he permits several important questions to be raised about the distribution of these organisms.

For example, the absence of *Palmata* in the North American fossil record is taken as support for the conclusion that the ancestor of *Acer circinnatum* was dispersed to North America in Pliocene or Quaternary times. But, while *Macrantha* and *Spicata* are both members of a purportedly ancient assemblage, no explanation is given, or need be given, as to why evidence of their presence does not appear in the fossil record of eastern North America. In his analysis, Wolfe establishes a rational scheme from the *context* of the past and present distributions of these organisms. Negative evidence, the absence of *Palmata* in the fossil record of western North America, is taken as support of dispersal, but the lack of fossil evidence of *Macrantha* and *Spicata* in the east is not used to question either the phylogeny or the scenario of distribution. Given the context, it is perhaps reasonable to take the same value of evidence in two different ways, for the fossil record and present distribution of *Acer* offer families of competing scenarios, rather than a single sequence of events. These are likely paths, but not precisely resolvable without a complete fossil record. The paper under discussion begins by assuming Ogata's phylogeny, and uses this with established dates from the fossil record to generate from the past distributions a logically coherent, most likely scenario of what may have established the present distribution.

The sections of *Acer* discussed here are, unfortunately, distributed only on two continents.[1] Since there are not unique elements of the genus in three areas, the conceptual parallax required for resolving areas in the vicariance method is not available here.[2] A geometric analogue would be the attempt to discern if a line were a plane, or a point a line, from a single point of observation. To determine if the distribution of lineages corresponds to vicariance events, one must compare at least two lineages. These should

[1] Conversations over many years with a friend and fellow graduate student, Tom Delendick, have informed me of the biology of the genus *Acer*. I hasten to add that he is not responsible for the views expressed here. The immense amount of chemical, morphological, and other data that he has gathered will, when published, very likely be of great value in sorting out the problems in the group.

[2] The use of three areas stands up well to questioning from another perspective. Although I do not know if this has been previously stated in the context of vicariance biogeography, we should expect biotic areas to occur in threes. The reason is profoundly simple. The most probable effect of the packing or cracking of planar figures is the production of three-way junctures. The nature of planar space itself gives us, on the average, areas in groups of three. It was noted more than 40 years ago that mountain chains do not conform to this pattern, but, continental plates very likely do conform. For an elegant discussion of the whole question of pattern in nature, see Stevens (1974).

be distantly related—each with unique elements, they should be of approximately the same geological age, and there should be adequate overlap of their ranges. While in the paper under consideration there are six endemic Asian sections of *Acer*, there is only one in western North America and there is none in eastern North America. As tantalizing as it may be to use a well known genus such as *Acer*, with its wealth of detail in the geological record, it cannot be used rigorously to test the vicariance model. I believe, however, that the practice of biogeography would benefit from a critical evaluation adequate to the vicariance approach, and I will attempt to outline one in what follows.

I pointed out previously that "kinds" are special sets that give more information than is required to construct them. In the context of vicariance biogeography, kinds are taxa that must embody information about the temporal production of the lineages to which they belong. With this requirement, it is possible to compare the distribution of two-to-many lineages in order to establish, by the presence of unique members of these lineages, the geographical areas that may have shared a peculiar sequence of past events. One is permitted to take neither the assemblages of organisms nor the clusters of areas as general sets with some random characteristics. The groups of organisms and of areas must be *kinds*, that share the same familial history and the same geological and climatic sequence.

Returning to the question of vicariance with regard to angiosperms (or any other group), one cannot critically test a biogeographical theory that purports to disclose more ancient versus more recent speciation events without a taxonomy adequate to this task. To test the theory, the phylogeny or cladogram must be radially self-critical with regard to the question of the temporal sequence of primitive/derived and generalized/specialized characters. Vicariance biogeography implies that geological events erect barriers that permit the genetic clock in the isolated populations to drift rapidly, while gene flow continues to damp genetic and morphological change in the unisolated populations. If the characters (character states) used by the taxonomist are not arranged in a sequence from generalized to specialized, i.e., ancestral to derived (a polarity), a practitioner of the vicariance school might logically maintain that the phylogeny or cladogram is a reflection of an ordering of sets, but not of kinds. One could logically maintain this with regard to Ogata's phylogeny of maples. In terms of a test of vicariance biogeography, with taxa whose relations may be specified in terms of specialized differentiae, but without an implied temporal sequence in the phylogeny, it is not possible to evaluate the correspondence of taxa with geographical and climatic events of the past. Many sets are ahistorical; lineages and geological events are not, but the specific genealogical figure is discernable only against the background of the many possible descent and dispersal scenarios implied by the context.

To question vicariance biogeography one must question phylogeny: What character(s) differentiates each taxon from all other taxa; and, what character(s) unites two groups, but separates these from all others? With answers to these questions, unique occurrences of unique taxa of different lineages in the same area should inform us, by the predictions of the theory, of similar distributions of as yet unstudied taxa of the same age. This should be a special place, a "kind" of place where, for example, the raising of mountains corresponded with the splitting of communities of organisms.[3]

As in all biogeography, the vicariance school uses contextual ordering of sets, but this enterprise is particularly concerned with the correspondence of lineages and places. The vicariance method cannot be tested with classical taxonomic orderings such as Ogata's sections of *Acer*, however, because the polarities embedded in these orderings do not embody a strictly linear sequence of characters, a requirement for the evaluation of correspondence between the temporality in the production of clades, and linear sequences in the history of the earth. This may prove problematic.

Vicariance biogeography requires linear sequences in character states. This requirement would make the theory untestable at present for major groups of organisms because this kind of information is present for some groups, but for many others it is not available. Angiosperms, ferns, and other plants suggest themselves here as essentially problematic. Reticulate evolution in some plants, their continued incestuous hybridizations, may place them beyond the present conceptual grasp of the vicariance school. Methods may be invented or imagined by which this intractable portion of the plant kingdom can be ordered in linear polarities of character states, but these have not yet appeared.[4]

From this discussion it would seem that biogeographers encounter sets of organisms and sets of areas. All biogeographers would hope to discover and intuit those special sets we call natural kinds, lineages of related organisms, and therefore some specific understanding of how the history of life is bound to the history of our planet. While all biogeographers sort through the sets to bring conceptual clarity to the context of distribution,

---

[3] This "kind" of place may correspond with "habitation" in Candolle's sense (Nelson 1978).

[4] Several of the most profound problems in the area of the idiosyncratic nature of plants are discussed in Levin (1979).

some attempt to attend to specific correspondence between the splitting of populations and the specific events in the history of the earth. Humans all know that methods are subject to error, and the methods compared here are no exceptions. The separation of major groups into sets based on similarity is likely to include, falsely, unrelated taxa in the same grouping. On the other hand, the sharp-edged conceptual tools of the vicariance school are likely to separate a taxon from its natural relatives because the creature, by reason of its particular environment and internal milieu, has established or maintained a course of development that makes it look like the ancestor or like some derived descendant with respect to the character state being used. But these criticisms may be taken as caveats; there may be a more serious problem in the future of vicariance biogeography.

All science is grounded in the theoretical and the conceptual. Experiments and hypotheses assume and imply frameworks of interpretation. I have already pointed out that vicariance may not be testable at present with regard to certain groups of plants. A kindred example might be the heritable variation proposed by Darwin as essential to his theory of evolution. Two generations passed before variation in heritable characteristics in terms of genetic laws was understood by the mainstream of the tradition. Two more generations passed before an adequate measure of genetic as opposed to phenetic variation was discovered. Mendelian genetics supported Darwin's postulate in phenotypic terms; electrophoresis and allied techniques supported Darwin in terms of the genes themselves. Heritable variability is at present quite testable, but for those persons not so fortunate to have lived this long, it was problematic. Another example should make this point even clearer. The relativity theories are often cited as good falsifiable theories. Even Einstein published the wrong value in 1907 for the curvature of light due to gravity (the published value also included an arithmetic error). Because of the war, the theory was not tested during the 1914 eclipse in Russia. Einstein was told that it could not be tested without an eclipse, which is false. Not until Einstein learned a new mathematical method—tensor calculus—beginning around 1912, and not until he used this method on the light gravitation problem in 1915 and 1916, was the correct value disclosed for the bending of light. Had the theory been tested early, it would have been falsified.[5]

In summary, vicariance biogeography requires phylogenies based on

[5] I am indebted to a friend and colleague, Herschel Snodgrass, for outlining this scenario for me in a conversation and subsequent note. For a description of some of these matters, see Hoffmann and Dukas (1973: 118 ff.).

linear evolutionary sequential characters in two distinct lineages with endemic elements in three areas. These requirements are based on the logical argument that two forms different from a third form are not necessarily different from one another. Without creative work and imagination, nature may not show herself in syllogisms. In any case, there remains the problem that given a linear evolutionary sequence without adequate fossil evidence, no *a priori* principle specifies the direction of evolution from simple to complex, or from complex to simple, elaborative, or reductive. The direction may be demonstrated by independant geological evidence on the history of the range of the organism or by experimentally uncovering the ancestral trait in the ontogeny of a derived member of the sequence.[6] A final problem is that only by clustering similar characters, by gestalt variations, can we reach some assurance that our kinds are as complete as those disclosed and embedded in nature. Vicariance biogeography, based on dissimilarity and uniqueness, lacks an intrinsic methodological directive that insures gathering all related members of a taxon, while the assumptions of dispersal biogeography too readily applied would show similarity in many groups that are more distantly related than is implied by their similar traits and common ranges.

In conclusion, even though vicariance biogeography may not be testable in certain groups of organisms at present, it is not yet clear if it is, in principle, untestable in these realms. In any event, many theories—like those of Copernicus, Einstein, and Darwin—were not testable or falsifiable for several generations, while some of Fermat's theorems still go unproven. The value of a theory is measured by its beauty, its applicability, what it discloses to the practitioner of science, and its usefulness in the world at large. If a theory does not lead practitioners to variations on the methodological themes available for encountering and producing information, it holds no value for science. Theory must motivate and orient the search for knowledge and truth; information must be realized and organized. This is the immediate test for vicariance biogeography. Human thoughts in human hands can bring the question to nature, but she will answer in her own time—which is history.

---

[6] An elegant description of this method of determining the direction of polarities is found in Basile (1969).

Response

J. A. Wolfe

NIKLAS' DISCUSSION of the problems of the relationships within *Acer* is based on the assumption that workers such as Ogata have no concept of "primitive" versus "advanced" characters (and hence have no concept of cladistic relationships). I strongly disagree. Ogata (1967) makes clear what he considers to have been the evolutionary trends in the various organs of *Acer*, and, indeed, he criticizes some other classifications that are based on "superficial appearance," i.e., on grade rather than on clade. Further, contrary to Niklas' assumption, the greatest disagreement among systematists has generally been on the classification of the more "primitive" sections of *Acer* (those with more generalized characters), whereas the more "advanced" sections (e.g., sections *Saccharina* and *Indivisa*) have not been the subject of disagreement. Systematists, including Ogata, do have concepts of "advanced" characters in *Acer*, and the relationships proposed are generally cladistic, even if no formal cladistic treatment was made.

Mankiewicz has stated that there are not "unique elements of . . . [*Acer*] in three areas," and thus vicariance methodologies cannot be applied. In fact, three areas are under discussion because the Atlantic North American region has long been considered floristically distinct from the Pacific North American region (Takhtajan 1969), that is, as a floristically different area. And each of the three areas (including the Sino-Japanese region) has endemic species. Moreover, if the known extinct species are used, then a number of species can be used in a three-taxon three-area analysis.

Indeed, my discussion of *Acer* centers on these three areas and points out that many sections are vicariant; each vicariant section obviously has (or had) endemic species in different areas. Consider, for example, sections *Macrantha*, *Rubra*, and *Saccharina*. *Macrantha* and *Rubra* (both series) were vicariated during the Miocene and probably by the same vicariant (climatic) event. The western American species of *Macrantha* (now extinct) is closest to eastern Asian species, but the western American species of both series of *Rubra* (now extinct) are closest to the eastern American species. The eastern Asian species of *Saccharina* (now extinct) is closest to the eastern American species, but, of course, I have inferred long-distance dispersal across the Atlantic for this section. The cladistic analysis of *Acer* in combination with a three-taxon three-area analysis would not necessarily indicate the past distributions within *Acer*.

Both Niklas and Mankiewicz imply that a critique of vicariance biogeography must be within the framework of principles and assumptions of vicariance biogeography. I strongly disagree. Perhaps the best critique will be independent of vicariance biogeography itself. That is, the purpose of vicariance biogeography is to reconstruct (or predict) how patterns of distribution came about; the data used are largely, if not entirely, based on extant taxa. I submit that the only validation of vicariance methodology must be based on paleontological data—these data are surely equally as valuable as tectonic data that relate to possible vicariant events. Only by recourse to paleontology can the past distributions predicted by vicariance biogeography be validated.

Hennig was well aware that fossils could provide an independent check on cladistic analysis. In stratigraphic (time) sequences, the appearance of certain grades later than other grades allows clear inferences as to which grades are advanced and which grades are primitive. Further, if the grades are represented by transitional morphological series, the data can be placed in a truly cladistic framework.

Not only can fossils provide an independent check on the assumptions made in a given cladistic analysis, but fossils can provide also an independent check on past distributional patterns hypothesized by vicariance biogeographers. This is what I have attempted; while the fossil record of *Acer* does support some vicariance, some long-distance dispersal also is supported. Moreover, in the instance of *Acer*, repeated dispersals and vicariant events are indicated. The concept of a fragmented biota is, I think, overly simplistic and not warranted either from the paleontological data or from considerations of the complexity of the influence of the environment on an organism or on evolving populations.

One of Croizat's major tracks is based on the floristic similarities between South America and Africa. The supposed vicariance Croizat infers is, as I have emphasized, negated by even a gross consideration of paleobotanical data. Detailed analyses of the type championed by Nelson, Rosen, and their colleagues may well yield valuable inferences on the past distributions of various groups of organisms, although even these must be judged in the light of paleontological data. Gross analyses of the type used by geofloral proponents or by Croizat, however, can only suggest possible past distributions and events, many of which may be demonstrated to be in serious error.

11

Methods of Paleobiogeography

C. Patterson

> Fossil life cannot of course genuinely contradict living life. (Croizat 1964:715)

> The fossil record, however, showed this view to be false . . . thus providing another example of how misleading it is to try to derive distributional histories from living forms alone. (Keast 1977b:261)

THE AIM of this paper is to review the role of fossils in historical biogeography. In particular, I am interested in the contrasting views of that role provided by the two epigraphs. Croizat, in developing vicariance biogeography, has always questioned the cardinal importance given to fossils in dispersal biogeography. The quotation from Keast is one of several that can be found in the writings of dispersal biogeographers (e.g., Darlington 1970a:11: "If, in the face of the fossil record, they say that this has been the [distributional] history of mammals, they invite ridicule"). If Croizat is right—if the distribution of fossils cannot contradict theories based on the distribution of living organisms—then fossils play a subsidiary role in historical biogeography. If Keast, Darlington, and others are right in holding that fossils, not living organisms, provide the key to historical biogeography, then that conclusion would be a strong criticism of vicariance biogeography as formulated by Croizat. However, it seems that both schools are right within their own frame of reference: fossils are of subsidiary importance in vicariance biogeography, but of cardinal importance in dispersal biogeography. Discussion of the reasons for this difference is one way of comparing the two approaches, and of meeting the aims of this symposium.

I tackle these questions by reviewing the role that fossils play, explicitly or implicitly, in various recent attempts to formulate a method of historical biogeography; then I apply those methods to an example—the marsupials. I find Ball's (1976) discussion to be the most useful starting point because he treats the philosophical aspects of biogeography at some length in an interesting way. But before discussing his method, and other recent proposals, I comment on the relationship between biogeography and systematics, something that Ball's essay introduces.

Analogy between Historical Biogeography and Systematics

> Zoogeography has had a fate very much like taxonomy.
> (Mayr, 1944:1)

Virtually every writer on historical biogeography remarks that biogeography is subordinate to systematics: Biogeography can be no better than the taxonomy it must use to describe distributions. Ball (1976:408) distinguishes three phases in the development of biogeography: "the descriptive or empirical phase, a narrative phase, and an analytical phase, the last two comprising historical biogeography." I suppose it is no coincidence that in the same issue of *Systematic Zoology* a book review by Rosen and Schuh treats taxonomy in terms of the last two of Ball's three phases. Rosen and Schuh (1976:505) write of "narrative evolutionary taxonomy" (cf. Bock 1978), and comment that "for Stebbins [the author under review] . . . evolutionary interpretation is a narrative rather than analytical undertaking." To Rosen and Schuh, the narrative phase of taxonomy is typified by those who believe that "fossils are the ultimate key to understanding historical relationships" (p. 506), whereas the analytical phase was initiated by Hennig's (1966) *Phylogenetic Systematics*.

In describing the narrative and analytical phases of historical biogeography, Ball does not allocate praise and blame so squarely as Rosen and Schuh, but he would, I think, agree that their assessment of the force behind analytical taxonomy, cladistics, is equally valid in biogeography. This is plain from several statements in his paper: e.g., "the phylogeneticists' insistence on working with rigidly monophyletic groups is one of their main contributions both to systematics and to biogeography" (1976:413).

If one allows that Ball's three phases (descriptive, narrative, and analytical) apply to systematics as well as to biogeography, then it is clear that in systematics, as in biogeography, only the last two phases have an historical content. Descriptive, or empirical, taxonomy includes much current work (alpha taxonomy) and the whole of taxonomy in the period before Darwin, when the role of the taxonomist was to discover, name, and define the immutable classes expressing the natural order (cf. Ghiselin 1969:81). Darwin, in advocating genealogy as the reality behind the natural order, first gave systematics an expressly historical basis. Thereafter, as Ghiselin (1969:83) puts it, "classification ceased to be merely descriptive, and became explanatory."

The narrative phase of systematics was, in my view, introduced by Haeckel (1866), and was developed over the succeeding one hundred years by innumerable specialists. The aim of those specialists was arboriculture—filling out the trunk, limbs, and twigs of the tree that Haeckel first sketched. Through this aim, systematics became preoccupied with historical narratives, with ancestors, and with fossils. As Rosen and Schuh see it (1976:505): "in this narrative approach, what matters is making a nice story, a pleasing picture, a satisfying panorama." Those are hard words, but they match my own opinion (Patterson 1977:632) on the stagnation produced by a century of "systematics of the pre-Darwinian kind with an historical explanation imposed upon it" in one major group of vertebrates.

The analytical phase of systematics began in the 1960s. It has been developed, independently to some extent, by three groups of workers: those who have adapted numerical methods to the reconstruction of phylogeny (e.g., Kluge and Farris 1969; Farris et al. 1970; Farris 1977); taxonomists who have been influenced by Hennig's *Phylogenetic Systematics*; and biochemists and others who have developed methods of reconstructing phylogeny from amino-acid sequences and other molecular data (e.g., Fitch and Margoliash 1967; Moore et al. 1973; Fitch 1977). An axiom common to these three groups is that the empirical data (the OTUs; the semaphoronts; the nucleotide sequences) are the terminal twigs of the tree; its limbs and trunk are abstract and hypothetical. This view of history as hypothesis distinguishes the analytical phase from the narrative phase. The method arrived at by these three groups is one that, in my understanding, can be summarized in six words: "interpret the distribution of homologies parsimoniously." The generality of this method is attested by its independent development by cladists, who apply it to organisms; by biochemists, who apply it to molecular sequences (which need not represent organisms; a cladogram of genes can be produced from paralogous sequences from the same organism—human globins, for example); and by linguists and stemmatists (Platnick and Cameron 1977), who apply it to artifacts. The superiority of this method over the eclectic or intuitive methods of narrative systematics lies in its simplicity, which makes its products fully accessible to criticism. In insisting on one property—*homology*, and one criterion—*parsimony*, analytical systematics seems to me to come as close to science as is likely, and these two features distinguish it from history.[1] Narrative systematics, in allowing eclectic methods, immunizes its products against criticism and has much the same status as history.

So I believe that we shall not develop an analytical historical biogeography until we can codify biogeographical method in some simple phrase like "interpret the distribution of homologies parsimoniously." In reviewing recent attempts to straighten out the methods of biogeography, I shall pursue this analogy between systematics and biogeography, looking for concepts that will replace "homology" in biogeography (can "homology" be replaced, for example, by "dispersal routes," "generalized tracks," "monophyletic groups," or "centers of endemism"?) and asking if parsimony is the overriding criterion in biogeography. In other words, I view historical biogeography as a cladist systematist. To anticipate, I find that traditional dispersal biogeography is closely related to evolutionary systematics; that Croizat's generalized tracks share many attributes with phenetic systematics; and that the cladistic vicariance method is nearest kin to phylogenetic systematics.

Ball's Method

Ball (1976), like many other recent writers on the methods of comparative biology, is a Popperian, an advocate of the hypothetico-deductive method

---

[1] I mean that unless historians can recognize some equivalent of homology, they should not claim to practice a science. Each historical discipline should seek or emphasize its own equivalent of homology. For example, in historical geology, magnetic reversals and the features of stratigraphic units deserve discussion from this point of view, as does the development of geological cladograms.

and falsifiable theories. He writes: "There are many inherent difficulties in attempting to adopt such tenets for enquiries into historical biogeography. Nonetheless, by attacking these we may achieve a truly meaningful state of the science" (p. 412). Ball's method is first to conduct a Hennigian analysis of the taxon under study. Having produced a cladogram of monophyletic groups (assumed to be true), the investigator imagines by a "creative leap" a story that will explain the geographical distribution of those groups. The initial criteria by which one judges such a hypothesis are its internal consistency and information content, or the quantity of facts it encompasses. The greater the information content of the hypothesis, the greater the number of things it forbids. The hypothesis is tested by deducing these forbidden consequences—the restrictions that the hypothesis places on nature—and then looking to see if any are violated. If so, the hypothesis is refuted, and the investigator must invent a new one and put it to the test.

Ball's example is a group of primitive freshwater planarians. His hypothesis includes a mixture of vicariance (in southern Gondwanaland) and dispersal (through the southern continents and into the northern hemisphere) and is constrained by other assumptions, such as that "the centre of dispersal, and probably of origin . . . lies . . . where the primitive forms are found, and where there is greatest taxonomic diversity" (p. 414), and that the current story of plate tectonics is correct (breakup of Gondwana, closure of Tethys, etc.). As potential falsifiers of the hypothesis, Ball cites four classes of facts: (1) "problematical taxa," known taxa that in current taxonomy seem to contradict the hypothesis (examples are found to have been wrongly described); (2) finds of taxa or given character complexes outside the predicted range (examples are interpreted as recently transported by man; p. 426); (3) "refutation of the phylogeny on which it is based" (p. 415); and (4) "perhaps the best area for refutation concerns regions across which dispersal, or vicariance, according to my hypothesis has not occurred" (p. 416). The example given is the North Atlantic. One (non-dugesiid) genus, *Planaria*, appears to necessitate a link across the North Atlantic because it occurs in Europe and in two eastern American areas. Ball predicts that the genus will turn out to be non-monophyletic, and he refers to indications (since fulfilled by Ball and Gourbault 1978) that this is so.

It is worth commenting on these four classes of facts. Classes (1) and (4) comprise known taxa that appear to contradict the hypothesis. The first thing one might say about such potential falsifiers is that either the author of the hypothesis was aware of their frailty before he framed it, or the hypothesis lacked internal consistency if it failed to account for these known distributions. Second, Ball proposes to accommodate these potential falsifiers by changing their position in the cladogram: as in class (3), the cladogram, not the geographical hypothesis, is vulnerable. Class (2) concerns taxa whose position in the cladogram is inimical to the geographical hypothesis. They are accommodated by appealing to human agency (the example given under class (4) seems amenable to the same explanation, should the monophyly of *Planaria* have been unassailable, because the American localities are in the vicinity of seaports). I do not mean to suggest that Ball uses human transportation and non-monophyly of taxa as means to immunize his theory. I want only to point out first, that the ease with which these falsifiers may be evaded is a sign of their weakness; and second, that the falsifiers are primarily at the level of the cladogram, rather than the map. Class (3), refutation of the cladogram, is therefore the primary target of these tests.

How does one refute or falsify a cladogram? Ball (1976:425) argues that it may be done in one of three ways: by new synapomorphies, by new taxa, or by re-evaluating characters previously accepted or rejected as synapomorphies. Platnick (1977) elaborates on this, pointing out that newly discovered taxa can hardly test cladograms because introducing a new taxon "is only a change in the nature of the problem (i.e., from a three-taxon to a four-taxon or larger problem)." Platnick concludes that cladograms are testable only by newly discovered synapomorphies, and that the "test" is parsimony; given conflicting sets of characters, we must conclude that "the largest set . . . reflects evolutionary history and that smaller sets . . . are not synapomorphies" (p. 439). "Testing" cladograms by this method is naturally a piecemeal procedure. Engelmann and Wiley (1977:7), for example, point out that testing complex cladograms "would require a prohibitive number of logical operations and would be impractical. . . . this difficulty can be avoided by assuming that some higher level phylogeny, preferably the most highly corroborated, is correct." Of course, whenever one of the taxa under consideration contains more than two terminal taxa, one will have to assume also that some lower level phylogeny is correct. Using these stratagems, one can test complex cladograms by treating them as a succession of three-taxon problems (what Løvtrup 1977 calls basic classifications), or four-taxon problems when a new taxon is introduced. Platnick's (1977) analysis shows that this "testing" is not testing in the Popperian sense. Rather, it is an instance of induction by complete exclusion; all possible cladograms (three in a three-taxon problem, 15 in a four-taxon problem) are known, and the preferred one is selected by eliminating all others. Hull (1973:22) points out that induction by complete exclusion is deduction in disguise.

So cladograms are not imaginative hypotheses. Rather, a cladogram is built up piecemeal by a deductive mode of choosing, among known alternatives, the pattern congruent with the largest set of characters rated as synapomorphous. Just as the cladogram is built up piecemeal, so it can be modified ("falsified") only piecemeal, because the accumulation of newly discovered or newly evaluated characters that may render a different pattern more parsimonious affects only one branching point at a time. It is true that the theory of relationships represented by a particular cladogram is more profoundly affected if branching points near the base are modified, but in Ball's cladogram (1976:figure 3), the base is a trichotomy and so is invulnerable, for as Platnick (1977) observes, a trichotomous junction says only that there is an unresolved problem. In other words, it says no more than "there are three taxa."

If we turn from the cladogram to the biogeographical hypothesis, and if there is, as I suppose, a direct analogy between systematics and biogeography, then a sound biogeographical hypothesis should result not from "a creative leap," as Ball argues, but from a deductive choice among known alternatives, and it should be tested in the same way as a cladogram in systematics. This does not correspond with Ball's account of his method, yet when he regards the geographical hypothesis as falsified (1977:32), the test is a change in the cladogram; the test affects only part of the geographical story (piecemeal testing), and it is accommodated by replacing the dispersal interpretation of that part with a vicariance interpretation.

Ball mentions one type of test that affects his geographical hypothesis rather than his cladogram—predictions concerning regions across which dispersal has not occurred (class (4) above). I suggest two others: (5) geological falsifiers; (6) finds of fossils. The example Ball gives under (4)—the North Atlantic—refers to this part of his hypothesis (pp. 414–5): "the *Dugesia gonocephala* group arose in Africa, and after closure of the Tethys Sea dispersed northwards into Palaearctis. . . . if the dugesiid planarians did not reach the northern hemisphere until after closure of the Tethys Sea then Laurasia, as a dispersal route between North America and Europe, was unavailable to them." Ball proposes that this part of the hypothesis could be falsified by finding taxonomic links across the North Atlantic. But what if the Tethyan "'Ocean' is only a geometric *artefact*," as Owen (1976:250) argues, and what if the Thulean land bridge across the North Atlantic was not interrupted until late Oligocene or early Miocene times, 20–24 Ma, as Nilsen (1978) argues? I offer these as examples of possible geological falsifiers of Ball's hypothesis. Like "falsifiers" of the cladogram, new geological evidence could contradict the hypothesis only piecemeal, and the contradiction is by no means decisive. For example, removal of Tethys from the Mesozoic map would leave Ball's story intact, for he specifies no date for the arrival of dugesiids north of Tethys except that they did not arrive there until the North Atlantic had opened. In the same way, a late Oligocene land bridge across the North Atlantic would leave Ball's story intact, for it specifies only that dugesiids arrived too late to make use of such a bridge. In other words, the predictions of the hypothesis are imprecise and compatible with widely divergent accounts of earth history.

Dugesiid flatworms have no fossil record and seem unlikely to acquire one. But it is worth considering the effect that fossils might have on Ball's hypothesis. Fossil dugesiids, once found, would be uninformative until they could be placed in the cladogram. Suppose a fossil, placed as the sister group of all Dugesiidae, were found in the Permian of Greenland. Could this falsify all or any of Ball's hypothesis? I think not, for the fossil could reasonably be interpreted as representing an extinct vicariant (Laurasian) sister group of the originally Gondwanian dugesiids. But suppose this Greenland Permian fossil were found to be a subtaxon or sister group of one of the terminal taxa (genera and subgenera) in Ball's cladogram. Such a fossil would give a minimum age for that taxon and for all the higher taxa represented by the branching points between it and the base of the clado-gram. These ages could contradict a large part of Ball's story by showing that the dating of the diversification and subsequent dispersal of the family had been underestimated. If the fossil belonged to a taxon known only from the southern hemisphere, it would greatly extend the range of that taxon (as would the discovery of a Recent Greenland species) and might call into question the Antarctic origin that Ball hypothesizes. If the fossil belonged to a northern taxon, the extension of range would be less drastic, but the dating could effectively destroy the northern dispersal part of the story.

In summary, Ball's method strikes me as still in the narrative phase. Although it differs from traditional biogeography by its reliance on cladistic analysis, its appeal to both dispersal and vicariance explanations, and its acceptance of the Popperian model of science, the predictions derived from the geographical narrative are vague, and the possibilities of falsification impinge primarily on the cladogram rather than on the geography. Fossils provide potential falsifiers of the dispersal part of the geographical narrative.

Rosen's 1976 Method

Rosen (1976a) sets out to apply Croizat's vicariance method to Caribbean biogeography. As Rosen summarizes it, the method consists of marking the distribution of disjunct components of monophyletic groups on the map, and linking the areas of each group by a line (track). When tracks linking sister taxa (Recent or fossil) repeatedly coincide, the massed lines mark a generalized track, assumed to link two or more biotas that are the vicariant fragments of a single ancestral biota. Events responsible for, or correlative with, fragmentation of the ancestral biota are then sought in historical geology.

Rosen recognizes four generalized tracks that end in the Caribbean region: a North American-Caribbean track and a South American-Caribbean track, both mainly terrestrial; and an eastern Pacific-Caribbean track and an eastern Atlantic-Caribbean track, both mainly marine. Having documented many components of these generalized tracks, Rosen points out that they may be interpreted either as the result of four separate dispersal routes into the Caribbean, or of vicariance events that subdivided ancestral marine and terrestrial biotas. The first interpretation demands that dispersal was relatively recent and remarkably well co-ordinated. The second, vicariance, interpretation demands events that isolated the eastern and western Atlantic, and the eastern Pacific from the Caribbean; and that allowed intermingling of North and South American biotas. Rosen regards the first interpretation as untestable because it appeals to co-ordinated migration or dispersal of organisms with "vastly different biological properties" (p. 445). Rosen describes two kinds of tests of the second interpretation.

The first test is to add further individual tracks to the map. Such tracks will be either congruent or incongruent with the generalized tracks previously resolved. Incongruent tracks can be interpreted in one of three ways (p. 433): as belonging to different generalized tracks, as dispersal, or as representing non-monophyletic groups. The third interpretation is independently testable, but the first two seem to me reasonable alternatives that nullify the test.

Rosen's second test is to compare the biogeographical model with the geological history of the region. Rosen pursues this in detail, adopting Malfait and Dinkelman's (1972) account of Caribbean history. He finds close agreement between that account and the biogeographical model in the following series of events: (1) development of a late Jurassic proto-Antillean archipelago linking North and South America, colonized by dispersal from both continents, and allowing limited dispersal of each continental biota to the other land mass; (2) displacement of the proto-Antilles to the east, as Pacific sea floor intruded between North and South America (the archipelago would have carried a mixed, and now isolated, North and South American biota, and the eastern Pacific marine biota would not enter the Caribbean);

(3) development of an epicontinental seaway that isolated eastern and western North America; (4) development of a new lower Central American archipelago that partially isolated the Caribbean from the eastern Pacific and was again populated by dispersal from north and south, allowing a second phase of dispersal between the North and South American biotas.

Rosen's complete theory, combining biogeography and geology, is thus a mixture of vicariance and dispersal. The concordance between biology and geology is striking and satisfying, but we should not forget that Wallace (1876), Matthew (1918), and Simpson (1950), for example, found equally satisfactory concordance between biology and a vastly different geological story. If the concordance between the tracks and Malfait and Dinkelman's geological story is a valid test of the vicariance model (and vice versa, according to Rosen 1976a:433), are there any further tests to which one can put this general explanation? I will consider two: developments in geology and fossils.

Malfait and Dinkelman's theory of Caribbean history is one among several alternatives (e.g., Owen's 1976:figure 7; and Carey's 1976:figures 99–102, 165, variants of the expanding earth model). Recent work calls into question the lynchpin of the Malfait and Dinkelman model—the idea that the floor of the southern Caribbean is part of the old Pacific floor. The magnetic lineations in the Colombian basin are aligned east-west, and age to the north (Christofferson 1976; Bowin 1976). They are thus totally inconsistent with Malfait and Dinkelman's hypothesis that this part of the Caribbean floor was originally part of the Farallon plate. And if part of the Pacific floor is not intruded here, then the whole story of eastward displacement of the proto-Antilles (with their biota) is without foundation. Recent accounts of Caribbean and eastern Pacific plate tectonics (Bowin 1976; Ladd 1976; Hey 1977; Mullins and Lynts 1977; Perfit and Heezen 1978; Lonsdale and Klitgord 1978) seem to be moving toward a story very different from that of Malfait and Dinkelman, but that story is still incoherent, especially in the lack of integration of work on opposite sides of the Isthmus of Panama. If the geological hypothesis is falsified, is Rosen's biological story affected? His tracks still stand, even if the congruent historical geology fades away. Toward the end of his paper, Rosen (p. 455) introduces a different method of testing his hypothesis, through its predictions about the relationships of taxa represented in three areas. This method is more fully exploited in Platnick and Nelson (1978) and Rosen (1978), and is discussed below. Here I will consider only one other possible test—the discovery of fossils.

Rosen (1976a:460) mentions as "an important test" of the biogeographical theory the possibility of finding fossil gars (*Lepisosteus*) between the Rio Grande and Nicaragua. The data on gars (Wiley 1976) are that *Atractosteus tropicus* (Costa Rica to southern Mexico) is the sister group of *A. spatula* (disjunct populations, a northern one in the United States and northern Mexico, and a southern one in Nicaragua and Costa Rica), *A.tristoechus* (Cuba and the Isle of Pines), and three fossil species (one from western Africa and two from North America). In proposing Mexican fossil gars as a test, Rosen adopts a different system of relationships in which the Antillean *A.tristoechus* is the sister group of vicariant populations of *A.tropicus*, but with either scheme it is hard to see how such fossils could test the biogeographical hypothesis. If Mexican fossil gars prove to be related to *A.spatula*, they would support Rosen's conjecture that the gap between the disjunct population of that species is due to extinction in the intermediate region. If the fossils prove to be related to *A.tropicus*, they might extend the range of that taxon northward, but would not affect the hypothesis. If the fossils prove to be related to *A.tristoechus*, they could refute the vicariance model for the species, but this refutation could plausibly be met (as in *Fundulus*, Rosen 1976a:458) by postulating dispersal of that species between Cuba and Mexico. In this example, the biogeographical hypothesis seems to be immune to testing by fossils.

Rosen (1976a:458) also allots a broader role to fossils in vicariance biogeography "by corroborating or refuting track boundaries based on recent organisms." But, as he says elsewhere (p. 433), "fossils . . . should occur within geographical boundaries set by the track or should form extensions of the track (i.e., should form a new track element, one end of which coincides with a terminus of a recent track)." Because "a track is no more than a line on a map connecting the disjunct populations of a species or the disjunct species of a monophyletic group," fossils found anywhere can do no more than extend a track, and I do not see how fossils could refute a generalized track.

Indeed, it is difficult to see how any new find of fossils could be incongruent with the vicariance method. Rosen emphasizes (p. 458) that one of the principal differences between dispersal and vicariance biogeography is in the age assigned to events. Dispersal biogeography sees present distributions as the result of relatively recent (especially Pleistocene) events, whereas the vicariance model implies that taxa were emplaced in remote times. Rosen stresses that fossils give only minimum ages, and because the vicariance model requires that taxa be in place before a geological event, it could hardly be disturbed by fossils of any age.

McKenna (1975a) has an interesting comment on the role of fossils in vicariance biogeography. In discussing a former Euramerican terrestrial biota, he suggests a contrast between "low resolution" data from Recent organisms and "high resolution" data from fossils. He means that the inference of a Euramerican generalized track from Recent organisms is derived from comparisons at a relatively high taxonomic rank, whereas Eocene fossil mammals give much more precise indications of continuity or discontinuity in the form of ties at low taxonomic rank. McKenna documents this argument by tabulating European mammalian genera of the Sparnacian (54–51 Ma) and Lutetian (49–45 Ma). His table shows that the Eurasian or Euramerican-Asian element is small (less than 5 percent) in both periods; the Euramerican element is about 55 percent in the early Eocene and only 14 percent in the Middle Eocene; and the European endemic element rises from about 30 percent in the early Eocene to 80 percent in the Middle Eocene. These are impressive figures, and perhaps they are unlikely to be much altered by subsequent finds or taxonomic revisions. McKenna concludes, in agreement with geological evidence on the opening of the North Atlantic, that the Euramerican biota was sundered about 49 Ma, and that the generalized track linking Europe and North America crosses the North Atlantic, not (as has sometimes been proposed) Asia and the Bering Strait. McKenna uses a refined version of a traditional paleontological method: estimation of provinciality from statistical comparison of fossil biotas. This method has a huge literature (e.g., Middlemiss et al. 1971; Hallam 1973a)—Ager (1973:18) calls it "mountains of paper"—and its results have traditionally been interpreted as dispersal (Hallam 1977b; Galton 1977; Wood 1977, to cite three recent examples). In adapting this method to the vicariance framework, McKenna seems to imply that the arrows on the Jurassic maps of Hallam (1977b:figures 1–3) and Galton (1977:figure 1), for example, need not imply migration routes or avenues of dispersal, but may be treated as tracks implying nothing more than an estimate of biotic similarity over some period of geological time.

Those comments recall Ball's (1976:421) criticism of vicariance biogeography. He writes: "questions may then be raised as to what do generalized tracks mean? How can they be explained? As statistical measures of overall similarity of disjunct biotas they mean about the same as measures of overall similarity in systematics." Although Rosen (1976a) insists that the groups whose distributions make up a generalized track must be monophyletic, this requirement seems equivalent to pheneticists' insistence that the attributes they select must be homologous (e.g., Jardine and Sibson 1971:169). I therefore believe that Ball's comment is a just assessment of the meaning of generalized tracks, one that Rosen (1978:167) would now accept (also Platnick and Nelson 1978; Nelson and Platnick 1979). The similarity between generalized tracks (and much else in biogeography) and phenetics is emphasized by this statement: "One of the kinds of zoogeographic questions in which taxonomic evidence is used is whether faunas A and B are more closely related to each other (i.e., *have more taxa in common*) than either is to fauna C" (Vuilleumier 1975:438; emphasis added). Here the equivalence of zoogeographical and phenetic relationship is made plain. Viewed in this way, much paleobiogeographical work may be adapted to the vicariance paradigm. For example, Fallaw's (1977; see also Flessa et al. 1978) assessment of trans-Atlantic commonality through time, by means of Simpson coefficients for the fossils of each epoch, can be seen as an assessment of variations in the strength of a North Atlantic track through time.

To sum up, Rosen's 1976 paper has great interest as a precise exposition of Croizat's vicariance method. Although Rosen added cladistic systematics to the method, its central concept—the generalized track—remains a phenetic concept. As such, I do not believe it can lift biogeography out of the narrative phase or meet the need for correspondence between systematics and biogeography. The importance Rosen gives to historical geology as a test of the biogeographical hypothesis seems also misplaced. In my view, subsequent developments in Caribbean geology are at odds with Rosen's story, but this in no way falsifies his empirical biological evidence, which still demands explanation. Finally, I note that vicariance biogeography seems immune to test by fossils, and that much current paleobiogeography is readily adapted to the vicariance framework.

Keast's method

Keast (1977b) reviews the "basic premises, concepts, methodology, and . . . major contributions" of biogeography. Simpson (1978a:219) cites the paper as "incomparably the best modern summary of the whole subject." Keast's paper is long, and I will concentrate on the parts of it dealing with fossils. Keast gives a good deal of attention to vertebrate paleontology, and this part of his work appeals to me as a reasoned response by a member of the Matthew-Simpson-Darlington tradition to the criticisms voiced by followers of Hennig and Croizat.

As a general summary of method, Keast writes (1977b:286):

It is not justifiable to try to come up with all-embracing generalizations. Rather analysis must proceed at the familial and generic level giving equal weight to original historical patterns, dispersal, distributional changes associated with climatic change, evolutionary changes in situ, and interrelationships with the associated biota.

The method Keast advocates is therefore eclectic within the dispersal framework. On fossils in particular, Keast reiterates his opinion that contemporary distributions may be misleading "in determining origins" (p. 270), "distributional histories" (p. 261), and "past distribution patterns" (p. 301). Therefore, in Keast's view, "vertebrate paleontology will remain the final arbiter in many matters of past history" (p. 258). Keast cites several examples to illustrate his opinion that inferences from Recent distributions may be contradicted by the fossil record. That idea is the theme of this paper, so it is necessary to discuss each of his examples.

(1) *Lungfishes.* Keast (1977b:figure 5) maps the distribution of Recent and fossil ceratodontids and of Devonian lungfishes to show that the present distribution of the group (*Neoceratodus*, Queensland; *Lepidosiren*, Amazon basin; *Protopterus*, tropical Africa) is misleading because it leads one to assume that the group is Gondwanian. To me, this example shows one weakness of Keast's eclectic method. By avoiding a commitment to any one point of view, Keast neglects the fact that there can be only one historical relationship between the spots on his maps, and the fact that a cladogram is the only device that can precisely express a theory of those historical relationships. Miles (1977:figure 157) provides a cladogram of living and fossil lungfishes. This shows Recent lungfishes (*Neoceratodus* and lepidosirenids) as a monophyletic group, and ceratodontids (*Neoceratodus†, Microceratodus†, Paraceratodus†, Ceratodus*) as paraphyletic. The fossil record of *Neoceratodus* and *Protopterus* extends the range of each within Australia and Africa, but not beyond either continent. Inferences about the history of Recent lungfishes are therefore unaffected by the fossil record, and Keast's first example shows only that it is misleading to discuss the distribution of groups without distinguishing monophyletic groups from para- and polyphyletic ones, that is, without a prior phylogenetic analysis.

(2) *Osteoglossomorph fishes.* Keast (1977b:258) writes: "osteoglossomorphs now exclusively southern were formerly widespread in the Northern Hemisphere." I assume that he means osteoglossoids (osteoglossiforms *sensu* Taverne 1977:5) rather than osteoglossomorphs because the hiodontids are now northern (as are all fossil hiodontoids). Osteoglossoids occur today in Africa (*Heterotis, Pantodon*), South America (*Osteoglossum, Arapaima*), Australia, New Guinea, and southeastern Asia (*Scleropages*). Fossil osteoglossoids extend the range of the group into the northern hemisphere (*Brychaetus*, marine Eocene, Europe; *Phareodus*, Eocene, western North America; *Platinx, Opsithrissops*, marine Paleocene-Eocene, Europe and western Asia; Taverne 1977, 1978; Patterson 1975).

The interrelationships of osteoglossoids are still questionable (Nelson 1973a; Patterson 1975; Taverne 1977). According to Taverne the better-known fossils (*Phareodus, Phareoides, Brychaetus, Musperia*) form a monophyletic group Phareodontinae, which is the sister group of the Osteoglossinae (*Osteoglossum, Scleropages*). If the fossils form a monophyletic group, their widespread distribution is most parsimoniously explained by a marine invasion involving this group alone (Nelson 1973a:9). The inference of connections among Africa, South America, Australasia, and Asia that might be drawn from Recent osteoglossoids is not yet affected by the fossil record. Keast's second example thus fails to show paleontology contradicting Recent distributions, but shows again that phylogenetic analysis should precede biogeographical inference.

(3) *Camels and peccaries.* These two groups will be discussed together because Keast adapts them from Matthew (1915), and their histories are based on similar arguments. Keast (1977b:258) writes that "camels (now confined to Asia and South America) appear first in the North American fossil record and peccaries (now almost completely Neotropical) formerly occurred in Africa and Europe." With these examples we reach the stronghold of traditional biogeography—the mammalian fossil record. Keast selects camels and peccaries from several other groups mentioned in his paper (1977b:figure 2) and analyzed in the same way by Matthew (1915; Wood's 1977 account of rodents is another recent example). The primary assumption behind these mammalian narratives is that the fossil record is complete, so that stratigraphic succession is a reliable guide, and the trunk of the phylogenetic tree is readily apparent in the record and may be placed on the map (cf. Hershkovitz 1972:314, on Matthew's "rule of thumb," that "the age and site of the oldest known representative of a taxon must be taken as the time and place of origin of that taxon"). The lungfish and osteoglossoid

examples discussed above show that phylogenetic analysis is an essential prerequisite for biogeographical inference. So far as I know, no phylogenetic analysis of camels or peccaries has been published, so that for me these examples are immune to criticism. Among the other groups of mammals that Keast cites—giraffes, bears, tapirs, pigs—only one, the giraffes, has been subjected to phylogenetic analysis (Hamilton 1978). I will discuss that group.

Concerning giraffes, Matthew (1939:81) wrote: "their dispersal center would appear to have been in south central Asia," and "They appear suddenly in the Upper Miocene of Europe, but an ancestral series is found in India as far back as the Upper Oligocene." Keast (1977b:255) redraws Matthew's map and adds: "Fossil giraffes, however, are now known from throughout Africa." Heintz (1975) draws a new map with palaeotragids radiating from a Libyan center. Those views may be contrasted with figure 11.1, a simplified version of Hamilton's (1978) cladogram.

Figure 11.1 makes one point obvious, that in discussing the origin and dispersal of a group with fossil representatives it may be necessary to distinguish two different groups and two different origins. The first group comprises all the descendants, living and extinct, of the latest common ancestor of living members of the group. The second comprises those fossil forms more closely related to the first than to any other. Hennig (1969) calls the first the "*group" and the second the "stem-group"; Jefferies (1979) calls them the "crown-group" and stem-group. These two groups are often not clearly distinguished until a cladistic analysis has been done.

Given the cladogram in figure 11.1, how could one decide on a center of origin, and hence on directions of dispersal, for crown- and stem-group giraffes? Two rules have been offered. The first is Matthew's rule of thumb that the site of the oldest fossils is the center of origin. The second is Hennigian analysis: "ancestral distribution is most parsimoniously estimated by . . . eliminating the unshared element when the descendant distributions are not completely different" (Nelson 1973b:314). For crown-group giraffoids, the first method gives India (*Giraffokeryx punjabensis*) and Mongolia ("*Palaeotragus*" *tungurensis*); the second gives western Africa. For giraffoids as a whole, the first method gives eastern and northern Africa, the second gives eastern Africa. Notice that the Hennigian approach for crown-group giraffoids, and both methods for giraffoids as a whole, suggest African origins—the same conclusion that would be drawn if we had no fossils and only the okapi and giraffe.

Matthew's "ancestral series" of giraffes in India includes various primitive pecorans and *Progiraffa*. Hamilton (1978) leaves *Progiraffa incertae sedis*

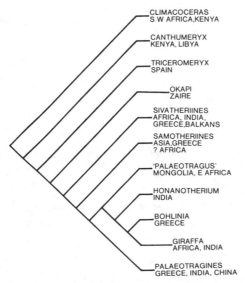

Figure 11.1. Cladogram of giraffoids. Extant
genera extend further to the right. The earliest
fossils are *Canthumeryx* (L. Miocene, ca 18 Myr),
followed by *Climacoceras*, *Triceromeryx*,
sivatheriines, and *"Palaeotragus"* (M. Miocene,
ca 14 Myr). Simplified from Hamilton (1978).

in the giraffoids, but new material suggests that *Canthumeryx* may be a
synonym of *Progiraffa* (Hamilton personal communication), which would give
Africa and India as the area of origin on an oldest fossil basis.

How might one reconcile these various hypotheses? There seem to be
only two reasonable ways: if all four answers were the same, one would
select that area as the area of origin. If the answers were not the same, as in
giraffes, one would combine the different areas, introducing a trend toward
cosmopolitan theories of origin. Such a trend is evident as the number of
fossil mammals grows. For example, Hershkovitz (1972:314) writes of South
American Tertiary mammal groups: "The uncertainties regarding their respective origins seem to increase rather than decrease with each new discovery."
This comment seems justified when one reads Simpson's latest opinions
(1978b) on these South American groups: "we simply do not know where
marsupials evolved" (p. 323) and "I must somewhat sadly say that the origin
of the Xenarthra, either phylogenetic or geographic, is unknown" (p. 324);
and on condylarths (and hence of South American ungulates): "The order
might have arisen in any continent except Antarctica plus Australia" (p. 327).
These statements may be compared with earlier opinions of Simpson and

others (summarized in Simpson 1978b), placing the origin of each of these groups, with more or less confidence, in one or another area. In these groups, as in the giraffe example, the trend of opinion modified with successive paleontological discoveries is toward uncertainty about centers of origin, which may be regarded as a trend toward an estimate of primitive cosmo-politanism.

How this trend will be influenced by future finds of fossils I cannot guess, for no one knows what may be found. Westoll (1958:82), discussing the ade-quacy of the vertebrate fossil record, proposes "a law of diminishing returns in exploration" as a guide. He means that at a certain stage "any new material tends more and more to confirm what has already been known or suspected." His discussion is concerned with Paleozoic fishes and tetrapods and with ecology and phylogeny rather than zoogeography. But several of Westoll's points have been vitiated by subsequent finds (for example, of marine Lower Paleozoic vertebrates, and of marine Upper Devonian *Bothriolepis* and lung-fishes), showing that in the Paleozoic the law of diminishing returns is not yet operating. But perhaps the law already applies in the zoogeography of Neogene mammals. Taking the elephants, probably the best-known group, as an example, Maglio's (1973:figure 15) phylogeny includes newly discovered fossil species as the ancestors of *Loxodonta*, *Elephas*, and the elephantines as a whole, amending previous phylogenies in a way that could hardly be more comprehensive. Maglio's monograph, like almost every fossil-based revision of a group, begins by mentioning the important new finds that necessitate the review. These new finds show the previous story of the individual group to be wrong, but more importantly they show the general assumption on which it was based—that the fossil record is complete—to be wrong.

In short, the fossil record continues to produce surprises, and there are no signs that a law of diminishing returns is operating. So we must expect further surprises. Thus Matthew's (1915) decision that elephants originated in Asia was a misleading deduction from the fossil record, as shown by Osborn (1942). In turn, Osborn's decision that elephants originated in South Africa was a misleading deduction from the fossil record, as shown by Maglio (1973). Whether, or when, Maglio's East African origin will fall, only time can tell. But in general, Keast's assertion that Recent distributions may be mislead-ing is a charge that can be laid equally well against the fossil record. The dif-ference is that Recent distributions may be regarded as completely known in many groups, whereas fossil distributions, even in those groups with the best fossil record, are an unknown proportion of an unknown quantity.

It is true, of course, that the fossil record may greatly extend the geographical range of a group, show that that range has been drastically altered by extinction, and give precious information on age. But Keast's opinion that Recent distributions are therefore misleading is an example of the constraints that paleontology has put on biogeography. It may be that current stories of the history of elephants and horses will stand the test of time (on crown-group horses, see Eisenmann 1979). But the idea that those mammalian groups are the paradigm by which we should interpret all others has not been helpful. It has led to the belief that in biogeography (as in systematics) fossils hold the key to understanding. So, in group after group, workers bemoan the lack of fossils or discuss existing fossils to the exclusion of all else. Recent distributions cannot mislead, for they provide the only unequivocal data of biogeography. Fossils complement those data by documenting extinctions and age of occupation of areas, but the information they provide is spotty and is further limited by problems of phylogenetic analysis of the parts preserved. Reliance on paleontology as "the final arbiter" (Keast's phrase) in biogeography has not given us access to the truth.

Method of Platnick and Nelson (1978) and Rosen (1978)

Platnick and Nelson (1978) propose a method of historical biogeography that Rosen (1978) puts into practice. The method combines Hennigian systematics with Croizat's vicariance approach and exploits the analogy between systematics and biogeography to the full. In brief, the method applies cladistics to biogeography by making cladograms of areas, which are tested by cladograms of individual taxa occupying those areas. Areas A and B are considered more closely related to each other than to area C not because they "have more taxa in common" (Vuilleumier 1975:438), but because their biotas share a more recent common ancestry.

In setting out the method, Platnick and Nelson begin by asking how we might discriminate between the two possible answers to the question: "why does this taxon occupy this area"? Either it evolved there, or it evolved elsewhere and dispersed into the area. The difference between the two interpretations (vicariance and dispersal) lies in the relationship between the age of the taxon and the age of the barriers limiting the area. Vicariance predicts that the taxon and the barriers have the same age; dispersal predicts that the barrier predates the taxon. Platnick and Nelson discuss the possibility of discriminating between the two by tests involving fossils and geological dating of barriers. The dispersal interpretation is tested only by fossils of that taxon, whereas the vicariance interpretation can be tested by other taxa, fossil or living, that should have been affected by the same barriers and that therefore should show relationships congruent with those of the taxon under study. In other words, dispersal treats each taxon as an individual case, whereas vicariance is a general explanation (Croizat's dictum that earth and life have evolved together), which may be presented as a cladogram of areas, and tested by cladograms of taxa.

Congruent taxon cladograms corroborate the vicariance explanation, but incongruent taxon cladograms need not falsify that explanation, for they may indicate dispersal of the incongruent taxa, or a different (older or younger) vicariance pattern. In the analogy with systematics, a cladogram of areas is a hypothesis of relationship between biotas; it corresponds to a hypothesis of relationship among taxa in systematics. Congruent cladograms of individual taxa occupying those areas correspond to synapomorphies, congruent character distributions in systematics. In systematics, incongruent character distributions may be rated as convergence, or may accumulate until they outnumber the original synapomorphies and "falsify" the original hypothesis of relationship. In Platnick and Nelson's biogeographical method, incongruent taxon cladograms might accumulate until they are numerous enough to corroborate a different area cladogram (if they are congruent among themselves) or to falsify the vicariance explanation (if they are randomly incongruent).

In Platnick and Nelson's method, the only useful taxa are those with endemic representatives in each of three or more areas and whose relationships are established, just as in systematics the only useful characters are those represented in three or more taxa and showing at least two states, one of which can be rated as derived. Rosen (1978) applies a method similar to that of Platnick and Nelson to the historical biogeography of Central America. Recognizing three areas of endemism (eastern North America above the Rio Grande; the Rio Panuco basin in Mexico; and southeastern Mexico and Central America), Rosen finds several taxa that relate the second and third more closely to each other than to the first. He then reviews the geological history of those areas, seeking events that could correlate with their sequential isolation. Finding several plausible geological events that isolate a few relatively stable areas, Rosen discusses how one might choose among plausible events of different ages, and concludes that fossils would be the most useful test.

Passing to the more general question of method in historical biogeography, Rosen shows that extended cladograms of two Middle

American groups of poeciliid fishes are largely congruent. Converting each taxon cladogram into a cladogram of areas and combining the two by deleting incongruent areas and those unique to just one, he produces a general cladogram of five areas. The probability that two groups will agree in a five-area cladogram is 1 in 105 (the number of possible dichotomous cladograms with five tips). If a third five-taxon, five-area cladogram were congruent, the probability falls to 1 in 11,025 (105^2); for three three-taxon, three-area cladograms the probability of congruence is 1 in 9; for four of these it is 1 in 27; and so on. If such cases are found, then the nonrandom distribution demands a nonrandom explanation—vicariance rather than dispersal. The explanation for the vicariance patterns can be sought in earth history. Rosen points out that geological data can also be arranged cladistically, giving the sequence of the breakup of Pangea as an example.

The method developed by Platnick, Nelson, and Rosen seems to meet the need, mentioned in the first section of this paper, for a biogeographical method that can be codified in a simple phrase like "interpret the distribution of homologies parsimoniously." In their method, "homologies" of systematics (synapomorphies) can be replaced by "sister groups," so that the biogeographical method is "interpret the geographical distribution of sister-groups parsimoniously." The parsimony criterion still applies (Rosen, 1978:186): if the sister-group relationships of several taxa agree with their distribution, parsimony demands a general explanation for the congruence. If the sister-group relationships are randomly incongruent, parsimony demands that the taxa have dispersed. And if the sister-group relationships present two (or more) patterns of congruence, parsimony demands that they represent two (or more) vicariant patterns of different ages, a possibility that is open to independent test (Platnick and Nelson 1978:15).

As for the role of fossils in this method, it can be summed up by: "we view the role of paleontology in historical biogeography as the same as its role in phylogenetic systematics, i.e., as an additional source of information for historical analysis" (Croizat et al. 1974:280). This additional information may extend the range of a taxon, showing that it formerly occupied an area where it is now extinct, or it may give a minimum age for a taxon. The age of fossils may be crucial in choosing between possible geological causes of a disjunction.

The Platnick, Nelson, and Rosen method has hardly yet been tried. In the remainder of this paper I attempt to evaluate it, against its competitors and consequences, by applying it to one of the classic groups of dispersal biogeography—the marsupial mammals.

Marsupials

I have selected the marsupials as a trial group for five reasons. First, they have always attracted the attention of biogeographers, and particularly since the rise of plate tectonics, discussions of marsupial history have been pouring out (a selective list confined to the last five years includes: Clemens 1977; Crochet 1978, 1979; Hoffstetter 1975; Keast 1977a; Kirsch 1977, 1979; Lavocat 1977; Martin 1975, 1977; Papavero 1977; Simpson 1978b). Second, the marsupials are suited to a discussion of the role of fossils in historical biogeography because they are mammals, the group that has always occupied the center of the stage in the subject. Third, all writers on marsupial biogeography have devoted most of their attention to the fossil record, and that record is considered tolerably good. Fourth, there is sufficient contrast between vicariance and different dispersal interpretations of marsupial history, and between Recent and fossil-based interpretations, for the group to illustrate these different approaches. And fifth, the interrelationships of marsupials are to some extent established, and their immediate sister-group relationships are established almost beyond doubt (Marshall 1979).

Living marsupials are concentrated in Australia, New Guinea and adjacent islands (Simpson 1965:figure 35), and in South and Central America. One species, *Didelphis virginiana*, ranges from Central America to southern Canada. This North American marsupial is the sister species of the Central and South American *D. marsupialis*, and these two are the sister group of *D. albiventris*, in temperate South America (Gardner 1973).

Fossil marsupials are reviewed by Tedford (1974) and Clemens (1977). They occur in Australia (Oligocene onward), New Guinea (Pliocene onward), South America (late Cretaceous onward), North America (late Cretaceous to Miocene, and Pleistocene to Recent), and Europe (early Eocene to Miocene). The Cretaceous Deltatheridiidae from Asia and, perhaps, North America (Kielan-Jaworowska 1975) may (Hoffstetter 1975) or may not (McKenna 1975b) be marsupials. The decision rests, at present, on dental formulae and disputed interpretations of the tooth replacement pattern in deltatheridiids and other primitive mammals (Archer 1978; Marshall 1979).

Interrelationships
Two phylogenies of marsupials have recently been published by Keast (1977a:figure 5.6, adapted from Tedford 1974) and by Kirsch (1977:figure 24). The two phylogenies have 23 terminal taxa in common (Kirsch's

includes five families absent in Keast's), of which 13 are living and ten are fossil. For the living groups, Kirsch's phylogeny is based primarily on his serological studies of 12 of the 13 Recent families (*Thylacinus* was not studied). His phylogeny is fully compatible with his phenogram (1977:figure 23) of serological evidence on those groups. Keast's phylogeny of the living groups differs in detail from Kirsch's; in figure 11.2*A* I have combined them into a cladogram by the method described by Nelson (1979). Lest that procedure be thought misleading, figure 11.2*B* shows the cladogram derived from Kirsch's phylogeny of Recent groups. Transforming the two phylogenies into a cladogram brings out the fact that both Keast and Kirsch treat the didelphids as an ancestral (paraphyletic) group. This means that didelphids have to be treated as equally closely related to more than one group, so that there is a basal polychotomy in the cladogram.

Among the living groups, the major inconsistency between Keast's and Kirsch's phylogenies is the position of the Australian *Thylacinus*. Keast maintains the consensus in relating *Thylacinus* to dasyurids, whereas Kirsch follows Archer (1976) and places *Thylacinus* as the sister group of the extinct South American borhyaenoids. If Archer is right, his views have important biogeographical consequences because Australian marsupials would not be monophyletic, and the marsupial cladogram would show a double link between Australia and South America. Marshall (1977) reviews the problem of borhyaenoid-thylacinid affinities, and finds it more probable that thylacinids are related to dasyurids, and borhyaenoids to didelphoids, although his arguments are far from conclusive. Here (figure 11.2*C*) I follow Marshall and assume that Australian marsupials are monophyletic. The sister group of Recent Australian marsupials is not yet resolved. Kirsch finds that the South American caenolestoids are serologically as distinct from didelphoids as they are from Australian marsupials, in agreement with earlier opinions based on anatomy. This implies that there are two monophyletic groups of Recent American marsupials—the didelphoids and the caenolestoids, either or both of which could be the sister group of the Australian assemblage (figure 11.3).

Fossil marsupials complicate the picture enormously (figure 11.2*C*). The three extinct Australian families Wynyardiidae, Thylacoleonidae, and Diprotodontidae fit into the Australian assemblage with little difficulty. There are six extinct American groups, Pediomyidae (Cretaceous, North and, perhaps, South America; Fox 1979b), Stagodontidae (Cretaceous, NA), Borhyaenoidea (Paleocene-Pliocene, SA), Groeberiidae (Oligocene, SA), Argyrolagidae (late Cenozoic, SA), and Polydolopidae (Paleocene-Eocene,

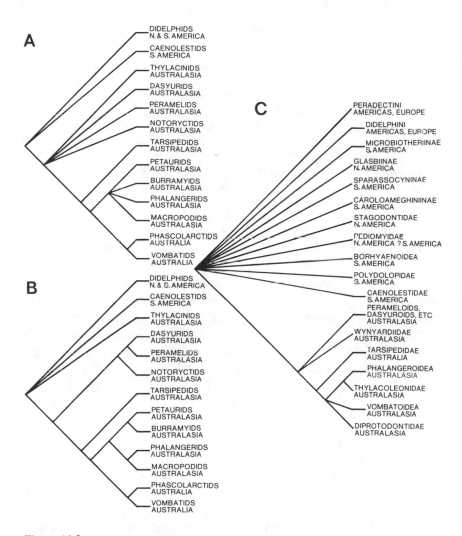

Figure 11.2. Cladograms of marsupials: A, Recent groups, derived by cladistic analysis (Nelson 1979) of the phylogenies of Keast (1977a) and Kirsch (1977), but following Keast on the position of thylacinids; B, Recent groups, derived from the phylogeny of Kirsch (1977); C, Recent groups simplified from A, fossil groups added. Extant groups extend further to the right.

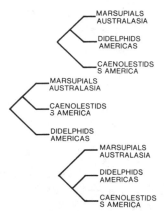

Figure 11.3. Alternative cladograms of Recent marsupial groups.

SA), and many extinct didelphids, assigned to five subfamilies. Of these, two are extinct South American (Caroloameghiniinae, Eocene; Sparassocyninae, Miocene-Pliocene), one is extinct North American (Glasbiinae, Cretaceous), and two are extant—one is South American (Microbiotheriinae, Eocene-Recent), and one, Didelphinae, is represented by fossils from North and South America (Cretaceous onward) and Europe (Eocene-Miocene). The Polydolopidae are placed as caenolestoids by Keast and Kirsch, but Clemens and Marshall (1976) write that there is no convincing evidence that they are closer to caenolestoids than to didelphoids. I follow Clemens and Marshall in figure 11.2*C.* The Groeberiidae and Argyrolagidae are of unknown relationships according to both Keast and Kirsch; they may not be marsupials (McKenna personal communication) and are omitted in figure 11.2. Marshall (1977:421) finds no synapomorphies between borhyaenoids and didelphoids, implying that borhyaenoids, too, are a distinct group; this is the position of both the stagodontids and pediomyids in Keast's and Kirsch's phylogenies.

Crochet (1978, 1979) reviews fossil didelphines (also Fox 1979a). Cretaceous didelphines such as *Alphadon* have traditionally been treated as ancestral marsupials, but Crochet places *Alphadon* (NA), *Albertatherium* (late Cretaceous, NA), and *Peradectes* (late Cretaceous-Paleocene, SA; Paleocene-Oligocene, NA; Eocene, Europe) in a tribe Peradectini, which he seems to regard as monophyletic. He puts the remaining North American and European didelphines in a tribe Didelphini. They comprise three genera: *Herpetotherium* (Eocene-Miocene, NA), *Peratherium* (Eocene-Oligocene, Europe), and *Amphiperatherium* (Eocene-Miocene, Europe), which Crochet regards as a monophyletic group related to a South American didelphine stock. Thus Crochet's work suggests that extra-South American didelphines have three links with South America, one Mesozoic link in Peradectini and two in Didelphini, one pre-Eocene link, and one (*D. virginiana*) more recent link.

In summary, the best available cladogram of Recent marsupials includes a basal trichotomy. Australian marsupials seem to be monophyletic, but American ones may not be so. Adding fossils to the cladogram produces a basal polychotomy, strengthens the North American representation, and introduces a new area, Europe, where two groups of didelphines occur.

Relationships

The relationships of marsupials as a whole are well established (Marshall 1979). The placentals are the sister group of the marsupials, and the monotremes are the sister group of marsupials and placentals (therians). Placentals are now found on all continents except Antarctica, but I accept that they have dispersed into Australasia fairly recently because only bats and murid rodents occur there. In South America, placentals and marsupials are coeval, so far as the Recent fauna and fossil record tell.

Monotremes are found only in Australia and New Guinea. It is generally argued that the fossil groups Multituberculata (late Jurassic to Eocene), Triconodonta (late Triassic to Jurassic), and Docodonta (late Jurassic) are related to monotremes, members of a monophyletic Prototheria (Kermack 1967; Hopson and Crompton 1969; Kermack and Kielan-Jaworowska 1971; Crompton and Jenkins 1973; McKenna 1975b; Marshall 1979). These fossil taxa would greatly extend the range of the Prototheria. Multituberculates occur in Asia, Europe, and North America; triconodonts occur in Asia, Africa, and Europe; and docodonts occur in Europe and North America. The grounds for associating the three fossil groups with the monotremes concern the side wall of the braincase, which is said to be formed by the anterior lamina of the petrosal in prototherians, and by the alisphenoid in therians. The prototherian anterior lamina of the petrosal is treated as a specialization, or synapomorphy, by all the authors cited. Rating this character as synapomorphous, however, has a remarkable consequence: the mammalian middle ear, with the included ear ossicles, evolved twice. This conclusion follows because a middle ear of this type is present in monotremes and therians, but in triconodonts, docodonts, and the Triassic *Kuehneotherium* (considered a therian), the reptilian jaw articulation, involving the middle ear bones, is still functional. This conclusion, that the middle ear of living mammals is a parallelism rather than a synapomorphy, is acceptable to the authors cited above, and to Kermack et al. (1973), and Parrington (1974), and is even considered beyond argument by Kermack (1975). The fact that there is no difference between the ear ossicles of monotremes and therians (e.g., Allin 1975:figure 4) is considered by Hopson (1969:215) as an indication of the efficiency of natural selection in producing "remarkably similar solutions to similar functional problems in long-separated lineages." There is, however, another way of looking at the similarities between monotremes and therians in the complexities of the middle ear; that they are synapomorphous. This approach requires an alternative explanation of the similarities in the side wall of the braincase of monotremes, triconodonts, and multituberculates; that they are not synapomorphous but either primitive or convergent.

The morphologists Presley and Steel (1976) review the homology of the mammalian alisphenoid. They conclude that the bone has two components, a ventral cartilage-bone (homologous with the quadrate ramus of the therapsid epipterygoid) and a dorsal membrane-bone, the lamina obturans (homologous with the anterior lamina of the petrosal of cynodonts and monotremes). In their opinion (Presley and Steel 1976:455, 457), fusion of the lamina obturans with the petrosal, as in monotremes, triconodonts, and multituberculates, is a primitive condition (also Kemp 1979:111, on cynodonts). Kuhn (1971), whose work on the development of *Tachyglossus* is not cited by Presley and Steel, reaches similar conclusions. He holds that only the basal part of the mammalian alisphenoid is homologous with the epipterygoid, and in *Tachyglossus* he found the lamina obturans to be an independent bone (cf. MacIntyre 1967). If the lamina obturans fuses with the petrosal in ontogeny, one gets the condition in *Ornithorhynchus*; if it fuses with the alisphenoid, one gets the therian condition. The ontogeny of the petrosal in triconodonts and multituberculates is, of course, unknown, but it seems more reasonable to regard the similarity with *Ornithorhynchus* (not *Tachyglossus*) as primitive, and the middle ear of monotremes and therians as synapomorphous. Evidence that multituberculates were viviparous (Kielan-Jaworowska 1979) is congruent with that interpretation because it allows multituberculates to be regarded as primitive therians (because of vivipary), so that it is not necessary to follow Kielan-Jaworowska's view that vivipary is yet another example of parallel evolution. I therefore regard the triconodonts and docodonts as stem-group mammals, not assignable to any Recent subgroup; the multituberculates as possible therians; and the monotremes as without

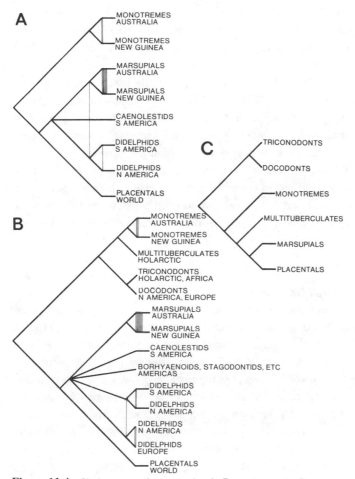

Figure 11.4. Cladograms of mammals: A, Recent groups; B,
Recent and fossil groups (Recent groups extend further to the
right; the vertical lines estimate the number of taxonomic links
between areas); C, an alternative cladogram of Recent and fossil
groups, with triconodonts and docodonts placed as stem-group
mammals, and multituberculates placed as stem-group therians.

known relatives outside Australasia. In short, I question the monophyly of the
Prototheria.[2]

    [2] I have now seen Griffiths' (1978) important account of the monotremes. He gives a very full
account of the development of the side wall of the braincase in *Tachyglossus* and writes (p. 313):
"There is no such thing . . . as a monotreme condition of the side wall of the braincase." Although
he is "an overt incorrigible typologist" (p. 331), Griffiths objects to the Prototheria in the sense of
the paleontologists cited above. Griffiths also has interesting comments on the supposed relationship between monotremes and multituberculates. (added in proof)

Figure 11.4 shows three alternative cladograms of monotremes, marsupials, and placentals, simplified to emphasize the relationships between the areas occupied by marsupials, and the effect of the fossil record. Recent animals (figure 11.4A) show a double link between Australia and New Guinea in monotremes, and a multiple link in marsupials. Between Australasia and South America, and between South and North America, there is a single link in Recent marsupials. Addition of fossils (figure 11.4B) adds extra Australia/New Guinea links in monotremes and marsupials; and two extra North/South America links, and two North America/Europe links in marsupials. In addition, the conventional view of prototherians (figure 11.4B) adds an Australia/world link in prototherians. The cladograms in figures 11.2 and 11.4 will be discussed from three methodological viewpoints: traditional, fossil-based dispersal biogeography; Hennigian dispersal biogeography; and cladistic vicariance.

Traditional Dispersal Interpretation

The numerous recent discussions of marsupial biogeography are almost all conducted within the traditional dispersal framework. Keast's (1977a) analysis is one of the most thorough. He evaluates seven different hypotheses of marsupial origin and dispersal, reviews the fossil record and the ecology and dispersal abilities of marsupials, and gives a detailed account of austral plate tectonics and past climates. The monotremes are not discussed, in accord with the dispersal paradigm that each taxon has its own history. But many other taxa with Australian/South American distributions are mentioned as being consistent with the marsupial story that Keast prefers. This story is that marsupials originated in North and/or South America about 100 Ma, and dispersed to Australia through a cool-temperate Antarctic bottleneck, probably in the early Tertiary. Keast does not discuss relationships within marsupials in detail, but he considers that South American marsupials are monophyletic (pp. 72, 84; "a basic dichotomy and independent radiation"), and his phylogeny (figure 5.6) shows North and South American marsupials as independent, monophyletic groups, except for the possibility that South American didelphids are of North American origin.

Martin (1977), in the same volume as Keast's contribution, reviews much of the same evidence and concludes that "the safest hypothesis" is one of western North American origins, dispersal to eastern North America and South America in the late Cretaceous, and island-hopping dispersal across Antarctica to Australia in the early Tertiary—a story very similar to

Keast's. Kirsch (1979) gives more attention to Recent marsupials, and argues for an Australian origin and dispersal through Antarctica and the Americas in the Cretaceous. Simpson (1978b) settles for a less restrictive hypothesis: the origin and early dispersal of marsupials involved four continents—Antarctica, Australia, and South and North America—and it is not possible to settle on one area of origin, or on the direction of dispersal. Simpson comments that his is a poor hypothesis from the Popperian standpoint because "it is not falsifiable by any evidence now in hand or known to be obtainable." The sort of evidence that is desirable, he says, is an adequate Cretaceous or Paleocene mammal fauna from Antarctica. But a paradoxical consequence of the Popperian approach to dispersal biogeography is that falsifiers would surely have to be sought in a continent not involved in the hypothesis, such as Africa or Asia.

If falsifiable hypotheses are in order, then according to Popper we should ask for bold, restrictive ones, and so prefer the two continents of Keast's hypothesis to the four of Simpson's; and Martin's western North America or Kirsch's Australia to Keast's New World. But is Martin's or Kirsch's hypothesis any more falsifiable than Simpson's? As shown earlier, potential tests of a biogeographical hypothesis impinge first of all on a phylogeny; if the hypothesis is based on an unfalsifiable phylogeny, it is immune. Keast, Martin, Kirsch, and Simpson offer no suggestions about marsupial phylogeny more precise than those included in figure 11.2. If those cladograms are the best current estimates of marsupial phylogeny, then they are unfalsifiable at the level involving more than one continent, for there is a basal trichotomy among living marsupials, and a polychotomy when fossils are added. In that situation, it is not possible to deduce falsifiable predictions about distribution. The Recent cladogram says only that there are three taxa: one Australasian, one South American, and one North/South American. Further finds, for example of Antarctic caenolestoids or Australian didelphoids, will extend the range of those taxa, but will not falsify any logical deduction from the phylogeny. Falsifiable predictions ensue only if additional assumptions are made; one example is Martin's (1977:98) assumption that the earliest unquestionable marsupial fossils can be taken as the site of the first radiation of the group. That assumption can be disallowed, as it is by Keast, Kirsch, and Simpson, or one can argue about the earliest marsupials and how they are to be recognized. Perhaps falsifiers of Simpson's four-continent hypothesis are already available—not in Antarctica, but in the Asian deltatheridiids. Here the argument founders in inconclusive discussions of dental formulae (McKenna 1975b; Archer 1978; Marshall 1979).

In summary, it seems unlikely that a choice can be made among stories of marsupial dispersal until there is an attempt to resolve the relationships of fossil and living marsupials and to solve problems such as the position of caenolestoids, the paraphyly of didelphids, and the status of deltatheridiids.

Hennigian Dispersal Interpretation

Hennigian biogeography, exemplified by Brundin (1966) and formalized by Nelson (1969), estimates ancestral distributions "by combining descendant distributions when they are completely different, and eliminating the unshared element when the descendant distributions are not completely different" (Nelson 1973b:314; cf. Ross 1974; Cracraft 1975a). The three cladograms of figure 11.4 are treated in this way in figure 11.5. Figure 11.5A shows that this method can lead to the conclusion that mammals arose in Australasia and dispersed from there (that conclusion is avoided if Recent Australasian placentals are regarded as late immigrants; figure 11.5D). The figure also shows that the area of origin of living marsupials cannot be resolved because of the basal trichotomy in the group.

Concerning the conclusion that mammals arose in Australasia, Darlington (1970a:11) writes: "This poses a dilemma for cladist biogeographers. If, in the face of the fossil record, they say that this has been the history of mammals, they invite ridicule." Figures 11.5B and C show the basis for this ridicule. According to conventional taxonomy, the fossil record of triconodonts, docodonts, and multituberculates leads to a Euramerican origin of prototherians, and of mammals as a whole (figure 11.5B). Figure 11.5C, with a different cladogram of triconodonts, docodonts, and multituberculates, gives an Australasian/Euramerican (i.e., cosmopolitan) origin for crown-group mammals, and a Euramerican origin when certain stem-group mammals are added. Figure 11.5D shows the effect on figure 11.5C of allowing that placentals have recently dispersed into Australasia. I judge that the Euramerican origins resolved in figure 11.5B and C are an estimate of the concentration of paleontologists, not of ancestral mammals. The basis for the two different estimates of crown-group mammal origins in figure 11.5B and C is reviewed above; they rest on interpretations of the lamina obturans in the side wall of the braincase. The cladist's conclusion of Australasian origins (figure 11.5A) invites ridicule in the face of the fossil record only if it is decisively contradicted by the fossil record, as in figure 11.5B. Yet the cladogram in figure 11.5B leads to a consequence that is perhaps equally worthy of ridicule, that the middle ear of monotremes and therians is a parallelism, not

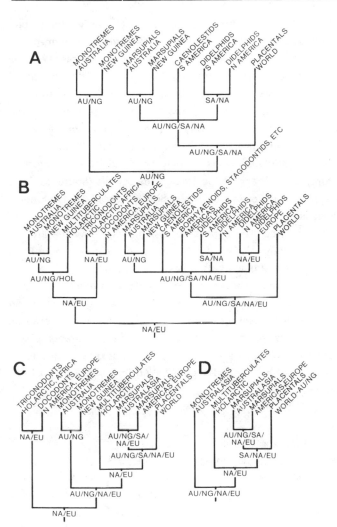

Figure 11.5. Hennigian dispersal analyses of ancestral distribution of mammals: A, cladogram of figure 11.4A, Recent groups; B, cladogram of figure 11.4B, Recent and fossil; C, cladogram of figure 11.4C, Recent and fossil; D, simplified version of C, with the assumption that placentals have recently dispersed into Australasia.

a synapomorphy. This consequence is avoided in figure 11.5C, where the area of origin of crown-group mammals is estimated as cosmopolitan. That estimate avoids all ridicule and is unlikely to be contradicted by the fossil record, but is little help to those seeking areas of origin and routes of dispersal.

There are other possible variants of figure 11.5C. For example, one might regard the deltatheridiids (Asia and North America) as stem-group marsupials, which would resolve ancestral marsupials as North American (the shared element of deltatheridian and crown-group marsupial distribution). I mention this only to emphasize that the Hennigian dispersal method is extremely sensitive to stem-group fossils, and that the assessment of the relationships of such fossils may depend only on one ambiguous character.

But after all, the "cladist dilemma" of Australian origins (figure 11.5A) need not rest on such ambiguous clues. It may be avoided by an effort to resolve the trichotomy at the base of the Recent marsupials (figure 11.3). If the Australian marsupials turn out to be more closely related to didelphoids than to caenolestoids, so that American marsupials are paraphyletic, then the area of marsupial origins would be estimated as American, and the area of origin of crown-group mammals would be more or less cosmopolitan, depending on the cladogram of placentals that was adopted.

In summary, the Hennigian dispersal method offers an infallible way to settle on centers of origin, and hence on centers of dispersal. But the method is so sensitive to fossils that in any group with a stem group it will settle on fossil localities or centers of paleontology. As a paleobiogeographical method, it is therefore reliable only if the fossil record is acknowledged to be complete. If that were so, the method would be no improvement on Matthew's rule of thumb.

Cladistic Vicariance Interpretation

The vicariance method estimates ancestral distributions "by adding the descendant distributions" (Nelson 1975:556). Nelson writes (p. 557) that in the vicariance framework, the method he had previously advocated—eliminating the unshared element in distributions—estimates not ancestral distributions, but "where barriers appeared, barriers that caused the splitting (vicariance) of ancestral species." The cladograms of figure 11.4 are treated in this way in figure 11.6.

As shown above, neither traditional nor Hennigian dispersal methods can yet say if or when marsupials dispersed into Australasia. Platnick and Nelson's (1978) method offers a possibility for resolving the question. Given the cladograms of figures 11.2 and 11.4, the vicariance biogeographer converts them into cladograms of areas, and asks whether that pattern has any generality; if it is congruent with area cladograms of other taxa. If so, the general pattern is interpreted as sequential speciation in response to splitting

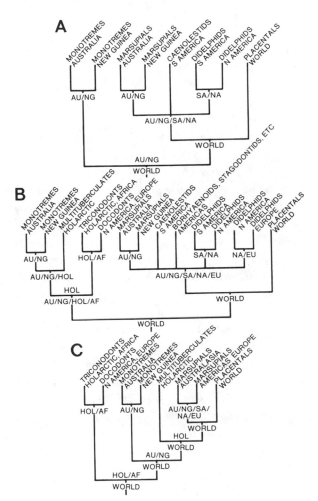

Figure 11.6. Vicariance analyses of ancestral distribution of mammals, same cladograms as figure 11.5A–C. Distributions on vertical lines are ancestral; distributions on horizontal lines are estimates of the location of barriers.

of an ancestral biota. If not, if the pattern is unique or nearly so, it is interpreted as the result of chance dispersal.

As understood here, Recent marsupials form a four-area pattern (figure 11.7A), with Australia and New Guinea, and North and South America, as two sister-group pairs. The trichotomy at the base of the Recent marsupial cladogram can be resolved in three ways (figure 11.3), of which two (the upper two in figure 11.3) give uninformative trichotomous area cladograms,

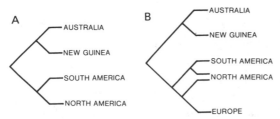

Figure 11.7. Area cladograms of marsupials: A, Recent groups; B, Recent and fossil.

with South America equally closely related to Australasia and North America, and only one (figure 11.3, bottom) is informative. The latter is adopted here. Adding fossils (figure 11.7*B*) introduces a fifth area, Europe, most closely related to North America according to Crochet's phylogenies (1978:figures 34, 241; 1979:1458), so that North America shows a double relationship with South America (*Didelphis*) and with Europe (fossils). The present distribution of *Didelphis virginiana* (Gardner 1973:figure 14) just overlaps that of known North American fossil marsupials, but the area cladogram could be made allopatric by accepting fossil, archeological, and historical evidence (Gardner 1973) that *D. virginiana* has recently dispersed northward, and dividing North America into two regions: southeastern (Recent), most closely related to South America; and northwestern (fossil), most closely related to Europe. That would produce a six-area cladogram. Alternatives are to treat the relationship among South America, North America, and Europe as a trichotomy, reflecting the reticulate relationship (cf. Harper and Platnick 1978:360); or to recognize two levels of North American relationships, an older one with Europe and a newer one with South America, and to hope that the fossil record or other data might distinguish the two levels in test groups. The latter is adopted here (figure 11.7*B*). The polychotomy at the base of the fossil and Recent marsupial cladogram (figure 11.2*C*) introduces further ambiguity because there is the possibility that certain South or North American marsupials might turn out to be most closely related to Australian marsupials, giving a different five-area pattern. But I assume that this possibility is remote.

The fossil record gives minimum ages for some of the areal relationships shown in figure 11.7. The North American/European relationship is pre-Eocene; the new South/North American relationship is pre-late Pleistocene; the old South/North American relationship (didelphids, pediomyids) is pre-Paleocene; the American/Australasian relationship is at least pre-Oligocene and, if the cladogram is correct, must predate the old South/North American relationship; the New Guinea/Australian relationship includes Pliocene or older elements.

Platnick and Nelson's method is to look at random for cladograms of taxa with representatives endemic in three or more of the five marsupial areas to see whether or not they relate the areas in the same way. Test groups may have five taxa in the five areas, four in four of them, or three in three of them. Other possible test groups are those with one undifferentiated species occupying two or more of the areas, producing four-taxon five-area tests, or three-taxon four-area tests. I believe that these could hardly test the marsupial pattern, for contradictory groups would have to contain a single species shared by one Australasian region and Europe, or by Europe and South America.

In a search for test groups, it would be prudent to choose those with fossil or other indications that they were commensurate in age with the marsupials. Cracraft (1975b:table 2) lists ten vertebrate groups of this sort, considered to demonstrate probable sister-group relationships between Australia and South America. These will serve as a first sample. Among them, one (lungfishes) occurs only in two of the marsupial areas; in one (suboscine birds) the Australasian and American groups are no longer thought to be related (Feduccia 1975); in two others, no cladistic information is available (meiolanid turtles, Gaffney 1975:428; parrots, Cracraft 1973:508); and for one, cladistic information is available, but is unreliable (leptodactyloid frogs, where Lynch's 1971 and 1973 cladograms of the group are mutually inconsistent). Area cladograms for the remaining five groups are shown in figure 11.8.

None of the cladograms in figure 11.8 is inconsistent with the marsupial area cladogram (figure 11.7). Osteoglossoid fishes and chelid turtles occupy only three of the marsupial areas, ratites occupy four, and the hylids and galliforms occupy all five. I was surprised by the congruence of all six groups, for intuitively I did not expect it. I attempted to quantify my surprise by calculating with Rosen's method (1978:180) the probability that all the cladograms should be congruent. This gives a probability of about 1 in 42,000 that the congruence is due to chance (three three-area cladograms, 1 in 27; one four-area, 1 in 15; one five-area, 1 in 105; a total of 1 in 42,525). I was not that surprised, and suppose that the calculation is spurious because it gives equal probability to all possible cladograms, whereas I judge that the Australia/New Guinea relationship is incontrovertible (see below). Lumping Australia and New Guinea gives a probability of 44 to 1 (one three-area and one four-area cladogram congruent with marsupials) that these five groups

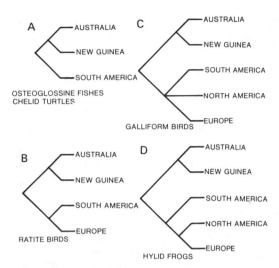

Figure 11.8. Area cladograms of certain vertebrate groups. A, osteoglossine fishes (*Osteoglossum* and *Scleropages*), omitting southeastern Asia, sister area (s-a) of Australia and New Guinea, and chelid turtles, after Gaffney (1977); B, higher ratite birds, after Cracraft (1972, 1973), omitting Africa, s-a of Europe; C, galliform birds, after Cracraft (1973), omitting Africa (s-a of Europe) and cosmopolitan phasianids—the trichotomy of the Americas and Europe results from sympatry of cracids and gallinuloidids in North America; D, hylid frogs, after Maxson and Wilson (1975), omitting Asia, ? s-a of Europe.

are distributed with marsupials for common historical reasons. If we accept that, it has the corollary that incongruent parts of the individual distributions require explanation. For example, if osteoglossids and marsupials are part of the ancient common biota of South America and Australasia, then the presence of *Scleropages* in southeastern Asia demands either that the fishes dispersed there or that marsupials became extinct there. Because none of the other groups in figure 11.8 occurs in southeastern Asia, dispersal of the one fish group is more parsimonious than extinction of five other groups. South American ratites are related to the African and European ostriches, according to Cracraft. If this group shares the same history as the marsupials, then either ratites became extinct in North America and dispersed to Africa, or marsupials became extinct in Africa. It might be easier to choose the more parsimonious of these alternatives if area cladograms for other taxa are brought in.

Keast (1973:tables 1, 2) published a list of taxa showing relationships of some sort between Australasia and South America. I have been able to find cladistic information only for a few of these. Area cladograms for some are shown in figure 11.9. Two of the classic austral disjunct groups, *Nothofagus* and chironomids, are incongruent with the marsupial area cladogram, but congruent with each other at the level shown in figure 11.9, although they differ when analyzed in more detail. The beeches relate northern- and southern-hemisphere areas among themselves, implying that the primary event in their history was separation of those two areas. *Nothofagus* is uninformative on the interrelationships of the southern-hemisphere areas. The chironomids also relate northern and southern areas among themselves, but in Brundin's (1966) cladograms the northern-hemisphere representatives of podonomines and diamesines are each most closely related to African taxa. These chironomids suggest a pattern of areal relationships different from that of the marsupials.

Figure 11.9 *C–F* shows five three-area cladograms, two four-area cladograms, and one five-area cladogram, all of which are congruent with the marsupial cladogram. Among these, four of the three-area cladograms (figure 11.9*C*) are congruent also with those of Fagaceae and chironomids (figure 11.9*A,B*). The fifth three-area cladogram (figure 11.9*F*) and the four- and five-area cladograms (figures 11.9*D,E*) are incongruent with Fagaceae and chironomids. Among the vertebrate groups in figure 11.8, the two three-area cladograms (figure 11.8*A*) are congruent with Fagaceae and chironomids, but the four- and five-area cladograms (figure 11.8*B–D*) are not. The ratite cladogram (figure 11.8*B*) would be congruent with those of Fagaceae and chironomids if Sibley's (personal communication) cladogram, based on DNA hybridization, were followed. This places rheas (S.America) as the sister group of kiwis (New Zealand) and emus (Australia) + cassowaries (Australia and New Guinea), with ostriches (Africa, fossil in Europe) as the sister group of that assemblage.

Thus two groups of chironomids, the Fagaceae, and an alternative ratite cladogram (one three-area, three four-area) all suggest a different pattern of areal relationships from the marsupial one. Figures 11.8 and 11.9 show six three-area cladograms (figures 11.8*A*, 11.9*C*) congruent with both patterns. The five-area marsupial pattern is corroborated by two three-area (figures 11.8*C*, 11.9*F*), three four-area (figures 11.8*B*, 11.9*D*, one of them the

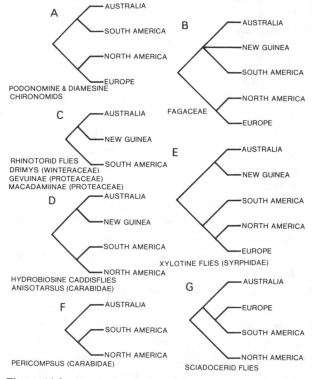

Figure 11.9. Area cladograms of certain plant and invertebrate groups. A, podonomine and diamesine chironomids, after Brundin (1966), omitting New Zealand (s-a of Australia and South America), Africa (s-a of Holarctic), and Asia (s-a of North America and/or Europe); B, Fagaceae, after Melville (1973) and Hanks and Fairbrothers (1976), omitting New Zealand (tetrachotomy with austral areas) and Asia (s-a of North America and/or Europe); C, *Drimys* (Winteraceae), after C. J. Humphries (personal communication), omitting New Caledonia, s-a of New Guinea; Gevuineae (Proteaceae), after Johnson and Briggs (1975), omitting New Caledonia, s-a of Australia and New Guinea; Macadamiinae (Proteaceae), after Johnson and Briggs (1975), omitting southeastern Asia, s-a of Australasia; and rhinotorid flies, after McAlpine (1968); D, hydrobiosine caddisflies, after Ross (1956), omitting New Zealand (trichotomy with Australia and New Guinea), and southeastern Asia (s-a of Australia and New Guinea); and *Anisotarsus* (Carabidae), after Noonan (1973), omitting New Zealand, s-a of Australia and/or New Guinea; E, *Chalcosyrphus* group of xylotine syrphids (Diptera), after Hippa (1978), omitting Asia, s-a of Europe and/or North America; F, *Pericompsus* (Carabidae), after Erwin (1974); G, Sciadoceridae (Diptera), after McAlpine and Martin (1966); the North American records are U. Cretaceous fossils, and the European records are Oligocene fossils.

alternative ratite cladogram), and two five-area (figures 11.8D, 11.9E) cladograms. Deleting the support common to both patterns (Australasian/South
American relationships and the alternative ratite cladograms) leaves marsupials only with the support of those groups (hylids and syrphids) showing
congruent three-area cladograms of South America, North America, and
Europe.

Another way of tackling the problem is to consider areas omitted from
the cladograms in figures 11.8 and 11.9. For example, southeastern Asia is
omitted three times (osteoglossines, macadamiines, hydrobiosines), always
as the sister area of Australia plus New Guinea. Ten other groups occupy
Australia and New Guinea, so that at present parsimony demands dispersal
of the three groups to southeastern Asia, rather than extinction of ten groups
there. This conclusion might be altered if further area cladograms repeatedly
demanded dispersal to southeastern Asia, or if fossils of marsupials and other
groups with Australasian relationships were found there. Africa is omitted
four times in figures 11.8 and 11.9 (two groups of chironomids, two groups
of birds), always as the sister area of a northern one. But Africa is the next
step in area cladograms of four of the taxa in figures 11.8 and 11.9 (osteoglossids, *Drimys*, Gevuinae—Madagascar only, Macadamiinae), and in others
showing Australasian/South American relationships such as Restionaceae
(Cutler 1972), aphroteniine chironomids, and galaxiine fishes (Rosen
1978:figure 24). In all those groups, except for galliform birds and Cracraft's
version of the ratites (figure 11.8B), Africa is the sister area of all the other
southern areas, To explore South American/African relationships further is
out of the question here (Cracraft 1975a:table 1), but among the taxa
considered here, Africa crops up too often for repeated dispersal to be parsimonious. I suggest that the taxa shown in figures 11.7–11.9, all with congruent Australasian/South American patterns, display two different patterns
beyond these areas. The first is the marsupial pattern, with younger relationships extending into northern areas, shown by galliforms, hylids,
hydrobiosines, *Anisotarsus*, *Chalcosyrphus* group xylotines, and *Pericompsus*.
The second is the chironomid pattern, with older relationships extending into
Africa, shown by ratites (Sibley's version), osteoglossids, *Drimys*, Restionaceae, Proteaceae, and galaxiine fishes.

Whether extensions of these patterns in the northern hemisphere and
southern hemisphere (e.g., New Zealand, New Caledonia) are more parsimoniously explained as dispersal or vicariance requires extended cladograms for
more taxa, or finds of fossils. For example, on present evidence the omission
of Asia three times in figures 11.8 and 11.9 (galliforms, hylids, syrphids),

always as the sister area of a northern one, demands either three separate dispersals or extinction in Asia of marsupials, caddisflies, and beetles.

Are these postulated vicariance patterns refutable? The obvious way to refute them is to find many taxa with incongruent area cladograms. But such taxa are not easy to find. Figure 11.9G shows one: sciadocerid flies. Their pattern is, so far, unique, and I regard it either as a vagary of the fossil record or as the pattern of a non-monophyletic group (cf. McAlpine and Martin 1966:figure 24). I assume that there exists a large class of area cladograms inconsistent with those in figures 11.7–11.9 for groups that have dispersed into Australasia from the north. Obvious examples are vicariant sister groups of those shown in figures 11.7–11.9 (e.g., placental mammals, the remaining xylotine syrphids), and more remote relatives of those groups (e.g., ranid frogs and carettochelid and trionychid turtles). But many such groups will give three- or four-area cladograms that are congruent with that of marsupials in relating Europe and North America more closely to each other than to one or both Australasian regions (e.g., Ross 1956, agapetine caddisflies; Erwin 1975, carabid *Tachyta*; Papavero 1977, botflies; and the Prototheria in conventional taxonomy, figure 11.4B). Area cladograms are likely to contradict the marsupial cladogram only by relating one northern area more closely to an Australasian one than to another northern one (e.g., figure 11.9G), or, if they include South America, by relating that to one northern area (e.g., figure 11.9G), or to Australasian and northern areas (as do the remaining xylotine syrphids; Hippa 1978).

On the scale of areas considered here, I therefore believe that bolstering the vicariance explanation by calculating the odds against congruence of area cladograms is spurious. It depends on the assumption that all cladograms are equally likely because "knowledge of the spatial arrangement of areas during the past is unavailable" (Platnick and Nelson 1978:15). But we can be fairly sure that, for example, New Guinea was never in contact with Europe while Australia was in the Caribbean.

I began this section by asking whether the cladistic vicariance method could say if or when marsupials dispersed into Australasia. Figures 11.8 and 11.9 suggest that if marsupials did walk into Australasia, they did so roughly in step with (or in opposition to—some in one direction, some in the other) plants, beetles, flies, fishes, frogs, turtles, and flighted and flightless birds. Parsimony demands that we regard these groups as part of an ancient common biota of Australasia and South America. Two patterns diverge from South America, an older one to Africa and a younger one to the north. The pattern involving Africa, South America, and Australasia is congruent with the late Mesozoic sequence of separation of those areas in current plate-tectonic theory, as Rosen (1978) shows, and is best explained by that sequence. The northern part of the marsupial pattern is younger, but late Cretaceous fossil marsupials in North and South America show that it was established by the late Mesozoic. The question whether marsupials walked into North America and thence into Europe demands more refined analysis of fossil American marsupials, and of many other groups with representatives in the Americas and Europe.

As for the place of origin of marsupials, I suppose that one existed, but I believe that attempts to localize it lie in biogeographical theory rather than in paleontological practice. The place of origin of crown-group marsupials may be parsimoniously resolved when the interrelationships of fossil and Recent marsupials are sorted out. I guess that it will include Australia and South America. The place of origin of stem-group marsupials is unlikely to be resolved more precisely.

In summary, my attempts to explore the cladistic vicariance method suggest that it holds the best hope for an analytical historical biogeography. I doubt, however, that it will be the panacea that cladistics is in systematics. The reasons for this are dispersal and extinction. In cladistic biogeography the result of dispersal (sympatry) is the same as the result of hybridization in systematics (irresolvable tri- or polychotomies in cladograms). Extinction has the same consequence in biogeography as in systematics—loss of useful information that can be reclaimed only from the fossil record. Paleontology therefore has a crucial role in cladistic vicariance biogeography. Without the possibility of documenting extinctions by means of fossils, I believe that cladistic biogeography would peter out in an infinite regression of parsimony arguments trying to reconcile incompletely overlapping area cladograms of different taxa.

Conclusions

Paleobiogeographers who have read this far may well be incensed by or indifferent to my line of argument. I apologize to them, and wish that they or their predecessors had devoted as many pages to method as have their neontological colleagues. As it is, paleobiogeographers seem to have regarded method as self-evident. And so, most paleobiogeography is either still in the descriptive stage, seeking to recognize provinces (areas of endemism), or it consists of little more than drawing arrows on maps—arrows that run from earlier fossil localities to later ones. I have not mentioned paleobiogeographical work with marine organisms, or with totally extinct groups, but I doubt that the methods used can be any different from those applicable in continental groups with living and fossil representatives.

My central aims is this paper have been to ask if fossils can contradict inferences from Recent distributions, and to look for a method of analytical paleobiogeography which utilizes the analogy between systematics and historical biogeography. That fossils can contradict Recent distributions is considered true only by dispersal biogeographers, who expect that fossils can localize centers of origin and hence directions of dispersal. Two rules for finding the center of origin of a group by means of fossils have been offered: that pointed to by the earliest fossils, and Hennig's progression rule. The first depends on the assumption that the fossil record is complete. When that assumption is found to have been wrong, and when new fossils suggest a different center of origin, one can redraw the arrows on the map, or become less sure about the center of origin (trend toward cosmopolitanism), or look for some other method of analysis. Hennigian dispersal analysis provides such a method and is one way to utilize the analogy between systematics and biogeography. Although Darlington (1970a:10) called this method "biogeography made easy," it does demand that a cladogram of the group be constructed, and that the fossils be fitted into it by means of synapomorphies—constraints that have so far been met in few groups. When they are met in groups with a reasonable fossil record, the method leads to the recognition of two groups—the crown group and the stem group—which may have had different centers of origin. In the crown group, fossils have the same status as Recent organisms, but the stem group contains only fossils, so that stem-group centers of origin are determined as decisively by fossils as they are in the oldest-fossil method (e.g., figures 11.1, 11.5). Hennig's progression rule therefore depends on the same assumption as the oldest-fossil method—that the fossil record is complete.

If it is agreed that the fossil record is incomplete, then fossils cannot decisively contradict evidence from Recent distributions. This is assumed to be true in vicariance biogeography. The generalized-track method treats fossils in the same way as living organisms, so that they become another source of information on phenetic relationships among biotas. The cladistic vicariance method explores the analogy between systematics and biogeography to the full. It demands that fossils be fitted into cladograms by means of synapomorphies before they become useful, but, as the marsupials show (figures 11.2, 11.7), poorly resolved taxon cladograms, with many fossil taxa entered only as polychotomies, may give usable area cladograms, so that the method is not always sensitive to exact placement of fossils. The role of fossils in the cladistic vicariance method is, first, to document extinctions, thereby extending the range of groups and allowing new areas and therefore new test groups to be brought in, and permitting a choice between general explanations involving multiple dispersals or multiple extinctions. Second, fossils, by giving minimum ages of occupation of areas, may insure that test groups are comparable, and permit a choice between geological events of different ages as correlatives of biological events.

Vicariance biogeographers (Croizat et al. 1974; Rosen 1976a, 1978; Platnick and Nelson 1978) stress the aim of correlating historical geology and historical biogeography. But I agree with Rosen (1978:186) that historical geology "neither tests nor in any way affects the generality of a biological area-cladogram." Several writers have remarked that plate-tectonic theory has had an unfortunate band-wagon effect in biogeography (more than 30 papers on marsupial biogeography in the last decade are one symptom). In the past, biogeography has been held back by allegiance to current geological theory. As Croizat has often said, the biological evidence stands, whether or not it matches fashionable geology. The effort of paleobiogeographers is better spent in analyzing the relationships of taxa and biotas then in reconciling distribution with today's historical geology.

Acknowledgments
I am grateful to many colleagues for advice, in particular W. R. Hamilton, C. J. Humphries, L. G. Marshall, M. C. McKenna, C. G. Sibley, and R. I. Vane-Wright; and to P. L. Forey, R. S. Miles, and R. I. Vane-Wright for comments on the manuscript.

Discussion

L. R. Parenti

DR. PATTERSON'S FIRST QUESTION, whether fossils can contradict inference from Recent distributions, has been fully answered. The second question, whether there is a method of analytical paleobiogeography that utilizes the analogy between systematics and historical biogeography, has been answered more completely than ever before; the answer, in my opinion, falls just one step short of fully integrating the two disciplines. The primary purpose of this discussion, therefore, is to elaborate certain of Patterson's points, rather than to criticize his discussions of biogeographical methods, with which I generally agree.

Patterson's reanalysis of the characters used to determine interrelationships of mammals is astute and demonstrates his belief that a well-constructed phylogeny is essential·to a sound biogeographical analysis. No one working on mammalian biogeography or systematics should ignore his work.

I have no disagreement with his conclusions concerning the assumptions underlying the use of fossils in Hennigian phylogenetic biogeography or dispersalist biogeography. The violation of their own assumption that the fossil record is complete is reason enough to reject the dispersalist and the Hennigian phylogenetic methods. Another reason to reject them, however, is that both methods deal with groups on an individual basis, ignoring the general significance of their distribution.

Platnick and Nelson (1978) remind us of a question we may ask in biogeography: How does a taxon come to occupy an area? Either it evolves there, or it evolves elsewhere and disperses into the area. The two explanations between which we choose are vicariance and dispersal. The major points of disagreement I have with Patterson concern the direct role that paleontology plays in such an analysis.

Patterson reminds us of the role of systematics by stating: "biogeography can be no better than the taxonomy it must use to describe distributions." He further states that fossils are of subsidiary importance in vicariance biogeography, but of cardinal importance in dispersal biogeography. Yet, he discusses three special roles fossils may play in vicariance biogeography: (1) arbiter of dispersal versus extinction; (2) indicator, of high resolution, of former land continuity; and, (3) evidence of a group's age to equal that of another. I comment on each of these to demonstrate that fossils play a role equivalent to that of Recent organisms in vicariance as well in cladistic vicariance biogeography.

I disagree with Patterson's conclusion about the importance of fossils that "without the possibility of documenting extinctions by means of fossils, . . . cladistic biogeography would peter out in an infinite regression of parsimony arguments." Fossils have been treated in vicariance models to extend tracks or ancestral biotas, a use that was passed along to cladistic vicariance biogeography. Rosen (1976a) states that a fossil either lies within the boundaries of a track or forms an extension of the track. One explanation of an individual track that does not correspond to a generalized track is that members of the taxon represented by the individual track have broken away from the parent biota and dispersed.

Thus, it is logical to conclude that fossils that form a unique track may be explained by dispersal into the area at some time in the past, before the time of fossilization. The cladograms of areas for groups found in the same areas as marsupials (Patterson's figure 11.8) may be used to illustrate this point. Patterson considers the areas omitted from the cladograms, commenting that their larger distribution needs some explanation. Southeastern Asia is an area omitted three times (from the cladograms of osteoglossines, galliforms, and hylids), and always as the sister area of Australia/New Guinea. Ten other groups occupy Australia and New Guinea without having any representatives in southeastern Asia; therefore, he states, parsimony demands dispersal into southeastern Asia of the three groups, rather than extinction of ten groups there. He continues: "This conclusion might be altered if further area cladograms repeatedly demanded dispersal to southeastern Asia, or if fossil marsupials and other groups with Australasian relationships were found there."

Dispersal and extinction, however, are not mutually exclusive explanations. If, for example, fossil marsupials were found in southeastern Asia, we would have one documented extinction, three hypothesized dispersals, and nine groups with hypothesized ancestral biotas not including southeastern Asia. Should we extend the ancestral biota of marsupials to include southeastern Asia, or invoke the parsimony criterion and postulate a dispersal, now of four groups, one of which is known as fossil? The distinction between dispersal and extinction that Patterson tries to make is not valid. By trying to distinguish between dispersal and extinction, he is in effect creating two different hypotheses for an extralimital distribution. The living ones dispersed; the fossils were taxa that "went extinct," implying, if this means something other than dispersal, that they evolved in that area.

Parsimony suggests an hypothesis: The three Recent taxa and one fossil taxon dispersed. Thus, our evaluation of dispersal versus vicariance (conformation to a pattern) is a parsimony problem. Fossils and Recent taxa play equivalent roles in the analysis. Extinction is documented by fossils, but extinction is important when related to a series of events of earth history, a practice which Patterson himself says is secondary to the discovery of patterns.

A second use of fossils that Patterson briefly mentions is recommended by McKenna (1975a). In discussing a former Euramerican terrestrial biota, McKenna suggests a contrast between "low resolution" data from Recent organisms, and "high resolution" data from fossils because the inference of a generalized track from Recent organisms is derived from comparisions at a relatively higher taxonomic rank than those of fossils, which give more precise indications of continuity. In my opinion, however, the taxonomic rank we assign to a taxon is its most artificial attribute. Recent organisms are in one sense more diverse, and it is likely that they will be divided by taxonomists into more groups than fossil specimens that by their very nature have a lower variability. The presence or absence of a taxon, regardless of its rank, constitutes the data of biogeographical analyses.

What then can be said about marsupial biogeography? Starting with the assumption that the cladogram presented is well-corroborated, Patterson converts it into a cladogram of areas (figure 11.7). The fact that North America is involved in a polychotomy with South America and Europe may indicate that, for the purpose of analysis, North America should, as suggested, be broken up into two regions. There is no reason to keep geographical boundaries just because they are familiar when our objective is the comparison of biotas.

Before discussing the pattern exhibited by all the groups compared with the marsupial pattern (figures 11.8–11.9), I consider the incongruent cladogram of figure 11.9g. Patterson says that this totally incongruent pattern may be due to a vagary of the fossil record or to the fact that sciadocerids may represent a nonmonophyletic group. From McAlpine and Martin's (1966) revision, it is apparent that the Sciadoceridae are not a monophyletic group. Some members are more closely related to the family Phoridae than to other sciadocerids.

As a general method of biogeographical analysis that integrates systematics and historical biogeography more completely than Patterson's discussion, I suggest a summary of the information contained in the remaining cladograms of figures 11.8 and 11.9. As one would do in a systematic study, each of these cladograms is viewed as a character-state tree telling us something about the genealogy of the areas.

That Australia/New Guinea and North America/Europe form sister areas is never contradicted in the cladograms (except in sciadocerids). South America is related to the Australian/New Guinean subset in nine groups, and it is related to the European/North American subset in eight groups (including the marsupials of figure 11.7). We could delete the three-area cladograms (figures 11.8A, 9C, 11.9F) from this analysis because they are consistent with both hypotheses for the relationships of South America; including them may be analogous to using a character that has not been surveyed in all taxa in a systematic study.

Nonetheless, attempting to summarize the information in these cladograms, or, parsimoniously interpreting the distribution of homologies, we would get a cladogram of the areas most like that of figure 11.9B. The only difference would be that New Guinea and Australia form a sister group. The placement of South America on this cladogram is tenuous because if we remove the three-area cladograms, South America is more parsimoniously assessed as the sister area of North America and Europe. That there are two patterns involving South America suggests that South America should be broken up into two areas for this analysis, one more closely related to Australia/New Guinea, the other to North America/Europe.

This reminds us of the original cladograms of marsupials (Patterson's figures 11.4A, 11.4B). *Didelphis* is one South American form related to

North American/European forms; while caenolestids are the other South American group that currently forms a multichotomy at the base of marsupial cladograms. If we use the most parsimonious cladogram of areas, as illustrated in figure 11.10, the cladograms of monophyletic groups that Patterson claims are inconsistent with the marsupial pattern are actually congruent. That is, if we accept that South America should be divided into two regions denoted as South America 1 and 2, we can use this area cladogram as our pattern. In such an analysis, the definition of a geographical area is analogous to the definition of a character. Both are homology problems and are therefore resolvable by invoking parsimony. From the cladograms in figures 11.8 and 11.9, it is nonparsimonious to conclude that South America is one area.

The cladogram of figure 11.10 may be used to illustrate the problem of delimiting an ancestral biota, or center of origin, using the Hennigian node-reconstruction method (as in Patterson's figure 11.5). A similar method has been applied by systematists (e.g., Farris 1970; Fitch 1970) to reconstruct

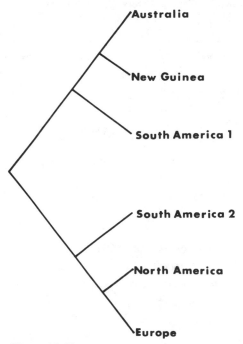

Figure 11.10. The cladogram of areas best supported by the cladograms of Patterson's figures 11.8 and 11.9, and the marsupial cladograms presented in his text.

the most parsimonious set of primitive states on a cladogram. In figure 11.10, if South America is not recognized as two areas, then the Hennigian method would recognize South America as the group's center of origin. Recognizing it as two areas gives us Australia/New Guinea/South America 1/South America 2/Europe/North America, which may be interpreted as a roughly cosmopolitan ancestral biota. Therefore, the method does work, but only if we can recognize parallel states beforehand.

Geological evidence for the separation of South America into two areas would support the view that the pattern is directly related to the previous separation of these land masses. Caenolestids occur in western South America, and all Recent species are found in parts of the Andes (Martin 1975). If caenolestids form a monophyletic group with Australian and New Guinean marsupials, their distribution—indeed the entire most parsimonious pattern as in figure 11.10—is in agreement with the idea that the flora and fauna of South America were derived from two sources (also Melville in this volume).

If the South American continent is not of hybrid origin, we may consider the idea that there is an older and a younger component to the pattern. If all older fossils are of groups found in Australia, New Guinea, or South America 1, we may conclude that this is the older portion of the pattern. The finding of an older fossil in Europe, North America, or South America 2 would force us to change our hypothesis. Unless the oldest fossils from both groups are the same age, we can always say which one, at our stage of analysis, is older. Therefore, such a conclusion seems trivial unless it can be correlated with information from other groups.

Finding overlapping distributions of groups in South America 1 or 2 would not provide further evidence for choosing between the hypotheses that the areas are geologically or temporally distinct. If the areas were geologically distinct, sympatry may simply represent dispersal after the land masses were united.

We may ask if the general pattern of figure 11.10 is consistent with any events of earth history. Patterson suggests that biologists have enough to do to get this far. Adding geological explanations is secondary to finding a pattern, and in no way tests the biological cladogram (Rosen 1978). Biogeographical methods other than vicariance and cladistic vicariance discuss marsupial distributions separately, disregarding all other animal and plant groups. Once other taxa have been considered, and a pattern found, as I believe is the case, it is no longer sufficient to discuss the history of groups individually.

The congruence of all the patterns allows us to seek an explanation of earth history of the pattern as a whole. Therefore, even though the oldest known fossil marsupial is late Cretaceous, the oldest fossils of the groups studied which support the pattern of figure 11.10 are those of the chironomid midges, the record of which extends into the Jurassic (Brundin 1966). The pattern itself, then, of which marsupials are a part, is a least as old as the mid-Jurassic. Therefore, I cannot agree with Patterson's statement that in a search for test groups, it would be prudent to choose those with fossil or other indications of age commensurate with that of the marsupials, unless he means that they share with marsupials a biogeographical pattern that would not be known until the patterns were analyzed.

Even if there were a general pattern, and if all these groups responded to the same events of earth history to create the pattern, fossil marsupials are too young to estimate the absolute age of the pattern. As for their role in deciding whether or not the pattern dictates an ancestral biota that is pre-Pangean, Pangean, or involving a Pacific continent, all marsupials might just as well be Recent.

The idea of Pacifica might be rejected on geological evidence, but one cannot reject it on the basis of minimum ages of individual groups. The general pattern and its minimum age suggest that the animals and plants were on the continental masses by at least the mid- or late Jurassic.

Choosing an established geological hypothesis to enhance the biological one requires caution. Even interpreting all higher order relationships within the framework of the breakup of Pangea may not be sufficient to explain the distribution. Many groups, both plant and animal, must have a pre-Pangean origin, and an attempt to impinge the cladogram onto a cladogram of the breakup may be a useless exercise.

In choosing among alternative geological hypotheses, fossils will aid only in rejecting hypotheses. For example, one may reject all hypotheses dealing with events younger than a fossil that was hypothesized to have dispersed, but could not have dispersed because it was already in place by the time of the geological event. Once such an hypothesis is rejected, any hypothesis that is older may be considered a possible reciprocal illuminator (in the sense of Rosen 1978).

In conclusion, Patterson summarizes the state of biogeography, and I fully agree that phylogeny reconstruction is a prerequisite to biogeographical analysis. The treatment of the cladograms of areas presented in the current paper provides a more complete integration of systematics and biogeography and is consistent with the goals of biogeography expressed in his paper.

Paleontology does not have a role in cladistic biogeography any more critical than that of neontology. Fossils do document extinctions, but they do not invariably document ancestral biotas. Cladistic biogeography is, therefore, not going to "peter out in an infinite regression of parsimony arguments," but may peter out when parsimony ceases to be the logical criterion we choose to apply.

Acknowledgments

G. Nelson and D. E. Rosen provided comments on an earlier draft, which greatly improved the presentation of ideas. Discussions with M. F. Mickevich and N. A. Neff contributed to the development of several of the arguments. L. F. Marcus courteously provided access to a computer facility, which allowed me to produce several typescripts with ease.

Response

C. Patterson

I AM GRATEFUL for Lynne Parenti's perceptive criticism of my paper. I believe that some of the differences between us are due only to my failure to be explicit on certain points.

Parenti's first criticism centers on a quote concerning possible finds of fossils of marsupials and other groups with Australasian relationships in southeastern Asia. She contends that I try to distinguish dispersal and extinction, and violate the parsimony criterion by suggesting that if fossil marsupials were found in southeastern Asia we might extend the ancestral Australasian biota to that region, rather than postulate dispersal of marsupials to southeastern Asia. I had no such intention, and the criticism could be avoided if I had added [three words]to the passage Parenti quotes: "This conclusion might be altered if further area cladograms repeatedly demanded dispersal to southeastern Asia, or if fossils of marsupials and [four or more] other groups with Australasian relationships were found there."

I agree with Parenti's comment on McKenna's (1975a) argument. On Sciadoceridae and "vagaries of the fossil record" I was aware that McAlpine and Martin (1966) interpreted sciadocerids as paraphyletic, but I had in mind other opinions (Hennig 1969:392; Griffiths 1972:71) on the status of the group.

Parenti's main contribution is a reinterpretation of my cladograms in figures 11.7–9. She concludes that the pattern they represent is most parsimoniously interpreted as one in which South America is divided into two areas. We could argue about the significance of the area cladograms relating South America to Australasia rather than to North America and Europe: by my count, if we omit three-area cladograms consistent with either hypothesis for South America, we get three groups relating it to Australasia (podonomines, diamesines, *Nothofagus*) and eight groups relating it to North America and Europe (didelphoid marsupials, ratites, galliforms, hylids, hydrobiosines, *Anisotarsus*, xylotines, *Pericompsus*). Treating each group as a character-state tree, parsimony would put South America with the northern areas, and we should rate the three indications of Australasian relationships as parallelisms or wrongly evaluated characters. But Parenti's alternative, division of South America into two areas, is interesting. To discuss it, we need some idea of where on the map to draw a line through South America. The only hint Parenti gives is that caenolestoid marsupials occur in western South America, and that Recent species are Andean. Two predictions of Parenti's hypothesis are therefore: (1) that caenolestoids share synapomorphies with Australasian marsupials, not with didelphoids; (2) that podonomines, diamesines and *Nothofagus* should be sympatric with caenolestoids, and the eight other groups (didelphoids, ratites, galliforms, etc.) should not. Regarding the first of these, L. G. Marshall (personal communication) cites sperm pairing as a synapomorphy uniting South American marsupials (caenolestoids and didelphoids); I have read of no plausible synapomorphies uniting caenolestoids and Australasian marsupials. Regarding the second prediction, podonomines and diamesines are Andean, broadly sympatric with caenolestoids, but *Nothofagus* is confined to southern South America, and is sympatric only with the caenolestid *Rhyncholestes*. The other two caenolestid genera, *Caenolestes* and *Lestoros*, live far to the north, where they are sympatric with didelphids (e.g., Hershkovitz 1972:figures 10, 16). Where, then, do we draw the line between the two parts of South America? Have caenolestids and chironomids dispersed to the north, into the territory of didelphids, or have didelphids dispersed into the northern territory of caenolestids and chironomids, while *Nothofagus* has become extinct there? These alternatives recall the Australasia/southeastern Asia problem discussed above. Like that problem, they could be explored through area cladograms of other taxa within South America, something that is well worth doing. However, I am not convinced that Parenti will avoid a regression of parsimony arguments. In suggesting a regression, I had in mind only the alternatives of dispersal and extinction. The difference between these alternatives is that extinction is, in principle, demonstrable by fossils, whereas dispersal is not, unless one assumes that the fossil record is complete. Parenti wishes to add a third alternative, subdivision of areas. I foresee a regression here, because incongruent area cladograms will demand finer and finer subdivision of areas.

I think, after all, that the major difference between Parenti and me is that I was viewing the cladistic vicariance method as one that needs trying out (for example, my use of the word "prudent," that Parenti complains of, implies not methodological prudence, but social prudence—having one's first efforts taken seriously), whereas she has accepted the method wholeheartedly, and seeks to push it to its limits. Good luck to her.

12

Biogeography: Past, Present, and Future

L. Croizat

FOR MOST of the last half-century, biological thinking in the English-speaking world—that is, virtually throughout science—has been dominated in matters biogeographical by notions stemming primarily from Darwin's *Origin of Species* (1859) and secondarily from Matthew's *Climate and Evolution* (1915). Endorsed and broadcast as fundamentally correct by George Gaylord Simpson and his associates (Ernst Mayr, Theodosius Dobzhansky, Philip J. Darlington, Jr., and others), these notions have ruled the mental and professional formation of at least two generations of biologists both within and without the particular fields of biogeography and systematic zoology. This they have done all the more pervasively because some of the main works of this school are richly informative and ably presented along a vast front of details.

Most readers, particularly when young, seem more interested in mastering details than in pondering generalities. For this reason, perhaps, the body of opinion quickly reached an axiomatic status in favor of the notions of Darwin and his followers. Veiled opposition to these notions, for example by Cain (1944; see Rosen 1976b), received no attention at all. Articulate opposition by this writer in a steady stream of publications in four languages was ignored as if nonexistent, on the grounds that it came from an author who, if not downright insane, was at least nonscientific in method and manner of writing (for part of this bibliography, see Nelson 1973b). The mental and academic climate then prevailing doubtless could not have been altered for many more years if the earth sciences, particularly geophysics of the last 20 years, had not made discoveries that dispose of Matthew's tenets, and that show on the rebound that Darwin's notions of "Geographical Distribution" are by no means as solid as they once were believed to be.

Panbiogeography (biogeography of the analytic and synthetic description) is today no longer disreputable. Once in circulation, it will in time cause a profound revolution throughout biology. Of this I am sure, for I have been among the very first to sense and enjoy the feeling of liberation, so pointedly underscored by Ball (1976), that follows the rejection of the conceptual props of Darwin's "Geographical Distribution": the concepts of centers of origin, means of dispersal, and casual migration.

Still, there are those who strive to shore up the now crumbling fortress of Darwinism. Gould, for example, writes (1976): "We are always ready to watch a theory fall under the impact of new data, but we do not expect a great and influential theory to collapse from a logical error in its formulation. . . . Even his [Darwin's] severest critics have never accused him of crass stupidity."

In contrast to Gould, I would be inclined to believe that a theory falls under the impact of new data precisely because it is vitiated by some (one or more) logical errors in its formulation. In my thought, a theory anticipates what the facts, when fully known, will demonstrate to be correct. Its failure, when the facts tell otherwise, points to a logical error in its formulation. And in my thought a *method*, unlike a *theory*, does not run ahead of the facts, but only analyzes and synthesizes them for the purpose of abstracting general rules about the normal operation of nature. In this sense, Darwin's "Geographical Distribution" is a *theory*; panbiogeography is a *method*.

True, no one would say that Darwin was guilty of gross stupidity. But he had most assuredly an excessive appetite for theorizing, which was well known to his own son (Himmelfarb 1959), and which is readily apparent to his discriminating readers. Grossly stupid he was not; indeed he was the contrary when it proved necessary to work out of tangles of his own making. But he was capable of incredible oversights, as I will show. Some persons may feel that the line between such oversights and sheer stupidity is tenuous. I personally feel no need to try to settle that issue, but I am convinced that Darwin fell short of being a genius.

Thinking as I do, I would have paid no attention at all to Gould and his opinion, but meditating upon his argument, I thought that Gould, even if wrong on every count, may still be given credit for opening the way to an interesting statement of the problem: Is it possible to find in the theorizing of Darwin and Matthew some logical error that disposes of it as a valid scientific instrument?

Thus formulated, the problem stands on a clear and factual basis beyond the province of mere opinion. It must be considered, naturally, with reference to the writings of Darwin and Matthew. I suppose that these texts, from which I will quote, have not received much critical attention from most of my readers. I would not blame them for any lack of critical appraisal—first, because biologists are only exceptionally disposed to check at the source the teachings that they imbibe during their formative years (Simpson, for example, through Matthew took Darwin for granted); second, because discovery of the true hinges of a "great and influential theory" formulated by a thinker such as Darwin is exceedingly difficult. Looking for black and white in a thick mess of gray is like searching for a lone seed in a haystack. To succeed, one must know exactly what he wants to find, and then patiently winnow tons of chaff in the hope of finding the only kernel fit to sprout.

In order to be as decisive as possible in what I argue and eventually conclude, I treat Darwin and Matthew separately, and then continue with comments on the work of both.

Darwin's "Geographical Distribution"

In the mature edition (sixth) of the *Origin*, Darwin states (chapter 12, *"Single Centres of supposed Creation,"* p. 32):

> We are thus brought to the question which has been largely discussed by naturalists, namely, whether species have been created at one or more points of the earth's surface. Undoubtedly there are many cases of extreme difficulty in understanding how the same species could possibly have migrated from some one point to the several distant and isolated points, where now found. Nevertheless the simplicity of the view that each species was first produced within a single region captivates the mind. He who rejects it, rejects the *vera causa* of ordinary generation with subsequent migration, and calls in the agency of a miracle.

This statement immediately renders it obvious that (1) Darwin had no idea worth mentioning of the process of species formation over space through time (he did not explain or discover, but only imagined, that a species issues from a particular center of origin, next to reach by active migration the "several distant and isolated points, where now found"); (2) caught on the short side of the argument, Darwin did not try to better the score, but counterattacked blindly by accusing any who would not believe him of rejecting the true cause of "ordinary generation with subsequent migration" and of appealing to "miracles."

The quality of Darwin's argument has serious implications; in my judgment it disqualifies Darwin as a theorist worthy of attention, and kills at the very moment of their birth two of the three fundamental props (the concepts of *center of origin* and *migration*) of his "Geographical Distribution,"—the eventual source of the "zoogeography" of Matthew, Simpson, Mayr, Darlington, Dobzhansky, and hosts of zoogeographers and phytogeographers who based their arguments and conclusions upon these concepts. The whole crashes at its birth, for its own parent admits that he does not understand the substance of the matter, while at the same time he invites his peers to share, and to exhibit, ignorance as a badge of common wisdom. Facing a major unknown, a true genius would recognize its importance and would steadily work until he had solved it, or at least until he had logically worked out some of its major difficulties. Under the vaults of Westminster, the distance may be short between the tombs of Isaac Newton and Charles Darwin, but with respect to their minds the two are poles apart.

The third prop of Darwin's "Geographical Distribution" is dealt with by him in a special section entitled "Means of Dispersal" (chapter 12). These means are identified as seeds carried by birds or distributed by marine currents, winds, etc. Curious is his warning that it is incorrect to call these means accidental: "the currents of the sea are not accidental, nor is the direction of prevalent gales of wind" (p. 329). Indeed, currents and gales result from the geography existing at the time of their circulating and blowing. Hence *means of dispersal* act on the average by norm, not by chance, in spite of appearances. And the rule, as a matter of observable fact, is that life and earth evolve together. Were it not so, Pleistocene would not follow Pliocene; nor would Pliocene follow Miocene.

In the *Origin* flashes of insight alternate with obscurity (chapter 12): "Whenever it is fully admitted, as it will some day be, that each species has proceeded from a single birthplace, and when in the course of time we know something definite about the means of distribution, we shall be enabled to speculate with security on the former extension of the land" (p. 324). This anticipation might seem reasonable to a naturalist ignorant of the facts of life, but surely not to him who knows them. First, on an "extension of the land," the "means of dispersal" (or "means of distribution") are neither more nor less than "means of survival." The "means" that a plant or animal employs to survive and to reproduce within its normal environment turn immediately into "means" of *active dispersal* if the normal environment enlarges because of favorable changes in geography, climate, ecology, etc. Thus, plants or animals adapted to live and reproduce along the fringes of a desert will readily turn their means of ordinary survival into means of active dispersal so as to occupy even the whole of a large desert if favorable conditions make it available to the life already on its fringes. The history of the Sahara during the last 15,000 years, for example, leaves little room for doubt on that score. Second, the hope that we may eventually know the "means of dispersal" of the majority of plants and animals is ludicrous. Not only are such "means" frequently considered "mysterious" by writers of the Darwinian tradition, but animals with "means" as different as, for example, those of earthworms and swallows are factually distributed over land and sea in a comparable scale of amplitude, proving that their different means of dispersal really had very little to do with bringing about the similarity of their distributions.

In summary of what is little by way of its pagination, but decisive, in my opinion, by way of its substance, the three classical props of Darwin's "Geographical Distribution" (meaning the zoogeography and phytogeography of many more recent authors) were stillborn—killed in the egg by their own parent author. It is incredible that, so far as I know, none of the scores of zoogeographers and phytogeographers who steered their efforts by means of Darwin's concepts ever seriously thought of checking for soundness the planks upon which he stood. Everyone has compiled everyone else in a rush of spurious orthodoxy and fictitious respectability. How sadly mistaken is he who feels certain that as a modern he can smile with impunity at the Middle Ages—so credulous, so prone to compilation, so ready to endorse piffle as legitimate knowledge, so inclined to place Augustine of Hippona before Bacon!

The chief difficulty presented to the reader by the *Origin* stems from the fact that its author was at the same time a good observer and a bad thinker. Because of this dualism, he who peruses the *Origin* as an Innocent without ideas of his own immediately sinks into a morass of examples and observations. Dizzy after reading a few pages, the Innocent is apt to view the *Origin* as a Bible, quite satisfied to believe that Solomon and Darwin share the same throne of wisdom.

Although Darwin proved incapable of formulating a viable theory of dispersal in the quoted text, he nevertheless was not far from achieving that viable theory that he so grandly muffed when opening the door to the concepts of *center of origin, migration,* and its *means* (chapter 12): "Undoubtedly many cases occur, in which we cannot explain how the same species could have passed from one point to the other. But the geographical and climatal changes, which have certainly occurred within recent geological times, must have rendered discontinuous the formerly continuous range of many species" (p. 321). This text may be illustrated by an example. Suppose that a species once was distributed throughout the area now occupied by the mountains that extend between Armenia and Taiwan, or, alternatively, along the shore of a former arm of the sea covering a sector of Venezuela from the central coast to the southwestern extremity of the country. Suppose, also, that because of later geological events this distribution became disrupted, leaving two widely separated populations at the extremities, or wings, of the original range. In this example, the sort visualized by Darwin and actually verified by the factual distributions of many plants and animals throughout the world, two remnants of the primitive distribution would vicariate even if separated by a distance judged to be long in terms of present mileage. These remnants would vicariate, or replace one another, within the area of the original (ancestral) distribution. Were a third or a fourth population to intervene between the two already considered, nothing of substance would change because the third or fourth remnant would also vicariate with the others, replacing them in particular areas. Thus, the number of populations and the mileage between them are secondary to the basically vicariant arrangement of such remnants that might persist from earlier distributions.

The two surviving populations in the wings would basically retain their initial positions: one in Armenia and the other in Taiwan; or, alternatively, one in northern and the other in southern Venezuela. The mileage intervening between them might seem impressive when reckoned as absolute distance, but neither of these populations would have moved a single yard in reaching the positions that they actually occupy on the map. In this case, the intervening distance would be real enough, but no migration would have been necessary to traverse it. A case of this kind, then, flatly contradicts the normal supposition that distance and migration are phenomena necessarily bound one with the other to the point of their being virtually the same.

It may be argued that if the populations now in a state of vicariance have not moved, the parent species itself must have actively migrated between Armenia and Taiwan at some earlier time or, alternatively, between one end of Venezuela and the other. This conclusion, however, does not necessarily follow, for it is possible that the parent species itself vicariated with other species far and near. In other words, the fact of migration becomes insignificant when vicariance is apparent. Thus we are led to the concept of *mobilism* vs. *immobilism* as an integral and fundamental aspect of organic evolution.

This concept (mobilism vs. immobilism) is fundamental. I pause for a moment to give it part of the attention it deserves. So far as known today, there have been in the history of the world four revolutions, two of which are of absolutely major proportions. These revolutions have been both geological (in the broad sense) and, on the rebound, biological, for earth and life evolve together. The existence of these revolutions is a matter of common knowledge, even if their full significance for evolution and dispersal may not as yet have been fully appreciated:

(1) Infracambrian Ice Age, about 600 Ma, was of long-lasting and severe glaciation. Its end marks the appearance in the fossil record of vascular plants, protozoans, poriferans, and, generally speaking, metazoans.

(2) Permo-Carboniferous Ice Age took place about 250 Ma, and was felt particularly in the southern hemisphere. Its end marks the appearance of very primitive mammals, birds, reptiles, and the first hints of modernization of insects, fishes, reptiles, and other groups.

(3) Alpine-Laramidian Orogeny, an age of active mountain building in the Old and New Worlds alike, began toward the end of the Cretaceous, about 80 Ma. It is responsible for the evolution of "modern" plants and animals evolving under the whip of its geological alterations that, as one may anticipate, also caused numerous extinctions. Thus, the surrection of the Andes and the Himalayas, for example, gave rise to numerous genera and species that today vicariate on their heights, and, by altering the course of winds, was instrumental in desiccating wide tracts of South America and Asia and in exterminating scores of mammals and other animals, for example, in Argentina, India, central Asia, and so on.

(4) Pliocene-Pleistocene Ice Ages closed the Tertiary, initiated the Recent, and, through renewed onsets of glaciation, destroyed a vast number of animals. *Homo* actively evolved and, in his role as hunter, was no doubt responsible for some part of this destruction.

These four ages doubtlessly altered the course of evolution. Plants and animals living under optimal conditions would likely have perished under the reverses of glacial cold and aridity or, in general terms, under conditions that they were unable to withstand. In disappearing, they would have left areas open to plants and animals that formerly had been marginal or were still genetically plastic—forms that took the lead, widely spread in all directions, and became dominant in the new ages opening.

I do not ask the reader to take literally the four ages that I have underscored above; a few lines of print cannot do justice to a history of a half-billion and more years. My purpose is only to sketch in a general way my understanding of the relationship between the evolution of the earth and the evolution of the life upon it. With this general statement as background, I now consider a particular example.

Mayr and Phelps (1967) elaborated a scheme of colonization by birds of the ancient cerros and mesas (Pantepui) of Venezuela. They postulate colonizing flights to Pantepui from the direction of the Andes, the coastal Venezuelan cordilleras, and, finally, the Brazilian Shield. In my judgment this scheme is false both in its chronology and in its biogeography (Croizat 1976).

It seems to me that the American continent developed none of the basic groups of modern plant and animal life. These groups would have reached it during the first upsurge of mobilism over trans-Atlantic and trans-Pacific tracks during the eras following the Permian and antedating the Cretaceous. Once in America, these groups apparently settled down to multiply and evolve in virtual immobilism. At the time there could have been no difference between Andean and Pantepuian worlds of life, for the Andes and cordilleras generally began to stir and rise only in the beginning of the Tertiary in a renewed period of mobilism, which eventually resulted in a multitude of species and genera that today vicariate geographically and altitudinally along the Andean chains and cordilleras. Naturally, the progenitors of these taxa would already have been in place at the time, for they could not otherwise have achieved their vicariant distributions the way they demonstrably did. An Andean and cordilleran world of life thus developed, distinct from a Pantepuian one, during an onset of partial mobilism. Yet because the progenitors of these worlds had been interrelated in ages before the Andean and cordilleran orogeny, their kinship would not have been altogether obliterated. Consequently Andean and cordilleran affinities are observable today in Pantepuian life, but these affinities do not imply the long-distance colonizing flights imagined by Mayr and Phelps, who suppose, mistakenly in my opinion, that the bird taxa of the tepuis are much too young, geologically speaking, to have evolved in place in relation to the geography.

I summarize this general sketch by stating that life and earth, too, never stay absolutely put, for there is a certain amount of alteration of already established ranges, that is to say, of migration, even in epochs of immobilism. But immobilism is the prime requirement for form-making, or speciation, in isolation. Without immobilism, vicariant distributions would be impossible. Epochs of general mobilism, in contrast, correspond to eras of marked and widespread geological alteration that destroys large amounts of preexisting flora and fauna in favor of plants and animals that are essentially weedy at the time. During periods of relatively slow and gradual mobilism, as for example the development of the Venezuelan Pantepui in relation to the more active orogeny of the Andes and cordilleras, the effects of mobilism and immobilism do combine quite closely in causing eventual form-making.

In my view, nothing of nature lends itself to hard and fast generalization beyond the essentials of a process. Yet nature's prime movers and manner of action are not beyond our grasp. They may be interpreted in particular cases with taste and measure. The interpretation may sometimes entail an apparent paradox, as for example, distance that is explained without appeal to active migration. The difficulty in understanding an intricate process, and the mind's natural repugnance for paradox, readily account for the fact that an author who, like Darwin, has the correct solution of a major problem almost within his grasp, may eventually lose his bearings and flounder into the inconsequential and erroneous instead of driving straight over the last few yards that still separate him from his goal.

Ernst Mayr seems another example. He has an excellent understanding of vicariant form-making (Mayr 1942). Yet as I see him, he is unable to dovetail vicariant form-making (a result of immobilism) and migration (a result of mobilism). As a taxonomist, he is an uncompromising "vicariist"; as a zoogeographer, he is also uncompromising, but he is a migrationist. Accordingly we find in his 1942 work a figure (figure 16) that lucidly explains the mainsprings and consequences of vicariance. Yet we read also of his zoogeography (Mayr *in litt.* to Bond 1948:208; cf. Croizat 1976:315): "The distances between the various Antilles are so much shorter than the wellsubstantiated jumps made by Pacific birds, I would not hesitate to accept transoceanic dispersal for the whole Antillean bird fauna without any major change of the present geological contours."

Darwin was one of the first naturalists to discover and report vicariance, nearly a century-and-a-half ago. But this epochal discovery fizzled out in his hands in a remarkable, even incredible, way. During his voyage on the *Beagle* (1831–36), he visited the Galapagos (15 September–20 October, 1835). The account of his observations on the islands fills the whole of a chapter of the *Voyage* (1839 and subsequent editions), and is particularly relevant within a work that, in my opinion, easily rates as one of his best—an imperishable monument to his talents as an observer. He writes (1846:145–46)[1]:

> The natural history of these islands is eminently curious, and well deserves attention. Most of the organic productions are aboriginal creations, found nowhere else; there is even a difference between the inhabitants of the different islands; yet all show a marked relationship with those of America, though separated from that continent by an open space of ocean between 500 and 600 miles in width. The archipelago is a little world within itself, or, rather, a satellite attached to America, whence it has derived a few stray colonists, and has received the general character of its indigenous productions. Considering the small size of these islands, we feel the more astonished at the number of their aboriginal beings, and at their confined range. Seeing every height crowned with its crater, and the boundaries of most of the lava-streams still distinct, we are led to believe that within a period geologically recent the unbroken ocean was here spread out. Hence, both in space and time, we seem to be brought somewhat near to that great fact—that mystery of mysteries—the first appearance of new beings on this earth.

Darwin's characterization of the islands seems factually exact; in my knowledge there is none better in so few lines of print. The islands do contain an endemic biota that is basically American; adventitious plants and animals are relatively few, and their presence does not alter the degree of endemism typical of the islands individually and collectively. Perfectly satisfactory as an observer, Darwin, in my opinion, forthwith flopped as a theorist, or better, as a thinker, when he reasoned that the unbroken ocean once was spread out where the islands now stand, and when he dreamed about the appearance of "new beings on this earth." We know today that Darwin was wrong in his

---

[1] Ed. Note: Croizat quotes from the second edition (1846) of Darwin's *Voyage*, which was altered from the original (1839), mainly to incorporate results that taxonomists achieved in their studies of the specimens that Darwin had collected. This passage does not appear in the original edition, but seems an adaptation of two passages, one earlier and one later, from the same chapter:

"The natural history of this archipelago is very remarkable: it seems to be a little world within itself; the greater number of its inhabitants, both vegetable and animal, being found nowhere else" (1839:454–55).

"I will not here attempt to come to any definite conclusions, as the species have not been accurately examined; but we may infer, that, with the exception of a few wanderers, the organic beings found on this archipelago are peculiar to it; and yet that their general form strongly partakes of an American character. It would be impossible for any one accustomed to the birds of Chile and La Plata to be placed on these islands, and not to feel convinced that he was, as far as the organic world was concerned, on American ground. This similarity in type, between distant islands and continents, while the species are distinct, has scarcely been sufficiently noticed. The circumstance would be explained, according to the views of some authors, by saying that the creative power had acted according to the same law over a wide area" (1839:474).

reasoning and in his dreaming, for geophysics has told us what to believe—in principle, if not in every detail of the geological history of the islands. But even without the help of geophysics, biogeography, as early as twenty-five years ago, did return clear and abundant evidence that Darwin had well understood the islands as an observer, but had wholly misunderstood them as a thinker (Croizat 1964:89–90).

On the strength of the above quotation, I am sure that what Darwin brings before his reader is a fragment of geological America that, because of the vicissitudes of tectonics and historical geology in general, was recast, apparently in early Tertiary times, into a number of islands beset by volcanism and in this respect similar to the none-too-distant Andes of Ecuador, the cordilleras of Panama, Costa Rica, El Salvador, Colombia, and so on.

On these tormented islands managed to evolve ancient plant and animal life inherited as a whole from the American continent at a general level of evolution corresponding to that ruling on the continent during the early Tertiary. Reacting to a violent history of volcanism, emersion, and submersion, this life evolved along lines of its own, but in no way contrary to the norms of organic evolution the world over. The peculiar birds of the islands, including the so-called Darwin finches, still show kinship to certain forms of the Lesser Antilles (as asserted by Bond 1950:167, against Lack 1947:101). This relationship might seem incredible were it not confirmed (Croizat 1976:182) by certain mammals and other forms such as the tortoises (Coizat 1976:522, citing Müller).

The question concerning how the islands were colonized by the progenitors of the plants and animals now living on them is one that might be asked of any area. The answer, in general, is that the islands were colonized in the same way as Costa Rica, Panama, Colombia, Ecuador, the United States, and the West Indies. It is difficult to understand upon what basis of fact and logic stand starry-eyed geographers who imagine that the islands are an exceptional locus of colonization and creation. It is true that, following their initial colonization, the islands worked out their own schemes of local form-making, but I can not see, however much I strain my imagination, that these schemes are more portentous than those ruling the evolution of life endemic to the Andes, to the serras of Brazil, to the Colombian Serranía de la Macarena, to the Pantepui of southeastern Venezuela, or to other areas of endemism the world over. Wonderment and chance have little place in nature, if nature acts by laws, distilling, so to speak, uncounted ponderables and imponderables through time and space into a final rule. What are the Galapagos in the scheme of nature—a pet lap-dog?

In the Galapagos "both in space and time, we seem to be brought somewhat near to that great fact—the mystery of mysteries—the first appearance of new beings on this earth," is a statement not quite as clear as most of Darwin's commentators seem to think—they who use Darwin's declaration to justify the islands as a marvel of zoogeography and natural selection. As a "satellite attached to America," can the Galapagos be the place reserved for the enactment of a mystery of mysteries?

I regret that the tyranny of space prevents my analyzing here the whole of the Darwinian account of life on the Galapagos (but I have not been remiss on a previous occasion: Croizat 1964:609 ff.). Hence I will concentrate on what Darwin related about vicariance (1846:166–72)[2]:

I have not as yet noticed by far the most remarkable feature in the natural history of this archipelago; it is, that the different islands, to a considerable extent, are

[2] Ed. note: Most of these six passages were added to later editions; some were much altered from the original edition (1839):

"It was confidently asserted, that the tortoises coming from different islands in the archipelago were slightly different in form; and that in certain islands they attained a larger average size than in others. Mr. Lawson maintained that he could at once tell from which island any one was brought. Unfortunately, the specimens which came home in the Beagle were too small to institute any certain comparison" (p. 465);

"It has been mentioned, that the inhabitants can distinguish the tortoises, according to the islands whence they are brought. I was also informed that many of the islands possess trees and plants which do not occur on the others. For instance the berry-bearing tree, called Guyavita, which is common on James Island, certainly is not found on Charles Island, though appearing equally well fitted for it. Unfortunately, I was not aware of these facts till my collection was nearly completed: it never occurred to me, that the productions of islands only a few miles apart, and placed under the same physical conditions, would be dissimilar. I therefore did not attempt to make a series of specimens from the separate islands. It is the fate of every voyager, when he has just discovered what object in any place is more particularly worthy of his attention, to be hurried from it. In the case of the mocking-bird, I ascertained (and have brought home the specimens) that one species (*Orpheus trifasciatus*, Gould) is exclusively found in Charles Island; a second (*O. parvulus*) on Albemarle Island; and a third (*O. melanotus*) common to James and Chatham Islands. The two last species are closely allied, but the first would be considered by every naturalist as quite distinct. I examined many specimens in the different islands, and in each the respective kind was *alone* present. These birds agree in general plumage, structure, and habits; so that the different species replace each other in the economy of the different islands. These species are not characterized by the markings on the plumage alone, but likewise by the size and form of the bill, and other differences. I have stated, that in the thirteen species of ground-finches, a nearly perfect gradation may be traced, from a beak extraordinarily thick, to one so fine, that it may be compared to that of a warbler. I very much suspect, that certain members of the series are confined to different islands; therefore, if the collection had been made on any *one* island, it would not have presented so perfect a gradation. It is clear, that if several islands have each their peculiar species of the same genera, when these are placed together, they will have a wide range of character. But there is not space in this work, to enter on this curious subject" (pp. 474–75).

inhabited by a different set of beings. My attention was first called to this fact by the vice-governor, Mr. Lawson, declaring that the tortoises differed from the different islands, and that he could with certainty tell from which island any one was brought. I did not for some time pay sufficient attention to this statement, and I had already partially mingled together the collections from two of the islands. I never dreamed that islands about fifty or sixty miles apart, and most of them in sight of each other, formed of precisely the same rocks, placed under a quite similar climate, rising to a nearly equal height, would have been differently tenanted; but we shall soon see that this is the case. It is the fate of most voyagers, no sooner to discover what is most interesting in any locality, than they are hurried from it; but I ought, perhaps, to be thankful that I obtained sufficient materials to establish this most remarkable fact in the distribution of organic beings. . . . The different islands probably have their representative species or races of the Amblyrhynchus [Iguanidae], as well as of the tortoise. My attention was first thoroughly aroused by comparing together the numerous specimens, shot by myself and several other parties on board, of the mock-ing-thrushes [Nesomimus], when, to my astonishment, I discovered that all those from Charles Island belonged to one species (Mimus trifasciatus); all from Albemarle Island to M. parvulus; and all from James and Chatham Islands (between which two other islands are situated as connecting links) belonged to M. melanotis. These two latter species are closely allied, and would, by some ornithologists, be considered as only well-marked races or varieties; but the Mimus trifasciatus is very distinct. Unfortu-nately most of the specimens of the finch tribe were mingled together; but I have strong reasons to suspect that some of the species of the sub-group Geospiza are confined to separate islands. . . . If we now turn to the Flora, we shall find the abo-riginal plants of the different islands wonderfully different. . . . The species of the Com-positae are particularly local, and Dr. Hooker has furnished me with several other most striking illustrations of the difference of the species on the different islands. He remarks that this law of distribution holds good both with those genera confined to the archipelago and those distributed in other quarters of the world. . . . It is the cir-cumstance that several of the islands possess their own species of the tortoise, mock-ing-thrush, finches, and numerous plants, these species having the same general habits, occupying analogous situations, and obviously filling the same place in the natural economy of this archipelago, that strikes me with wonder. It may be suspected that some of these representative species, at least in the case of the tortoise and of some of the birds, may hereafter prove to be only well-marked races; but this would be of equally great interest to the philosophical naturalist. . . . The only light which I can throw on this remarkable difference in the inhabitants of the dif-ferent islands is, that very strong currents of the sea, running in a westerly and W. N. W. direction, must separate, as far as transportal by the sea is concerned, the southern islands from the northern ones; and between these northern islands a strong N. W. current was observed, which must effectually separate James and Albemarle Islands. As the archipelago is free to a most remarkable degree from gales of wind, neither the birds, insects, nor lighter seeds would be blown from island to island. And lastly, the profound depth of the ocean between the islands, and their apparently recent (in a geological sense) volcanic origin, render it highly unlikely that they were ever united; and this, probably, is a far more important consideration than any other, with respect to the geographical distribution of their inhabitants. Reviewing the facts here given, one is astonished at the amount of creative force, if such an expression may be used, displayed on these small, barren, and rocky islands, and still more so at its diverse yet analogous action on points so near each other. I have said that the Galapagos Archipelago might be called a satellite attached to America, but it should rather be called a group of satellites, physically similar, organically distinct, yet intimately related to each other, and all related in a marked, though much lesser degree, to the great American continent.

In this text, Darwin reported one of the most remarkable sets of observations ever made by a naturalist. He perceived the importance of vicariance as a fundamental law of nature; he saw that "species" and "subspecies" (understood in the usual taxonomic sense) could not be discriminated absolutely, inasmuch as their limits are subject to the play of individual opinion; and he adopted the happy term "representative" as applied to species and subspecies. He was assured that casual means of dispersal among the islands were of little importance; he was satisfied that the plants and animals of the islands were basically American in their relationships. Thus, he had the whole of evolution and panbiogeography snugly in his hands by 1836. All that remained for him to do was to reason, from his own observations in the light of the axiom that earth and life evolve together, that it could not be true that the ocean unbounded lay forever there, where the Galapagos now stand; that the islands could not have originated, burning and lifeless, from the depths of the eastern Pacific, but do on the contrary represent the fragments, altered by later vulcanism, of an earlier history, of a former extension of the American mainland already tenanted by ancestral plants and animals.

It is incredible that Darwin, master of factual observations of paramount biological significance, proved unable to reach obvious conclusions; that he lost himself in hazy speculations about "creative forces" and, later, about the "origin of species." It is no doubt true that at times even the keenest minds muff what in retrospect seems unmuffable, but this excuse can hardly apply in Darwin's case. In order to proceed toward a judgment fair to everyone and everything concerned, let us ask whether Darwin was really unaware of the intimate bond between the history of the earth and that of the life upon it. The answer is clear: absolutely not. In the *Voyage*, chapter 20 is entitled "Keeling Island:—Coral Formations." In the conclusion of what Darwin most creditably expounds on the origin of atolls, he writes (1846:280–81)[3]:

[3] Ed. note: No comparable passage seems to exist in the original edition (1839). In his book on coral reefs, however, Darwin states (1842:142): "The immense surfaces on the map, which, both by our theory and by the plain evidence of upraised marine remains, have undergone a change of level either downwards or upwards during a late period, is a remarkable fact."

We must feel astonished at the vastness of the areas which have suffered changes in level either downwards or upwards, within a period not geologically remote. It would appear, also, that the elevatory and subsiding movements follow nearly the same laws.... Nor can I pass quite over the probability of the former existence of large archipelagoes of lofty islands, where now only rings of coral-rock scarcely break the open expanse of the sea, throwing some light on the distribution of the inhabitants of the other high islands, now left standing so immensely remote from each other in the midst of the great oceans. The reef-constructing corals have indeed reared and preserved wonderful memorials of the subterranean oscillations of level.

In chapter 21 he remarks that a specimen of tufaceous material collected on the "oceanic" island of Ascension in the mid-Atlantic was found to be composed almost wholly of organic remnants of freshwater infusoria and 25 different kinds of siliceous tissues of plants, chiefly grasses. He then asks (1846:297)[4]: "Where on the face of the earth can we find a spot, on which close investigation will not discover signs of that endless cycle of change to which this earth has been, is, and will be subjected?" Thus, did he ruin with a single stroke his theory that, biogeographically speaking, there are islands "continental" as opposed to "oceanic," anticipating by some 125 years the discovery on Ascension of remarkable crustaceans just as relictual, if not more so, than the specimens collected by Darwin (as commented on by Croizat 1976:99 ff.).

Darwin's "Geographical Distribution," based on the concepts of center of origin, migration, and means of dispersal, fell upon, and was propagated by, an uncritical and unthinking host of naturalists from 1859 to this day. The certificate of its birth leaves no doubt that Darwin preached from ignorance, not from knowledge. Hence, the question about how he could—having directly and efficiently observed and reported in the *Voyage* (1) the interplay of life and earth, (2) vicariance at work in different realms of life, and (3) the relative value of taxonomic ranks—next indulge in such a summary (*Origin*, chapter 12:30):

Undoubtedly there are many cases of extreme difficulty in understanding how the same species could possibly have migrated from some one point to the several distant and isolated points, where now found. Nevertheless the simplicity of the view that each species was first produced within a single region captivates the mind. He who rejects it, rejects the *vera causa* of ordinary generation with subsequent migration, and calls in the agency of a miracle.

The miracle, if such it be, is that Darwin did not recall at all in 1859

---

[4] Ed. note: No comparable passage seems to exist in the original edition (1839).

what he had seen in the Galapagos some 25 years earlier, of the "migrations" of the giant tortoises and mocking-thrushes, distributed among the different islands—not by migration of the extant species, or subspecies as they might be regarded, but by a process of vicariant form-making effected basically *in situ*, within a parent group already widespread over the region before its fragmentation into different islands. Indeed, this parent group did in its turn vicariate with other aggregates originally widespread in the Antilles, Central America, the East African Islands, and so on, in an endless process of immobilism and vicariant form-making, only occasionally broken by spells of mobilism and active enlargement or diminution of range—all without the chance migration and jumps of the zoogeographic, i.e., Darwinian, mode of explanation.

Who would be so grossly "stupid" (I borrow the epithet from Gould 1979), who, in contemplating the skies, could imagine a star migrating from some center of origin, thanks to its individual (and possibly mysterious) means of dispersal, to the place now occupied by Polaris, or by a star of the Southern Cross? Who would be so foolish as to tackle the dispersal of avian life under the assumption that first he must be sure, before beginning, of the location of some 30,000 centers of origin for as many species or subspecies of birds (Croizat 1976:549)? Why, when fabulating that water is "a most effective barrier for land birds," does an ornithologist fail to mention that certain "superspecies" of White-Eyes of the Central Solomon Islands are distributed quite as vicariously as the tortoises and mocking-thrushes of the Galapagos (Mayr 1942:227)?

The answer is simple and direct. Darwin, and whoever followed, or still follows, him never synthesized the facts of nature within an efficient doctrine of dispersal and form-making, that is, a genuinely scientific biogeography. In short, the whole of the "Geographical Distribution" of Darwin expired at its birth because of a "logical error in its formulation" (I again borrow from Gould 1976). Darwin was indeed a good observer, but, alas, an indifferent thinker. Being made of the same tender stuff, thousands of specialists, expert in sundry branches of biology, but less well grounded as a whole, did blithely walk the same primrose path of "geographical distribution" and "zoogeography."

I would not claim, but do not hesitate to acknowledge, that I have done for the liberation of my peers (Ball 1976) what Darwin could have done after debarking from the *Beagle* with the treasure of his own observations, instead of chasing a will-o-the-wisp—the origin of species—under the assumption that artificial and natural selection are homologous processes.

In summary, I judge that Darwin's "geographical distribution," and the zoogeography and phytogeography that it sired, are worthless as instruments of learning. The text expounding the stuff attracts those unaccustomed to exactitude in thought because of its lavish display of more or less harmoniously related details. It repels those persons who, satisfied that 2 and 5 are true as numbers, do not yet accept that $2+2=5$. In summary, the line is by now sharply and finally drawn: Either the Darwinians bury me, or I them.

Matthew's *Climate and Evolution*

Matthew's work opens with a thesis of five dicta, which I quote and comment upon:

(1) Secular climatic change has been an important factor in the evolution of land vertebrates and the principal known cause of their present distribution.

Comment: Land vertebrates are but a small part of biogeography; and secular climatic change is but a small part of geology.

(2) The principal lines of migration in later geological epochs have been radial from Holarctic centers of dispersal.

Comment: The distributions of Tertiary mammals, when shown on a map of a northern polar projection, may create the illusion of Holarctic centers of dispersal. But this illusion is obviously insufficient to justify Matthew's contention as a general theory of biogeography.

(3) The geographic changes required to explain the present distribution of land vertebrates are not extensive and for the most part do not affect the permanence of the oceans as defined by the continental shelf.

Comment: The distribution of land vertebrates may be invoked as the main prop of a theory of dispersal. But vertebrates alone cannot settle the matter. Also, it is false that oceans have been permanent in the way Matthew claims.

(4) The theories of alternations of moist and uniform with arid and zonal climates, as elaborated by Chamberlin, are in exact accord with the course of evolution of land vertebrates, when interpreted with due allowance for the probable gaps in the record.

Comment: "Probable gaps in the record" do not justify affirmations of a theory presented with supporting evidence that is clearly insufficient.

Chamberlin's theories, however understood, are not in "exact accord with the course of evolution" of life at large.

(5) The numerous hypothetical land bridges in temperate tropical and southern regions, connecting continents now separated by deep oceans, which have been advocated by various authors, are improbable and unnecessary to explain geographic distribution. On the contrary, the known facts point distinctly to a general permanency of continental outlines during the later epochs of geologic time, provided that due allowance be made for the known or probable gaps in our knowledge.

Comment: It might be true that there has been a "general permanency of continental outlines during the later epochs of geological time," particularly "if due allowance be made." Yet it is patently false that this "general permanency" renders land bridges "improbable and unnecessary."

In my view Matthew's theory is not a tool of scientific investigation, but merely the unsupported opinion of a specialist in mammalian paleontology who speaks on matters beyond his specialty. How this opinion came to dominate American and world biology would be a conundrum were we lacking information that Simpson believed in Matthew's dicta and actively worked, together with his associates, to spread them (Simpson 1976).

Simpson relates that his interests have been multifarious—biogeography being one of them. He wavered at first between the viewpoints of Schuchert and Matthew, and eventually endorsed the latter. To my mind, Simpson's account of these early days plainly means that he was incapable of synthesizing the main points of the different disciplines with which he had to contend. If I may speak of my own experience, I soon found that the facts of the distribution of life at large, consulted in full freedom of theoretical preferences, immediately proved fallacious the taboo against trans-Atlantic dispersal, a taboo to which Simpson has clung for many years in seemingly flat subservience to Matthew. This seems not a matter of opinion, but of plain fact. Even at this late date, when Simpson faces the ruin of his own "zoogeography," he insists that a serious student (myself) is a member of the lunatic fringe simply for having done what he (Simpson) should have done at the beginning.

Darwin's *Origin of Species*

This article would not be adequate if, following the theories of Darwin and Matthew on dispersal, it failed to put on record a few notes on Darwin's theory of evolution. Willis made it quite clear years ago that there is no validity in theories of evolution and dispersal that jar one against the other (Willis 1940). So grave are the deficiencies of Darwin's "geographical distribution," that we ask whether his "natural selection" is any better.

Certain hints in the *Voyage* suggest that Darwin as an evolutionist is no better than he was as a biogeographer. With reference to the peculiar iguanid lizards of the Galapagos, he writes (1846:161)[5]: "They are both herbivorous, although the kind of vegetation on which they feed is so very different. . . . the form of the mouth may almost be compared to that of the tortoise: one is led to suppose that this is an adaptation to their herbivorous appetites."
It seems to me a plain fact that appetites, of whatever sort, depend in the first place upon the type of mouth and the dentition of the creature seeking food. It is conceivable, especially over time, that a given mouth, its dentition, and its food might all fit together, but it is inconceivable in my view that the food molds the mouth and dentition required to partake of it. Although man devises and manufactures an instrument necessary to accomplish a purpose, an animal lives only with what nature fits it at birth. Accordingly, the iguanas of the Galapagos eat what they do with the mouth that inheritance placed in their heads. Fitted with a different mouth, they would partake of different food, as will an old man turned edentate, without the help of contrivances, no longer eat what he did earlier in life. Thus the structure, or instrument, precedes and determines its use; for without structure, or instrument, use cannot follow.

Darwin seems to have taken for granted, as if instinctively, that use molds the structure. For him, the availability of a certain kind of food adapts the type of mouth and dentition required to partake of it. This means that nature reasons, as it were, like man; nature works to a purpose to devise the mouth fit to the food, acting for the good, in this case, of the animal if not the plant. This viewpoint, characteristic of Darwin and his theory of natural selection, is the source of the teleological bias that eventually stultifies his theory, which presupposes that natural selection works for what is advantageous to this or that organic being, plant or animal, in its struggle for existence.

Supposedly a staunch Darwinian, Simpson maintains that today natural selection should not be understood in terms of struggle for existence

---

[5] Ed. note: This passage is slightly modified from the original edition (1839): "They are both herbivorous, although the kind of vegetation consumed in each case is so very different. Mr. Bell has given the name to the genus from the shortness of the snout: indeed, the form of the mouth may almost be compared to that of the tortoise. One is tempted to suppose this is an adaptation to their herbivorous appetites" (pp. 471–72).

(Simpson 1949:221). If even Simpson is unsatisfied with Darwin's notion, the question arises as to what Darwin himself thought about the concept:

Natural selection will never produce in a being any structure more injurious than beneficial to that being, for natural selection acts solely by and for the good of each. . . . Natural Selection tends only to make each organic being as perfect as, or slightly more perfect than, the other inhabitants of the same country with which it comes into competition. (*Origin*, chapter 6, "Utilitarian Doctrine," pp. 162–63)

It is generally acknowledged that all organic beings have been formed on two great laws—Unity of Type, and the Conditions of Existence. By unity of type is meant that fundamental agreement in structure which we see in organic beings of the same class, and which is quite independent of their habits of life. On my theory, unity of type is explained by unity of descent. The expression of conditions of existence, so often insisted on by the illustrious Cuvier, is fully embraced by the principle of natural selection. For natural selection acts by either now adapting the varying parts of each being to its organic and inorganic conditions of life; or by having adapted them during past periods of time: the adaptations being aided in many cases by the increased use or disuse of parts, being affected by the direct action of the external conditions of life, and subjected in all cases to the several laws of growth and variation. Hence, in fact, the law of the Conditions of Existence is the higher law; as it includes, through the inheritance of former variations and adaptions, that of Unity of Type. (Ibid., "Summary," pp. 166–67)

The first text quoted could be augmented by reference to others of the same tenor. It is the essence of Darwin's thought and requires little comment. Competition and struggle are fundamental to natural selection, which could not take place if all things of nature were in peaceful harmony. The second text is significant on several counts. Long before Darwin's time it was understood that organic beings have been formed in accordance with two laws: inheritance and environmental influence. If we suppose that a seal and a penguin owe their peculiarities to a marine environment, it is still certain that, by inheritance, a seal is a mammal; and a penguin is a bird. Inheritance is a factor that, once admitted, allows no doubt. Environmental influence is debatable, even once admitted, for more often than not it is held responsible for analogies, not homologies, of structure. Hence environment plays second fiddle to inheritance, which, within the broad concept of "type of organization," is the factor that rules out teeth in the bill of a penguin without proscribing them from the mouth of a seal, regardless of the environment and its pressures (see, e.g., Simpson 1949:23 for "type of organization").

Darwin admits that "adaptations. . . . ['by the direct action of the external conditions of life' are] subjected in all cases to the general laws of growth and variation" (Ibid.); and that "the chief part of the organization of every living creature is due to inheritance; and consequently, though each being assuredly is well fitted for its place in nature, many structures have now no very close and direct relation to present habits of life" (*Origin*, "Utilitarian Doctrine," p. 160). He also says:

We may easily err in attributing importance to characters, and in believing that they have been developed through natural selection. We must by no means overlook the effects of the definite action of changed conditions of life,—of so-called spontaneous variations, which seem to depend in a quite subordinate degree on the nature of the conditions,—of the tendency to reversion to long-lost characters,—of the complex laws of growth, such as of correlation, compensation, of the pressure of one part on another, etc.... But structures thus indirectly gained, although at first of no advantage to a species, may subsequently have been taken advantage of by its modified descendants, under new conditions of life and newly acquired habits. (Ibid., "Organs of Little Apparent Importance," pp. 157–58).

The mind of a genius is well balanced between things that are and things that should and will be. It gets hold of the substances of a question raised by observable facts and their logical interrelations, and reasons out a set of conclusions. If means to this end are unavailable at the moment, it labors to supply the means, ever conscious of its purposes. Thus were the minds of Kepler and Newton, the former more on the intuitive side, the latter on the synthesizing side of the ledger.

Within Darwin, two different persons seemed to be at odds: one was a shrewd observer; the other was an uncompromising, even rabid, theorist. I judge that, had he been a genius, Darwin would have reasoned from the enormous treasure of observations and impressions gained from his voyage, and would have given to the world of the 1850s a work of sterling value, to last through the ages in point of principle and method. Alas, he was seduced by the notion that artificial and natural selection are fundamentally the same process; and he was forced to build a theory in which the will and purpose of the human and artificial breeder is matched by some extrahuman purpose in nature and natural breeding. This purpose, as eventually codified by Darwin, is natural selection:

This preservation of favourable individual differences and variations, and the destruction of those which are injurious, I have called Natural Selection, or the Survival of the Fittest.... Some [writers] have even imagined that natural selection induces variability, whereas it implies only the preservation of such variations as arise and are beneficial to the being under its conditions of life. (Ibid., chapter 4, "Natural Selection," p. 63)

Darwin tried to give natural selection first place before inheritance, which led him into fundamental contradictions. He could not deny that laws of growth dominate the stage of life independent of natural selection; and that adaptation through environmental influence is subject in all cases to laws of growth and variation independent of natural selection.

Thus caught on his own hook, Darwin squirmed through long pages of the *Origin*, trying without much success to fit a multitude of facts to natural selection. Among many other takers of the Darwinian bait, Simpson tried to show it palatable, if only it were digested with a new understanding (Simpson 1949:268):

Darwin was one of history's towering geniuses and ranks with the greatest heroes of man's intellectual progress. He deserves this place first of all because he finally and definitely established evolution as a fact, no longer a speculation or an alternative hypothesis for scientific investigation. His second greatest achievement was correct identification of a major element in the rise of adaptation: natural selection. It must, however, be noted that the modern concept of natural selection has been considerably broadened and refined and is not quite the same as Darwin's. . . . In the modern theory natural selection is differential reproduction, plus the complex interplay in such reproduction of heredity, genetic variation, and all the other factors that affect selection and determine its results.

In my view Simpson proves unequal to the task of explaining what is, or what might be, the "complex interplay" about which he dreams. If natural selection is to be understood by appeal to differential reproduction, heredity, and genetic variation, the conclusion seems to follow that inheritance (or, to be frank, Darwin's "laws of growth") precede and mold natural selection. In his thought Simpson seems moored today to the very same peg to which Darwin fastened himself in 1859.

Gould seems to beat a different path. He affirms: "The essence of Darwinism lies in its claim that natural selection creates the fit. Variation is ubiquitous and random in direction. It supplies the raw material only. Natural selection directs the course of evolutionary change. It preserves favorable variants and builds fitness gradually" (Gould 1976:28). I observe that no species ever manages to survive forever; each becomes extinct with time. Hence natural selection, even at best, creates fitness only for a time. Yet variation is not random in direction; it occurs only within limits set by types of organization. Birds are birds, be they colibris, ostriches, or penguins—each fit to survive until its extinction in its natural environment. As a Darwinian, Gould supposes that types of organization come about through micromutations, transmitted and augmented by inheritance, that no one has ever been able to demonstrate. But even if "variation" were supposed to supply the "raw material" of evolution, on what would natural selection work if "variation" did not first supply the raw material? Neo-Darwinians, seldom write about the difficulties that beset their point of view. The arguments of Simpson, Gould, and other Neo-Darwinians seem never to rise above the level of unsupported affirmation and neglect of pertinent literature critical of their stance.

Summary

G. Nelson

BIOGEOGRAPHY IN its historical aspect is a science that developed during the nineteenth century, stemming primarily from the activities of European naturalists such as Buffon, Humboldt, Candolle, and others of their time. An early synthesis by Candolle (1820) considered areas of plant endemism and their possible causes. Wallace (1876, 1880) followed with a synthesis of animal distribution, explained within the context of evolution by natural selection and dispersal from northern centers of origin on an earth stable in its main geographical features. Wallace's synthesis, at least in North America, quickly achieved prominence and remained generally stable and unchallenged for about 100 years (Nelson 1978).

The revival of continental drift during the 1960s was the doom of Wallace's synthesis (dispersalist biogeography). That dynamic concept of earth history made it clear that the 100-odd-year tradition of dispersalism was based on some fundamental error. A suggestion of a possible cause and remedy was supplied by Brundin (1966), who coupled Hennig's (1950) notions of cladistics with repetitive vicariant distributions of freshwater midges of the temperate parts of the southern continents. One result was that Croizat's panbiogeography was brought into the light of present relevance where, fused with cladistics, it matured into vicariance biogeography.

The problem that was clarified in the process was a problem of pattern, or order in nature, understandable in the form of a cladogram, a branching diagram of relationships. Some theoretical development was necessary before the possibilities of a cladistic treatment of geographical distribution could be realized (Rosen 1978; Platnick and Nelson 1978); distribution as a biological fact seemed inherently too complex to most biogeographers, with the notable exception of Croizat, to suggest an underlying simplicity of patterns that could be summarized in a cladogram. Gradually, however, vicariance biogeography developed with its concern for areas of endemism and for the interrelationships of the endemic forms of life living in them. In retrospect, vicariance biogeography, under the stimulus of plate tectonics, Croizat's synthesis, and Hennig's cladistics, picked up the subject where Candolle left it when he died 140 years ago. In this sense, vicariance biogeography has proved to be an alternative to the tradition of biogeography that has often been associated with the names of Charles Darwin and Alfred Wallace.

Vicariance biogeography is not an attempt to explain everything, or even the greater part, of the geographical distribution of plants and animals, for its focus is allopatric differentiation as manifested by the phenomenon of endemism. It is historical, rather than ecological, and corresponds to Candolle's study of "habitations," rather than to his study of "stations." It begins by asking one question: Is there a cladogram of areas of endemism? Or, in other words: Are areas of endemism interrelated among themselves in a way analogous to the interrelationships of the species of a certain group of organisms?

The long and sometimes complex argument about cladistics, as exemplified in the pages of *Systematic Zoology*, teaches that fundamental concepts of cladistics are not always easily grasped by persons unfamiliar with them, and are often ungraspable by persons trained to think in other ways. A cladistic approach to biogeography compounds the argument by transferring it to a different domain of empirical investigation—distributions of endemic forms of life. Considered as specimens, or species, distributions are difficult to work with. They cannot be dried, pickled, or pinned according to standard museum techniques of preparation and storage. They are not even directly observable, except as they may be rendered on maps. And they are sensitive to revisionary change, in accordance with the vagaries of taxonomic practice, when species are lumped or split. Some persons believe that distributions, like behaviors, are evanescent in their capacity to change in the temporal dimension. Distributions are sometimes dismissed as abstract phenomena that, like shadows, are without much if any reality in time and space. Yet distributions have at least one redeeming value, for they are of potential interest to all persons studying life and its history. Hence what is true about them does not derive from the pronouncements of any single specialist no matter how expert he might be in his detailed knowledge of a certain group of organisms. What is true about distributions in a general sense derives from knowledge of life in all its forms. To the extent that the same distributions are exemplified by different groups of organisms, they pose a general problem inviting divergent specialists to interact in search of a general solution. Biogeography is in this sense an interdisciplinary synthesis not only within biological systematics itself, but a synthesis among life, earth, and planetary sciences. Therein is the redeeming value of the study of distributions; no other focus brings together, within a common theoretical framework, these diverse investigations and even others that extend beyond (Carey 1978).

The contributors to this symposium were asked to critique the present state of vicariance biogeography. Science being the overspecialized type of activity that it is, the results were predictable enough, and they are recorded in the presentations published in this volume—a fair cross section of response from scientists concerned, or willing to become concerned, with biogeography in one sense or another. The committee that organized the symposium went to some length to insure a diversified group of contributors, so as to avoid a symposium that would merely voice its approval and thereby propagandize in favor of vicariance biogeography.

The first day, with presentations by Udvardy, Simberloff et al., Brundin, Erwin, and nine discussants, was a philosophical free-for-all, centering on dispersal versus vicariant interpretations of distribution. Most of the participants forgot to mention that dispersalism, in its traditional guise, is no longer an issue, having already been rendered obsolete by the revolution in the earth sciences, if not previously by the synthesis of Croizat (1952, 1958, 1960, 1964, 1968a, 1968b, 1976)—an author whose ideas have generally been dismissed by traditional dispersalists as either radical or impenetrable, and whose books, like Scharff's (1899, 1911), went uncited by traditional dispersalists in their blind adherence to the status quo. Rather than to identify the error inherent in traditional dispersalism, most contributors fretted with the notion of "dispersal" in a different guise, which renders it the same as Croizat's concept of "mobilism." It was for Brundin, among the symposium participants, to codify this view of "dispersal" in its modern sense, in relation to its general cause: removal of preexisting barriers. In Croizat's terms, the removal of barriers allows "means of survival" to become "means of dispersal," and marks the shift from a period of "immobilism" to a period of "mobilism." Indeed, one main area of philosophical agreement among participants of this symposium is this restricted concept of "dispersal" (Udvardy, Brundin, Erwin, Haffer, Prance, Tattersall). That the restricted concept is merely a restatement of Croizat's "mobilism" was not, however, generally recognized or acknowledged by the participants, many of whom stressed that "dispersal" and vicariant interpretations are complementary, not exclusive, concepts.

The second day focused on the biogeography of the Pacific, which seemingly remains the last frontier of global investigation. Presentations by Solem, Melville, Hallam, and Nur and Ben-Avraham, and nine discussants left the audience with mixed reactions to a possible Pacifica continent and its biological implications. By the day's end many persons were convinced that there is a real problem. In response to Melville's presentation in particular, the discussion provoked some denunciations of the Pacifica theory (because it differs from current orthodoxy) that were reminiscent of those made earlier in this century against Wegener's presentation of continental drift (because it clashed with what was then widely accepted as truth by geologists of that time). Only Edmunds pointed out that widespread acceptance is not the same as truth and that widespread acceptance is not a relevant measure of the worth of a theory.

The third day dealt with refuge theory in South America, and paleontology in general, with presentations by Haffer, Wolfe, Patterson, and six discussants. The afternoon concluded with the reading of Croizat's manuscript (by Luis Rivas). An added evening session featured a presentation by Mary Mickevich, and some additional remarks on the Indian Ocean by Nur. The day's highlight was the contrast between Wolfe and Patterson in their presentations and in their different approaches to the interpretation of information about fossils. It is in this area (paleontology) that a cladistic approach to biogeography is apt to provoke the greatest controversy, if, as seems likely, human history tends to repeat. As a group, paleontologists were the last to learn the lessons of cladistics, and they are apt to be the last to learn whatever vicariance biogeography has to teach them.

Rather than to review the philosophical contributions paper by paper, I elect first merely to list what I consider the obstacles consciously or unconsciously raised by, or liable to be read into the presentations of, the contributors. They are obstacles to understanding what seems to be, in retrospect no doubt, a fairly simple question: Is there a general cladogram of areas of endemism? This question presupposes the possiblity that there is such a cladogram or, if not, that there are more than one that, taken together, specify real relations existing in the natural world. The question presupposes also that whatever answer is reached will be real knowledge of the natural world. That this question cannot be answered today, except in a tentative way, is a reflection of the progress, or lack of progress, in biogeography since Candolle (1820). That this question seems difficult for some persons to understand is at best a reflection of the human condition, bound as it is to precepts acquired early in life. For most of the participants of this symposium (about this there is no doubt), the precepts acquired were those of dispersal over a stable geography—the precepts inherent in traditional dispersalism.

To itemize the obstacles to perception and to understanding displayed by one's colleagues, or merely read into their words, is a thankless task that is apt to be resented by author and reader alike. I do it not to engender their resentment, nor to show expertise in analysis. If creating obstacles is in some sense a mistake, then knowledge of them is best acquired from one's personal experience in making them. There is no sense, in short, in pointing out mistakes of others (be they well intentioned authors who nevertheless mislead, or well intentioned readers who nevertheless misconstrue) unless the mistakes have been one's own as well; hence I claim them all as my own in my capacity both as an author and as a reader. My purpose is to pinpoint those stumbling blocks that seem real enough to me, that have been created by authors or may be created by readers, and that, therefore, may trouble the understanding of one and all. I do not consider the following list definitive, nor authoritative, for such are not possibilities to which I aspire. Biogeography has too long been riddled with definitive authority. What the field needs now is a simplification of theory that will open the field to future investigation. What it needs are questions, not answers. Without them, it will remain what, perhaps, it still is: a nineteenth-century science that, for a while, has become interesting once again.

The stumbling blocks in the following list are each organized in the form of a premise and a conclusion. As such they are unambiguous, even if fallacious for one reason or another: because the premise is merely false, or at least debatable; because the conclusion merely restates the premise; or because the conclusion does not follow from the premise. Stated as such, the 35 items would probably be rejected by all of the authors with whom I associate them—and perhaps by many readers as well. To anticipate their criticism, I suppose that the critics would charge that the list is one of straw men. I suppose also that the critics would charge that I render their words, or their readings, absurd by taking them to extremes. I would respond, however, by asserting that I merely render the thoughts and readings unambiguous. To leave them in an ambiguous state, qualified by expressions such as "in some cases," "probably," "might be," "is possible," "may be true," etc., would be to leave them as they can already be abundantly found in the current literature and the many discussions of it.

(1) *Higher taxa:* Higher taxa (and their geographical distributions) are artifacts of classification; therefore they are unreal (Udvardy).

(2) *Correct classification:* Present classification is not totally correct; therefore it is uninformative (Short, Brundin, Erwin, Solem, Niklas).

(3) *Unique histories:* Each taxon has a unique history; therefore taxa are incomparable (Short, Koopman).

(4) *Dispersal:* Much dispersal has occurred; therefore distributions of organisms are random (Short).

(5) *Oceanic islands:* Endemic life exists on mid-ocean islands; therefore ancestral species dispersed there over water (Short, Koopman, Howden).

(6) *Vagility:* Organisms disperse; therefore vagility must be considered first (Short, Erwin).

(7) *Cattle Egret:* the Cattle Egret crossed the Atlantic unaided by human agency; therefore other organisms have also done so (Short, Koopman).

(8) *Equiprobable topologies:* Cladogram topologies have equal probabilities of occurrence; therefore taxonomists must have made cladograms accordingly (Simberloff et al.).

(9) *Nonrandom sampling:* Sampling can be biased; therefore vicariance biogeographers have taken biased samples (Simberloff et al.).

(10) *Ghosts:* Missing data can disagree with an area cladogram; therefore they will disagree when found (Simberloff et al.).

(11) *Sympatric speciation:* Sympatric speciation occurs; therefore it explains allopatric distributions (Simberloff et al., Smith, Slater).

(12) *Random model:* Nature is nonrandom; therefore random models are unnatural (Terborgh).

(13) *Center of origin:* Centers of origin are apparent; therefore they exist (Terborgh, Brundin, Solem, Melville, Hallam, Wolfe).

(14) *Regression analysis:* Faunal similarity and interisland distance are significantly correlated; therefore they are causally related (Terborgh).

(15) *Deviations:* There are deviations from the norm; therefore the deviations are to be explained by any theory purporting to explain the norm (Smith).

(16) *Point origin:* A center of origin is not a point; therefore centers of origin exist (Smith, Brundin).

(17) *Peripheral apomorphy:* Speciation involves isolation of a peripheral population; therefore apomorphic populations are peripherally located geographically (Brundin).

(18) *Progression rule:* The progression rule has been applied; therefore it is true (Brundin).

(19) *Dispersal concealed:* Dispersal occurs; therefore vicariance biogeographers conceal its occurrence (Brundin, Slater).

(20) *Monotopism:* It is inconceivable that the same species (or genus) can evolve in more than one place; therefore it can't (Brundin, Haffer).

(21) *Amphitropical distribution:* Amphitropical distributions have been caused by dispersal; therefore vicariance biogeography is wrong (Brundin).

(22) *Simple mechanisms:* Nature is complex; therefore simple causal mechanisms are unnatural (Erwin, Koopman, Howden).

(23) *Semantics:* Human communication is difficult; therefore semantics is the big problem (Erwin).

(24) *Taxonomic level:* There is a correlation between age of origin and taxonomic level; therefore genera are older than species, families are older than genera, etc. (Erwin, Koopman, Wolfe).

(25) *Taxon pulses:* Taxon pulses arise through competition and adaptation; therefore competition and adaptation determine the course of evolution and dispersal (Erwin).

(26) *Evolutionary process:* Evolution is a process; therefore the process must first be understood before its results can be investigated (Erwin).

(27) *Numerous possibilities:* The same type of distribution can be achieved in different ways; therefore it has been achieved in different ways (Koopman, Solem).

(28) *Improbable/probable:* Probabilities are what they are; therefore the improbable becomes probable with time (Koopman).

(29) *Founder effect:* The founder effect is important; therefore it is important (Howden).

(30) *Fossil evidence:* Fossil evidence is the most important; therefore it will be the most important when it is found (Solem).

(31) *Insufficient evidence:* Present evidence is incomplete; therefore it is insufficient (Solem).

(32) *Pacifica:* The Pacifica hypothesis does not gibe with currently accepted views; therefore the hypothesis is wrong (Haugh, Hallam).

(33) *Earliest fossil:* The earliest fossil of a group is the best estimate of

the group's age; therefore a group without any, or only with young, fossils cannot be old (Haugh, McKenna, Wolfe).

(34) *Young groups:* Groups without old fossils are young; therefore their ancestors must have dispersed rather than have been involved in old vicariance events (Haugh, McKenna, Wolfe, Niklas).

(35) *Fossil record:* The fossil record is incomplete; therefore it cannot be used to test hypotheses (Niklas).

If the items display a common theme, it is the wonder of the kaleidoscope (Udvardy, Erwin): Nature is marvelously complex; hence no explanation of it will suffice unless the explanation is equally complex and marvelous. Yet a kaleidoscope is fully explained, scientifically if not aesthetically, by the optical properties of a few mirrors appropriately arranged, if not by the movement that, induced in some bits of colored glass, produces a particular arrangement of the bits. Such is the power of scientific theories that as simple statements explain simple regularities, if not all of the particular manifestations of the regularities.

An instructive example from the history of genetics is the marvelously complex array of hereditary factors faced by T. H. Morgan earlier in this century. Looking for repetitive elements of pattern, Morgan and his group of students in the "fly room" of Columbia University sorted factors into "linkage groups" of genes inherited together, and found them numerically correlated with chromosome number in *Drosophila melanogaster* (Allen 1978:164):

> There were as many linkage groups, determined by breeding data, as there were chromosome pairs determined by cytological observations. As a result of these two lines of work (the chiasmatype theory and the working out of linkage groups) by 1914 it became even more clear to Morgan that the chromosome interpretation of the Mendelian laws was a theory of enormous power. The two theories were not incompatible, but in fact seemed to be two sides of the same coin.

Thus, the "Mendelian-Chromosome Theory" of inheritance was developed, for which Morgan received the Nobel Prize in 1933.

The "linkage groups" of the biogeographer are no more or no less than congruent cladograms specifying the interrelationships of endemic forms of life; the "chromosomes" are the structural features of the earth's crust, "that is, major features of the earth past and present fit to influence the course of life by fixing biogeographic boundaries, primary and secondary centers of form-making, etc." (Croizat 1964:115–16). The correlation between the two is the guts of vicariance biogeography, just as the correlation between linkage groups and chromosomes is the guts of Morgan's contributions to genetics.

That there might exist a parallelism between one theory (Morgan's) and another (Croizat's) will come as no surprise to persons familiar with science in general and with the nature of its theories. Such a parallelism would, however, be denied by many persons within the fields of biological systematics and biogeography, who view the one (Morgan's) as respectable and the other (Croizat's) as outlandish. The explanation for this polarity, which is perhaps somewhat diminished at present, was suggested a few years ago by Robert MacArthur, who, now deceased, was probably totally unaware of vicariance biogeography:

> To do science is to search for repeated patterns, not simply to accumulate facts, and to do the science of geographical ecology is to search for patterns of plant and animal life that can be put on a map. The person best equipped to do this is the naturalist who loves to note changes in bird life up a mountainside, or changes in plant life from mainland to island, or changes in butterflies from temperate to tropics. But not all naturalists want to do science; many take refuge in nature's complexity as a justification to oppose any search for patterns (MacArthur 1972:1).

It is my impression that, amid all of the philosophical repartee of the symposium, the only issue at stake was already pinpointed by MacArthur.

One aspect on which MacArthur does not comment, is why anyone should oppose a search for patterns. Because he attributed this opposition to many naturalists, one may wonder what motivation prompts the opposition. I have often wondered, but can do no more here than suggest a possible motivation, namely that naturalists, specialized as they are, seek to maintain what they feel is their right to pontificate over all knowledge impinging upon their specialty. It is a right—one might better say *rite*,—that has been maintained throughout the history of biological systematics, if not geology, and it is especially tangible within the literature of traditional dispersalism. It is a rite that has gone uncontested except most notably by Croizat. That he contested it without inhibition explains in my opinion why traditional dispersalists classed him as untouchable, and his books as uncitable. Croizat noted (1964:iv):

> It is obvious that never having thought of doing what I myself did, and bound through thick and thin by narrow 'specialities,' . . . my peers could not understand what I had planned to do, how I was developing it, and why it must after all be so disturbing to their accustomed standards of opinion.

The general justification for Croizat's challenge to the specialist and to his rite of pontification is, perhaps, well stated by a contemporary American philosopher (Bahm 1977:73):

> When views representing "the illiteracy of the specialist" become propagated, the result is popular, public, and even "scientific" illiteracy. There is no more serious danger from specialization than the unwitting propagation of such partial ignorance in the name of the specialist as an authority. The mistaken confidence that views expressed on the authority of specialists are always really the best is a form of self-deception. Not until considerable competence in interdisciplinary studies has been achieved can one distinguish with confidence what is genuine and what is biased knowledge in each of several specialties.

Biogeography in Croizat's view is an interdisciplinary study that has long suffered in the hands of one or another specialist-as-an-authority. He chose a candid, at times merciless, style of expression in the hope that, in the long run, it would be for the best.

The long run, however, is not yet over. Hence it is for you, the reader, to judge for yourself the current state of the art, keeping in mind, perhaps, Croizat's perception of it in an earlier period (1964:xii):

> A cock in the barnyard and a man in a position of influence and power have—with very rare exceptions on the part of the latter—the very same basic reactions. Both are happy to be what they are, not at all inclined to tolerate intruders and poachers on their chosen premises, jealous custodians of what they believe to be orthodox standards, inclined —the cock when not the man—to strut about pompously and to share with their hens the crumbs aroung the yard. This picture, reduced to a minimum of course, is not malicious or lacking in due respect to bird and man. It is just that life is *so*, every being tending to perform in function of what it is, getting meanwhile the most for the least. Man may not know it by instinct, but if he has paused to meditate about the things of the barnyard and of the university he is bound to learn the truth. . . .

In summary (1964:xviii): "An appallingly high rate of learned illiteracy besots us from all sides."

Croizat's books were not universally ignored at the time of their appearance, for they received few but generally favorable reviews, one of which I miscited in a previous connection (Nelson 1973b) and which I now quote in part (review of Croizat's *Panbiogeography*, Corner 1959:237):

> This is the amplification of the principles put forward by Croizat in his *Manual of Phytogeography* (1952), their betterment and their application to zoology. I will

neither praise it nor condemn it, but state that it is the most important contribution to plant and animal distribution that has appeared. It is not a class-book, but an emporium, and right glad we must be that one mind has planned it. Here are plants, animals, rocks, men, books, theories, jewels of genius, and much tripe, displayed with astonishing salesmanship. Here is learning as of Gibbon, garrulity as of Montaigne, homeliness as of Bunyan, conceit as of Shaw, pervaded with Darwinian love of nature and common sense. I use these unscientific words because Croizat deals with the immense biology which transcends physics and chemistry, which we shall lose if rising generations are not inspired. Panbiogeography is the story of "Flesh and rocks" and, for the first time, in this bottomless pit of antiquity, I have been shown whereon to stand.

The notion of a mid-Pacific continent has an old history, going back into the nineteenth century at least, when observers wondered if the many Pacific islands were merely the mountaintops of a sunken continent. Darwin came to view the Pacific as an old and stable feature, as did Wegener when he clumped the continents together by closing the Atlantic Ocean in his reconstruction of the predrift configuration, essentially the viewpoint of the modern continental-drift school.

Croizat early commented on Pacific distributions in relation to Wegener's notions: "I do not see, for instance, how, to repeat, it is possible at all to figure out dispersal [distribution] on and around the Pacific in the lights of 'wegenerism...'" (Croizat, 1958:5). This is a stance for which Croizat has been criticized by authors who mistakenly believe that he rejected continental drift as false. The problem was not that drift was false, but that it was false for what it affirmed to be the history of the Pacific. Croizat counseled (1958:6):

If biogeography is ever to win the respect of the geologist, *biogeography must stand first of all on its own legs as an independent, analytical science, rigorously eschewing theories about which geologists themselves are not at peace.* This I see as the very first and most essential aim of the inquirer in dispersal, that a science of the kind is put in act, free of entanglements, mistress in her own house, and I should feel that "wegenerism" had better keep off the premises, even if we should think well of it, in principle. After—but certainly not before—we have our own house in order, then we may start wondering whether an added balcony *à la Wegener* might grace the facade a little more.

The possibilities for a Pacific continent within modern continental-drift theory (plate tectonics) were considered by Nur and Ben-Avraham and their discussants. There is a possibility, but evaluation of it hinges upon what is a "continental" remnant as opposed to an "island arc." There seems general agreement that island-arc systems have, for example, been incorporated into the western margin of North America. And there is agreement also that Japan is a classic island-arc system, if not the Philippines as well. Whereas geologists may bicker among themselves as to whether Japan and the Philippines are in some sense "continental," no biogeographer would hesitate to accept both as continental on the testimony of their biotas. Hence the fine points of geological interpretation are to some extent irrelevant if geological structures such as Japan and the Philippines have drifted about the Pacific, and have been incorporated in the lands around its margin. The only point at issue is whether these possible events could have happened recently enough to be reflected in the distributions of extant organisms. Here the paleontologists, for their part, cite the evidence of the fossil record—namely the absence of old fossils for groups with distributions that seem trans-Pacific, or amphitropical with a Pacific axis. And there the matter stands, itself adrift on a sea of negative evidence. True, it is negative evidence of the sort that paleontologists never tire of exhibiting as their standard stock-in-trade. It is evidence of the sort that is always subverted by subsequent discovery of older fossils. Discovery of such older fossils is one of the thrills of paleontology. I can do no more than suggest that subsequent generations of paleontologists may be thrilled beyond the wildest dreams of those alive today.

One possible tectonic explanation for Pacific distributions, not dealt with in this symposium, is earth expansion. Its chief advocate is Carey (1976:figure 170), whose map of the Pacific in the early Mesozoic shows an "Eo-Pacific" ocean much reduced east-to-west, but of considerable extent north-to-south—a concept that, like Wegener's, allows the Pacific to be the world's oldest ocean. Shields commented (1978:380):

> It is too bad Carey could not present a Pacific Ocean closure (other than figure 170) in his comprehensive earth synthesis. Instead, he clings to the idea that the Alaskan orocline must be straightened, thus creating a Jurassic Pacific, with an "Eopacific" starting in Permo-Carboniferous times. However, there is no evidence for such an ocean from DSDP drilling.

What, then, has been the history of the Pacific? Did it, like the Atlantic and Indian Oceans, begin to open in the Mesozoic? Or is the Pacific the "odd man out," in having a much longer history?

Croizat's generalizations of the facts of distribution tend to be true to his counsel, in omitting reference to "theories about which geologists themselves are not at peace" (1964:32): *"There is . . . a general process of evolution over space, in time, by form which has had for its effect that the same genus, even species, is today located on both sides of the Atlantic, Pacific, Indian oceans, etc., etc."* Earth expansion, if the process brought all ocean basins into existence at about the same time, is one possible explanation behind the "general process of evolution," of which the results are vicariant distributions of organisms across all of today's oceans (Shields 1979).

Until recently it could be said (Shields 1978:380) that "Plate tectonics differs little from earth expansion except in the Pacific region, and in the size of the earth. An expanding earth may not be readily apparent, but it is difficult to understand why many tectonicists steadfastly reject the idea without delving into it more deeply."

As presented by Nur and Ben-Avraham, the possibility of a Pacifica hypothesis framed within the constraints of plate tectonics now seems to leave little difference between earth expansion and plate tectonics, at least as these theories can be viewed by the biogeographer. The Pacifica hypothesis perhaps has the advantage over the expansion theory in allowing for considerable south-to-north displacement, which is a tectonic process that might explain amphitropical and bipolar distributions both of marine and terrestrial forms of life.

Paleontology and the "crucial fossil evidence" were left for the finale of the regular sessions of the symposium. Wolfe's presentation ran true to the tradition of dispersalism, whereas Patterson's explored vicariance interpretations of various fossil and Recent groups. The contrast between the two cuts to the heart of the symposium. To my mind the difference is so clear-cut that it is best appreciated by reading the two accounts without any further commentary upon them.

As for the symposium as a whole, what can be said of its accomplishments? First, that any symposium is a mixture of science and theater, usually with the theater predominating. In a symposium a little science goes a long way, and the science has been touched on above. As theater, the symposium was well acted and enthusiastically received by a large audience. It was staged in an institution responsive enough to make its resources available for what some of it staff deemed a dubious undertaking. In this age, when our institutions have a tendency toward nonresponsive irresponsibility, I for one am reassured by having witnessed the American Museum of Natural History commit itself once again to furthering the science that brought it into being and that, hopefully, will keep it healthy and active. As theater, lastly, the symposium sparkled under the direction of Virginia Ferris, who presided and coaxed from one and all—cast and the audience alike—the best that they could deliver.

References

AAPG. 1966–1973. *Geological Highway Maps (Mid-Continent Region, Southern Rocky Mountain Region, Northern Rocky Mountain Region, Texas)*. Tulsa: American Association of Petroleum Geologists.

Abbott, I. 1977. "Species richness, turnover, and equilibrium in insular floras near Perth, Western Australia." *Australian Journal of Botany*, 25(2):193–208.

Abbott, I., L. K. Abbott, and P. R. Grant. 1977 "Comparative ecology of Galápagos ground finches (*Geospiza* Gould): Evaluation of the importance of floristic diversity and interspecific competition." *Ecological Monographs*, 47(2):151–84.

Abbott, R. T. 1960, "The genus *Strombus* in the Indo-Pacific." In R. T. Abbott, ed., *Indo-Pacific Mollusca*, 1(2):33–134. Delaware Museum of Natural History, Greenville.

Ab'Saber, A. N. 1977. "Espaços ocupados pela expansão dos climas secos na América do Sul, por ocasião dos períodos glaciais quaternários." *Paleoclimas*, no. 3 pp. 1–19. Instituto de Geografia, Universidade de São Paulo.

Adachi, M. 1976. "Paleogeographic aspects of the Japanese Paleozoic-Mesozoic geosyncline." *Twenty-fifth International Geological Congress, Abstracts*, 1:263.

Adams, C. G. 1967 "Tertiary Foraminifera in the Tethyan, American, and Indo-Pacific provinces." In C. G. Adams and D. V. Ager, eds., *Aspects of Tethyan Biogeography*, pp. 195–217. Publications of the Systematics Association (London), no. 7.

Ager, D. V. 1973. *The Nature of the Stratigraphical Record*. London: Macmillan; New York: Halstead Press.

Alexander, R. D. and T. E. Moore. 1962. "The evolutionary relationships of 17-year and 13-year cicadas, and three new species (Homoptera, Cicadidae, *Magicicada*)." Ann Arbor: University of Michigan, *Miscellaneous Publications of the Museum of Zoology*, no. 121, pp. 1–59.

Allen, G. E. 1978. *Thomas Hunt Morgan: The Man and His Science.* Princeton, N.J.: Princeton University Press.

Allen, R. T. and G. E. Ball. 1980. "Synopsis of Mexican taxa of the *Loxandrus* series (Coleoptera: Carabidae: Pterostichini)." *Transactions of the American Entomological Society,* 105(4):481–575.

Allen T. F. H. and J. F. Koonce. 1973. "Multivariate approaches to algal stratagems and tactics in systems analysis of phytoplankton." *Ecology,* 54(6):1234–46.

Allin, E. F. 1975. "Evolution of the mammalian middle ear." *Journal of Morphology,* 147(4):403–37.

Alvarez, W., D. V. Kent, I. Premoli-Silva, R. A. Schweickert, and R. L. Larson. 1979. "Franciscan limestone deposited at 17° south paleolatitude." *Abstracts with Programs of the Geological Society of America,* 11(3):66.

Anderson, P. 1976. "Oceanic crust and arc-trench gap tectonics in southwestern British Columbia." *Geology* (Boulder), 4(7): 443–46.

Andersson, H. 1977. "Taxonomic and phylogenetic studies on Chloropidae (Diptera) with special reference to Old World genera." *Entomologica Scandinavica,* Supplementum 8, pp. 1–200.

Andrade-Lima, D. de. 1953. "Notas sôbre a dispersão de algumas espécies vegetais no Brasil." Universidade do Recife, *Anais da Sociedade de Biologia de Pernambuco,* 11(1):25–49.

—— 1976. "Preservation of the flora of northeastern Brasil." In G. T. Prance and T. S. Elias, eds., *Extinction Is Forever,* pp. 234–44. New York: New York Botanical Garden.

—— 1981. "Present-day forest refugia in northeastern Brasil." In G. T. Prance, ed., *Proceedings of the 5th Association for Tropical Biology Symposium,* In press. New York: Columbia University Press.

Andrews, E. C. 1916. "The geological history of the Australian flowering plants." *The American Journal of Science,* series 4, 42(249):171–232.

Andrews, J. E., G. Packham, J. V. Eade, B. K. Holdsworth, D. L. Jones, G. de V. Klein, L. W. Kroenke, T. Saito, S. Shafik, D. B. Stoeser, and G. J. Van der Lingen. 1975. "Site 289." *Initial Reports of the Deep Sea Drilling Project* (Washington, D.C.), 30:231–398.

Archer, M. 1976. "The dasyurid dentition and its relationships to that of didelphids, thylacinids, borhyaenids (Marsupicarnivora) and peramelids (Peramelina: Marsupialia)." *Australian Journal of Zoology,* Supplementary series, no. 39, pp. 1–34.

—— 1978. "The nature of the molar-premolar boundary in marsupials and a reinterpretation of the homology of marsupial cheekteeth." *Memoirs of the Queensland Museum,* 18(2):157–64.

Armstrong, D. M. 1977. "Dispersal vs. dispersion: Process vs. pattern." *Systematic Zoology,* 26(2):210–11.

Asama, K. 1959. "Systematic study of so-called *Gigantopteris.*" *Science Reports of Tohoku University: Geology,* series 2, 31(1):1–72.

Asama, K., A. Hongnusonthi, J. Iwai, E. Kon'no, S. S. Rajah, and M. Veeraburas. 1975. "Summary of the Carboniferous and Permian plants from Thailand, Malaysia and adjacent areas." *Geology and Palaeontology of Southeast Asia,* 15:77–101.

Ashton, P. S. 1969. "Speciation among tropical forest trees: Some deductions in the light of recent evidence." *Biological Journal of the Linnean Society* (London), 1(1–2):155–96.

Ashworth, A. C. 1979. "Quaternary Coleoptera studies in North America: Past and present." In T. L. Erwin, G. E. Ball, D. R. Whitehead, and A. L. Halpern, eds., *Carabid Beetles: Their Evolution, Natural History, and Classification*, pp. 395–406. The Hague: W. Junk.

Atwater, T. 1973. "Studies of sea-floor spreading and plate movements in the Pacific Basin." In D. H. Tarling and S. K. Runcorn, eds., *Implications of Continental Drift to the Earth Sciences*, 1:213–17. London and New York: Academic Press.

Aubréville, A. 1976. "Centres tertiaires d'origine, radiations et migrations des flores angiospermiques tropicales." *Adansonia*, series 2, 16(3):297–354.

Audley-Charles, M. G. 1978. "The Indonesian and Philippine Archipelagoes." In M. Moullade and A. E. M. Nairn, eds., *The Phanerozoic Geology of the World*, 2: *The Mesozoic*, pp. 165–207. Amsterdam: Elsevier Scientific.

Axelrod, D. I. 1963. "Fossil floras suggest stable, not drifting, continents." *Journal of Geophysical Research*, 68(10):3257–63.

—— 1970. "Mesozoic paleogeography and early angiosperm history." *Botanical Review*, 36(3):177–319.

—— 1975. "Evolution and biogeography of madrean-Tethyan sclerophyll vegetation." *Annals of the Missouri Botanical Garden*, 62(2):280–334.

Babcock, E. B. 1947. "The genus *Crepis*, part 1: The taxonomy, phylogeny, distribution, and evolution of *Crepis*." *Publications in Botany of the University of California*, 21:1–197.

Bahm, A. J. 1977. *The Specialist: His Philosophy, His Disease, His Cure*. Albuquerque: World Books.

Bailey, I. W. 1949. "Origin of the angiosperms: Need for a broadened outlook." *Journal of the Arnold Arboretum*, 30(1):64–70.

Baker, H. B. 1938–1941. "Zonitid snails from Pacific islands, parts 1–4." *Bulletin of the Bernice P. Bishop Museum*, no 158, pp. 1–102; no. 165, pp. 103–201: no. 166, pp. 202–370.

Baker, R. R. 1978. *The Evolutionary Ecology of Animal Migration*. London: Hodder and Stoughton.

Bakker, R. T. 1978. "Dinosaur feeding behaviour and the origin of flowering plants." *Nature* (London), 274(5672):661–63.

Ball, G. E. 1965. "The genus *Scaphinotus* (Coleoptera: Carabidae) and the Pleistocene Epoch in southwestern United States." In P. Freeman, ed., *Proceedings of the 12th International Congress of Entomology*, pp. 460–61. London: Royal Entomological Society of London.

—— 1975. "Pericaline Lebiini: Notes on classification, a synopsis of the New World genera, and a revision of the genus *Phloeoxena* Chaudoir (Coleoptera: Carabidae)." *Quaestiones Entomologicae*, 11(2):143–242.

—— 1978. "The species of the Neotropical genus *Trichopselaphus* Chaudoir (Coleoptera: Carabidae: Harpalini): Classification, phylogeny and zoogeography." *Quaestiones Entomologicae*, 14(4):447–89.

Ball, I. R. 1976. "Nature and formulation of biogeographical hypotheses." *Systematic Zoology*, 24(4):407–30.

—— 1977. "On the phylogenetic classification of aquatic planarians." *Acta Zoologica Fennica*, no. 154, pp. 21–35.

Ball, I. R. and N. Gourbault. 1978. "The phyletic status of the genus *Planaria* (Platyhelminthes, Turbellaria, Tricladida)." *Bijdragen tot de Dierkunde*, 48(1):29–34.

Banarescu, P. 1978. "Some critical reflexions on Hennig's phyletical concepts." *Zeitschrift für Zoologische Systematik und Evolutionsforschung*, 16(2):91–101.

Banner, A. H. and D. M. Banner. 1974. "Contributions to the knowledge of the alpheid shrimp of the Pacific Ocean, part 17." *Pacific Science*, 28(4):423–37.

Barker, P. F. and J. Burrell. 1977 "The opening of the Drake Passage." *Marine Geology*, 25(1–3):15–34.

Barker, P. H. 1967. "Bathymetry of Fiordland continental margin." *New Zealand Journal of Science*, 10(1):128–37.

Barnard, P. D. W. 1973. "Mesozoic floras." In N. F. Hughes, ed., *Organisms and Continents Through Time*, pp. 175–87. Special Papers in Palaeontology of the Palaeontological Association (London), no. 12; Publications of the Systematics Association, no. 9.

Baroyan, O. V., ed. 1965. *Metodij Mediko-Geograficheskih Issledovanii*. Moscow: Geographical Society of the USSR.

Basile, D. V. 1969. "Toward an experimental approach to systematics and phylogeny of leafy liverworts." In J. E. Gunckel, ed., *Current Topics in Plant Science*, pp. 120–33. New York and London: Academic Press.

Bates, H. W. 1881–1884. "Insecta: Coleoptera," vol. 1, pt. 1., pp. 1–316. In F. D. Godman and O. Salvin, eds., *Biologia Centrali-Americana*, London: published by the editors.

Bate-Smith, E. C. 1978. "Systematic aspects of the astringent tannins of *Acer* species." *Phytochemistry*, 17(11):1945–48.

Beck, C. B. 1976. "Origin and early evolution of angiosperms: A perspective." In C. B. Beck, ed., *Origin and Early Evolution of Angiosperms*, pp. 1–10. New York: Columbia University Press.

Ben-Avraham, Z. and A. Nur. 1976. "Slip rates and morphology of continental collision belts." *Geology* (Boulder), 4(11):661–64.

Ben-Avraham, Z. and S. Uyeda. 1973. "The evolution of the China Basin and the Mesozoic paleogeography of Borneo." *Earth and Planetary Science Letters*, 18(2):365–76.

Berggren, W. A. 1972. "A Cenozoic time-scale—some implications for regional geology and palaeobiogeography." *Lethaia*, 5(2):195–215.

Berggren, W. A. and C. D. Hollister. 1977. "Plate tectonics and paleocirculation—commotion in the ocean." *Tectonophysics*, 38(1):11–48.

Berggren, W. A. and J. D. Phillips. 1969. *Influence of Continental drift on the Distribution of Tertiary Benthonic Foraminifera in the Caribbean and Mediterranean Regions*. Contributions of the Woods Hole Oceanographic Institution, no. 2376.

Blackwelder, R. E. 1977. "Twenty five years of taxonomy." *Systematic Zoology*, 26(2):107–37.

Blundell, D. J. 1962. "Palaeomagnetic investigations in the Falkland Islands Dependencies." *Scientific Reports of the British Antarctic Survey*, no. 39, pp. 1-24.

Bock, W. J. 1978. "Comments on classifications as historical narratives." *Systematic Zoology*, 27(3):362-64.

Bock. W. J. and G. von Wahlert. 1963. "Two evolutionary theories—a discussion." *British Journal for the Philosophy of Science*, 14:140-46.

Bond, J. 1948. "Origin of the bird fauna of the West Indies." *The Wilson Bulletin*, 60(4):207-29.

—— 1950. *Check-List of Birds of the West Indies*. Philadelphia: The Academy of Natural Sciences of Philadelphia.

Bostwick, D. A. and M. K. Nestell. 1967. "Permian Tethyan fusulinid faunas of the northwestern United States." In C. G. Adams and D. V. Ager, eds., *Aspects of Tethyan Biogeography*, pp. 93-102. Publications of the Systematics Association (London), no. 7.

Bowin, C. 1976. "Caribbean gravity field and plate tectonics." *Special Papers of the Geological Society of America*, no 169, pp. 1-79.

Bradshaw, A. D. 1971. "Plant evolution in extreme environments." In R. Geed, ed., *Ecological Genetics and Evolution*, pp. 20-50. London: Blackwell.

Brady, R. 1980. "Natural selection: An examination of the criteria by which a theory is judged." *Systematic Zoology*, 28(4):600-21.

Briggs, J. C. 1974. "Operation of zoogeographic barriers." *Systematic Zoology*, 23(2):248-56.

Brown, D. A., K. S. Campbell, and K. A. W. Crook. 1968. *The Geological Evolution of Australia and New Zealand*. Oxford, London, Edinburgh, New York, Toronto, Sydney, Paris, Braunschweig: Pergamon Press.

Brown, K. S., Jr. 1976. "Geographical patterns of evolution in Neotropical Lepidoptera: Systematics and derivation of known and new Heliconiini (Nymphalidae: Nymphalinae). "*Journal of Entomology*, series B, 44(3):201-42.

—— 1977. "Centros de evolução, refugios quaternários, e conservação de patrimônios genéticos na região neotropical: Padrões de diferenciação em Ithomiinae (Lepidoptera: Nymphalidae)." *Acta Amazônica*, 7(1):75-137.

—— 1979. *Ecologia Geográfica e Evolução nas Florestas Neotropicais. Parte VI na Série, "Padrões Geográficos de Evolução em Lepidópteros Neotropicais*. São Paulo, Brazil: Universidade Estadual de Campinas (Tese, Livre Docência, Area de Ecologia).

Brown, K. S., Jr. and A. N. Ab'Saber. 1979. "Ice-age forest refugia and evolution in the Neotropics: Correlation of paleoclimatological, geomorphological and pedological data with modern biological endemism." *Paleoclimas*, no. 5, pp. 1-30. Universidade de São Paulo, Instituto de Geografia.

Brundin, L. 1966. "Transantarctic relationships and their significance." *Kungliga Svenska Vetenskapsakademiens Handlingar*, series 4, 11(1):1-472.

—— 1968. "Application of phylogenetic principles in systematics and evolutionary theory." In T. Orvig, ed., *Current Problems in Lower Vertebrate Phylogeny: Nobel Symposium 4*, pp. 473-95. Stockholm: Almqvist and Wiksell; New York, London, Sydney: Interscience Publishers.

—— 1972a. "Evolution, causal biology, and classification." *Zoologica Scripta*, 1(3–4):107–20.

—— 1972b. "Phylogenetics and biogeography." *Systematic Zoology*, 21(1):69–79.

—— 1975. "Circum-Antarctic distribution patterns and continental drift." *Mémoires du Muséum d'Histoire Naturelle*, new series, series A, Zoologie, 88:19–27.

—— 1976. "A Neocomian chironomid and Podonominae-Aphroteniinae (Diptera) in the light of phylogenetics and biogeography." *Zoologica Scripta*, 5(3–4):139–60.

Brundin, L. and O. A. Saether. 1978. "*Buchonomyia burmanica* sp. n. and Buchonomyiinae, a new subfamily among the Chironomidae (Diptera)." *Zoologica Scripta*, 7(4):269–75.

Brunet, M. 1977. "Les mammifères et le problème de la limite Eocène-Oligocène en Europe." In *Faunes de Mammifères du Paléogène d'Eurasie*, pp. 11–27. Colloque International, Centre National de la Recherche Scientifique. Geobios, Mémoire Spécial, no. 1. Lyon: Université Claude-Bernard, Département de Géologie.

Bullard, E. C., J. E. Everett, and A. G. Smith. 1965. "The fit of the continents around the Atlantic." In *Symposium on Continental Drift*, pp. 41–51. Philosophical Transactions of the Royal Society, London, series A, Mathematical and Physical Sciences, vol. 258, no. 1088.

Burchfiel, B. C. and G. A. Davis. 1975. "Nature and controls of cordilleran orogenesis, western United States: Extensions of an earlier synthesis." In J. H. Ostrom and P. M. Orville, eds., *Tectonics and Mountain Ranges*, pp. 363–96. American Journal of Science, vol. 275-A.

Bush, G. L. 1975a. "Sympatric speciation in phytophagous parasitic insects." In P. W. Price, ed., *Evolutionary Strategies of Parasitic Insects*, pp. 187–206. New York and London: Plenum Press.

—— 1975b. "Modes of animal speciation." *Annual Review of Ecology and Systematics*, 6:339–64.

Cain, S. A. 1944. *Foundations of Plant Geography*. New York: Harper; reprint, New York: Hafner, 1971.

Cande, S. C., R. L. Larson, and J. L. LaBrecque. 1978. "Magnetic lineations in the Pacific Jurassic quiet zone." *Earth and Planetary Science Letters*, 41(4):434–40.

Cande, S. C. and P. D. Rabinowitz. 1978. "Mesozoic seafloor spreading bordering conjugate continental margins of Angola and Brazil." In *Proceedings of the 10th Offshore Technological Conference*, pp. 1869–72. Houston.

Candolle, A.-P. de. 1820. "Géographie botanique." In *Dictionnaire des Sciences Naturelles*, 18:359–422. Strasbourg and Paris: F. G. Levrault; reprint, in F. N. Egerton, ed., *Ecological Phytogeography in the Nineteenth Century*, New York: Arno Press, 1977.

Carey, S. W. 1976. *The Expanding Earth*. Developments in Tectonics, no. 10. Amsterdam, Oxford, New York: Elsevier.

—— 1978. "A philosophy of the earth and universe." *Papers and Proceedings of the Royal Society of Tasmania*, 112:5–19.

Carlquist, S. 1965. *Island Life: A Natural History of the Islands of the World*. Garden City, N.Y.: Natural History Press.

—— 1966a. "The biota of long-distance dispersal, 1: Principles of dispersal and evolution." *The Quarterly Review of Biology*, 41(3):247–70.

—— 1966b. "The biota of long-distance dispersal, 2: Loss of dispersibility in Pacific Compositae." *Evolution*, 20(1):30–48.

—— 1966c. "The biota of long-distance dispersal, 3: Loss of dispersibility in the Hawaiian flora." *Brittonia*, 18(4):310–35.

—— 1966d. "The biota of long-distance dispersal, 4: Genetic systems in the floras of oceanic islands." *Evolution*, 20(4):433–55.

—— 1967. "The biota of long-distance dispersal, 5: Plant dispersal to Pacific islands." *Bulletin of the Torrey Botanical Club*, 94(3):129–62.

—— 1974. *Island Biology*. New York and London: Columbia University Press.

Carson, H. L. 1970. "Chromosome tracers of the origin of species." *Science* (Washington, D.C.), 168(3938):1414–18.

Carson, H. L., D. E. Hardy, H. T. Spieth, and W. S. Stove. 1970. "The evolutionary biology of the Hawaiian Drosophilidae." In M. K. Hecht and W. C. Steere, eds., *Essays in Evolution and Genetics in Honor of Theodosius Dobzhansky: A Supplement to Evolutionary Biology*, pp. 437–543. New York: Appleton-Century-Crofts.

Carson, H. L. and K. Y. Kaneshiro. 1976. "*Drosophila* of Hawaii: Systematics and ecological genetics." *Annual Review of Ecology and Systematics*, 7:311–45.

Case, J. E., L. G. Duran S., A. Lopez R., and W. R. Moore. 1971. "Tectonic investigations in western Colombia and eastern Panama." *Bulletin of the Geological Society of America*, 82(10):2685–2711.

Chaney, R. W. 1947. "Tertiary centers and migration routes." *Ecological Monographs*, 17(2):139–48.

—— 1959. "Miocene floras of the Columbian Plateau, part 1: Composition and interpretation." *Contributions to Paleontology of the Carnegie Institution of Washington*, no. 617, pp. 1–134.

Chapman, F. M. 1917. "The distribution of bird-life in Colombia: A contribution to a biological survey of South America." *Bulletin of the American Museum of Natural History*, 36:1–729.

—— 1926. "The distribution of bird-life in Ecuador: A contribution to a study of the origin of Andean bird-life." *Bulletin of the American Museum of Natural History*, 55:1–784.

Charig, A. J. 1973. "Jurassic and Cretaceous dinosaurs." In A. Hallam, ed., *Atlas of Palaeobiogeography*, pp. 339–52. Amsterdam, London, New York: Elsevier.

Chodorowski, A. 1959. "Ecological differentiation of turbellarians in Harsz-Lake." *Polskie Archiwum Hydrobiologii*, Polska Akademia Nauk, 6:33–73.

Christofferson, E. 1976. "Colombian Basin magnetism and Caribbean Plate tectonics." *Bulletin of the Geological Society of America*, 87(9):1255–58.

Churkin, M., Jr. 1974. "Paleozoic marginal ocean basin-volcanic arc systems in the cordilleran foldbelt." In R. H. Dott and R. Shaver, eds., *Modern and Ancient Geosynclinal Sedimentaton: Deep-Sea Pelagic Sediments and Ophiolite Assemblages*, pp. 174–92. Special Publications of the Society of Economic Paleontologists and Mineralogists, no. 19.

Churkin, M., Jr. and G. D. Eberlein. 1977. "Ancient borderland terranes of the North American cordillera: Correlation and microplate tectonics." *Bulletin of the Geological Society of America*, 88(6):769–86.

Clemens, W. A. 1977. "Phylogeny of the marsupials." In B. Stonehouse and D.

Gilmore, eds., *The Biology of the Marsupials*, pp. 51–68. London and Basingstoke: Macmillan; Baltimore, London, Tokyo: University Park Press.

Clemens, W. A. and L. G. Marshall. 1976. "American and European Marsupialia." *Fossilium Catalogus I: Animalia*, part 123, pp. 1–114. Gravenhage: W. Junk.

Coates, A. G. 1973. "Cretaceous Tethyan coral-rudist biogeography related to the evolution of the Atlantic Ocean." In N. F. Hughes, ed., *Organisms and Continents Through Time*, pp. 169–74. Special Papers in Palaeontology of the Palaeontological Association (London), no. 12; Publications of the Systematics Association, no. 9.

Cobbing, E. J. 1978. "The Andean geosyncline in Peru, and its distinction from Alpine geosynclines." *Journal of the Geological Society* (London), 135(2):207–18.

Colbert, E. H. 1973. *Wandering Lands and Animals*. New York: Dutton; 1974; London: Hutchinson.

Cole, L. C. 1954. "The population consequences of life history phenomena." *The Quarterly Review of Biology*, 29(2):103–37.

Colinvaux, P. A. 1964. "The environment of the Bering land bridge." *Ecological Monographs*, 34(3):297–329.

—— 1979. "The ice-age Amazon." *Nature* (London), 278(5703):399–400.

Collette, B. B. 1974. "Geographic variation in the Central Pacific halfbeak, *Hyporhamphus acutus* (Günther)." *Pacific Science*, 28(2):111–22.

Coney, P. J. 1979. "Mesozoic-Cenozoic cordilleran plate tectonics." In R. B. Smith and G. P. Eaton, eds., *Cenozoic Tectonics and Regional Geophysics of the Western Cordillera*, pp. 33–50. Memoirs of the Geological Society of America, no. 152.

Connor, E. F. and D. Simberloff. 1978. "Species number and compositional similarity of the Galápagos flora and avifauna." *Ecological Monographs*, 48(2):219–48.

Connor, E. F. and D. Simberloff. 1979. "The assembly of species communities: chance or competition?" *Ecology* 60(6):1132–40.

Cooke, C. M., Jr. and Y. Kondo. 1960. "Revision of Tornatellinidae and Achatinellidae (Gastropoda, Pulmonata)." *Bulletin of the Bernice P. Bishop Museum*, no. 221, pp. 1–303.

Corner, E. J. H. 1959. "Panbiogeography" [review of Croizat 1958]. *The New Phytologist*, 58(2):237–38.

Coryndon, S. C. and R. J. G. Savage. 1973. "The origin and affinities of African mammal faunas." In N. F. Hughes, ed., *Organisms and Continents Through Time*, pp. 121–35. Special Papers in Palaeontology of the Palaeontological Association (London), no. 12; Publications of the Systematics Association, no. 9.

Cox, C. B. 1973. "Systematics and plate tectonics in the spread of marsupials." In N. F. Hughes, ed., *Organisms and Continents Through Time*, pp. 113–19. Special Papers in Palaeontology of the Palaeontological Association (London), no. 12; Publications of the Systematics Association, no. 9.

—— 1974. "Vertebrate palaeodistributional patterns and continental drift." *Journal of Biogeography*, 1(2):75–94.

Cracraft, J. 1972. "The relationships of the higher taxa of birds: Problems in phylogenetic reasoning." *The Condor*, 74(4):379–92.

—— 1973. "Continental drift, paleoclimatology, and the evolution and biogeography of birds." *Journal of Zoology*, (London), 169(4):455–545.

—— 1974a. "Continental drift and vertebrate distribution." *Annual Review of Ecology and Systematics*, 5:215–61.

—— 1974b. "Phylogeny and evolution of the ratite birds." *The Ibis*, 116(4):494–521.

—— 1975a. "Historical biogeography and earth history: Perspectives for a future synthesis." *Annals of the Missouri Botanical Garden*, 62(2):227–50.

—— 1975b. "Mesozoic dispersal of terrestrial faunas around the southern end of the world." *Mémoires du Muséum National d'Histoire Naturelle*, new series, series A, Zoologie, 88:29–52.

Crampton, G. C. 1929. "The terminal abdominal structures of female insects compared throughout the orders from the standpoint of phylogeny." *Journal of the New York Entomological Society*, 37(4):453–96.

Creer, K. M. 1964. "A reconstruction of the continents for the Upper Palaeozoic from palaeomagnetic data." *Nature* (London), 203(4950):1115–20.

—— 1973. "A discussion of the arrangement of palaeomagnetic poles on the map of Pangaea for epochs in the Phanerozoic." In D. H. Tarling and S. K. Runcorn, eds., *Implications of Continental Drift to the Earth Sciences*, 1:47–76. London and New York: Academic Press.

Crochet, J.-Y. 1978. *Les Marsupiaux du Tertiaire d'Europe*. Thesis, Université du Languedoc.

—— 1979. "Données nouvelles sur l'histoire paléogéographique des Didelphidae (Marsupialia)." *Comptes Rendus des Séances de l'Académie des Sciences*, Paris series D, 288(19):1457–60.

Croizat, L. 1952. *Manual of Phytogeography*. The Hague: W. Junk.

—— 1958. *Panbiogeography*, vols. 1, 2a, 2b. Caracas: published by the author.

—— 1960. *Principia Botanica*, vols. 1a, 1b. Caracas: published by the author.

—— 1964. *Space, Time, Form: The Biological Synthesis*. Caracas: published by the author.

—— 1968a. "Introduction raisonnée à la biogéographie de l'Afrique." *Memórias da Sociedade Broteriana*, 20:1–451.

—— 1968b. "The biogeography of the tropical lands and islands east of Suez-Madagascar; with particular reference to the dispersal and form-making of *Ficus* L., and different other vegetal and animal groups." *Atti dell'Istituto Botanico e Laboratorio Crittogamico dell'Università di Pavia*, series 6, 4:1–400.

—— 1971. "Polytopisme ou monotopisme? Le cas de *Viola parvula* Tin. et de plusieurs autres plantes et animaux." *Boletim da Sociedade Broteriana*, series 2, 45:379–433.

—— 1976. "Biogeografia analítica y sintética ("panbiogeografia") de las Américas." *Biblioteca de la Academia de Ciencias Físicas, Matemáticas y Naturales* (Caracas), 15–16:1–454, 455–890.

—— 1978. "Deduction, induction, and biogeography." *Systematic Zoology*, 27(2):209–13.

Croizat, L., G. Nelson, and D. E. Rosen. 1974. "Centers of origin and related concepts." *Systematic Zoology*, 23(2):265–87.

Crompton, A. W. and F. A. Jenkins, Jr. 1973. "Mammals from reptiles; A review of mammalian origins." *Annual Review of Earth and Planetary Sciences*, 1:131–55.

Cronquist, A. 1968. *The Evolution and Classification of Flowering Plants*. Boston, New York, Atlanta, Geneva, Dallas, Palo Alto: Houghton Mifflin.

Cullen, D. J. 1967. "A note on the regional structure of the southwest Pacific." *New Zealand Journal of Science*, 10(3):813–15.

Cutler, D. F. 1972. "Vicarious species of Restionaceae in Africa, Australia, and South America." In D. H. Valentine ed., *Taxonomy Phytogeography and Evolution*, pp. 73–83. London and New York: Academic Press.

D'Allura, J. A., E. M. Moores, and L. Robinson. 1977. "Paleozoic rocks of the northern Sierra Nevada: Their structural and paleogeographic implications." In J. H. Stewart, C. H. Stevens, and A. E. Fritsche, eds., *Paleozoic Paleogeography of the Western United States: Pacific Coast Paleogeography Symposium 1*, pp. 395–408. Los Angeles: Pacific Section, Society of Economic Paleontologists and Mineralogists.

Dalziel, I. W. D. 1979. "The early (pre-Middle Jurassic) history of the Scotia Arc region: A review and progress report." In C. Craddock, ed., *IUGS Third Symposium on Antarctic Geology and Geophysics*, in press. Madison, Wisconsin (August 1977).

Dalziel, I. W. D. and D. H. Elliot. 1971. "Evolution of the Scotia Arc." *Nature* (London), 233(5317):246–52.

Danner, W. R. 1965. "Limestones of the western cordilleran eugeosyncline of southwestern British Columbia, western Washington and northern Oregon." In A. G. Jhingran, ed., *Dr. D. N. Wadia Commemorative Volume*, pp. 113–24. Calcutta: Mining, Geological, and Metallurgical Institute of India.

Darlington, P. J., Jr. 1943. "Carabidae of mountains and islands: Data on the evolution of isolated faunas, and on atrophy of wings." *Ecological Monographs*, 13(1):37–61.

—— 1957. *Zoogeography: The Geographical Distribution of Animals*. New York: Wiley.

—— 1965. *Biogeography of the Southern End of the World: Distribution and History of Far-Southern Life and Land, with an Assessment of Continental Drift*. Cambridge: Harvard University Press.

—— 1970a. "A practical criticism of Hennig-Brundin 'phylogenetic systematics' and Antarctic biogeography." *Systematic Zoology*, 19(1):1–18.

—— 1970b. "Carabidae on tropical islands, especially the West Indies." *Biotropica*, 2(1):7–23.

—— 1971. "The carabid beetles of New Guinea, part 4: General considerations; analysis and history of fauna; taxonomic supplement." *Bulletin of the Museum of Comparative Zoology*, 142(2):129–337.

Darwin, C. 1839. *Journal of Researches into the Geology and Natural History of the Various Countries Visited by H. M. S. Beagle under the Command of Captain Fitzroy, R. N. from 1832 to 1836*. London: Henry Colburn; reprint, New York: Hafner 1952.

—— 1842. *The Structure and Distribution of Coral Reefs*. Cornhill: Smith, Elder;

reprints, Cornhill: Smith, Elder, 1851; Berkeley and Los Angeles: University of California Press 1962.

—— 1846. *Journal of Researchers into the Natural History and Geology of the Countries Visited During the Voyage of H. M. S. Beagle Round the World, under the Command of Capt. Fitz Roy, R. N.*, vol. 2. New York: Harper.

—— 1859. *On the Origin of Species by Means of Natural Selection, or the Preservation of Favoured Races in the Struggle for Life.* London: John Murray; reprints, Cambridge: Harvard University Press, 1964; New York, Atheneum, 1967.

—— 1872. *The Origin of Species by Means of Natural Selection, or the Preservation of Favoured Races in the Struggle for Existence.* 6th ed. London: John Murray.

Davies, M. S. and R. W. Snaydon. 1973. "Physiological differences among populations of *Anthoxanthum odoratum* L. collected from the Park Grass experiment, Rothamsted, 1: Response to calcium; 2: Response to aluminum." *Journal of Applied Ecology*, 10(1):33–45, 47–55.

Davis, M. B. 1976. "Pleistocene biogeography of temperate deciduous forests." *Geoscience and Man*, 13:13–26.

Den, N., W. J. Ludwig, S. Murauchi, J. I. Ewing, H. Hotta, N. T. Edgar, T. Yoshii, T. Asanuma, K. Hagiwara, T. Sato, and S. Ando. 1969. "Seismic-refraction measurements in the northwest Pacific Basin." *Journal of Geophysical Research*, 74(6):1421–34.

Den, N., W. J. Ludwig, S. Murauchi, M. Ewing, H. Hotta, T. Asanuma, T. Yoshii, A. Kubotera, and K. Hagiwara. 1971. "Sediments and structure of the Eauripik-New Guinea Rise." *Journal of Geophysical Research*, 76(20):4711–23.

Dengo, G. 1973. *Estructura Geológica, Historia Tectónica y Morfologia de América Central.* 2d ed. Mexico City: Centro Regional de Ayuda Técnica, Agencia para el Desarrollo Internacional.

Dettman, M. E. and G. Playford. 1969. "Palynology of the Australian Cretaceous: A review." In K. S. W. Campbell, ed., *Stratigraphy and Paleontology: Essays in Honour of Dorothy Hill*, pp. 174–210. Canberra: Australian National University Press.

Dewey, J. F. and J. M. Bird. 1970. "Mountain belts and the new global tectonics." *Journal of Geophysical Research*, 75(14):2625–47.

Dewey, J. F., W. C. Pitman, III, W. B. F. Ryan, and J. Bonnin. 1973. "Plate tectonics and the evolution of the alpine system." *Bulletin of the Geological Society of America*, 84(10):3137–80.

Diamond, J. M. 1972. "Biogeographic kinetics: Estimation of relaxation times for avifaunas of southwest Pacific islands." *Proceedings of the National Academy of Sciences of the United States of America*, 69(11):3199–3203.

—— 1975. "Assembly of species communities." In M. L. Cody and J. M. Diamond, eds., *Ecology and Evolution of Communities*, pp. 342–444. Cambridge and London: Belknap Press of Harvard University Press.

Diamond, J. M. and A. G. Marshall. 1976. "Origin of the New Hebridean avifauna." *The Emu*, 76(4):187–200.

Dickinson, W. R. 1971. "Plate tectonic models of geosynclines." *Earth and Planetary Science Letters*, 10(2):165–74.

—— 1976. "Sedimentary basins developed during evolution of Mesozoic-Cenozoic arc-trench system in western North America." *Canadian Journal of Earth Sciences*, 13(9):1268–87.

Dietz, R. S. and J. C. Holden. 1970. "Reconstruction of Pangaea: Breakup and dispersion of continents, Permian to present." *Journal of Geophysical Research*, 75(26):4939–56.

Dilley, F. C. 1973. "Larger Foraminifera and seas through time." In N. F. Hughes, ed., *Organisms and Continents Through Time*, pp. 155–68. Special Papers in Palaeontology of the Palaeontological Association (London), no. 12; Publications of the Systematics Association, no. 9.

Dixon, J. R. 1979. "Origin and distribution of reptiles of lowland tropical rainforest of South America." In W. E. Duellman, ed., *The South American Herpetofauna: Its Origin, Evolution, and Dispersal*, pp. 217–40. Monographs of the Museum of Natural History, University of Kansas, no. 7.

Dott, R. H. and R. L. Batten. 1976. *The Evolution of the Earth*. New York: McGraw-Hill.

Douglass, R. C. and M. K. Nestell. 1972. "Fusulinid Foraminifera from southern Chile." *Anais da Academia Brasileira de Ciências*, Suplemento, 44:119–23.

Doyle, J. A. 1977. "Patterns of evolution in early angiosperms." In A. Hallam, ed., *Patterns of Evolution as Illustrated by the Fossil Record*, pp. 501–46. Developments in Palaeontology and Stratigraphy, vol. 5. Amsterdam, Oxford, New York: Elsevier.

Doyle, J. A., P. Biens, A. Doerenkamp, and S. Jardiné. 1977. "Angiosperm pollen from the pre-Albian Lower Cretaceous of equatorial Africa." *Bulletin des Centres de Recherches Exploration-Production Elf-Aquitaine*, 1(2):451–73.

Edmunds, G. F., Jr. 1975. "Phylogenetic biogeography of mayflies." *Annals of the Missouri Botanical Garden*, 62(2):251–63.

Edmunds, G. F., Jr., S. L. Jensen, and L. Berner. 1976. *The Mayflies of North and Central America*. Minneapolis: University of Minnesota Press.

Ehrendorfer, F. 1953. "Ökologisch-geographische Mikro-Differenzierung einer Population von *Galium pumilum* Murr. s. str." *Österreichische Botanische Zeitschrift*, 100(4–5):616–38.

—— 1959. "Differentiation-hybridization cycles and polyploidy in *Achillea*." In *Genetics and Twentieth Century Darwinism*, pp. 141–52. Cold Spring Harbor Symposia on Quantitative Biology, vol. 24.

Eisenmann, V. 1979. "Caractères évolutifs et phylogénie du genre *Equus* (Mammalia, Perissodactyla)." *Comptes Rendus des Séances de l'Académie des Sciences* (Paris), series D, 288(5):497–500.

Ekman, S. 1953. *Zoogeography of the Sea*. London: Sidgwick and Jackson (reprint, 1967).

Emsley, M. G. 1965. "Speciation in *Heliconius* (Lep., Nymphalidae): Morphology and geographic distribution." *Zoologica* (New York), 50(4):191–254.

Endler, J. A. 1977. *Geographic Variation, Speciation, and Clines*. Monographs in Population Biology, no. 10. Princeton, N.J.: Princeton University Press.

Engelmann, G. F. and E. O. Wiley. 1977. "The place of ancestor-descendant relationships in phylogeny reconstruction." *Systematic Zoology*, 26(1):1–11.

Erwin, T.L. 1970. "A reclassification of bombadier beetles and a taxonomic revision of the North and Middle American species (Carabidae: Brachinida)." *Quaestiones Entomologicae*, 6(1):4–215.

—— 1974. "Studies of the subtribe Tachyina (Coleoptera: Carabidae: Bembidiini), part II: A Revision of the New World-Australian genus *Pericompsus* LeConte." *Smithsonian Contributions to Zoology*, no. 162, pp. 1–96.

—— 1975. "Studies of the subtribe Tachyina (Coleoptera: Carabidae: Bembidiini), part III: Systematics, phylogeny and zoogeography of the genus *Tachyta* Kirby." *Smithsonian Contributions to Zoology*, no. 208, pp. 1–68.

—— 1979a. "A review of the natural history and evolution of ectoparisitoid relationships in carabid beetles." In T. L. Erwin, G. E. Ball, D. R. Whitehead, and A. L. Halpern, eds., *Carabid Beetles: Their Evolution, Natural History, and Classification*, pp. 479–84. The Hague: W. Junk.

—— 1979b. "Thoughts on the evolutionary history of ground beetles: Hypotheses generated from comparative faunal analyses of lowland forest sites in temperate and tropical regions." In T. L. Erwin, G. E. Ball, D. R. Whitehead and A. L. Halpern, eds., *Carabid Beetles: Their Evolution, Natural History, and Classification*, pp. 539–92. The Hague: W. Junk.

Erwin, T. L., G. E. Ball, D. R. Whitehead, and A. L. Halpern, eds., 1979. *Carabid Beetles: Their Evolution, Natural History, and Classification*. The Hague: W. Junk.

Evans, R. 1978. "Origin and significance of evaporites in basins around Atlantic margin." *Bulletin of the American Association of Petroleum Geologists*, 62(2):223–34.

Fallaw, W. C. 1977. "Trends in trans-North Atlantic commonality among Phanerozoic invertebrates, and plate tectonic events." *Bulletin of the Geological Society of America*, 88(1):62–66.

Farris, J. S. 1970. "Methods for computing Wagner trees." *Systematic Zoology*, 19(1):83–92.

—— 1977. "On the phenetic approach to vertebrate classification." In M. K. Hecht, P. C. Goody, and B. M. Hecht, eds., *Major Patterns in Vertebrate Evolution*, pp. 823–50. New York and London: Plenum Press.

Farris, J. S., A. Kluge, and M. J. Eckhardt. 1970. "A numerical approach to phylogenetic systematics." *Systematic Zoology*, 19(2):172–89.

Feduccia, A. 1975. "Morphology of the bony stapes in the Menuridae and Acanthisittidae: Evidence for oscine affinities." *The Wilson Bulletin*, 87(3):418–20.

Feller, W. 1950. *An Introduction to Probability Theory and Its Applications*, 1. New York: Wiley.

—— 1957. *An Introduction to Probability Theory and Its Applications*. 2d ed. New York: Wiley.

Felsenstein, J. 1978. "The number of evolutionary trees." *Systematic Zoology*, 27(1):27–33.

Feyerabend, P. 1975. *Against method*. London: NLB; reprint, London: Verso, 1978.

Fischer, J. F. 1976. "Global tectonics and the cordilleran orocline." *Geotimes*, 21(9):18–19.

Fisher, F. J. F. 1965. "The alpine ranunculi of New Zealand." *Bulletin of the New Zealand Department of Scientific and Industrial Research*, no. 165, pp. 1–192.

Fitch, W. M. 1970. "Distinguishing homologous from analogous proteins." *Systematic Zoology*, 19(2):99–113.

—— 1977. "The phyletic interpretation of macromolecular sequence information: Simple methods." In M. K. Hecht, P. C. Goody, and B. M. Hecht, eds., *Major Patterns in Vertebrate Evolution*, pp. 169–204. New York and London: Plenum Press.

Fitch, W. M. and E. Margoliash. 1967. "Construction of phylogenetic trees." *Science* (Washington, D.C.), 155(3760):279–84.

Fittkau, E. J. 1962. "Die Tanypodinae (Diptera: Chironomidae)." *Abhandlungen zur Larvalsystematik der Insekten*, 6:1–453.

Fitzpatrick, J. W. 1973. "Speciation in the genus *Ochthoeca* (Aves: Tyrannidae)." *Breviora*, no. 402, pp. 1–13.

—— 1980. "Some aspects of speciation in South American flycatchers." *Proceedings of the 17th International Ornithological Congress*, in press.

Flessa, K. W., J. M. Miyazaki, and W. C. Fallaw. 1978. "Trends in trans-North Atlantic commonality among Phanerozoic invertebrates, and plate tectonic events: Discussion and reply." *Bulletin of the Geological Society of America*, 89(3):476–80.

Florin, R. 1963. "The distribution of conifer and taxad genera in time and space." *Acta Horti Bergiani*, 20(4):121–312.

Förster, R. 1978. "Evidence for an open seaway between northern and southern proto-Atlantic in Albian times." *Nature* (London), 272(5649):158–59.

Forbes, E. 1846. "On the connexion between the distribution of the existing fauna and flora of the British Isles, and the geological changes which have effected their area, especially during the epoch of the northern drift." *Memoirs of the Geological Survey of Great Britain, and of the Museum of Economic Geology in London*, 1:336–432.

Forsythe, R. and C. Mpodozis. 1979. "Proto-Pacific crust in southern Chile." *Abstracts with Programs of the Geological Society of America*, 11(3):78.

Fosberg, F. R. 1948. "Derivation of the flora of the Hawaiian Islands." In E. C. Zimmerman, *Insects of Hawaii*, 1:107–19, Honolulu: University of Hawaii Press.

—— 1962. "Marotiri (Bass Rocks) Austral Islands." *Atoll Research Bulletin*, no. 162, pp. 9–10.

Fosberg, F. R. and M.-H. Sachet. 1966. "*Lebronnecia*, gen. nov. (Malvaceae) des Iles Marquises." *Adansonia*, series 2, 6(3):507–10.

Foster, R. J. 1974. "Eocene echinoids and the Drake Passage." *Nature* (London), 249(5459):751.

Fox, K. J. 1978. "The transoceanic migration of Lepidoptera to New Zealand—a history and a hypothesis on colonization." *New Zealand Entomologist*, 6(4):368–80.

Fox, R. C. 1979a. "Mammals from the Upper Cretaceous Oldman Formation, Alberta, 1: *Alphadon* Simpson (Marsupialia)." *Canadian Journal of Earth Sciences*, 16(1):91–102.

—— 1979b. "Mammals from the Upper Cretaceous Oldman Formation, Alberta, 2: *Pediomys* Marsh (Marsupialia)." *Canadian Journal of Earth Sciences*, 16(1):103–13.

Freeland, G. L. and R. S. Dietz. 1971. "Plate tectonic evolution of Caribbean-Gulf of Mexico region." *Nature* (London), 232(5305):20–23.

Freeman, J. A. 1945. "Studies in the distribution of insects by aerial currents." *The Journal of Animal Ecology*, 14(2):128–54.

Fryxell, P. A. 1965a. "A revision of the Australian species of *Gossypium* with observations of the occurrence of *Thespesia* in Australia (Malvaceae). *Australian Journal of Botany*, 13(1):70–102.

—— 1965b. "Stages in the evolution of *Gossypium* L." *Advancing Frontiers of Plant Sciences*, 10:31–55.

Fürsich, F. T. and R. M. Sykes, 1977. "Palaeobiogeography of the European boreal realm during Oxfordian (Upper Jurassic) times: A quantitative approach." *Neues Jahrbuch für Geologie und Paläontologie, Abhandlungen*, 155(2):137–61.

Funnell, B. M. and A. G. Smith. 1968. "Opening of the Atlantic Ocean." *Nature* (London), 219(5161):1328–33.

Furumoto, A. S., J. P. Webb, M. E. Odegard, and D. M. Hussong. 1976. "Seismic studies on the Ontong Java Plateau." *Tectonophysics*, 34(1–2):71–90.

Furumoto, A. S., W. A. Wiebenga, J. P. Webb, and G. H. Sutton. 1973. "Crustal structure of the Hawaiian Archipelago, nothern Melanesia, and the Central Pacific Basin by seismic refraction methods." *Tectonophysics*, 20(1–4):153–64.

Gaffney, E. S. 1975. "A phylogeny and classification of the higher categories of turtles." *Bulletin of the American Museum of Natural History*, 155(5):387–436.

—— 1977. "The side-necked turtle family Chelidae: A theory of relationships using shared derived characters." *American Museum Novitates*, no. 2620, pp. 1–28.

Galton, P. M. 1977. "The Upper Jurassic ornithopod dinosaur *Dryosaurus* and a Laurasia-Gondwanaland connection." In R. M. West, ed., *Paleontology and Plate Tectonics with Special Reference to the History of the Atlantic Ocean*, pp. 41–54. Special Publications in Biology and Geology of the Milwaukee Public Museum, no. 2.

Gardiner, F. P. and R. L. Haedrich. 1978. "Zonation in the deep benthic megafauna." *Oecologia*, 31(3):311–17.

Gardner, A. L. 1973. "The systematics of the genus *Didelphis* (Marsupialia: Didelphidae) in North and Middle America." Texas Tech University, *Special Publications of The Museum*, no. 4, pp. 1–81.

Garner, H. F. 1974, *The Origin of Landscapes: A Synthesis of Geomorphology*. New York, London, Toronto: Oxford University Press.

—— 1975. "Rainforests, deserts and evolution." In *Simpósio International sobre o Quaternário*, pp. 127–33. Anais da Academia Brasileira de Ciencias, Suplemento, vol. 47.

Germeraad, J. H., C. A. Hopping, and J. Muller. 1968. "Palynology of Tertiary sediments from tropical areas." *Review of Palaeobotany and Palynology*, 6(3–4):189–348.

Ghiselin, M. T. 1969. *The Triumph of the Darwinian Method*. Berkeley, Los Angeles, London: University of California Press.

Glennie, K. W., M. G. A. Boeuf, M. W. Hughes Clarke, M. Moody-Stuart, W. F. H. Pilaar, and B. M. Reinhardt. 1973. "Late Cretaceous nappes in Oman Mountains and their geologic evolution." *Bulletin of the American Association of Petroleum Geologists*, 57(1):5–27.

Gobbett, D. J. 1967. "Palaeozoogeography of the Verbeekinidae (Permian Foraminifera)." In C. G. Adams and D. V. Ager, eds., *Aspects of Tethyan Biogeography*, pp. 77–91. Publications of the Systematics Association (London), no. 7.

Goin, C. J. and O. B. Goin. 1973. "Antarctica, isostacy, and the origin of frogs." *Quarterly Journal of the Florida Academy of Science*, 35(2–3):113–29.

Gose, W. A. and D. G. Swartz. 1977. "Palaeomagnetic results from Cretaceous sediments in Hondouras: Tectonic implications." *Geology* (Boulder), 5(8):505–8.

Gothan, W. and H. Weyland. 1964. *Lehrbuch der Paläobotanik*. Berlin: Akademie-Verlag.

Gould, S. J. 1976. "Darwin's untimely burial." *Natural History* (New York), 85(8):24–30.

Gould, S. J., D. M. Raup, J. J. Sepkoski, Jr., T. J. M. Schopf, and D. S. Simberloff. 1977. "The shape of evolution: A comparison of real and random clades." *Paleobiology*, 3(1):23–40.

Graham, S. A., W. R. Dickinson, and R. V. Ingersoll. 1975. "Himalayan-Bengal model for flysch dispersal in the Appalachian-Ouachita system." *Bulletin of the Geological Society of America*, 86(3):273–86.

Grant, P. R. 1970. "Colonization of islands by ecologically dissimilar species of mammals." *Canadian Journal of Zoology*, 48(3):545–53.

Grant, V. 1971. *Plant Speciation*. New York and London: Columbia University Press.

Gray, A. 1859. "Diagnostic characters of new species of phaenogamous plants, collected in Japan by Charles Wright, botanist of the U.S. North Pacific Exploring Expedition (published by request of Captain John Rodgers, Commander of the expedition), with observations upon the relations of the Japanese flora to that of North America and of other parts of the northern temperate zone." *Memoirs of the American Academy of Arts and Sciences*, new series, vol. 6, part 2, year 1858, no. 9, pp. 377–449.

—— 1878. "Forest geography and archaeology." *The American Journal of Science and Arts*, series 3, 16(92):85–94; 16(93):183–96.

Gregory, J. W. 1925. "Continental drift." [review of Wegener, 1924]. *Nature* (London), 115(2886):255–57.

Gressitt, J. L. 1974. "Insect biogeography." *Annual Review of Entomology*, 19:293–321.

Gressitt, J. L., R. D. Leech, and K. A. J. Wise. 1963. "Entomological investigations in Antarctica." *Pacific Insects*, 5(2):287–304.

Griffiths, G. C. D. 1972. *The Phylogenetic Classification of Diptera Cyclorrhapha, with Special Reference to the Male Postabdomen*. Series Entomologica, no. 8. The Hague: W. Junk.

Griffiths, J. R. 1971. "Reconstruction of the south-west Pacific margin of Gondwanaland." *Nature* (London), 234(5326):203–7.

Griffiths, M. 1978. *The Biology of the Monotremes*. New York and London: Academic Press.

Guilday, J. E., P. S. Martin, and A. D. McCrady. 1964. "New Paris No. 4: A late Pleistocene cave deposit in Bedford County, Pennsylvania." *Bulletin of the National Speleological Society*, 26(4):121-94.

Guppy, H. B. 1906. *Observations of a Naturalist in the Pacific Between 1869 and 1899*, vol. 2: *Plant-Dispersal*. London: Macmillan.

Guzman, E. J. and Z. de Cserna. 1963. "Tectonic history of Mexico." In O. E. Childs and B. W. Beebe, eds., *Backbone of the Americas*, pp. 113-29. Memoirs of the American Association of Petroleum Geologists, no. 2.

Haeckel, E. 1866. *Generelle Morphologie der Organismen*. Berlin: Georg Reimer.

Haffer, J. 1967. "Speciation in Colombian forest birds west of the Andes." *American Museum Novitates*, no. 2294, pp. 1-57.

—— 1969. "Speciation in Amazonian forest birds." *Science* (Washington, D.C.), 165(3889):131-37.

—— 1970a. "Geologic-climatic history and zoogeographic significance of the Urabá region in northwestern Colombia." *Caldasia* (Bogotá), 10(50):603-36.

—— 1970b. "Entstehung und Ausbreitung nord-Andiner Bergvögel." *Zoologische Jahrbücher, Abteilung für Systematik, Okologie, und Geographie der Tiere*, 97(3):301-37.

—— 1974. *Avian Speciation in Tropical South America, with a Systematic Survey of the Toucans (Ramphastidae) and Jacamars (Galbulidae)*. Publications of the Nuttall Ornithological Club (Cambridge), no. 14.

—— 1978. "Distribution of Amazon forest birds." *Bonner Zoologische Beiträge*, 29(1-3):38-78.

Hall, R. 1976. "Ophiolite emplacement and the evolution of the Taurus suture zone, southeastern Turkey." *Bulletin of the Geological Society of America*, 87 (7):1078-88.

Hall, R. E. and K. R. Kelson. 1959. *The Mammals of North America*, vols. 1-2. New York: Ronald Press.

Hallam, A. 1967a. "The bearing of certain palaeozoogeographic data on continental drift." *Palaeogeography, Palaeoclimatology, Palaeoecology*, 3(2):201-41.

—— 1967b. "A discussion." In C. G. Adams and D. V. Ager, eds., *Aspects of Tethyan Biogeography*, p. 310. Publications of the Systematics Association (London), no. 7.

—— 1973b. "Distributional patterns in contemporary terrestrial and marine animals." In N. F. Hughes, ed., *Organisms and Continents Through Time* pp. 93-105. Special Papers in Palaeontology of the Palaeontological Association (London), no. 12; Publications of the Systematics Associations no. 9.

—— 1974. "Changing patterns of provinciality and diversity of fossil animals in relation to plate tectonics." *Journal of Biogeography*, 1(4):213-25.

—— 1975. *Jurassic Environments*. Cambridge, London, New York, Melbourne: Cambridge University Press.

—— 1976. "Geology and plate tectonics interpretation of the sediments of the Mesozoic radiolarite-ophiolite complex in the Neyriz region, southern Iran." *Bulletin of the Geological Society of America*, 87(1):47-52.

—— 1977a. "Jurassic bivalve biogeography." *Paleobiology*, 3(1):58-73.

—— 1977b. "Biogeographic evidence bearing on the creation of Atlantic seaways in the Jurassic." In R. M. West, ed., *Paleontology and Plate Tectonics with Special Reference to the History of the Atlantic Ocean*, pp. 23–34. Special Publications in Biology and Geology of the Milwaukee Public Museum, no. 2.

—— 1977c. "Secular changes in marine inundation of USSR and North America through the Phanerozoic." *Nature* (London), 269(5631):769–72.

—— 1978. "Eustatic cycles in the Jurassic." *Palaeogeography, Palaeoclimatology, Palaeoecology*, 23(1–2):1–32.

Hallam, A., ed. 1973a. *Atlas of Palaeobiogeography*. Amsterdam, London, New York: Elsevier.

Hallier, H. 1912. "Uber frühere Landbrücken, Pflanzen- und Völkerwanderungen zwischen Australaien und Amerika." Leiden, *Mededeelingen van's Rijks Herbarium*, 13(13):1–32.

Hamilton, W. 1969. "Mesozoic California and the underflow of Pacific mantle." *Bulletin of the Geological Society of America*, 80(12):2409–30.

—— 1970. "The Uralides and the motion of the Russian and Siberian platforms." *Bulletin of the Geological Society of America*, 81(9):2553–76.

Hamilton, W. R. 1978. "Fossil giraffes from the Miocene of Africa and a revision of the phylogeny of the Giraffoidea." *Philosophical Transactions of the Royal Society of London*, B. Biological Sciences, 283(996):165–229.

Hammond, S. R., L. W. Kroenke, F. Theyer, and D. L. Keeling. 1975. "Late Cretaceous and Palaeogene palaeolatitudes of the Ontong Java Plateau." *Nature* (London), 255(5503):46–47.

Hanks, S. L. and D. E. Fairbrothers. 1976. "Palynotaxonomic investigation of *Fagus* L. and *Nothofagus* Bl.: Light microscopy, scanning electron microscopy, and computer analysis." In V. H. Heywood, ed., *Botanical Systematics*, 1:1–141. London, New York, San Francisco: Academic Press.

Harper, C. W., Jr. and N. I. Platnick. 1978. "Phylogenetic and Cladistic hypotheses: A debate." *Systematic Zoology*, 27(3):354–62.

Harrington, H. J. 1962. "Paleogeographic development of South America." *Bulletin of the American Association of Petroleum Geologists*, 46(10):1773–1814.

Hayes, D. E. and J. Ringis. 1973. "Seafloor spreading in the Tasman Sea." *Nature* (London), 243(5408):454–58.

Hays, J. D. and W. C. Pitman, III. 1973. "Lithospheric plate motion, sea-level changes and climatic and ecological consequences." *Nature* (London), 246(5427):18–22.

Heck, K. L., Jr. and E. D. McCoy. 1978. "Long-distance dispersal and the reef-building corals of the eastern Pacific." *Marine Biology*, 48(4):349–56.

—— 1979. "Biogeography of seagrasses: Evidence from associated organisms." *Proceedings of the New Zealand Oceanographic Institution*, in press.

Hedley, C. 1899. "A zoogeographic scheme for the mid-Pacific." *Proceedings of the Linnean Society of New South Wales for the Year 1899*, 24, part 3, no. 95, pp. 391–423.

Heintz, E. 1975. "Origine, migration, et paléobiogéographie des Palaeotraginae (Giraffidae, Artiodactyla) antévallésiens." In *Problèmes Actuels de Paléontologie (Evolution des Vertébrés)*, 2: 723–29. Colloques Internationaux du Centre National de la Recherche Scientifique (Paris), no. 218.

Heirtzler, J. R., G. O. Dickson, E. M. Herron, W. C. Pitman, III, and X. Le Pichon.

1968. "Marine magnetic anomalies, geomagnetic field reversals, and motions of the ocean floor and continents." *Journal of Geophysical Research,* 73(6):2119–36.

Henderson, J. 1935. *Fossil Non-Marine Mollusca of North America.* Special Papers of the Geological Society of America, no. 3, pp. 1–313.

Hennig, W. 1950. *Grundzüge einer Theorie der phylogenetischen Systematik.* Berlin: Deutscher Zentralverlag.

—— 1954. "Flügelgeäder und System der Dipteren unter Berücksichtigung der aus dem Mesozoikum beschriebenen Fossilien." *Beitrage Entomologicae,* 4(3–4):245–388.

—— 1965. "Phylogenetic systematics." *Annual Review of Entomology,* 10:97–116.

—— 1966. *Phylogenetic Systematics.* Urbana: University of Illinois Press; reprint, 1979.

—— 1969. *Die Stammesgeschichte der Insekten.* Frankfurt am Main: Waldemar Kramer.

—— 1970. "Insektenfossilien aus der unteren Kreide 2: Empididae (Diptera, Brachycera)." *Stuttgarter Beiträge zur Naturkunde,* no. 214, pp. 1–12.

—— 1972. "Insektenfossilien aus der unteren Kreide 4: Psychodidae (Phlebotominae), mit einer kritischen Übersicht über das phylogenetische System der Familie und die bisher beschriebenen Fossilien (Diptera)." *Stuttgarter Beiträge zur Naturkunde,* no. 241, pp. 1–69.

Herrero-Ducloux, A. 1963. "The Andes of western Argentina." In O. E. Childs and B. W. Beebe, eds., *Backbone of the Americas,* pp. 16–28. Memoirs of the American Association of Petroleum Geologists, no. 2.

Herron, E. M. 1972. "Sea-floor spreading and the Cenozoic history of the East-Central Pacific." *Bulletin of the Geological Society of America,* 83(6):1671–91.

Hershkovitz, P. 1972. "The Recent mammals of the Neotropical region: A zoogeographic and ecological review." In A. Keast, F. C. Erk, and B. Glass, eds., *Evolution, Mammals and Southern Continents,* pp. 311–431. Albany: State University of New York Press.

Hey, R. 1977. "Tectonic evolution of the Cocos-Nazca spreading center." *Bulletin of the Geological Society of America,* 88(10):1404–20.

Hicken, A. and E. Irving. 1977. "Tectonic rotation in western Canada." *Nature* (London), 268(5617):219–20.

Hickey, L. J. 1979. "Changes in the angiosperm flora across the Cretaceous-Tertiary boundary." In W. A. Berggren and Van Couvering, eds., *Catastrophies and Earth History: The New Uniformitarianism,* in press. Princeton: Princeton University Press.

Hickey, L. J. and J. A. Doyle. 1977. "Early Cretaceous fossil evidence for angiosperm evolution." *Botanical Review,* 43(1):3–104.

Hilde, T. W. C., S. Uyeda, and L. Kroenke. 1976. "Evolution of the western Pacific and its margin." In C. L. Drake, ed., *Geodynamics: Progress and Prospects,* pp. 1–15. Washington, D.C.: American Geophysical Union.

—— 1977. "Evolution of the western Pacific and its margins." *Tectonophysics,* 38(1–2):145–65.

Hillhouse, J. 1977. "Paleomagnetism of the Triassic Nikolai Greenstone, McCarthy Quadrangle, Alaska." *Canadian Journal of Earth Sciences*, 14(11):2578–92.

Himmelfarb, G. 1959. *Darwin and the Darwinian Revolution*. London: Chatto and Windus; Garden City, N.J.: Doubleday; reprints, Garden City, N.J.: Anchor Books, Doubleday, 1962; New York: Norton, 1968.

Hippa, H. 1978. "Classification of Xylotini (Diptera, Syrphidae)." *Acta Zoologica Fennica*, no. 156, pp. 1–153.

Hirvenoja, M. 1973. "Revision der Gattung *Cricotopus* Van der Wulp und ihrer Verwandten (Diptera, Chironomidae)." *Annales Zoologici Fennici*, 10(1):1–363.

Hoffmann, B. and H. Dukas. 1973. *Albert Einstein: Creator and Rebel*. New York: New American Library.

Hoffstetter, R. 1975. "Les marsupiaux et l'histoire des mammifères: Aspects phylogéniques et chorologiques." In *Problèmes Actuels de Paléontologie (Evolution des Vertébrés)*, 2:591–610. Colloques Internationaux du Centre National de la Recherche Scientifique (Paris), no. 218.

Holden, J. C. and R. S. Dietz. 1972. "Galapagos gore, NazCoPac triple junction and Carnegie/Cocos Ridges," *Nature* (London), 235(5336):266–69.

Holloway, J. D. 1977. *The Lepidoptera of Norfolk Island, Their Biogeography and Ecology*. Series Entomologica, no. 13. The Hague: W. Junk.

Holmes, A. 1965. *Principles of Physical Geology*. Revised ed. London: Nelson; New York: Ronald Press.

Hooker, J. D. 1860. *Botany of the Antarctic Voyage of H. M. Discovery Ships "Erebus" and "Terror" in the Years 1839–1843, under the Command of Captain Sir James Clark Ross, part 3: Flora Tasmaniae*. London: Lovell Reeve.

Hopson, J. A. 1969. "The origin and adaptive radiation of mammal-like reptiles and nontherian mammals." *Annals of the New York Academy of Sciences*, 167(1):199–216.

Hopson, J. A. and A. W. Crompton. 1969. "Origin of mammals." In T. Dobzhansky, M. K. Hecht and W. C. Steere, eds., *Evolutionary Biology*, 3:15–72. New York: Appleton-Century-Crofts.

Houtz, R. and F. J. Davey. 1973. "Seismic profiler and sonobuoy measurements in Ross Sea, Antarctica." *Journal of Geophysical Research*, 78(17):3448–68.

Howden, H. F. 1971. "Terrestrial zoogeography" [Review of Udvardy, 1969]. *Ecology*, 52(1):191.

—— 1980. "Zoogeography of some Australian Coleoptera as exemplified by the Scarabaeoidea." In *Ecological Biogeography in Australia*, The Hague: W. Junk, in press.

Hsü, K. J. and R. Ohrbom. 1969. "Mélanges of San Francisco Peninsula—geologic reinterpretation of Type Franciscan." *Bulletin of the American Association of Petroleum Geologists*, 53(7):1348–67.

Hubbard, J. P. 1973. "Avian evolution in the aridlands of North America." *The Living Bird*, Cornell Laboratory of Ornithology, no. 12, pp. 155–96.

Hughes, T. 1975. "The case for creation of the North Pacific Ocean during the Mesozoic Era." *Palaeogeography, Palaeoclimatology, and Palaeoecology*, 18(1):1–43.

Hull, D. L. 1973. *Darwin and His Critics: The Reception of Darwin's Theory of Evolution by the Scientific Community*. Cambridge: Harvard University Press.

Hultén, E. 1928. "On the American component in the flora of eastern Siberia." *Svensk Botanisk Tidskrift*, 22(1–2):220–29.

—— 1937a. *Flora of the Aleutian Islands and Westernmost Alaska Peninsula with Notes on the Flora of Commander Islands*. Stockholm: Aktiebolaget Thule.

—— 1937b. *Outline of the History of Arctic and Boreal Biota during the Quarternary Period*. Stockholm: Aktiebolaget Thule.

Hurley, P. M. 1971. "Possible inclusion of Korea, central and western China and India in Gondwanaland." *Eos*, 52(4):356.

Igo, H. 1964. "Permian fusulinids of Nyukawa, central Japan, part 1." *Journal of Paleontology*, 38(4):637–49.

Illies, J. 1961. "Phylogenie und Verbreitungsgeschichte der Ordnung Plecoptera." In *Verhandlungen der Deutschen Zoologischen Gesellschaft, year 1960*, pp. 384–94. Zoologischer Anzeiger, Supplementband, vol. 24.

Irving, E. and R. W. Yole. 1972. "Paleomagnetism and kinematic history of mafic and ultramafic rocks in fold mountain belts." In *The Ancient Oceanic Lithosphere*, pp. 87–95. Publications of the Earth Physics Branch (Ottawa), vol. 42, no. 3.

Jacob, K. H. and K. Hamada. 1972. "The upper mantle beneath the Aleutian Island arc from pure-path Rayleigh-Wave dispersion data." *Bulletin of the Seismological Society of America*, 62(6):1439–53.

Jain, S. K. 1975. "Population structure and the effects of breeding system." In O. H. Frankel and J. G. Hawkes, eds., *Crop Genetic Resources for Today and Tomorrow*, pp. 15–36. Cambridge, London, New York, Melbourne: Cambridge University Press.

Jain, S. K. and D. R. Marshall. 1968. "Simulation of models involving mixed selfing and random mating, 1: Stochastic variation in outcrossing and selection parameters." *Heredity*, 23(3):411–32.

James, D. E. 1971a. "Plate tectonic model for the evolution of the central Andes." *Bulletin of the Geological Society of America*, 82(12):3325–46.

—— 1971b. "Andean crustal and upper mantle structure." *Journal of Geophysical Research*, 76(14):3246–71.

—— 1973. "The evolution of the Andes." *Scientific American*, 229(2):60–69.

Jansa, L. F. and J. A. Wade. 1975. "Geology of the continental margin off Nova Scotia and Newfoundland." In *Offshore Geology of Eastern Canada, 2: Regional Geology*, pp. 51–105. Papers of the Geological Survey of Canada (Ottawa), no. 74–30.

Janzen, D. H. 1971. "Seed predation by animals." *Annual Review of Ecology and Systematics*, 2:465–92.

Jardine, N. and R. Sibson. 1971. *Mathematical Taxonomy*. London, New York, Sydney, Toronto: Wiley.

Jarzen, D. M. and G. Norris. 1975. "Evolutionary significance and botanical relationships of Cretaceous angiosperm pollen in the western Canadian interior." In *Proceedings of the 6th Annual Meeting of the American Association of Stratigraphic Palynologists*, pp. 47–60. Geoscience and Man, vol. 11.

Jeannel, R. 1926–1928. "Monographie des Trechinae: Morphologie comparée et distribution géographique d'un groupe de coléoptères." *L'Abeille, Journal d'Entomologie*, 32:221–550; 33:1–592; 35:1–808.

—— 1946–1949. *Coléoptères Carabiques de la Region Malgache*, parts 1–3. Faune de l'Empire Français, vols. 6, 10, 11. Paris: Office de la Recherche Scientifique Coloniale.

Jefferies, R. P. S. 1979. "The origin of chordates—a methodological essay." In M. R. House, ed., *The Origin of Major Invertebrate Groups*, pp. 443–77. London and New York: Academic Press.

Jenks, W. F., ed. 1956a. *Handbook of South American Geology:* Memoirs of the Geological Society of America, no. 65.

—— 1956b. "Peru". pp. 219–47. In W. F. Jenks, ed., *Handbook of South American Geology*. Memoirs of the Geological Society of America, no. 65.

Johnson, C. G. 1969. *Migration and Dispersal of Insects by Flight*. London: Methuen.

Johnson, C. G. and J. Bowden. 1972. "Problems related to the transoceanic transport of insects, especially between the Amazon and Congo areas." In B. J. Meggers, E. S. Ayensu, and W. D. Duckworth eds., *Tropical Forest Ecosystems in Africa and South America: A Comparative Review*, pp. 207–22. Washington, D.C.: Smithsonian Institution Press.

Johnson, L. A. S. and B. G. Briggs. 1975. "On the Proteaceae—the evolution and classification of a southern family." *Botanical Journal of the Linnean Society* (London) 70(2):83–182.

Jones, D. L., W. P. Irwin, and A. T. Ovenshine. 1972. "Southeastern Alaska—a displaced continental fragment?" *Professional Papers of the Geological Survey* (Washington, D.C.), no. 800-B, pp. 211–17.

Jones, D. L., N. J. Silberling, and J. Hillhouse, 1977. "Wrangellia—a displaced terrane in northwestern North America." *Canadian Journal of Earth Sciences*, 14(11):2565–77.

Jones, M., R. Van der Voo, M. Churkin, Jr., and G. D. Eberlein. 1977. "Paleozoic paleomagnetic results from the Alexander Terrane of southeastern Alaska." *Eos*, 58(12):1126.

Jong, P. C. de. 1976. "Flowering and sex expression in *Acer* L.: A biosystematic study." *Mededelingen Landbouwhogeschool Wageningen*, 76(2):1–201.

Kanaev, V. F. and N. N. Turko. 1976. "Morphology and volcanism of the Indian Ocean floor." In H. Aoki and S. Iizuka, eds., *Volcanoes and Tectonosphere*, pp. 35–60. Tokyo: Tokai University Press.

Karig, D. E. 1971. "Origin and development of marginal basins in the western Pacific." *Journal of Geophysical Research*, 76(11):2542–61.

Kauffman, E. G. 1973. "Cretaceous Bivalvia." In A. Hallam, ed., *Atlas of Palaeobiogeography*, pp. 353–83. Amsterdam, London, New York: Elsevier.

Kavanaugh, D. H. and J. Negre. 1979. "Notiokasini—a new tribe of Carabidae (Coleoptera) from southeastern South America." Manuscript.

Kawai, N., K. Hirooka, and T. Nakajima. 1969. "Palaeomagnetic and potassium-argon age informations supporting Cretaceous-Tertiary hypothetic bend of the main island Japan." *Palaeogeography, Palaeoclimatology, Palaeoecology*, 6(4):277–82.

Keast, A. 1961. "Bird speciation on the Australian continent." *Bulletin of the Museum of Comparative Zoology*, 123(8):305–495.

—— 1973. "Contemporary biotas and the separation sequence of the southern continents." In D. H. Tarling and S. K. Runcorn, eds., *Implications of Continental Drift to the Earth Sciences* 1: 309–43. London and New York: Academic Press.

—— 1977a. "Historical biogeography of the marsupials." In B. Stonehouse and D. Gilmore, eds., *The Biology of Marsupials*, pp. 69–95. London and Basingstoke: Macmillan Press; Baltimore, London, Tokyo: University Park Press.

—— 1977b. "Zoogeography and phylogeny: The theoretical background and methodology to the analysis of mammal and bird fauna." In M. K. Hecht, P. C. Goody, and B. M. Hecht, eds., *Major Patterns in Vertebrate Evolution*, pp. 249–312. New York and London: Plenum Press.

Keigwin, L. D. 1978. "Pliocene closing of the Isthmus of Panama, based on biostratigraphic evidence from nearby Pacific Ocean and Caribbean Sea cores." *Geology* (Boulder), 6(10):630–34.

Kemp, E. M. 1978. "Tertiary climatic evolution and vegetation history in the southeast Indian Ocean region." *Palaeogeography, Palaeoclimatology, Palaeoecology*, 24(3):169–208.

Kemp, T. S. 1979. "The primitive cynodont *Procynosuchus*: Functional anatomy of the skull and relationships." *Philosophical Transactions of the Royal Society of London*, series B: Biological Sciences, 285:73–122.

Kennedy, W. J. and W. A. Cobban. 1976. "Aspects of ammonite biology, biogeography, and biostratigraphy." *Special Papers in Palaeontology of the Palaeontological Society* (London), no. 17, pp. 1–94.

Kennett, J. P. 1977. "Cenozoic evolution of Antarctic glaciation, the circum-Antarctic Ocean, and their impact on global paleoceanography." *Journal of Geophysical Research*, 82(27):3843–60.

Kennett, J. P. and R. E. Houtz. 1973. "Deep-sea drilling in the roaring 40s." *Geotimes*, 18(7):14–17.

Kennett, J. P., R. E. Houtz, P. B. Andrews, A. R. Edwards, V. A. Gostin, M. Hajos, M. A. Hampton, D. G. Jenkins, S. V. Margolis, A. T. Ovenshine, and K. Perch-Nielsen. 1974. "Development of the circum-Antarctic current." *Science* (Washington, D.C.), 186(4159):144–47.

Kermack, K. A. 1967. "The interrelations of early mammals." In C. Patterson and P. H. Greenwood, eds., *Papers on Fossil Vertebrates*, pp. 241–49. The Journal of the Linnean Society of London, Zoology, vol. 47, no. 311.

—— 1975. "The complex of early mammals." In *Problèmes Actuels de Paléontologie* (*Evolution des Vertébrés*), 2:563–71. Colloques Internationaux du Centre National de la Recherche Scientifique, no. 218.

Kermack, K. A. and Z. Kielan-Jaworowska. 1971. "Therian and non-therian mammals." In D. M. Kermack and K. A. Kermack, eds., *Early Mammals*, pp. 103–15. Zoological Journal of the Linnean Society (London), supplement, vol. 50, no. 1.

Kermack, K. A., F. Musset, and H. W. Rigney. 1973. "The lower jaw of *Morganucodon*." *Zoological Journal of the Linnean Society* (London), 53(2):87–175.

Kerney, M. P., ed., 1976. *Atlas of the Non-Marine Mollusca of the British Isles*. Cambridge: Conchological Society of Great Britain and Ireland and the Biological Records Centre, Institute of Terrestrial Ecology.

Key, K. H. L. 1976. "A generic and suprageneric classification of the Morabinae (Orthoptera: Eumastacidae), with description of the type species and a bibliography of the subfamily." *Australian Journal of Zoology*, Supplementary Series, no. 37, pp. 1–185.

Kielan-Jaworowska, Z. 1974. "Migrations of the Multituberculata and the late Cretaceous connections between Asia and North America." *Annals of the South African Museum*, 64:231–43.

—— 1975. "Results of the Polish-Mongolian palaeontological expeditions, part 6: Evolution of the therian mammals in the late Cretaceous of Asia, part 1, Deltatheridiidae." *Palaeontologia Polonica*, no. 33, pp. 103–32.

—— 1979. "Pelvic structure and nature of reproduction in Multituberculata." *Nature* (London), 277(5695):402–3.

Kinzey, W. 1981. "Distribution of neotropical primates and the model of Pleistocene forest refugia." In G. Prance, ed., *The Biological Model of Diversification in the Tropics*, in press, New York: Columbia University Press.

Kirsch, J. A. W. 1977. "The comparative serology of Marsupialia, and a classification of marsupials." *Australian Journal of Zoology*, Supplementary Series, no. 52, pp. 1–152.

—— 1979. "Les marsupiaux." *La Recherche*, 10:108–16.

Kluge, A. and J. S. Farris. 1969. "Quantitative phyletics and the evolution of anurans." *Systematic Zoology*, 18(1):1–32.

Kondo, Y. 1962. "The genus *Tubuaia*, Pulmonata, Achatinellidae." *Bulletin of the Bernice P. Bishop Museum*, no. 224, pp. 1–49.

—— 1968. "Partulidae: Preview of anatomical revision." *The Nautilus*, 81(3):73–77.

—— 1973. "*Samoana* of the Society Islands (Pulmonata: Partulidae)." *Malacological Review*, no. 6, pp. 19–23.

Krassilov, V. A. 1975. "Climatic changes in eastern Asia as indicated by fossil floras, 2: Late Cretaceous and Danian." *Palaeogeography, Palaeoclimatology, Palaeoecology*, 17(2):157–72.

Kristofferson, Y. 1978. "Sea-floor spreading and the early opening of the North Atlantic." *Earth and Planetary Science Letters*, 38(2):273–90.

Kuhn, H.-J. 1971. "Die Entwicklung und Morphologie des Schädels von *Tachyglossus aculeatus*." *Abhandlungen der Senckenbergischen Naturforschenden Gesellschaft*, no. 528, pp. 1–224.

Kurtén, B. 1967. "Continental drift and the palaeogeography of reptiles and mammals." *Commentationes Biologicae, Societas Scientiarum Fennica*, 31(1):1–8.

Lack, D. 1947. *Darwin's Finches*. Cambridge: Cambridge University Press; reprint, New York: Harper, 1961.

Ladd, J. W. 1976. "Relative motion of South America with respect to North America and Caribbean tectonics." *Bulletin of the Geological Society of America*, 87(7):969–76.

Lancelot, Y. 1978. "Relations entre évolution sédimentaire et tectonique de la Plaque pacifique depuis le Crétacé Inférieur." *Mémoires de la Société Géologique de France*, new series, 57(134):1–40.

Lancelot, Y. and R. L. Larson, 1975. "Sedimentary and tectonic evolution of the northwestern Pacific." *Initial Reports of the Deep Sea Drilling Project* (Washington, D.C.), 32:925–39.

Landis, C. A. and D. S. Coombs. 1967. "Metamorphic belts and orogenesis in southern New Zealand." *Tectonophysics*, 4(4–6):501–18.

Larson, R. L. and C. G. Chase. 1972. "Late Mesozoic evolution of the western Pacific Ocean." *Bulletin of the Geological Society of America*, 83(12):3627–44.

Larson, R. L. and J. W. Ladd. 1973. "Evidence for the opening of the South Atlantic in the early Cretaceous." *Nature* (London), 246(5430):209–12.

Larson, R. L., H. W. Menard, and S. M. Smith. 1968. "Gulf of California: A result of ocean-floor spreading and transform faulting." *Science* (Washington, D.C.), 161(3843):781–83.

Larson, R. L. and W. C. Pitman, III. 1972. "World-wide correlation of Mesozoic magnetic anomalies, and its implications." *Bulletin of the Geological Society of America*, 83(12):3645–62.

Lattin, G. de. 1957. "Die Ausbreitungszentren der holarktischen Landtierwelt." In *Verhandlungen der Deutschen Zoologischen Gesellschaft*, pp. 380–410. Zoologischer Anzeiger, Supplementband, no. 20.

—— 1967. *Grundriss der Zoogeographie*. Stuttgart: Gustav Fischer.

Laubscher, H. and D. Bernoulli. 1977. "Mediterranean and Tethys." In A. E. M. Nairn, W. H. Kanes, and F. G. Stehli, eds., *The Ocean Basins and Margins*, vol. 4A: *The Eastern Mediterranean, pp. 1–28*. New York and London: Plenum Press.

Laughton, A. S., D. H. Matthews, and R. L. Fisher. 1970. "The structure of the Indian Ocean." In A. E. Maxwell, ed., *The Sea: Ideas and Observations in the Study of the Seas*, vol. 4, part 2, pp. 543–86. New York, London, Sydney, Toronto: Wiley-Interscience.

Lavocat, R. 1977. "Sur l'origine des faunes sud-américaines de mammifères du Mésozoïque terminal et du Cénozoïque ancien." *Comptes Rendus des Séances de l'Académie des Sciences, Paris*, series D, 285(16):1423–26.

Leopold, E. B. and H. D. MacGinitie. 1972. "Development and affinities of Tertiary floras in the Rocky Mountains." In A. Graham, ed., *Floristics and Paleofloristics of Asia and Eastern North America*, pp. 147–200. Amsterdam, London, New York: Elsevier.

Le Pichon, X. and J. Francheteau. 1978. "A plate-tectonic analysis of the Red Sea-Gulf of Aden area." In O. H. Oren, ed., *Structure and Tectonics of the Eastern Mediterranean*, pp. 369–406. Tectonophysics, vol. 46, nos. 3–4.

Le Pichon, X. and D. E. Hayes. 1971. "Marginal offsets, fracture zones, and the early opening of the South Atlantic." *Journal of Geophysical Research*, 76(26):6283–93.

Levandowsky, M. 1972. "Ecological niches of sympatric phytoplankton species." *The American Naturalist*, 106(947):71–78.

Levandowsky, M. and B. S. White. 1977. "Randomness, time scales, and the evolution of biological communities." In M. K. Hecht, W. C. Steere, and B. Wallace, eds., *Evolutionary Biology*, 10:69–161. New York and London: Plenum Press.

Levin, D. A. 1979. "The nature of plant species." *Science* (Washington, D.C.), 204(4391):381–84.

Levin, D. A. and H. W. Kerster. 1974. "Gene flow in seed plants." In T. Dobzhansky, M. K. Hecht, and W. C. Steere, eds., *Evolutionary Biology*, 7:139–220. New York and London: Plenum Press.

Li, H.-L. 1952. "Floristic relationships between eastern Asia and eastern North America." *Transactions of the American Philosophical Society*, new series, 42(2):371–429. Reprint Philadelphia: Morris Arboretum, 1971.

Lindroth, C. H. 1945–1949. "Die fennoskandischen Carabidae, eine tiergeographische Studie 1, spezieller Teil; 2, Die Karten; 3, Allgemeiner Teil—zugleich eine biogeographische Prinzipdiskussion." Meddelanden fran Göteborgs Musei Zoologiska Avdelning, nos. 109, 110, 122. *Göteborgs Kungliga Vetenskaps- och Vitterhets-samhälles Handlingar*, Sjätte Följden, series B: Matematiska och Naturvetenskapliga Skrifter, 4(1):1–709; 4(2):1–277; 4(3):1–911.

—— 1961–1969. "The ground-beetles (Carabidae, excl. Cicindelinae) of Canada and Alaska, parts 1–6." *Opuscula Entomologica*, Supplementum, no. 20, pp. 1–200; no. 24, pp. 201–408; no. 29, pp. 409–648; no. 33, pp. 649–944; no. 34, pp. 945–1192; no. 35, pp. i–xlviii.

Lindroth, C. H., H. Andersson, H. Bödvarsson, and S. H. Richter. 1973. *Surtsey, Iceland: The Development of a New Fauna, 1963–1970, Terrestrial Invertebrates.* Entomologica Scandinavica, Supplementum 5. Copenhagen: Munksgaard.

Lloyd, J. J. 1963. "Tectonic history of the South Central-American orogen." In O. E. Childs and B. W. Beebe, eds., *Backbone of the Americas*, pp. 88–100. Memoirs of the American Association of Petroleum Geologists, no. 2.

Lloyd, M. and H. S. Dybas. 1966. "The periodical cicada problem, 2: Evolution." *Evolution*, 20(4):466–505.

Løvtrup, S. 1977. *The Phylogeny of Vertebrata*. London, New York, Sydney, Toronto: Wiley.

Lonsdale, P. and K. D. Klitgord. 1978. "Structure and tectonic history of the eastern Panama Basin." *Bulletin of the Geological Society of America*, 89(7):981–99.

Lotsy, J. P. 1916. *Evolution by Means of Hybridization*. The Hague: Martinus Nijhoff.

Lynch, J. D. 1971. "Evolutionary relationships, osteology, and zoogeography of leptodactyloid frogs." *Miscellaneous Publications of the Museum of Natural History*, University of Kansas, no. 53, pp. 1–238.

—— 1973. "The transition from archaic to advanced frogs." In J. L. Vial, ed., *Evolutionary Biology of Anurans: Contemporary Research on Major Problems*, pp. 133–82. Columbia: University of Missouri Press.

—— 1979. "The amphibians of the lowland tropical forests." In W. E. Duellman, *The South American Herpetofauna: Its Origin, Evolution and Dispersal*, pp. 189–215. Monographs of the Museum of Natural History, University of Kansas, no. 7.

McAlpine, D. K. 1968. "The genus *Cairnsimyia* Malloch (Diptera, Heleomyzidae, Rhinotorini)." *Records of the Australian Museum*, 27(12):263–83.

McAlpine, J. F. and J. E. H. Martin. 1966. "Systematics of Sciadoceridae and relatives with descriptions of two new genera and species from Canadian amber and erection of family Ironomyiidae (Diptera: Phoroidea)." *The Canadian Entomologist*, 98(5):527–44.

MacArthur, R. H. 1972. *Geographical Ecology: Patterns in the Distribution of Species*. New York, Evanston, San Francisco, London: Harper and Row.

MacArthur, R. H. and E. O. Wilson. 1963. "An equilibrium theory of insular zoogeography." *Evolution*, 17(4):373–87.

—— 1967. *The Theory of Island Biogeography*. Monographs in Population Biology, no. 1. Princeton, N.J.: Princeton University Press.

M'Closkey, R. T. 1978. "Niche separation and assembly in four species of Sonoran desert rodents." *The American Naturalist*, 112(986):683–94.

MacDonald, W. D. and P. M. Hurley. 1969. "Precambrian gneisses from northern Colombia, South America." *Bulletin of the Geological Society of America*, 80(9):1867–72.

McDowall, R. M. 1978. "Generalized tracks and dispersal in biogeography." *Systematic Zoology*, 27(1):88–104.

Macedo, M. and G. T. Prance. 1978. "Notes on the vegetation of Amazonia 2, the dispersal of plants in Amazonian white sand campinas: The Campinas as functional islands." *Brittonia*, 30(2):203–15.

McElhinny, M. W. 1973a. *Palaeomagnetism and Plate Tectonics*. Cambridge: Cambridge University Press.

—— 1973b. "Palaeomagnetic results from Eurasia." In D. H. Tarling and S. K. Runcorn, eds., *Implications of Continental Drift to the Earth Sciences*, 1:77–85. London and New York: Academic Press.

MacGinitie, H. D. 1962. "The Kilgore flora: A late Miocene flora from northern Nebraska." *Publications in Geological Sciences of the University of California*, 35(2):67–158.

MacIntyre, G. T. 1967. "Foramen pseudovale and quasi-mammals." *Evolution*, 21(4):834–41.

McKenna, M. C. 1972. "Eocene final separation of the Eurasian and Greenland-North American landmasses." *Twenty-Fourth International Geological Congress*, Section 7: Paleontology, pp. 275–81.

—— 1973. Sweepstakes, filters, corridors, Noah's arks, and beached Viking funeral ships in palaeogeography." In D. H. Tarling and S. K. Runcorn, eds., *Implications of Continental Drift to the Earth Sciences*, 1:295–308. London and New York: Academic Press.

—— 1975a. "Fossil mammals and early Eocene North Atlantic land continuity." *Annals of the Missouri Botanical Garden*, 62(2):335–53.

—— 1975b. "Toward a phylogenetic classification of the Mammalia." In W. P. Luckett and F. S. Szalay, eds., *Phylogeny of the Primates*, pp. 21–46. New York and London: Plenum Press.

Maglio, V. J. 1973. "Origin and evolution of the Elephantidae." *Transactions of the American Philosophical Society*, new series, 63(3):1–149.

Malfait, B. T. and M. G. Dinkelman. 1972. "Circum-Caribbean tectonic and igneous activity and the evolution of the Caribbean Plate." *Bulletin of the Geological Society of America*, 83(2):251–71.

Mallory, W. W., ed. 1972. *Geologic Atlas of the Rocky Mountain Region, United States of America*. Denver: Rocky Mountain Association of Geologists.

Mani, M. S. 1968. *Ecology and Biogeography of High Altitude Insects*. Series Entomologicae, vol. 4. The Hague: W. Junk.

Markl, R. G. 1978. "Further evidence for the early Cretaceous breakup of Gondwanaland off southwestern Australia." *Marine Geology*, 26(1–2):41–48.

Marks, J. G. 1956. "Pacific coast geologic province." In W. F. Jenks ed., *Handbook of

South American Geology, pp. 277–88. Memoirs of the Geological Society of America, no. 65.

Marshall, L. G. 1977. "Cladistic analysis of borhyaenoid, dasyuroid, didelphoid, and thylacinid (Marsupialia: Mammalia) affinity." *Systematic Zoology*, 26(4):410–25.

—— 1979. "Evolution of metatherian and eutherian (mammalian) characters: A review based on cladistic methodology." *Zoological Journal of the Linnean Society* (London), 66(4):369–410.

Martin, P. G. 1970. "The Darwin Rise hypothesis of the biogeographical dispersal of marsupials." *Nature* (London), 225(5228):197–98.

—— 1975. "Marsupial biogeography in relation to continental drift." *Mémoires du Muséum National d'Histoire Naturelle*, new series, series A, Zoologie, 88:216–36.

—— 1977. "Marsupial biogeography and plate tectonics." In B. Stonehouse and D. Gilmore, eds., *The Biology of Marsupials*, pp. 97–115. London and Basingstoke: Macmillan; Baltimore, London, Tokyo: University Park Press.

Mason, H. L. 1947. "Evolution of certain floristic associations in western North America." *Ecological Monographs*, 17(2):201–10.

—— 1949. "Evidence for the genetic submergence of *Pinus remorata.*" In G. L. Jepson, E. Mayr, and G. G. Simpson, eds., *Genetics, Paleontology, and Evolution*. pp. 356–62. Princeton, N.J.: Princeton University Press; reprint, New York: Atheneum, 1963.

Mathias, M. E. and L. Constance. 1955. "The genus *Oreomyrrhis* (Umbelliferae): A problem in south Pacific distribution." *Publications in Botany of the University of California*, 27(6):347–416.

Matthew, W. D. 1915. "Climate and evolution." *Annals of the New York Academy of Sciences*, 24:171–318.

—— 1918. "Affinities and origin of the Antillean mammals." *Bulletin of the Geological Society of America*, 29:657–66.

—— 1939. *Climate and evolution.* Second edition, revised and enlarged, arranged by Edwin Harris Colbert, preface by William King Gregory, with critical additions by the author and others and a bibliography of his scientific works by Charles Lewis Camp and Vertress Lawrence VanderHoof. Special Publication of the New York Academy of Sciences, no. 1.

Matthews, J. V., Jr. 1979. "Late Tertiary carabid fossils from Alaska and the Canadian archipelago." In T. L. Erwin, G. E. Ball, D. R. Whitehead, and A. L. Halpern, eds., *Carabid Beetles: Their Evolution, Natural History, and Classification*, pp. 425–45. The Hague: W. Junk.

Mattson, P. H. 1972. "Plate tectonics in the Caribbean." *Nature* (London): 235(5334):155–56.

Maxson, L. R. and A. C. Wilson. 1975. "Albumin evolution and organismal evolution in tree frogs (Hylidae)." *Systematic Zoology*, 24(1):1–15.

Mayr, E. 1942. *Systematics and the Origin of Species from the Viewpoint of a Zoologist*. New York: Columbia University Press.

—— 1944. "Wallace's line in the light of recent zoogeographic studies." *The Quarterly Review of Biology*, 19(1):1–14.

—— 1954. "Change of genetic environment and evolution." In J. Huxley, A. C.

Hardy, and E. B. Ford, eds., *Evolution as a Process*, pp. 157–80. London: George Allen and Unwin; reprint, New York: Collier Books, 1963.

—— 1963. *Animal Species and Evolution*. Cambridge: Belknap Press of Harvard University Press.

—— 1969. *Principles of Systematic Zoology*. New York: McGraw-Hill.

—— 1979. "Modes of speciation," [review of White, 1978]. *Systematic Zoology*, 27(4):478–82.

Mayr, E. and W. H. Phelps, Jr. 1967. "The origin of the bird fauna of the south Venezuelan highlands." *Bulletin of the American Museum of Natural History*, 136(5):269–328 (Spanish translation, 1971: *Boletin de la Sociedad Venezolana de Ciencias Naturales*, 29(121):309–401).

Mayr, E. and L. L. Short. 1970. *Species Taxa of North American Birds: A Contribution to Comparative Systematics*. Publication of the Nuttall Ornithological Club (Cambridge), no. 9.

Melville, R. 1966. "Continental drift, Mesozoic continents and the migrations of the angiosperms." *Nature* (London), 211(5045):116–20.

—— 1967. "The distribution of land around the Tethys Sea and its bearing on modern plant distribution." In C. G. Adams and D. V. Ager, eds., *Aspects of Tethyan Biogeography*, pp. 291–310. Publications of the Systematics Association (London), no. 7.

—— 1969. "Leaf venation patterns and the origin of the angiosperms." *Nature* (London), 224(5215):121–25.

—— 1973. "Continental drift and plant distribution." In D. H. Tarling and S. K. Runcorn, eds., *Implications of Continental Drift to the Earth Sciences*, 1:439–46. London and New York: Academic Press.

—— 1975. "The distribution of Australian relict plants and its bearing on angiosperm evolution." *Botanical Journal of the Linnean Society* (London), 71(2):67–88.

Menard, H. W. 1964. *Marine Geology of the Pacific*. New York, San Francisco, Toronto, London: McGraw-Hill.

Menard, H. W. and E. L. Hamilton, 1963. "Paleogeography of the tropical Pacific." In J. L. Gressit, ed., *Pacific Basin Biogeography*, pp. 193–217. Honolulu: Bishop Museum Press.

Mengel, R. M. 1964. "The probable history of species formation in some northern wood warblers (Parulidae)." *The Living Bird* (Cornell Laboratory of Ornithology), no. 3, pp. 9–43.

Meyen, S. V. 1971. "On the origin and relationship of the main Carboniferous and Permian floras and their bearing on general palaeogeography of this period of time." In *Proceedings of the Second Gondwana Symposium*, pp. 551–55. Pretoria: Council for Scientific and Industrial Research.

Meyer, R. P., W. D. Mooney, A. L. Hales, C. E. Helsely, G. P. Woollard, D. M. Hussong, L. W. Kroenke, and J. E. Ramirez. 1976. "Project Narino 3: Refraction observations across a leading edge, Malpelo Island to the Colombian Cordillera Occidental." In G. H. Sutton, M. H. Manghnani, and R. M. Moberly, eds., *The Geophysics of the Pacific Ocean Basin and Its Margin*, pp. 105–32. Monographs of the American Geophysical Union, no. 19.

Middlemiss, F. A., P. F. Rawson, and G. Newall, eds. 1971. *Faunal Provinces in Space and Time*. Liverpool: Seel House.

Miles, R. S. 1977 "Dipnoan (lungfish) skulls and the relationships of the group: a study based on new species from the Devonian of Australia." *Zoological Journal of the Linnean Society* (London), 61(1–3):1–328.

Mill, J. S. 1887. *A System of Logic, Ratiocinative and Inductive; Being a Connected View of the Principles of Evidence and the Methods of Scientific Investigation*. 8th ed. New York: Harper.

Milnes, A. G. 1978. "Structural zones and continental collision, central Alps." In K. L. Burns et al., eds., *Structural Characteristics of Tectonic Zones*, pp. 369–92. Tectonophysics, vol. 47, nos. 3–4.

Milson, J. and I. E. Smith. 1975. "Southeastern Papua: Generation of thick crust in a tensional environment?" *Geology* (Boulder), 3(3):117–20.

Minato, M. and Y. Fujiwara. 1964. "Palaeomagnetism and palaeoclimatology of the Japanese Islands." *Proceedings of the Japan Academy*, 40(2):116–20.

Molnar, P., T. Atwater, J. Mammerickx, and S. M. Smith. 1975. "Magnetic anomalies, bathymetry, and the tectonic evolution of the South Pacific since the late Cretaceous." *Geophysical Journal*, 40(3):383–420.

Molnar, P. and P. Tapponnier. 1975. "Cenozoic tectonics of Asia: Effects of a continental collision." *Science* (Washington, D.C.), 189(4201):419–26.

Monger, J. W. H. and C. A. Ross. 1971. "Distribution of fusulinaceans in the western Canadian cordillera." *Canadian Journal of Earth Sciences*, 8(2):259–78.

Moore, G. W., J. Barnabas, and M. Goodman. 1973. "A method for constructing maximum parsimony ancestral amino acid sequences on a given network." *Journal of Theoretical Biology*, 38(3):459–85.

Moore, H. E. Jr. 1973. "Palms in the tropical forest ecosystems of Africa and South America." In B. J. Meggers, E. S. Ayensu, and W. D. Duckworth, eds., *Tropical Forest Ecosystems in Africa and South America: A Comparative Revew*, pp. 63–88. Washington, D.C.: Smithsonian Institution.

Moreau, R. E. 1952. "Africa since the Mesozoic: With particular reference to certain biological problems." *Proceedings of the Zoological Society of London*, 121(4):869–913..

—— 1963. "Vicissitudes of the African biomes in the late Pleistocene." *Proceedings of the Zoological Society of London*, 141(2):395–421.

Morley, B. 1972. "The distribution and variation of some gesneriads on Caribbean islands." In D. H. Valentine, ed., *Taxonomy Phytogeography and Evolution*, pp. 239–57. London and New York: Academic Press.

Morrison, R. P. 1962. *A Resumé of the Geology of South America*. Toronto: Institute of Earth Sciences, University of Toronto.

Müller, P. 1973. *The Dispersal Centres of Terrestrial Vertebrates in the Neotropical Realm*. Biogeographica, vol. 2. The Hague: W. Junk.

Muller, J. 1970. "Palynological evidence on early differentiation of angiosperms." *Biological Reviews of the Cambridge Philosophical Society*, 45(3):417–50.

Mullins, H. T. and G. W. Lynts. 1977. "Origin of the northwestern Bahama Platform: Review and reinterpretation." *Bulletin of the Geological Society of America*, 88(10):1447–61.

Murauchi, S., N. Den, S. Asano, H. Hotta, T. Yoshii, T. Asanuma, K. Hagiwara, K. Ichikawa, T. Sato, W. J. Ludwig, J. I. Ewing, N. T. Edgar, and R. E. Houtz. 1968. "Crustal structure of the Philippine Sea." *Journal of Geophysical Research*, 73(10):3143–71.

Murauchi, S., W. J. Ludwig, N. Den, H. Hotta, T. Asanuma, T. Yoshii, A. Kubotera, and K. Hagiwara. 1973. "Seismic refraction measurements on the Ontong Java Plateau northeast of New Ireland." *Journal of Geophysical Research*, 78(35):8653–63.

Murray, A. E., Jr. 1970. "A monograph of the Aceraceae." Ph.D. dissertation, Pennsylvania State University.

Narain, H. 1973. "Crustal structure of the Indian subcontinent." *Tectonophysics*, 20(1–4):249–60.

Nelson, G. 1969. "The problem of historical biogeography." *Systematic Zoology*, 18(2):243–46.

—— 1973a. "Notes on the structure and relationships of certain Cretaceous and Eocene teleostean fishes." *American Museum Novitates*, no. 2524, pp. 1–31.

—— 1973b. "Comments on Leon Croizat's biogeography." *Systematic Zoology*, 22(3):312–20.

—— 1975. "Historical biogeography: An alternative formalization." *Systematic Zoology*, 23(4):555–58.

—— 1976. "Biogeography, the vicariance paradigm, and continental drift." *Systematic Zoology*, 24(4):490–504.

—— 1978. "From Candolle to Croizat: Comments on the history of biogeography." *Journal of the History of Biology*, 11(2):269–305.

—— 1979. "Cladistic analysis and synthesis: Principles and definitions, with a historical note on Adanson's *Familles des Plantes* (1763–1764)." *Systematic Zoology*, 28(1):1–21.

Nelson, G. and N. I. Platnick. 1979. "The perils of plesiomorphy: Widespread taxa, dispersal and phenetic biogeography." *Systematic Zoology*, 27(4):474–77.

Nilsen, T. H. 1978. "Lower Tertiary laterite on the Iceland-Faeroe Ridge and the Thulean land bridge." *Nature* (London), 274(5673):786–88.

Noonan, G. R. 1973. "The anisodactylines (Insecta: Coleoptera: Carabidae: Harpalini): Classification, evolution, and zoogeography." *Quaestiones Entomologicae*, 9(4):266–480.

Norton, I. O. and J. G. Sclater. 1979. "A model for the evolution of the Indian Ocean and the breakup of Gondwanaland." *Journal of Geophysical Research*, 84(B12):6803–30.

Nur, A. and Z. Ben-Avraham. 1977. "Lost Pacifica continent." *Nature* (London), 270(5632):41–43.

—— 1978. "Speculations on mountain building and the lost Pacifica continent." *Journal of the Physics of the Earth*, Supplement, 26:21–37.

Ogata, K. 1965. "A dendrological study on the Japanese Aceraceae, with special reference to the geographical distribution." *Bulletin of the Tokyo University Forests*, no. 60, pp. 1–99.

—— 1967. "A systematic study of the genus *Acer*." *Bulletin of the Tokyo University Forests*, no. 63, pp. 89–206.

Osborn, H. F. 1942. *Proboscidea*, vol. 2. New York: American Museum of Natural History.

Owen, H. G. 1976. "Continental displacement and expansion of the earth during the Mesozoic and Cenozoic." *Philosophical Transactions of the Royal Society of London*, series A: Physical Sciences, 281(1303):223–91.

Packham, G. and J. E. Andrews. 1975. "Results of Leg 30 and the geological history of the southwest Pacific arc and marginal sea complex." *Initial Reports of the Deep Sea Drilling Project* (Washington, D.C.), 30:691–705.

Pálmason, G. 1971. "Crustal structure of Iceland from explosion seismology." *Visindafélag Islendinga*, no. 40, pp. 1–187.

Papavero, N. 1977. *The World Oestridae (Diptera), Mammals, and Continental Drift*. Series Entomologicae, no. 14. The Hague: W. Junk.

Parodiz, J. J. 1969. "The Tertiary non-marine Mollusca of South America." *Annals of the Carnegie Museum*, 40:1–242.

Parrington, F. R. 1974. "The problem of the origin of the monotremes." *Journal of Natural History* (London), 8(4):421–26.

Parsons, B. and J. G. Sclater. 1977. "An analysis of the variation of the ocean floor bathymetry and heat flow with age." *Journal of Geophysical Research*, 82(5):803–27.

Pate, V. S. L. 1946. "The generic names of the Sapygidae and their type species (Hymenoptera: Aculeata)." *Entomological News*, 57(9):219–21.

Patterson, C. 1975. "The distribution of Mesozoic freshwater fishes." *Mémoires du Muséum National d'Histoire Naturelle*, new series, series A, Zoologie, 88:156–174.

—— 1977. "The contribution of paleontology to teleostean phylogeny." In M. K. Hecht, P. C. Goody, and B. M. Hecht, eds., *Major Patterns in Vertebrate Evolution*, pp. 579–643. New York and London: Plenum Press.

Patton, W. W., Jr. and I. L. Tailleur. 1977. "Evidence in the Bering Strait region for differential movement between North America and Eurasia." *Bulletin of the Geological Society of America*, 88(9):1298–1304.

Paynter, R. A., Jr. 1972. "Biology and evolution of the *Atlapetes schistaceus* species-group (Aves: Emberizinae)." *Bulletin of the Museum of Comparative Zoology*, 143(4):297–320.

—— 1978. "Biology and evolution of the avian genus *Atlapetes* (Emberizinae)." *Bulletin of the Museum of Comparative Zoology*, 148(7):323–69.

Payton, C. E., ed. 1977. *Seismic Stratigraphy—Applications to Hydrocarbon Exploration*. Memoirs of the American Association of Petroleum Geologist, no. 26.

Perfit, M. R. and B. C. Heezen. 1978. "The geology and evolution of the Cayman Trench." *Bulletin of the Geological Society of America*, 89(8):1155–74.

Peters, W. L., J. G. Peters and G. F. Edmunds, Jr. 1979. "The Leptophlebiidae of New Caledonia, 1: Introduction and systematics." *Cahiers de l'Office de la Recherche Scientifique et Technique Outre-Mer (ORSTOM)*, Série Hydrobiologie, 12(2):1–21.

Pilsbry, H. A. and C. M. Cooke. 1915–1916. *Manual of Conchology*, Second series: *Pulmonata*, vol. 23. Philadelphia: Academy of Natural Sciences of Philadelphia.

Pitman, W. C., III. 1978. "Relationship between eustacy and stratigraphic sequences of passive margins." *Bulletin of the Geological Society of America*, 89 (9):1389–1403.

Pitman, W. C., III, E. M. Herron, and J. R. Heirtzler. 1968. "Magnetic anomalies in the Pacific and sea floor spreading." *Journal of Geophysical Research*, 73(6):2069–85.

Pitman, W. C., III and M. Talwani. 1972. "Sea-floor spreading in the North Atlantic." *Bulletin of the Geological Society of America*, 83(3):619–46.

Platnick, N. I. 1976. "Concepts of dispersal in historical biogeography." *Systematic Zoology*, 25(3):294–95.

—— 1977. "Cladograms, phylogenetic trees, and hypothesis testing." *Systematic Zoology*, 26(4):438–42.

Platnick, N. I. and H. D. Cameron. 1977. "Cladistic methods in textual, linguistic, and phylogenetic analysis." *Systematic Zoology*, 26(4):380–85.

Platnick, N. I. and W. J. Gertsch. 1976. "The suborders of spiders: A cladistic analysis." *American Museum Novitates*, no. 2607, pp. 1–15.

Platnick, N. I. and G. Nelson. 1978. "A method of analysis for historical biogeography." *Systematic Zoology*, 27(1):1–16.

Pojarkova, A. I. 1933. "Botanico-geographical survey of the maples in USSR, in connection with the history of the whole genus *Acer* L." In B. K. Schischkin, ed., *Flora et Systematica Plantae Vasculares*, pp. 224–374. Acta Institui Botanici Academiae Scientiarum Unionis Rerum Publicarum Soveticarum Socialisticam, series 1, fasc. 1. Botanicheskovo Instituta. Leningrad: Akademia Nauk SSSR, Trudy.

Ponomarenko, A. G. 1977. "Mesozoic Coleoptera." *Transactions of the Paleontological Institute*, Moscow, 161:1–204.

Popper, K. R. 1959. *The Logic of Scientific Discovery*. New York: Basic Books; London: Hutchinson.

—— 1962. *Conjectures and Refutations: The Growth of Scientific Knowledge*. London: Routledge and Kegan Paul; New York: Basic Books; reprint New York and Evanston: Harper and Row, 1968.

Porter, D. M. 1976. "Geography and dispersal of Galapagos Islands vascular plants." *Nature* (London) 264(5588):745–46.

Powell, C. M. and P. J. Conaghan. 1973. "Plate tectonics and the Himalayas." *Earth and Planetary Science Letters*, 20(1):1–12.

Prakash, U. and E. S. Barghoorn. 1961. "Miocene fossil woods from the Columbia basalts of central Washington." *Journal of the Arnold Arboretum*, 42(2):165–95.

Prance, G. T. 1973. "Phytogeographic support for the theory of Pleistocene forest refuges in the Amazon Basin, based on evidence from distribution patterns in Caryocaraceae, Chrysobalanaceae, Dichapetalaceae and Lecythidaceae." *Acta Amazônica*, 3(3):5–28.

—— 1978. "The origin and evolution of the Amazon flora." *Interciencia*, 3(4):207–22.

—— 1979. "The taxonomy and phytogeography of the Chrysobalanaceae of the Atlantic coastal forests of Brazil." *Revista Brasileira de Botanica* 2(1):19–39.

Prance, G. T., W. A. Rodrigues, and M. F. da Silva. 1976. "Inventário florestal de um hectare de mata de terra firme km 30 da Estrada Manaus-Itacoatiara." *Acta Amazônica*, 6(1):9–35.

Presley, R. and F. L. D. Steel. 1976. "On the homology of the alisphenoid." *Journal of Anatomy*, 121(3):441–59.

Quine, W. V. 1969. *Ontological Relativity and Other Essays*. New York and London: Columbia University Press.

Raup, D. M. 1977. "Probabilistic models in evolutionary paleobiology." *American Scientist*, 65(1):50–57.

Raup, D. M., S. J. Gould, T. J. M. Schopf, and D. S. Simberloff. 1973. "Stochastic models of phylogeny and the evolution of diversity." *The Journal of Geology* (Chicago), 81(5):525–42.

Raven, P. H. 1979. "Plate tectonics and southern hemisphere biogeography." In K. Larsen, ed., *Tropical Botany*, in press. London and New York: Academic Press.

Raven, P. H. and D. I. Axelrod. 1972. "Plate tectonics and Australasian paleo-biogeography." *Science* (Washington, D.C.), 176(4042):1379–86.

—— 1974. "Angiosperm biogeography and past continental movements." *Annals of the Missouri Botanical Garden*, 61(3):539–673.

—— 1975. "History of the flora and fauna of Latin America." *American Scientist*, 63(4):420–29.

Read, C.B. and S. H. Mamay. 1964. "Upper Palaeozoic floral zones and floral provinces of the United States." *Professional Papers of the Geological Survey* (Washington, D.C.), no. 454-K, pp. 1–19.

Rees, W. J. 1964. "A review of breathing devices in land operculate snails." *Proceedings of the Malacological Society of London*, 36(2):55–67.

Reichardt, H. 1979. "The South American carabid fauna: Endemic tribes and tribes with African relationships." In T. L. Erwin, G. E. Ball, D. R. Whitehead, and A. L. Halpern, eds., *Carabid Beetles: Their Evolution, Natural History, and Classification*, pp. 319–25. The Hague: W. Junk.

Reinig, W. F. 1937. *Die Holarktis: Ein Beitrag zur diluvialen und alluvialen Geschichte der zirkumpolaren Faunen- und Florengebiete*. Jena: Gustav Fischer.

—— 1950. "Chorologische Voraussetzungen für die Analyse von Formenkreisen." In A. von Jordans and F. Peus, eds., *Syllegomena Biologica; Festschrift zum 80. Geburtstage von Herrn Pastor Dr. Med. h. c. Otto Kleinschmidt*, pp. 346–78. Leipzig: Geest and Portig.

Richards, H. G. 1974. "Tectonic evolution of Alaska." *Bulletin of the American Association of Petroleum Geologists*, 58(1):79–105.

Richards, P. W. 1969. "Speciation in the tropical rain forest and the concept of the niche." *Biological Journal of the Linnean Society* (London), 1(1–2):149–53.

Ricklefs, R. E. and G. W. Cox. 1972. "Taxon cycles in the West Indian avifauna." *The American Naturalist*, 106(948):195–219.

Ridley, H. N. 1930. *The Dispersal of Plants Throughout the World*. Ashford: L. Reeve.

Ries, A. C. 1978. "The opening of the Bay of Biscay—a review." *Earth Sciences Review*, 14(1):35–63.

Rivero, J. A. 1970. "On the origin, endemism and distribution of the genus *Stefania* Rivero (Amphibia, Salientia) with a description of a new species from southeastern Venezuela." *Boletin de la Sociedad Venezolana de Ciencias Naturales*, 28(117–18):456–81.

Rosa, D. 1918. *Ologenesi*. Firenze: R. Bemporad and Figlio.

Rosen, D. E. 1974a. "The phylogeny and zoogeography of salmoniform fishes, and the relationships of *Lepidogalaxias salamandroides*." *Bulletin of the American Museum of Natural History*, 153(2):265–326.

—— 1974b. "Space, time, form: the biological synthesis." [Review of Croizat 1964]. *Systematic Zoology*, 23(2):288–90.

—— 1976a. "A vicariance model of Caribbean biogeography." *Systematic Zoology*, 24(4):431–64.

—— 1976b. "Foundations of plant geography" [review of Cain, 1944]. *Systematic Zoology*, 24(4):489–90.

—— 1978. "Vicariant patterns and historical explanation in biogeography." *Systematic Zoology*, 27(2):159–88.

Rosen, D. E. and R. M. Bailey. 1963. "The poeciliid fishes (Cyprinodontiformes), their structure, zoogeography, and systematics." *Bulletin of the American Museum of Natural History*, 126(1):1–176.

Rosen, D. E. and R. T. Schuh. 1976. "Flowering plants: Evolution above the species level" [review of Stebbins, 1974]. *Systematic Zoology*, 24(4):504–6.

Ross, C. A. 1967. "Development of fusulinid (Foraminiferida) faunal realms." *Journal of Paleontology*, 41(6):1341–54.

Ross, H. H. 1956. *Evolution and Classification of the Mountain Caddisflies*. Urbana: University of Illinois Press.

—— 1974. *Biological Systematics*. Reading: Addison-Wesley.

Saether, O. A. 1970. "Nearctic and Palaearctic *Chaoborus* (Diptera: Chaoboridae)." *Bulletin of the Fisheries Research Board of Canada*, no. 174, pp. 1–57.

—— 1971. "Nomenclature and phylogeny of the genus *Harnischia* (Diptera: Chironomidae)." *The Canadian Entomologist*, 103(3):347–62.

—— 1976. "Revision of *Hydrobaenus, Trissocladius, Zalutschia, Paratrissocladius*, and some related genera (Diptera: Chironomidae)." *Bulletin of the Fisheries Research Board of Canada*, no. 195, pp. 1–287.

—— 1977. "Female genitalia in Chironomidae and other Nematocera: Morphology, phylogenies, keys." *Bulletin of the Fisheries Research Board of Canada*, no. 197, pp. i–viii, 1–209.

Sahni, A. and V. Kumar. 1974. "Palaeogene palaeobiogeography of the Indian subcontinent." *Palaeobiogeography, Palaeoclimatology, Palaeoecology*, 15(3): 209–26.

Sahni, B. 1936. "Wegener's theory of continental drift in the light of palaeobotanical evidence." *Journal of the Indian Botanical Society*, 15(5):319–32.

—— 1939. "The relationship of the *Glossopteris* flora with the Gondwana glaciation." *Proceedings of the Indian Academy of Sciences*, 9B:1–6.

St. John, H. 1935. [Mangarevan expedition: report on botany]. *Bulletin of the Bernice P. Bishop Museum*, no. 133, pp. 56–58.

Salomonsen, F. 1976. "The main problems concerning avian evolution on islands." In H. J. Frith and J. H. Calaby, eds., *Proceedings of the 16th International Ornithological Congress*, pp. 585–602. Canberra: Australian Academy of Science.

Saporta, G. de. 1865. "Etudes sur la végétation du sud-est de la France à l'époque tertiaire, deuxième partie, 3." *Annales des Sciences Naturelles*, Botanique, series 5, 4:2–264.

Savage, J. M. 1974. "The isthmian link and the evolution of Neotropical mammals." *Contributions in Science of the Natural History Museum, Los Angeles County,* no. 260, pp. 1–51.

Savin, S. M., R. G. Douglas, and F. G. Stehli. 1975. "Tertiary marine paleotemperatures." *Bulletin of the Geological Society of America*, 86(11):1499–1510.

Scharff, R. F. 1895. "Etudes sur les mammifères de la région holarctique. et leurs relations avec ceux des régions voisines." *Mémoires de la Société Zoologique de France*, 8:436–74.

——— 1899. *The History of the European Fauna.* London: Walter Scott; New York: Scribner.

——— 1907. *European Animals: Their Geological History and Geographical Distribution.* London: Archibald Constable; New York: Dutton.

——— 1911. *The Distribution and Origin of Life in America.* London: Archibald Constable; 1912, New York: Macmillan.

Schauensee, R. M. de. 1952. "A review of the genus *Sporophila*." *Proceedings of the Academy of Natural Sciences of Philadelphia*, 104:153–96.

Schlee, D. 1968. "Vergleichende Merkmalsanalyse zur Morphologie und Phylogenie der *Corynoneura*-Gruppe (Diptera, Chironomidae), zugleich eine allgemeine Morphologie der Chironomiden-Imago." *Stuttgarter Beiträge zur Naturkunde*, no. 180, pp. 1–150.

Schlee, D. and H.-G. Dietrich. 1970. "Insektenführender Bernstein aus der Unterkreide des Libanon." *Neues Jahrbuch für Geologie und Paläontologie, Monatshefte*, 1970, no. 1, pp. 40–50.

Schlinger, E. I. 1974. "Continental drift, *Nothofagus*, and some ecologically associated insects." *Annual Review of Entomology*, 19:323–43.

Schminke, H. K. 1973. "Evolution, System und Verbreitungsgeschichte der Familie Parabathynellidae (Bathynellacea, Malacostraca)." *Mikrofauna des Meeresboden*, 24:1–192.

Schofield, E. K. and P. A. Colinvaux. 1969. "Fossil *Azolla* from the Galapagos Islands." *Bulletin of the Torrey Botanical Club*, 96(6):623–28.

Schopf, J. M. 1970a. "Gondwana paleobotany." *Antarctic Journal of the United States*, 5(3):62–66.

——— 1970b. "Relation of floras of the southern hemisphere to continental drift." *Taxon*, 19(5):657–74.

Schuchert, C. 1955. *Atlas of Paleogeographic Maps of North America.* New York: Wiley; London; Chapman and Hall.

Schuchert, C. and C. O. Dunbar. 1950. *Outlines of Historical Geology*, 4th ed. New York: Wiley.

Schultz, R. J. 1969. "Hybridization, unisexuality, and polyploidy in the teleost *Poeciliopsis* (Poeciliidae) and other vertebrates." *The American Naturalist*, 103(934):605–19.

Schuster, R. M. 1972a. "Continental movements, 'Wallace's Line' and Indomalayan-

Australasian dispersal of land plants: Some eclectic concepts." *Botanical Review*, 38(1):3–86.

—— 1972b. Evolving taxonomic concepts in the Hepaticae, with special reference to circum-Pacific taxa." *Journal of the Hattori Botanical Laboratory*, no. 35, pp. 169–201.

—— 1976. "Plate tectonics and its bearing on the geographical origin and dispersal of angiosperms." In C. B. Beck, ed., *Origin and Early Evolution of Angiosperms*, pp. 48–138. New York: Columbia University Press.

Schweickert, R. A. 1976. "Early Mesozoic rifting and fragmentation of the cordilleran orogen in the western USA." *Nature* (London), 260(5552):586–91.

Schweickert, R. A. and D. S. Cowan. 1975. "Early Mesozoic tectonic evolution of the western Sierra Nevada, California." *Bulletin of the Geological Society of America*, 86(10):1329–36.

Schwerdtfeger, F. 1968. *Ökologie der Tiere*, 2: *Demökologie*. Hamburg: Paul Parey.

Sclater, J. G., R. N. Anderson, and M. L. Bell. 1971. "Elevation of ridges and evolution of the central eastern Pacific." *Journal of Geophysical Research*, 76(32): 7888–7915.

Sclater, J. G., S. Hellinger, and C. Tapscott. 1977. "The paleobathymetry of the Atlantic Ocean from the Jurassic to the present." *The Journal of Geology* (Chicago), 85(5):509–22.

Segawa, J. and S. Oshima. 1975. "Buried Mesozoic volcanic-plutonic fronts of the north-western Pacific island arcs and their tectonic implications." *Nature* (London), 256(5512):15–19.

Selander, R. K. 1971. "Systematics and speciation in birds." In D. S. Farner, J. R. King, and K. C. Parkes, eds., *Avian Biology*, 1:57–147. New York and London: Academic Press.

Sepkoski, J. J. 1978. "A kinetic model of Phanerozoic taxonomic diversity, 1: Analysis of marine orders." *Paleobiology*, 4(3):223–51.

Sherff, E. E. 1937a. "The genus *Bidens*, Part 1." *Publications of the Field Museum*, Botanical Series, 16(388):1–709.

—— 1937b. "Some Compositae of southeastern Polynesia (*Bidens, Coreopsis, Cosmos*, and *Oparanthus*)." *Occasional Papers of the Bernice P. Bishop Museum*, 12(19):1–19.

Shields, O. 1978. "The expanding earth" [review of Carey, 1976]. *Systematic Zoology*, 27(3):379–81.

—— 1979. "Evidence for initial opening of the Pacific Ocean in the Jurassic." *Palaeogeography, Palaeoclimatology, Palaeoecology*, 26(3–4):181–220.

Shor, G. G., Jr., H. K. Kirk, and H. W. Menard. 1971. "Crustal structure of the Melanesian area." *Journal of Geophysical Research*, 76(11):2562–86.

Short, L. L. 1975. "A zoogeographic analysis of the South American chaco avifauna." *Bulletin of the American Museum of Natural History*, 154(3):163–352.

Silver, L. T. and T. H. Anderson. 1974. "Possible left-lateral early to middle Mesozoic disruption of the southwestern North American craton margin." *Abstracts with Programs of the Geological Society of America*, 6(7):955–56.

Simberloff, D. S. 1970. "Taxonomic diversity of island biotas." *Evolution*, 24 (1):23–47.

—— 1974. "Equilibrium theory of island biogeography and ecology." *Annual Review of Ecology and Systematics*, 5:161–82.

—— 1978. "Using island biogeographic distributions to determine if colonization is stochastic." *The American Naturalist*, 112(986):713–26.

—— 1979. "Dynamic equilibrium island biogeography: The second stage." *Proceedings of the 17th International Congress of Ornithology*, in press.

Simberloff, D. and E. F. Connor. 1979. "Q-mode and R-mode analyses of biogeographic distributions: Null hypotheses based on random colonization." In G. P. Patil and M. L. Rosenzweig, eds., *Contemporary Quantitative Ecology and Related Ecometrics*, pp. 123–38. Fairfield, Md.: International Cooperative Publishing House.

—— 1980. "Missing species combinations. Manuscript.

Simpson Vuilleumier, B. B. 1971. "Pleistocene changes in the fauna and flora of South America." *Science* (Washington, D.C.), 173(3999):771–80.

Simpson, B. B. 1974. "Glacial migrations of plants: Island biogeographical evidence." *Science* (Washington, D.C.), 185(4152):698–700.

—— 1975. "Pleistocene changes in the flora of the high tropical Andes." *Paleobiology*, 1(3):273–94.

—— 1978. "Biosystematics and biogeography." In J. A. Romberger, ed., *Beltsville Symposia in Agricultural Research, 2: Biosystematics in Agriculture*, pp. 151–72. Montclair, N.J.: Allanheld and Osmund.

—— 1979. "Quaternary biogeography of the high montane regions of South America." In W. E. Duellman, ed., *The South American Herpetofauna: Its Origin, Evolution and Dispersal*, pp. 157–188. Monographs of the Museum of Natural History, University of Kansas, no. 7.

Simpson, B. B. and J. Haffer. 1978. "Speciation patterns in the Amazonian forest biota." *Annual Review of Ecology and Systematics*, 9:497–518.

Simpson, G. G. 1949. *The Meaning of Evolution: A Study of the History of Life and of Its Significance for Man*. New Haven: Yale University Press.

—— 1950. "History of the fauna of Latin America." *American Scientist*, 38(3):361–89.

—— 1952. "Probabilities of dispersal in geologic time." *Bulletin of the American Museum of Natural History*, 99(3):163–76.

—— 1953. *Evolution and Geography*. Eugene: Oregon State System of Higher Education.

—— 1965. *The Geography of Evolution*. Philadelphia and New York: Chilton Books; reprint, New York: Capricorn Books, 1967.

—— 1976. "The compleat palaeontologist?" *Annual Review of Earth and Planetary Sciences*, 4:1–13.

—— 1978a. "Variations and details of macroevolution" [review of Hecht et al. 1977]. *Paleobiology*, 4(2):217–21.

—— 1978b. "Early mammals in South America: Fact, controversy, and mystery." *Proceedings of the American Philosophical Society*, 122(5):318–28.

Skinner, J. W. and G. L. Wilde. 1966. "Permian fusulinids from Pacific northwest and Alaska." *Paleontological Contributions of the University of Kansas*, paper 4, pp. 1–64.

Skottsberg, C. 1960. "Remarks on the plant geography of the southern cold temperate zone." *Proceedings of the Royal Society* (London), Series B, Biological Sciences, 152(949):447–57.

Smith, A. C. 1970. "The Pacific as a key to flowering plant history." In Harold L. Lyon Arboretum Lecture Number One, pp. 1–26. Honolulu: University of Hawaii.

Smith, A. G. 1976. "Plate tectonics and orogeny: A review." *Tectonophysics,* 33(3–4):215–85.

Smith, A. G. and J. C. Briden. 1977. *Mesozoic and Cenozoic Paleocontinental Maps.* Cambridge, London, New York, Melbourne: Cambridge University Press.

Smith, F. E. 1972. "Spatial heterogeneity, stability, and diversity in ecosystems." In E. S. Deevey, ed., *Growth by Intussusception: Ecological Essays in Honor of G. Evelyn Hutchinson,* pp. 307–35. Transactions of the Connecticut Academy of Arts and Sciences, vol. 44.

Smith, G. L. 1972. "Continental drift and the distribution of Polytrichaeceae." *Journal of the Hattori Botanical Laboratory,* 35:41–49.

Snider-Pelligrini, A. 1859. *La Création et Ses Mystères Dévoilées.* Paris: A. Franck.

Snogerup, S. 1967. "Studies in the Aegean flora, 9: *Erysimum* sect. *Cheiranthus,* B, variation and evolution in the small-population system." *Opera Botanica,* no. 14, pp. 1–86.

Snow, D. W. 1975. "The classification of the manakins." *Bulletin of the British Ornithological Club,* 95(1):20–27.

Solem, A. 1959. "Systematics and zoogeography of the land and freshwater Mollusca of the New Hebrides." *Fieldiana: Zoology,* 43(1–2):1–359.

——1964. "*Amimopina,* an Australian enid land snail." *The Veliger,* 6(3):115–20.

——1969. "Basic distribution of non-marine mollusks." In *Proceedings of the symposium on Mollusca,* pp. 231–47. Symposium Series, Marine Biological Association of India, no. 3, part 1.

—— 1973. "Island size and species diversity in Pacific island land snails." *Malacologia,* 14(1–2):397–400.

——1976. *Endodontoid Land Snails from Pacific Islands (Mollusca: Pulmonata: Sigmurethra),* part 1: *Family Endodontidae.* Chicago: Field Museum of Natural History.

—— 1978a. "Cretaceous and Early Tertiary camaenid land snails from western North America (Mollusca: Pulmonata)." *Journal of Paleontology,* 52(3):581–89.

——1978b. "Classification of the land Mollusca." In V. Fretter and J. Peake, eds., *Pulmonates,* 2A:49–97. London, New York, San Francisco: Academic Press.

—— 1979a. "Biogeographic significance of land snails, Paleozoic to Recent." In J. Gray and A. J. Boucot eds., *Proceedings of the 37th Annual Biology Colloquim,* pp. 277–87. Corvallis: Oregon State University Press.

—— 1979b. "A theory of land snail biogeographic patterns through time." In, Van der Spoel, S., A. C. Van Bruggen, and J. Lever, eds., *Pathways in Malacology,* pp. 225–49. Amsterdam: Sixth European Malacological Congress.

—— In press. *Endodontoid land snails from Pacific islands,* part 2: *Families Punctidae and Charopidae, Zoogeography.* Chicago: Field Museum Press of Natural History.

Solem, A. and E. Yochelson. 1979. "North American Paleozoic land snails, with a summary of other Paleozoic non-marine snails." *Professional Papers of the Geological Survey* (Washington, D.C.), no. 1072, pp. 1–42.

Stapleton, R. P. and E. M. Beer. 1976. "'Upper Jurassic' sediments of South Africa." *Nature* (London), 264(5581):49.

Stearns, H. T. and T. K. Chamberlain. 1967. "Deep cores of Oahu, Hawaii and their bearing on the geologic history of the Central Pacific Basin." *Pacific Science*, 21(2):153–65.

Stebbins, G. L., Jr. 1940. "Studies in the Cichorieae: *Dubyaea* and *Soroseris*, endemics of the Sino-Himalayan region." *Memoirs of the Torrey Botanical Club*, 19(3):1–76.

—— 1950. *Variation and Evolution in Plants*. New York: Columbia University Press.

—— 1959. "The role of hybridization in evolution." *Proceedings of the American Philosophical Society*, 103(2):231–51.

—— 1971. "Adaptive radiation of reproductive characteristics in angiosperms, 2: Seeds and seedlings." *Annual Review of Ecology and Systematics*, 2:237–60.

—— 1974. *Flowering Plants: Evolution Above the Species Level*. Cambridge: Belknap Press of Harvard University Press.

Stebbins, R. C. 1966. *A Field Guide to Reptiles and Amphibians*. Boston: Houghton Mifflin.

Stegmann, B. 1938. "Principes généraux des subdivisions ornithogéographiques de la région paléarctique." *Faune de l'URSS, Oiseaux*, vol. 1, no. 2. Institut Zoologique de l'Académie des Sciences de l'URSS, new series, no. 19. Moscow and Leningrad: Académie des Sciences de l'URSS.

—— 1939. "Eine neue Darstellungsmethode der biogeographischen Gliederung." *Chronica Botanica*, 5(1):50–52.

Stehlin, H. G. 1909. "Remarques sur les faunules de mammifères des couches éocènes et oligocènes du Bassin de Paris." *Bulletin de la Société Géologique de France*, series 4, 9(7–8):488–520.

Steiner, J. 1967. "The sequence of geological events and the dynamics of the Milky Way Galaxy; the present cosmic year, a preliminary study." *Journal of the Geological Society of Australia*, 14(1):99–132.

Steinhauser, P., S. A. Vincenz, and S. M. Dasgupta. 1972. "Palaeomagnetism of some Lower Cretaceous lavas on Jamaica." *Eos*, 53(4):356–57.

Stevens, P. S. 1974. *Pattern in Nature*. Boston and Toronto: Little, Brown.

Steyermark, J. A. 1979a. "Plant refuge and dispersal centers in Venezuela: Their relict and endemic element." In K. Larsen and L. B. Holm-Nielsen, eds., *Tropical Botany*, pp. 185–221. London and New York: Academic Press.

—— 1979b. "Flora of the Guyana highland: Endemicity of the generic flora of the Venezuelan tepuis." *Taxon* 28(   ):45–54.

—— 1981. "Relationships of some Venezuelan forest refuges with lowland tropical floras." In G. T. Prance, ed., *The Biological Model of Diversification in the Tropics*, in press. New York: Columbia University Press.

Stose, G. W. 1950. *Geologic Map of South America*. New York: Geological Society of America.

Strid, A. 1970. "Studies in the Aegean flora, 16: Biosystematics of the *Nigella arvensis* complex with special reference to the problem of nonadaptive radiation." *Opera Botanica*, no. 28, pp. 1–169.

Strong, D. R., Jr. 1980. "Null hypotheses in ecology." *Synthese*, 43(2):271–85.

Summerhayes, C. P. 1967. "Note on the Macquarie Ridge and the Tonga-Kermadec complex: Are they parts of the mid-ocean ridge system?" *New Zealand Journal of Science*, 10(3):808–12.

Sutton, G. H., G. L. Maynard, and D. M. Hussong. 1971. "Widespread occurrence of a high-velocity basal layer in the Pacific crust found with repetitive sources and sonobouys (with discussion)." In J. G. Heacock, ed., *The Structure and Physical Properties of the Earth's Crust*, pp. 193–209. Monographs of the American Geophysical Union (Washington, D.C.), no. 14.

Symons, D. T. A. 1971. "Paleomagnetic notes on the Karmutsen basalts, Vancouver Island, British Columbia." *Papers of the Geological Survey of Canada*, no. 71-24, pp. 9–24.

Takhtajan, A. 1969. *Flowering Plants Origin and Dispersal*. Washington, D.C., Smithsonian Institution Press; Edinburgh: Oliver and Boyd.

Talwani, M. and O. Eldholm. 1977. "Evolution of the Norwegian-Greenland Sea." *Bulletin of the Geological Society of America*, 88(7):969–99.

Tanai, T. 1978a. "Taxonomical investigations of the living species of the genus *Acer* L., based on vein architecture of leaves." *Journal of the Faculty of Science, Hokkaido University*, series 4, Geology and Minerology, 18(3):243–82.

—— 1978b. "Taxonomical reinvestigations of the genus *Acer* L., based on vein architecture of leaves." *The Journal of Japanese Botany*, 53(3):65–83.

Tattersall, I. and N. Eldredge. 1977. "Fact, theory, and fantasy in human paleontology." *American Scientist*, 65(2):204–11.

Taverne, L. 1977. "Ostéologie, phylogénèse et systématique des téléostéens fossiles et actuels du super-ordre des ostéoglossomorphes, première partie." Académie Royale de Belgique, *Mémoires de la Classe des Sciences*, Collection in-8°, series 2, 42(3):1–235.

—— 1978. "Ostéologie, phylogénèse et systématique des téléostéens fossiles et actuels du super-ordre des ostéoglossomorphes, deuxième partie." Académie Royale de Belgique, *Mémoires de la Classe des Sciences*, Collection in-8°, series 2, 42(6):1–213.

Te, G. A. 1976. "A summary of pulmonate distribution information contained in Zilch's 1959–1960 monograph: Gastropoda, Teil 2, Euthyneura." *Malacological Review*, no. 9, pp. 39–53.

Tedford, R. H. 1974. "Marsupials and the new paleogeography." In C. A. Ross, ed., *Paleogeographic Provinces and Provinciality*, pp. 109–26. Special Publications of the Society of Economic Paleontologists and Mineralogists (Tulsa), no. 21.

Terborgh, J. 1973. "Chance, habitat and dispersal in the distribution of birds in the West Indies." *Evolution*, 27(2):338–49.

—— 1974. "Preservation of natural diversity: The problem of extinction prone species." *BioScience*, 24(12):715–22.

Termier, H. and G. Termier. 1960. *Atlas de Paléogéographie*. Paris: Masson.

Thorne, R. F. 1963. "Biotic distribution patterns in the tropical Pacific." In J. L.

Gressitt, ed., *Pacific Basin Biogeography*, pp. 311–50. Honolulu: Bishop Museum Press.

—— 1973. "Floristic relationships between tropical Africa and tropical America." In B. J. Meggers, E. S. Ayensu, and E. D. Duckworth, eds., *Tropical Forest Ecosystems in Africa and South America: A Comparative Review*, pp. 27–47. Washington, D.C.: Smithsonian Institution Press.

—— 1974. "A phylogenetic classification of the Annoniflorae." *Aliso*, 8(2):147–209.

—— 1976. "Where and when might the tropical angiospermous flora have originated?" *Bulletin of the Singapore Botanical Garden*, 29:183–89.

—— 1978. "Plate tectonics and angiosperm distribution." *Notes from the Royal Botanic Garden* (Edinburgh), 36(2):297–315.

Tozer, E. T. 1956. "Uppermost Cretaceous and Paleocene non-marine molluscan faunas of western Alberta." *Memoirs of the Geological Survey of Canada*, no. 280, pp. i–v, 1–125.

Tschopp, H. J. 1956. "Upper Amazon Basin geological province." In W. F. Jenks, ed., *Handbook of South American geology*, pp. 253–67. Memoirs of the Geological Society of America, no. 65.

Turcotte, D. L. and K. Burke. 1978. "Global sea-level changes and the thermal structure of the earth." *Earth and Planetary Science Letters*, 41(3):341–46.

Tuxen, S. L. 1978. "Protura (Insecta) and Brazil during 400 million years of continental drift." *Studies of Neotropical Fauna and Environment*, 13(1):23–50.

Udvardy, M. D. F. 1963a. "Zoogeographical study of the Pacific Alcidae." In J. L. Gressitt, ed., *Pacific Basin Biogeography*, pp. 85–111. Honolulu: Bishop Museum Press.

—— 1963b. "Bird faunas of North America." In C. G. Sibley, ed., *Proceedings of the 13th International Ornithological Congress*, 2:1147–67. Baton Rouge: The American Ornithologists' Union.

—— 1969. *Dynamic Zoogeography with Special Reference to Land Animals*. New York, Cincinnati, Toronto, London, Melbourne: Van Nostrand Reinhold.

—— 1970. "Mammalian evolution: Is it due to social subordination?" *Science* (Washington, D.C.), 170(3955):344–45.

Underwood, A. J. 1978. "The detection of non-random patterns of distribution of species along a gradient." *Oecologia*, 36(3):317–26.

Uyeda, S. and Z. Ben-Avraham. 1972. "Origin and development of the Philippine Sea." *Nature*, Physical Sciences, 240(104):176–78.

Vagvolgyi, J. 1976. "Body size, aerial dispersal, and origin of the Pacific land snail fauna." *Systematic Zoology*, 24(4):465–88.

—— 1978. "Why are so many minute land snails on the Pacific islands: A response to Leon Croizat." *Systematic Zoology*, 27(2):213.

Vail, P. R., R. M. Mitchum, Jr., and S. Thompson, III. 1977. "Seismic stratigraphy and global changes of sea level, part 4: Global cycles of relative changes of sea level." In C. Payton, ed., *Seismic Stratigraphy—Applications to Hydrocarbon Exploration*, pp. 83–97. Memoirs of the American Association of Petroleum Geologists, no. 26.

Valencio, D. A. and J. F. Vilas. 1970. "Palaeomagnetism of some Middle Jurassic lavas from south-east Argentina." *Nature* (London), 225(5229):262–64.

Valentine, J. W. 1971. "Plate tectonics and shallow marine diversity and endemism, an actualistic model." *Systematic Zoology*, 20(3):253–64.

—— 1973. *Evolutionary Paleoecology of the Marine Biosphere*. Englewood Cliffs, N.J.: Prentice-Hall.

Van Andel, T. H., J. Thiede, J. G. Sclater, and W. W. Hay. 1977. "Depositional history of the South Atlantic Ocean during the last 125 million years." *The Journal of Geology* (Chicago), 85(6):651–98.

Van Balgooy, M. M. J. 1960. "Preliminary plant-geographical analysis of the Pacific." *Blumea*, 10(2):385–430.

—— 1971. "Plant-geography of the Pacific as based on a census of phanerogam genera." *Blumea*, Supplement, 6:1–222.

Van Bruggen, A. C. 1967. "An introduction to the pulmonate family Streptaxidae." *The Journal of Conchology*, 26(3):181–88.

—— 1978. "Land molluscs." In M. J. A. Werger, ed., *Biogeography and Ecology of Southern Africa*, 2:877–923. Monographiae Biologicae, vol. 31. The Hague: W. Junk.

Van der Hammen, T. 1974. "The Pleistocene changes of vegetation and climate in tropical South America." *Journal of Biogeography*, 1(1):3–26.

Van der Pijl, L. 1969. *Principles of Dispersal in Higher Plants*. Berlin, Heidelberg, New York: Springer Verlag.

Van der Voo, R., F. J. Mauk and R. B. French. 1976. "Permian-Triassic continental configurations and the origin of the Gulf of Mexico." *Geology* (Boulder), 4(3):177–80.

Van Hinte, J. E. 1976a. "A Jurassic time scale." *Bulletin of the American Association of Petroleum Geologists*, 60(4):489–97.

—— 1976b. "A Cretaceous time scale." *Bulletin of the American Association of Petroleum Geologists*, 60(4):498–516.

Van Steenis, C. G. G. J. 1962. "The land-bridge theory in botany with particular reference to tropical plants." *Blumea*, 11(2):235–372.

—— 1971. "*Nothofagus*, key genus of plant geography, in time and space, living and fossil, ecology and phylogeny." *Blumea*, 19(1):65–98.

Vanzolini, P. E. and E. E. Williams. 1970. "South American anoles: The geographic differentiation and evolution of the *Anolis chrysolepis* species group (Sauria, Iguanidae)." *Arquivos de Zoologia* (São Paulo), 19(1–2):1–298.

Varga, Z. 1975. "Zoogeographische Gliederung der paläarktischen Orealfauna." In H. Malicky, ed., Verhandlungen der Sechsten Internationalen Symposiums über Entomofaunistik in Mitteleuropa, pp. 263–84. The Hague: W. Junk.

Vine, F. J. 1966. "Spreading of the ocean floor: New evidence." *Science* (Washington, D.C.), 154(3755):1405–15.

Voous, K. H. 1963. "The concept of faunal elements or faunal types." In C. G. Sibley, ed., *Proceedings of the 13th International Ornithological Congress*, 2:1104–8. Baton Rouge: The American Ornithologists' Union.

Vuilleumier, F. 1969. "Pleistocene speciation in birds living in the high Andes." *Nature* (London), 223(5211):1179–80.

—— 1970. "Insular biogeography in continental regions, 1: The northern Andes of South America." *The American Naturalist*, 104(938):373–88.

—— 1971. "Generic relationships and speciation patterns in *Ochthoeca, Myiotheretes, Xolmis, Neoxolmis, Agriornis,* and *Muscisaxicola." Bulletin of the Museum of Comparative Zoology,* 141(5):181–232.

—— 1975. "Zoogeography." In D. S. Farner, J. R. King, and K. C. Parkes, eds., *Avian Biology,* 5:421–96. New York, San Francisco, London: Academic Press.

—— 1978. "Qu'est-ce que la biogéographie?" *Compte Rendu des Séances de la Société de Biogéographie,* year 54(475):41–66.

—— 1980. "Speciation in birds of the high Andes." In *Proceedings of the 17th International Ornithological Congress,* in press.

Vuilleumier, F. and D. Simberloff. 1980. "Ecology vs. history as determinants of patchy and insular distributions in high Andean birds." In M. K. Hecht, W. C. Steere, and B. Wallace, eds., *Evolutionary Biology* 12:235–379. New York and London:Plenum.

Wagner, W. 1962. "Dynamische Taxionomie, angewandt auf die Delphaciden Mitteleuropas." *Mitteilungen aus dem Hamburgischen Zoologischen Museum,* 60:111–80.

Walker, J. W. 1971. "Pollen morphology, phytogeography, and phylogeny of the Annonaceae." *Contributions from the Gray Herbarium,* no. 202, pp. 1–131.

—— 1976. "Comparative pollen morphology and phylogeny of the ranalean complex." In C. B. Beck, ed., *Origin and Early Evolution of Angiosperms.* pp. 241–99. New York: Columbia University Press.

Wallace, A. R. 1876. *The Geographical Distribution of Animals,* vols. 1–2. London: Macmillan; New York: Harper; reprint, New York and London: Hafner, 1962.

——1880. *Island Life.* London: Macmillan (1881, New York: Harper and Brothers).

Wasserman, A. O. 1970. "Polyploidy in the common tree toad, *Hyla versicolor* Le Conte." *Science* (Washington, D.C.), 167(3917):385–86.

Watson, H. 1934. "*Natalina* and other South African snails." *Proceedings of the Malacological Society of London,* 21(3):150–96.

Watson, P. J. 1970. "Evolution in closely adjacent plant populations, 6: An entomophilous species, *Potentilla erecta,* in two contrasting habitats." *Heredity,* 24(3):407–22.

Webb, S. D. 1976. "Mammalian faunal dynamics of the great American interchange." *Paleobiology,* 2(3):220–34.

—— 1978. "A history of savanna vertebrates in the New World, part 2: South America and the great interchange." *Annual Review of Ecology and Systematics,* 9:393–426.

Weeks, L. G. 1947. "Paleogeography of South America." *Bulletin of the American Association of Petroleum Geologists,* vol. 31, part 2, no. 7, pp. 1194–1241.

—— 1948. "Paleogeography of South America." *Bulletin of the Geological Society of America,* 59(3):249–82.

Wegener, A. 1912a. "Die Entstehung der Kontinente." *Dr. A. Petermanns Mitteilungen aus Justus Perthes' Geographischer Anstart,* year 58 (April), pp. 185–95; (May), pp. 253–56; (June), pp. 305–309.

—— 1912b. "Die Entstehung der Kontinente." *Geologische Rundschau,* 3(4):276–92.

—— 1915. *Die Entstehung der Kontinente und Ozeane.* Sammlung Vieweg, no. 23. Braunschweig: Vieweg.

—— 1924. *The Origin of Continents and Ocean Basins.* London: Methuen.

—— 1966. *The Origin of Continents and Oceans.* Translated from the fourth revised German edition by John Biram. New York: Dover.

Weissel, J. K. and R. N. Anderson. 1978. "Is there a Caroline Plate?" *Earth and Planetary Science Letters*, 41(2):143–58.

Weissel, J. K. and D. E. Hayes. 1972. "Magnetic anomalies in the southeast Indian Ocean." In D. E. Hayes, ed., *Antarctic Oceanology,* vol. 2: *The Australian-New Zealand Sector,* pp. 165–96. Antarctic Research Series of the American Geophysical Union, vol. 19.

Weissel, J. K., D. E. Hayes, and E. M. Herron. 1977. "Plate tectonics synthesis: The displacements between Australia, New Zealand, and Antarctica since the late Cretaceous." *Marine Geology,* 25(1–3):231–77.

Westoll, T. S. 1958. "The origin of continental vertebrate faunas." *Transactions of the Geological Society of Glasgow,* 23:79–105.

White, M. J. D. 1978. *Modes of Speciation.* San Francisco: W. H. Freeman.

Whitehead, D. R. 1972. "Classification, phylogeny, and zoology of *Schizogenius* Putzeys (Coleoptera: Carabidae: Scaritini)." *Quaestiones Entomologicae,* 8(3): 131–348.

Whittaker, R. H. 1967. "Gradient analysis of vegetation." *Biological Reviews of the Cambridge Philosophical Society,* 42(2):207–64.

Wiebes, J. T. 1968. "Catalogue of the Coleoptera Cetoniidae in the Leiden Museum 1: *Goliathus* Lamarck, sensu lato." *Zoologische Mededelingen,* Rijksmuseum van Natuurlijke Historie (Leiden), 43(3):19–40.

Wiley, E. O. 1976. "The phylogeny and biogeography of fossil and Recent gars (Actinopterygii: Lepisosteidae)." *Miscellaneous Publications of the Museum of Natural History,* University of Kansas, no. 64, 1–111.

Willis, J. C. 1940. *The Course of Evolution by Differentiation or Divergent Mutation Rather Than by Selection.* Cambridge: Cambridge University Press.

Wilson, E. O. 1961. "The nature of the taxon cycle in the Melanesian ant fauna." *The American Naturalist,* 95(882):169–93.

Wilson, J. T. 1963. "Hypothesis of earth's behavior." *Nature* (London), 198(4884):925–29.

Windhausen, A. 1931. *Geologia Argentina.* Buenos Aires: Jacobo Peuser.

Winterer, E. L. 1976. "Anomalies in the tectonic evolution of the Pacific." In G. H. Sutton, M. H. Manghnani, and R. M. Moberly, eds., *The Geophysics of the Pacific Ocean Basin and Its Margin,* pp. 269–78. Monographs of the American Geophysical Union, no. 19.

Wolfe, J. A. 1966. "Tertiary plants from the Cook Inlet region, Alaska." *Professional Papers of the Geological Survey* (Washington, D.C.), no. 398B, pp. 1–32.

—— 1969. "Neogene floristic and vegetational history of the Pacific northwest." *Madroño,* 20(3):83–110.

—— 1971. "Tertiary climatic fluctuations and methods of analysis of Tertiary floras." *Palaeogeography, Palaeoclimatology, Palaeoecology,* 9(1):27–57.

—— 1972. "An interpretation of Alaskan Tertiary floras." In A. Graham, ed., *Floristics and Paleofloristics of Asia and Eastern North America*, pp. 201–33. Amsterdam, London, New York: Elsevier.

—— 1975. "Some aspects of plant geography of the northern hemisphere during the late Cretaceous and Tertiary." *Annals of the Missouri Botanical Garden*, 62(2):264–79.

—— 1977. "Paleogene floras from the Gulf of Alaska region." *Professional Papers of the Geological Survey* (Washington, D.C.), no. 997, pp. 1–108.

—— 1978. "A paleobotanical interpretation of Tertiary climates in the northern hemisphere." *American Scientist*, 66(6):694–703.

Wolfe, J. A., J. A. Doyle, and V. M. Page. 1975. "The bases of angiosperm phylogeny: Paleobotany." *Annals of the Missouri Botanical Garden*, 62(3):801–24.

Wolfe, J. A. and T. Tanai. 1980. "The Miocene Seldovia Point flora from the Kenai Group, Alaska." *Professional Papers of the Geological Survey* (Washington, D.C.), no. 1105, pp. 1–52.

Wood, A. E. 1977. "The Rodentia as clues to Cenozoic migrations between the Americas and Europe and Africa." In R. M. West, ed., *Paleontology and Plate Tectonics With Special Reference to the History of the Atlantic Ocean*, pp. 95–109. Special Publications in Biology and Geology of the Milwaukee Public Museum, no. 2.

Woollard, G. P. 1975. "The interrelationships of crustal and upper mantle parameter values in the Pacific." *Reviews of Geophysics and Space Physics*, 13(1):87–137.

Wright, H. E. and D. G. Frey, eds., 1965. *The Quaternary of the United States*. Princeton: Princeton University Press.

Wright, S. 1960. "On the number of self-incompatibility alleles maintained in equilibrium by a given mutation rate in a population of a given size: A reexamination." *Biometrics*, 16(1):61–85.

Yü, W. 1977. "Cretaceous and Early Tertiary non-marine gastropods from south China with their stratigraphical significance." *Acta Paleontologica Sinica*, 16(2): 191–216.

Ziegler, A. M., C. R. Scotese, M. E. Johnson, W. S. McKerrow, and R. K. Bambach. 1977. "Paleozoic biogeography of continents bordering the Iapetus (pre-Caledonian) and Rheic (pre-Hercynian) Oceans." In R. M. West, ed., *Paleontology and Plate Tectonics With Special Reference to the History of the Atlantic Ocean*, pp. 1–22. Special Publications in Biology and Geology of the Milwaukee Public Museum, no. 2.

Zimmerman, E. C. 1948. *Insects of Hawaii*, vol. 1. Honolulu: University of Hawaii Press.

Zwick, P. 1979. "Revision of the stonefly family Eustheniidae (Plecoptera) with emphasis on the fauna of the Australian region." *Aquatic Insects*, 1:17–50.

Author Index